Fundamentals of
Structural Analysis

Fundamentals of Structural Analysis

Samuel E. French, Ph.D., P.E.
Structural Engineer
University of Tennessee at Martin

WEST PUBLISHING COMPANY
Minneapolis/St. Paul   New York   Los Angeles   San Francisco

Production: The Book Company
Cover photograph: Courtesy American Institute of Steel Construction
Composition and Art: Fog Press
Production, Prepress, Printing and Binding by West Publishing Company.

WEST'S COMMITMENT TO THE ENVIRONMENT

In 1906, West Publishing Company began recycling materials left over from the production of books. This began a tradition of efficient and responsible use of resources. Today, up to 95 percent of our legal books and 70 percent of our college and school texts are printed on recycled, acid-free stock. West also recycles nearly 22 million pounds of scrap paper annually—the equivalent of 181,717 trees. Since the 1960s, West has devised ways to capture and recycle waste inks, solvents, oils, and vapors created in the printing process. We also recycle plastics of all kinds, wood, glass, corrugated cardboard, and batteries, and have eliminated the use of Styrofoam book packaging. We at West are proud of the longevity and the scope of our commitment to the environment.

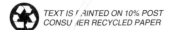 TEXT IS PRINTED ON 10% POST CONSUMER RECYCLED PAPER   PRINTED WITH SOY INK

British Library Cataloguing-in-Publication Data. A catalogue record for this book is available from the British Library.

Copyright © 1995   By West Publishing Company
                          610 Opperman Drive
                          P.O. Box 64526
                          St. Paul, MN 55164-0526

Printed in the United States of America

02 01 00 99 98 97 96 95   8 7 6 5 4 3 2 1 0

Library of Congress Cataloging-in-Publication Data

French, Samuel E., 1930–
    Fundamentals of structural analysis / Samuel E. French.
        p.   cm.
    Includes bibliographical references and index.
    ISBN 0-314-03929-5
    1. Structural analysis (Engineering)   I. Title.
TA645.F73 1994
624.1'71—dc20   94-2551
                                           CIP

Contents

Preface

This book presents the analysis of simple structures. It is intended for use in the first course in structural analysis at the university level. The second course in such a sequence normally begins where this text stops, with the matrix analysis of multispan, multistory frames.

The primary emphasis in this text is placed on analysis rather than on design. The examples used to illustrate the theory have been selected both from the design of buildings and from the design of construction falsework, but the focus remains on the theoretical analysis of reactions, loads, and deformations rather than on the design of members. Separate studies in the design of timber, steel, masonry, and concrete members would follow this introductory study into structural analysis very naturally.

Two generations ago, the classical methods of analysis, such as those developed and used in this book, were found to be so readily understandable that they became (and still are) the cornerstones of structural analysis. The problem came in using them: manual evaluation of discontinuous integrals and manual solution of large arrays of simultaneous equations proved to be so tedious and cumbersome (and so subject to numerical error) that other, less exact and less understandable methods were substituted. Probably every engineering graduate of those days remembers coursework in which the mathematics involved in the solutions became the paramount concern, leaving the engineering significance of the problem badly blurred if not lost.

In today's practice, the availability of extremely powerful mathematics software at modest cost removes the labor and tedium from the classical methods of analysis. Mathematics software such as Maple, MathCAD, Matlab, and Mathematica, permit users to evaluate the mathematics of the classical solutions with a minimum of drudgery and numerical error. In today's market, even handheld calculators, such as HP 48S and TI 82, have some capability to perform integrations and to solve matrices.

The concept of coupling the classical methods of structural analysis with computer-aided evaluation of the mathematics is termed the *neoclassical* approach to engineering. The author is a strong proponent of the neoclassical methods, particularly for teaching and learning structural analysis, since understanding structural response to load remains always at the forefront; the distracting and time-consuming evaluation of the mathematics becomes a side issue, not a dominant issue.

The neoclassical approach is followed in this text. Initially, the introductory problems on a subject are solved using manual methods entirely, including manual evaluation of the mathematics. Then, as understanding of the structural response increases and as the evaluation of the mathematics becomes increasingly cumbersome, the evaluation of the mathematics is gradually shifted to the computer.

Computer programming of problems in structural analysis is not included in this text. Like other secondary issues in structural analysis, programming can very easily become a distraction, diverting attention from the focus on the response of structures to load. The programming of problems in structural analysis is left to special coursework devoted exclusively to computer applications.

In this text, the fundamental concepts of structural analysis are developed using statically determinate systems. The development of these fundamental concepts occupies the first fourteen chapters; in the final chapters, the concepts are extended very naturally into an introduction to indeterminate beams and frames. Very deliberately, the early chapters are focused on analytical concepts, without having that focus diffused by parallel studies of structural systems. The final chapters are then focused on structural systems, without having that focus diffused by parallel studies of analytical concepts.

The sharp break between the presentations of determinate systems and of indeterminate systems produces a second beneficial effect: the text provides a complete treatment of determinate structures, with no "loose ends" left to be resolved in later coursework. This feature should be especially attractive to students in a curriculum where the study of indeterminate structures is considered to have only secondary importance; in such cases, further coursework in indeterminate structures may be omitted altogether.

The distinction between statically determinate structural systems and statically indeterminate structural systems is an important one. In a statically determinate structural system, the reactions and forces in every member can be computed from statics alone—that is, without considering the deformations of the structure. Typical examples of such statically determinate structural systems are the braced frame, the diaphragm-and-shearwall system, the braced post-and-beam system, and all of the more common types of trussed systems.

In contrast, statically indeterminate systems require the inclusion of additional conditions (beyond the statics conditions) in order to produce a solution. These additional conditions are almost always deformation conditions. Statically indeterminate systems constitute only a small fraction of the total number of structures that are built, but in general these structures command a very high level of visibility and attention. The most common structure belonging to this type of system is the continuous rigid frame—the basic structure used in the large multistory skyscrapers that so often appear as symbols of modern technology. However visible they may be, skyscrapers are not a common project in a typical engineering office; only a small percentage of an average structural engineer's working life is devoted to the design of such rarely encountered projects.

Of the two types of systems, statically determinate systems constitute the overwhelming majority of all building construction in contemporary practice. These structures and systems, usually less than 50 or 60 feet high, are routinely designed and built every day in practically every city and town in the world; these simple structures and falsework systems dominate the industry. Such structures are almost always designed with a statically determinate structural system, rather than an indeterminate system, because the simpler determinate system offers real advantages in cost, ease of fabrication, and ease of construction. The methods of analysis presented in this introductory text are completely adequate for performing the final analysis and design of any of these common, everyday structures or falsework systems.

Of course, students who specialize in structural engineering will continue their studies into more complex structural systems such as continuous rigid frames, space frame, plates, and shells. They will, in fact, spend years studying such special systems, but the fundamental concepts used in all of their advanced studies will be the concepts developed here, in their first course in structural analysis.

In comparison, students who specialize in construction can readily limit their formal study of structural analysis to the statically determinate systems included in this text. While they may quite often find themselves responsible for the analysis and design of elaborate systems of falsework and formwork, such systems will themselves be composed entirely of simple, statically determinate structures. In designing these systems, the designer must employ rigorously correct measures to control deformations. Neither wasteful overdesign nor dangerous underdesign can be tolerated. Consequently, even though the skills of falsework designers may indeed be limited to this one type of simple structural system, their design skill with this one type of system often has to be at least as good as that of their fellow students who went on to specialize in structural engineering. This text pays special attention to the needs of these designers of construction falsework.

This text is intended to serve as a general reference, both for students who wish to continue into the more advanced topics in structural analysis and for students who wish to end their studies here. For those who wish to continue, the concepts presented in this text are the fundamental ones on which all structural analysis is based; subsequent studies can continue quite smoothly into more advanced topics. For those who wish to end their study of structural analysis here, the presentations of the basic structural systems included herein are complete; the study of structural analysis can conveniently be ended at this point, with no critical "loose ends" to be picked up later.

The methods of analysis used throughout modern structural engineering are calculus-based; calculus is therefore a necessary prerequisite to the study of structures, particularly for a fundamental study of the type presented here. Even so, the calculus-based solutions themselves have a very simple form, are highly repetitive, and rapidly become routine. Students who have taken the usual basic coursework in differential and integral calculus will be quite comfortable in handling the simple calculus-based methods that are used in this text and throughout all of elementary structural analysis.

In developing the presentations in this text, the author has assumed that the student has already completed the usual preparatory courses in statics and strength of materials at the university level. It is also assumed that the student is familiar with the flexure formula and the beam shear equation, and has had some drill in their use. And finally, it is assumed that the student has had some exposure to the phenomenon of column buckling.

This text includes examples and problems both in imperial units of feet, pounds, slugs, and seconds and in SI units of meters, newtons, kilograms, and seconds. An exception is made in Chapters 13 and 14, which are presented only in imperial units, because these chapters are based on the provisions of American building codes, which are written in imperial units.

As with his earlier books, the author is again indebted to his wife, Sherry, who typed the manuscript of this text. Her unwavering support of these speculative ventures has at times made the difference between continuing the project and abandoning it; the author will be forever thankful for her quiet encouragement.

I also wish to thank the following reviewers: Irtishad Ahmad, Florida International University; Cam Andres, Southern Alberta Institute of Technology; Same Beadles, Southern College of Technology; Micahel Bluhm, Kansas State University; Corey Finnegan, Southern Alberta Institute of Technology; Walter Gerstle, University of New Mexico; Cathy French, University of Minnesota; Burton Henderson, University of Arkansas—Little Rock; M.R. Kianoush, Ryerson Polytechnic University; Lee Lowery, Texas A&M University, College Station, Texas; Michael Kupferman, Wentworth Institute of Technology, Boston, Massachusetts; William Nash, University of Massachusetts—Amherst; Steve Rakus, Seneca College of Applied Arts and Technology; Charles Rich, Oklahoma State University; Jimmy Smith, Texas Tech University; Richard Zbinden, Oregon Institute of Technology.

—S.E.F.

Stately precast columns precast in fiberglass reinforced
forms. (Photograph courtesy Portland Cement Association,
reprinted by permission.)

CHAPTER

1

Classifications, Conventions, Customs, and Practices

The study of structures is invariably treated in two parts. The first part of the study consists of the analysis of structures, in which the loads acting on each member of a building or structural system are determined. The second part of the study consists of the selection of the structural members themselves, in which the size and shape of each member are selected such that each can safely sustain the loads just determined.

Much later in the study of structures, after some degree of maturity and perspective have been developed, the study also includes the interaction between the loadings and the related design. In these more advanced studies, the overall structural system (rather than single members) is analyzed and examined. Further, the spans, materials, and foundation systems are varied, and the end results are analyzed and compared. The type of structural system itself can then be varied, altered, modified, and refined to produce the most appropriate structural system for the particular design conditions.

From such comparative studies, a student can develop a sense of design. That sense of design, in turn, warns the maturing student that, when shearwalls become too short, foundation loads can become too high; or when spans become too long, story heights can become too high; or when allowable soil pressures are low, a rigid frame structure might be more appropriate than a braced frame.

But all such extensive studies must start with a first step. This textbook is meant to serve as that first step—an introduction to the fundamental methods of structural analysis. Succeeding studies in the design of members—whether steel, timber, or concrete—will follow these initial studies very naturally into structural analysis.

In any discipline, including that of structural analysis and design, certain traditions, conventions, customs, and practices have been developed over the years. Persons engaged in the business understand these traditional practices and they can communicate with each other in well-known and familiar terms within the framework of these practices. They are the practices that form the common core of skills in the study of structural analysis; and which are the subject of this chapter.

It should not be inferred that traditional practices will be archaic or out-dated. In many (if not most) cases, traditional practices have come into existence and remained there simply because they consistently produce better results than anything else that has been tried. In addition, these practices possess a very reassuring advantage: they have been tried; they are known to work.

The practices discussed and presented in succeeding chapters are largely limited to tried and proven traditional practices. Specialized methods or adaptations that have only a few applications are avoided. Such specialized applications can always be handled alternatively by standard traditional methods, although the traditional methods may be considerably less elegant. More advanced studies into structural analysis address many of these specialized methods, which are largely derived from the more classical methods presented in this text. In today's practice, however, the purpose of specialized methods may not be to produce a savings in man-hours or labor; in many cases their biggest single advantage is that they are easier to program.

In this chapter, some of the more common conventions and customs used in the industry are introduced and discussed. Although these conventions and customs are by no means binding, they are widely used and are generally familiar to professionals in the practice. They form a starting point of terminology and concepts for the formal study of structures.

1.1 CLASSIFICATIONS

The broadest and most general classification of structures is based on their method of structural analysis: structures are either statically determinate or statically indeterminate. Statically determinate structures can be analyzed using only the conditions of simple statics; statically indeterminate structures require additional conditions, usually involving the deformations of the structure. Means of distinguishing between these two broad classifications are presented in Chapter 2.

Within either of these two broad classifications, structures are subdivided into smaller groups by their configuration or use. The following classifications are typical:

beams	rings	thin shells
columns	arches	tension structures
frames	space frames	inflated structures
shear panels	plates	

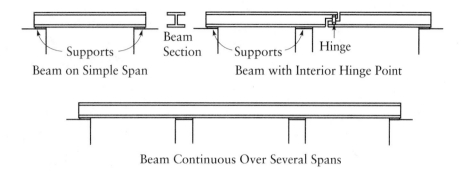

FIGURE 1-1 Typical beams.

Each of these classifications is described in detail in the following subsections.

Beams

Beams are structural members that distribute their loads transversely by flexure to a support point. Beams may be single-span or multiple-span, as indicated in Figure 1-1. Further, beams may be sloped or horizontal, and they sometimes have interior hinge points. Beams are by far the most common type of structure; much of the study of structural analysis is devoted entirely to beams.

Columns

Columns are structural members that carry their loads axially rather than transversely. Short, fat columns may be loaded to such a point that the load actually crushes the material. Long, slender columns are more likely to buckle under the higher axial loads, and they will fail by buckling long before the stresses are high enough to crush the material. Columns may also be continuous over several stories, as shown in Figure 1-2.

The sloped member shown in Figure 1-3 acts partly as a beam (transferring its loads transversely by flexure) and partly as a column (transferring its load axially along the length of the member). The member might therefore be described either as a beam carrying an axial load or as a column carrying a flexural load. The dividing line between these two cases is very ill-defined in structural analysis. Fortunately, the distinction is not important in the analytical methods presented in this text.

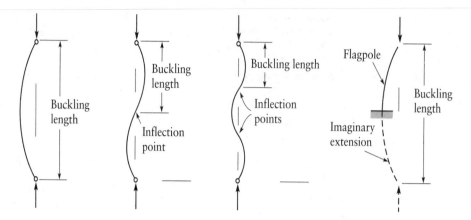

FIGURE 1-2 Typical columns.

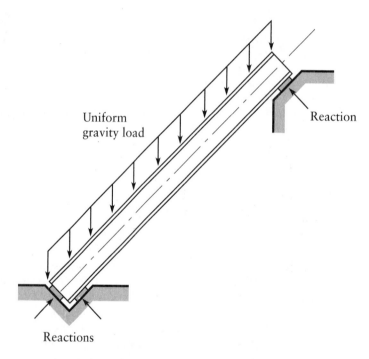

FIGURE 1-3 Beam under axial load or column under flexural load.

Rigid Frames

Rigid frames are a relatively recent innovation in structural design. A rigid frame is a structural member that carries its flexural loads continuously around an unyielding rigid joint. Several typical frames are shown in Figure 1-4.

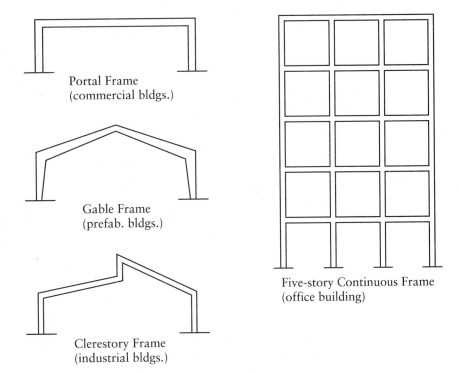

Portal Frame
(commercial bldgs.)

Gable Frame
(prefab. bldgs.)

Clerestory Frame
(industrial bldgs.)

Five-story Continuous Frame
(office building)

FIGURE 1-4 Typical frames.

In earlier centuries, it was not technically possible to build rigid frames in the configurations shown in Figure 1-4; the rigidity of the joints could not be maintained. But with the advent of modern structural steel—with its riveted, bolted, or welded joints—the rigid frame quickly became one of the more popular structures in the industry. Architects like its clean crisp lines and its open uncluttered spans; builders like its speed of construction; and investors like its low cost. The rigid frame structure will likely keep its popularity in the industry for many years to come.

In more recent years, the rigid frame structure has been extended to reinforced concrete construction as well as to steel construction. Reinforced concrete frames are now very popular and are widely used in parts of the world where steel is so expensive that structural steel frames could never have been competitive in cost. Of the four most popular construction materials (steel, concrete, timber, and masonry), only steel and reinforced concrete lend themselves to rigid frame configurations; consequently, for the foreseeable future, rigid frames will probably be limited to construction in steel or in reinforced concrete.

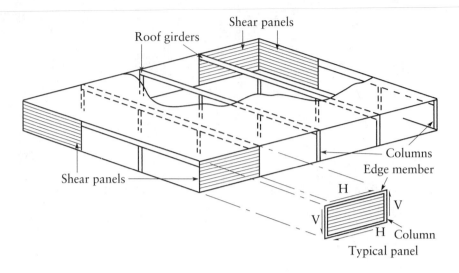

FIGURE 1-5 Typical shear panels.

Shear Panels

Shear panels are planar structural members that carry in-plane shearing forces from one side of the panel to the other side of the panel. Shear panels are usually large rectangular members, with a length-to-height ratio up to 4:1 or even more. Typical shear panels in a building are shown in Figure 1-5.

The term *shear panel* is used rather loosely. The shear panel of Figure 1-5 might be a solid masonry wall, a plywood wall on wood studs, or a rectangular steel frame with cross bracing at its interior. So long as the panel can transmit shearing forces from one side to the other, it can be called generically a shear panel.

In most cases, a shear panel is the structure used to resist wind or earthquake loading. The applied loads are thus the two horizontal loads indicated as H in Figure 1-5. By themselves, these two loads form a couple that tends to rotate the panel; they must be resisted by an opposing couple, such as the two forces indicated as V. In every case, therefore, a shear panel must be loaded by two opposing couples, such as those shown in Figure 1-5.

Rings

Rings are closed frames. Some typical rings are shown in Figure 1-6. Rings need not be round or square or even regular. They may be any shape, so long as they form a closed frame.

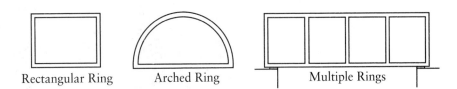

FIGURE 1-6 Typical rings.

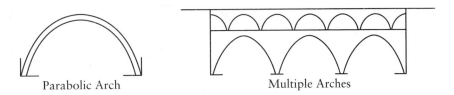

FIGURE 1-7 Typical arches.

Rings are statically indeterminate. When a ring is used as a shear panel, for example, the forces inside it cannot be computed by simple statics; rotations of the joints must be included in the computations. Rings are not one of the more common structures in today's construction, but they may be used occasionally when the architect requires a panel that for some reason cannot be cross-braced.

Arches

Arches are one of the older man-made structures. Early arch structures include the Roman-era aqueducts of Portugal and Spain—still in use after some 2000 years. Typical arch structures are shown in Figure 1-7.

Many of the bridges of earlier centuries utilized the arch. Commonly the foundations for the arch were unmortared rubble piers, since hydraulic cement (the type that hardens under water) had not yet been developed. The arch itself was typically built of stone or brick masonry, depending on the availability of materials.

The feature of the arch that made it attractive to the ancients was its ability to carry loads without producing high tensile stresses due to flexure. Consequently, materials having little or no tensile strength, such as stone or masonry, could be used to create open spans. In three dimensions, the arch becomes a vault; the vaulted ceiling was used throughout Europe for church construction during the Renaissance.

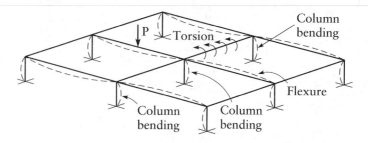

FIGURE 1-8 Typical space frame.

Space Frames

Space frames are frames that have been extended into the third dimension. Their analysis is so distinctive that they are generally classified separately from the more common two-dimensional frames. A typical space frame made from pipe is shown in Figure 1-8.

A space frame distributes its loads both by bending and by torsion. In most cases, the analysis becomes so tedious that only the smallest space frames can be analyzed manually. With the advent of the computer, however, analysis of the space frame has become readily possible, even for very large arrays. As a result, the space frame has become increasingly popular in recent years.

In practice, the space frame may also be designed in a pattern of rings, producing large three-dimensional plates. Such structures are quite functional as platforms in space, serving as mounts both for solar cells to collect power and for antenna arrays in communications devices. Very likely, the space frame will become a common and useful structure in space.

Plates

Plates are planar structures that carry transverse loads. Both the loads and the supports are normal to the plane of the plate. A typical plate structure is shown in Figure 1-9.

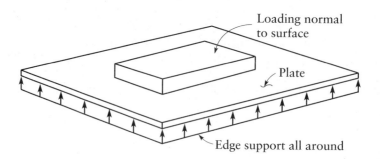

FIGURE 1-9 Typical plate.

Plate structures are statically indeterminate, and their analysis is quite complex. Tables of stresses in plates have been prepared for various boundary conditions, and these tables are generally used in design calculations; an independent analysis for stresses in a plate structure is rarely performed.

One beneficial fringe use of the theory of plates is in teaching mathematics. The defining equation for bending in plates is a nonhomogeneous fourth-order partial differential equation (a Poissonian equation). Teaching the solution of this equation provides an ideal opportunity to teach the use of Fourier series, the evaluation of multiple boundary conditions, and the application of finite differences in two dimensions. In addition to its value in actual applications of plates as a type of structure, studying the solution of the plate equation thus carries many worthwhile benefits in the study of applied mathematics.

Thin Shells

Thin shells are three-dimensional continuous surfaces that distribute their load in three dimensions throughout the shell. In the more traditional theory of shells, the surface conforms to a generating equation of some sort, such as a paraboloid, an ellipsoid, a sphere, or a hyperbolic paraboloid. Some typical shells are shown in Figure 1-10.

Thin shells have a great deal of appeal to engineers because of their incredible strength and their unusual economy of materials. They are very expensive to fabricate or to form, however, and they have very limited architectural applications. Except in special applications, demand for traditional thin shell structures seems unlikely to increase substantially in the foreseeable future.

Tension Structures

Tension structures support their loads through primary tension members. The suspension bridge is probably the best-known application of tension structures, although in recent years many innovative designs have been tried in other configurations using this class of structure. Some typical tension structures are shown in Figure 1-11.

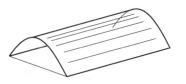

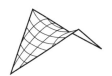

Cylindrical Barrel Shell   Spherical Dome   Hyperbolic Paraboloid

FIGURE 1-10 Typical shells.

Suspension Bridge   Cable-Suspended Roof

FIGURE 1-11 Typical tension structures.

Tension structures are a distinctly modern innovation in structures. Until the development of steel and steel cables in the late nineteenth century, no commonly available tensile material could sustain the high stresses that occur in almost any tension structure.

The biggest single advantage that tension structures offer is their long open spans. Except when a project design absolutely requires such spans (bridges, covered coliseums, hangars), these expensive and unusual structures are rarely appropriate design choices. As high-strength steel becomes more readily available and less costly, however, more and more experimental designs for tension structures are likely to appear in the future; perhaps some surprises will evolve.

Inflated Structures

Inflated structures, or air-supported structures, are closed membranes supported entirely by air pressure inside the membrane. The pressure differential between the inside and the outside of the membrane is quite small—usually less than 6 inches of water. In most cases, the membrane is far from being airtight; makeup air is supplied continuously by low-pressure, high-volume blowers. Some typical inflated structures are shown in Figure 1-12.

Inflated structures are another modern innovation whose applications so far have been limited to projects that require large open coverage, such as sports stadiums. They have also been used in settings where their uniqueness is meant to attract attention, such as in some of the construction for the Olympic games. Some promising experimentation has been done in adapting this type of structure for use as construction falsework; only a small amount of air pressure (up to 36 inches of water) will support extremely large loads during construction stages.

Trusses

Trusses are a particular type of construction used in fabricating structural members. Trusses were not included in any of the structural classifications given earlier in this chapter, since most of the classifications given earlier could include a truss configuration. Beams, frames, rings, arches, plates, and shells can all be built as trusses. Typical examples of such construction are shown in Figure 1-13.

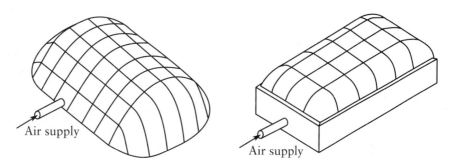

FIGURE 1-12 Typical inflated structures.

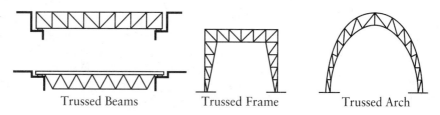

Trussed Beams   Trussed Frame   Trussed Arch

FIGURE 1-13 Typical truss configuration.

It might be argued that trusses are better classified as a type of construction than as a class of structure. Truss configurations are an important topic in the study of structures, however, and in earlier times they constituted a very large part of the study of structures. In more recent years, the cost of fabricating trusses has discouraged their use somewhat, although they remain a viable and prominent part of the industry.

A truss configuration is simply a system of triangulated members, as indicated in Figure 1-13. In three dimensions, a truss configuration becomes a system of tetrahedrons, which can be extended or configured into any desired three-dimensional shape. The analysis of two-dimensional truss configurations for their loads and deformations is treated in Chapters 5 and 6 of this text; the analysis of three-dimensional truss configurations is left to more advanced study.

Hinged Beams and Three-hinged Arches

Hinged beams and three-hinged arches are another type of construction used to obtain special features in the design. Hinge points may be deliberately introduced at advantageous points in continuous beams, rigid frames, or arches to reduce them to statically determinate structures; such a feature can often alleviate serious problems with foundation settlements. Alternatively, depending on the circumstances, incorporating a hinge point in a frame or an arch can relieve potential problems with thermal stresses. The analysis for reactions in hinged beams and three-hinged arches are treated in elementary statics; but for readers desiring a review, a brief summary is presented as an appendix to this text.

1.2 CONVENTIONS

Conventions in structural analysis regarding signs and symbols are generally the same as those introduced in standard texts on elementary strength of materials. As indicated in Figure 1-14, shear is positive if the left side moves up with respect to the right; moment is positive if it places tension on the bottom of the member; deflection is positive if the member lies above its original position; and slope is positive if the tangent points upward to the right.

For vertical or sloping members, the foregoing sign conventions can sometimes be confusing. To distinguish which side of a vertical member is up or down, top or bottom, or left or right, the viewer turns such that the coordinate distance x or y along the member increases to the viewer's right. The viewer is then correctly oriented to the member insofar as all the foregoing sign conventions are concerned.

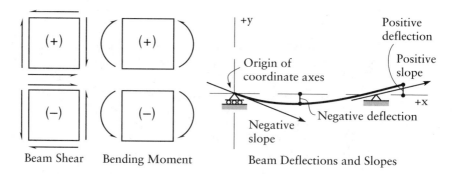

Beam Shear   Bending Moment   Beam Deflections and Slopes

FIGURE 1-14 Sign conventions.

The symbols commonly used for sketching structural supports in two dimensions are usually self-explanatory. Even so, there is very little standardization of such symbols and some confusion or misinterpretation can result. The symbols that will be used throughout this text are shown in Table 1-1, along with a description of their reactions.

1.3 CUSTOMS

Over the years, certain customs have evolved in the presentation of a structural analysis. Every analysis must be checked by someone else; and unfamiliar or "gimmick" solutions are more likely to slow down the review process than to speed things up. The customs described in this section comprise a few of the more commonly observed customs in the presentation of a structural analysis.

Loads on Sloping Members

Loads on sloping members are customarily shown on the horizontal or vertical projection, rarely if ever along the slope. A typical example is shown in Figure 1-15, for loads on a sloping roof beam. One way to compute the dead load on this member along its horizontal projection is to compute its total dead load, 15 ft × 31 lb/ft = 465 lb, and then to divide this load by the projected length of 12 ft to obtain the projected dead load of 39 plf. The dead load on the sloping roofing surface has similarly been converted to projected load.

TABLE 1-1 Standard Symbols

Hinged Support	Sketch Symbol	Horiz. and vert. reactions (pos. or neg.) Moment = 0 Deflection = 0 No resistance to rotation
Hinged Support	Sketch Symbol	Horiz. and vert. reactions (pos. or neg.) Moment = 0 Deflection = 0 No resistance to rotation
Roller Support	Sketch Symbol	Vertical reaction only (pos. or neg.) Moment = 0 Deflection = 0 No resistance to rotation
Roller Support	Sketch Symbol	Vertical reaction only (pos. or neg.) Moment = 0 Deflection = 0 No resistance to rotation
Slotted sleeve Guided End	Sketch Symbol	Reaction normal to guide (pos. or neg.) Develops moment (pos. or neg.) No resistance to deflection Rotation = 0
Fixed End	Sketch Symbol	Horiz. and vert. reactions (pos. or neg.) Develops moment (pos. or neg.) Deflection = 0 Rotation = 0

The wind load on the roof beam is similarly shown on the vertical projection. This approach is consistent; when the wind load is computed (Chapter 13), it is computed for the vertical projection. With such a consistent approach, the treatment of wind loads on a structure is greatly simplified.

The reasons for such a custom lie in the way that moments, shears, and deflections are computed. In such computations, the coordinate axes for the shear and the moment are taken as the horizontal and vertical x- and y-axes; for simplicity, loads are taken on the same axes. As a result, no conversions or corrections need to be made in the shear and moment equations, and all succeeding calculations will be consistent.

Temperature Growth on Curved or Sloping Members

Temperature growth on curved or sloping members is similarly shown along the vertical or horizontal projection, as shown in Figure 1-15. In effect, the thermal growth is simply computed as its x and y components. Such a custom eliminates many extraneous calculations, since the temperature growth is already expressed in its differential horizontal movement Δx and in its differential vertical movement Δy.

Centerline Sketches

Centerline sketches are used for the structural analysis; sketches for steel, timber, masonry, and concrete members are made to the centerline of the member. It is also customarily assumed throughout all of structural analysis that the deformations of the structure are so small compared to the centerline dimensions that such deformations can be ignored. For example, a column exactly 18 feet long will compress slightly under its axial load, but its length is nonetheless taken as being exactly 18 feet in all calculations. Slight variations in centerline dimensions due to flexure, torsion, axial load, shear, or temperature effects are ignored in the stress analysis.

Dimensions of Members

Dimensions of members are taken to centerline of bearing or to centerline of supporting member, as shown in Figure 1-16. Again, this custom could require the use of an extra step in the design of concrete (where dimensions are taken to face of supports). As before, however, the advantages of having a consistent approach outweigh this exception to the rule.

Allowable Working Stresses

Allowable working stresses are still widely used for designing members in all the common structural materials except concrete, although alternative methods based on ultimate loads are gradually becoming standard practice. The design of the members is performed for ultimate load conditions, but it is assumed that all materials—including concrete—will spend their service life entirely within their elastic range of deformations. Such a custom may at first seem to be inconsistent, but it is not. Related studies in ultimate load design show that stresses at day-to-day service levels are indeed kept within elastic ranges.

The foregoing list of customs that have evolved around the analysis of determinate structures is by no means complete, but it does include the more prominent customs that will appear throughout the remainder of this text. Other prominent customs have evolved in structural analysis but apply only to indeterminate structures. Those customs are introduced in the chapters on indeterminate structures, in the context of the discussions there.

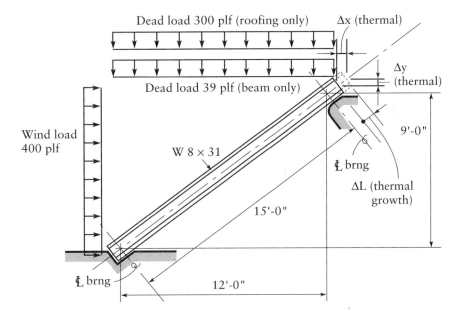

FIGURE 1-15 Loads on sloping members.

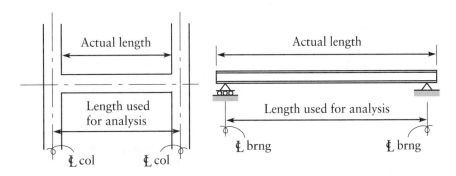

FIGURE 1-16 Dimension to ℄ bearing or to ℄ support.

1.4 PRACTICES

In applications of the theory of structures, certain practices are observed that are sometimes arbitrary, sometimes inaccurate, and sometimes only rough approximations. A few of these practices are discussed in the following paragraphs. Others are discussed in subsequent chapters of this text when they are first encountered, in the context of a particular application.

It is the practice in structural analysis to treat all loads in accordance with certain preconceived groupings, regardless how well the actual load fits into that grouping. A heavy safe, for example, is treated as a concentrated load. It does not matter that the safe may actually be 2 feet square, thus distributing its load over some 4 square feet of floor space. The load is considered to be best represented as a concentrated load, and it is so represented in the analysis.

As a second example, the load delivered by a series of closely spaced joists to their supporting beam is invariably treated as a continuous uniform load, rather than as a series of discrete concentrated loads. Such an approximation is shown in the sketch of Figure 1-17. In the joist system of Figure 1-17, each joist is designed to carry the dead and live loads halfway to the next joist; such loads are treated as uniform loads, as shown. The beam supporting these joists, in turn, is designed as if the entire floor system were delivered as a uniform load rather than as the discrete reactions of the joists; the load is simply treated as a uniform load, as shown. Only in rather severe cases, such as a *very* wide spacing of joists, are the joist loads treated as discrete loads on the supporting beam.

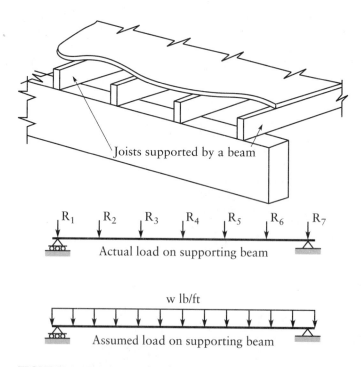

FIGURE 1-17 Discrete loads vs. uniform loads.

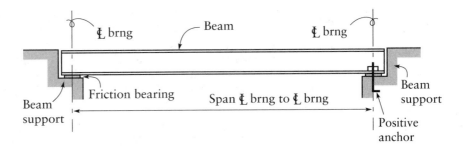

FIGURE 1-18 Beam bearings.

With regard to beam supports, it is customary to treat beam supports as frictionless supports if there is no deliberately placed restraint to their movement. The left support shown in Figure 1-18, for example, must in fact develop a significant horizontal reaction due to friction (about 30% of the vertical load) before sliding can occur. Nonetheless, it is treated in the analysis as a simple support, developing only a vertical reaction.

An exception to the practice of ignoring friction in bearings occurs in highway bridge design, where the design codes require that friction restraints be acknowledged and included. In buildings and in lighter structures, however, such a refinement tends not to be observed.

In foundation design, it is customary to limit all settlements to some nominal amount—say, 1 inch—and then to assume that any differential settlement that may occur between two adjacent footings is some lesser amount—say, ¾ inch. Clearly, myriad combinations of differential settlements between individual foundations might occur, even in a small building. If the differential settlements between two adjacent footings is less than about ¾ inch, however, the total stress in any of the structural members in the building can be expected to change less than 15% due to foundation settlements. For this amount of change, a separate analysis for differential settlements of the foundations is not considered necessary and is rarely performed in practice.

Stresses in statically determinate structures are unaffected by foundation settlements; only continuous structures experience stress buildups due to foundation settlements. In fact, the elimination of such foundation problems is often a decisive factor in the choice between a determinate system and an indeterminate system for the project design. In all cases, however, differential settlements can produce nonstructural effects such as broken windows, binding doors, and openings in siding; settlements may have to be considered at least to some degree even in the design of statically determinate structures.

In a similar context, myriad combinations of temperature or thermal effects might occur in a routine structure over a year's time, in view of the temperature variations that may be encountered both inside and outside the building. It is not common practice, however, to analyze the structure for loads or stresses due to temperature variations. Rather, the structure is conscientiously designed and detailed to prevent such loads and stresses from occurring; no special analysis is then required. Random and unpredictable loads or stresses due to temperature effects are thus relegated to the overall factor of safety for the design.

As a related matter, the numerical errors that occur in calculations during the design process constitute a serious hazard in the industry. When such errors lie undiscovered until late in the design stages (or even into construction stages) corrective measures are sometimes unbelievably expensive. For that reason, the industry demonstrates an intense fixation on checking calculations, sometimes two or even three times, with each checker having to initial the calculations as being correct and usable.

To accommodate the practice of checking, rechecking, and double-checking, the person initiating the calculations must follow familiar conventions, customs, and practices that permit accurate, thorough, and fast checks to be made on the calculations. The customs and practices described in the foregoing sections are only a few of the standard practices that prevail in a design office, but they provide a starting point for the calculations presented in this text. The young designer will learn other standard customs and practices through exposure, experience, and embarassment.

1.5   UNITS OF MEASUREMENT

Both imperial units and SI units are used in this textbook, although in the use of SI units the United States lags behind the rest of the world. It is somewhat ironic that the imperial system used in the United States is commonly called the British system, when the British themselves have already switched completely to SI units, both in manufacturing and in construction. In the United Kingdom, even the building codes and the design codes are now published only in SI units.

The use of SI units in engineering practice is occasionally at variance with the use of SI units in the physical sciences. A good example can be found in the British Code of Practice CP 110, which sets forth the design code for reinforced concrete in the United Kingdom. As long ago as 1976, CP 110 adopted newtons per square millimeter as the standard unit of stress; the prescribed SI units of Pa, MPa, and GPa (endorsed internationally as the "proper" units of stress) do not appear in the 1976 code.

Other variations in the use of SI units have also evolved over the years since worldwide adoption of the SI system. When the SI (or metric) system is used in working drawings, it is customary to give all lengths in millimeters—thus obviating the need to use any abbreviations for units, such as m, cm, or mm. This practice also eliminates any problems in trying to find the decimal point in sun-faded blueprints or in trying to deduce the units when the abbreviation happens to be missing. Further, a standard dimensional accuracy of 1 mm is automatically achieved, although dimensioning closer than 10 mm is rare (except in design calculations).

In engineering calculations, the practice is not so consistent; it could even be regarded as somewhat casual. Units of length are usually expressed in mm, but they may be given either in meters or in millimeters (or even mixed), as the designer prefers. Even so, using abbreviations for length is generally unnecessary, since it should always be obvious whether the units are meters or millimeters.

In general, engineering calculations expressed in SI units do not use second-tier names such as pascals or hertz. Nor are the higher multipliers (such as mega- and giga-) used. Units of stress in today's practice are invariably given in newtons/square millimeter, rather than in megapascals, since N/mm^2 is subject to dimensional analysis and MPa is not.

This textbook follows the practice of giving dimensions in millimeters in all dimension sketches and of omitting the abbreviations unless they become absolutely necessary. And in keeping with the practice, second-tier names are not used in calculations.

REVIEW QUESTIONS

Boldface Review Question numbers indicate that the question is answered in the Answer Section at the back of the book.

1. What are the two broad classifications of structures according to their methods of analysis?
2. Name five types of structures typed according to their configuration.
3. Distinguish between the failure modes of long columns and of short columns.
4. At what point does a beam carrying a small axial load become a column carrying a large flexural load?
5. Of what materials are rigid frames commonly built?
6. In view of the answer to question 5, why aren't rigid frames commonly built of other materials?
7. Sketch the system of loads to be expected on a shear panel.
8. What feature of the arch makes it a practical masonry structure?
9. What is the distinguishing feature between the way rigid frames carry loads and the way space frames carry loads?
10. What is the primary advantage of adding a hinge in the middle of an arch?
11. What is the positive sense of shear on a horizontal member?
12. What is the positive sense of moment on a horizontal member?
13. What is the positive sense of slope on a horizontal member?
14. What is the positive sense of deflection on a horizontal member?

15. Answer questions 11, 12, 13, and 14 for situations where the member is vertical.

16. What is the advantage of converting loads into their horizontal and vertical projections?

17. How are friction beam bearings usually handled in the structural analysis of buildings?

18. How are differential foundation settlements usually handled in the structural analysis of buildings?

19. How are differential temperature effects usually handled in the structural analysis of buildings?

20. Why is there such an emphasis on using well-known methods of analysis (rather than specialized methods) in performing the structural analysis of a building?

Reinforced concrete bridge at Blaydon-on-Tyne, England.
(Photograph courtesy Portland Cement Association,
reprinted by permission.)

2

Loads and Reactions on Beams

The general topics of loads and reactions presented in this chapter are the same ones introduced in earlier coursework in elementary statics; there, however, they were discussed at a very basic level for a very general audience. In the presentations here, these topics are extended and expanded into more specific civil engineering structures, to include the definitions, nomenclature, and approaches commonly used in civil engineering practice. The approaches, symbols, methods, and practices presented in this chapter are those that are used in the practice, and that will be used throughout the remainder of this text.

The approaches in this chapter utilize only two-dimensional statics. In the design of most conventional structures, such as buildings, towers, and construction falsework, there is little need for the complexities of three-dimensional statics. The structure is commonly analyzed in one plane for loads within that plane, and then again in a perpendicular plane for loads in that second plane; both analyses require only simple two-dimensional statics. Only in specialized fields such as aircraft or shipbuilding do structural designs routinely address the more complex three-dimensional loads and the structure's three-dimensional response to these loads. (A notable exception in civil engineering is the space frame—a three-dimensional structure for which the analysis is usually performed by a digital computer.)

The structural frames of the building in Figure 2-1, for example, would be analyzed for loads that could occur in two perpendicular directions. The analysis of column B2 would have to include loading along frame line B for its effects on the column, and then loading along frame line 2 for its effects on the column. The analysis of each frame would remain a two-dimensional problem, but the combination of these two two-dimensional analyses would account for the total three-dimensional loads acting on column B2.

Similarly, the beams within each frame may be analyzed in two dimensions, even though the loads tributary to these beams come from the third direction. The standard practices used in the industry (and presented in this text) produce efficient and realistic design of these members under such simplifying conditions. Even so, the prudent designer must always be aware that structures do have a third dimension and that the overall design must include measures to exclude unwanted effects (such as torsion) from that third dimension.

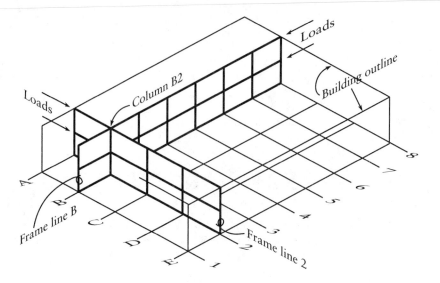

FIGURE 2-1 Two two-dimensional structural frames.

2.1 DEFINITIONS AND CONCEPTS

As used in this text, the term *structure* has two definitions. The first involves the term's generic meaning: anything that is built of interrelated elements. Thus a structure in the generic sense may be a building, a truss, a tower, a bridge, or any other man-made configuration whose purpose is to carry a load.

The second definition of structure is the more specific one used in civil engineering. In a building (or a tower or a falsework system), the structure is composed of the members that provide the primary load-carrying system for the overall building. The collapse of a member that is classified as structure would contribute to the collapse of the building.

This second definition warrants some elaboration. When a building is in its design stages, certain walls, columns, mullions, floor slabs, elevator shafts, and such are set aside as structure. They alone are designed to sustain the vertical and lateral loads that can occur on the building. All other walls, mullions, floors, and such are nonstructural—that is, while they may have other very vital functions to perform, they are not designated to carry primary building loads. Consequently, insofar as structural loading is concerned, these nonstructural elements are simply dead load.

Frequently a rather fine line separates structural items from nonstructural items, where by definition a structural item is one whose failure would contribute to the collapse of the building. For example, a window mullion for a large plate glass window does carry a wind load and it does deliver that load to the building frame, but it is not (usually) considered to be a part of the building structure. While its failure might create expensive damage, such failure would not contribute to the collapse of the building.

Project drawings that show the load-carrying members of a building are termed the *structural drawings*. Typically, the structural drawings exclude all features of the building that are not a part of the structural load-carrying system. As a result, the structural drawings are usually quite brief, accounting for only about 5% to 10% of the total number of drawings for a building project. The structural drawings do, however, include the foundations and the basic soils information, and they usually indicate such things as floor slab recesses for tile or floor coverings (since these can affect the strength of the slab).

2.2 LOADS AND LOAD SYSTEMS

The forces and force systems that act on a structure are called *loads*. Commonly, loads may be caused by such things as gravity, wind, earthquake, temperature changes, water pressure, fluid concrete pressure (for form design), earth pressure, and foundation settlements. In routine structures, the following types of load frequently occur:

1. Concentrated load—a wheel load, a safe, a column load, or any heavy load that is applied over a small contact area (Fig. 2-2).

2. Uniformly distributed load, such as a concrete slab that is carried by repeating joists or the part of a roof load that is carried by a single beam (Fig. 2-3).

3. Uniformly varying load, such as pressure from standing water or pressure created by fluid concrete in its forms before the concrete sets (Fig. 2-4).

4. Irregularly varying load, such as pressure created by high-velocity winds passing over a roof surface or along a wall line (Fig. 2-5).

5. Applied moment, such as a moment produced by a beam or column where it is rigidly framed (welded) to another (Fig. 2-6).

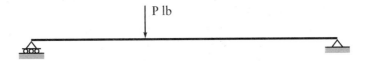

FIGURE 2-2 Concentrated load.

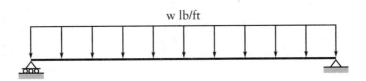

FIGURE 2-3 Uniform load.

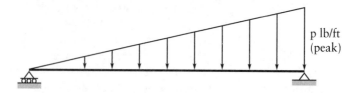

FIGURE 2-4 Hydrostatic load.

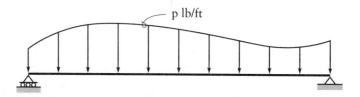

FIGURE 2-5 Irregular load.

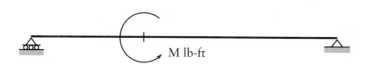

FIGURE 2-6 Applied moment.

The foregoing loads may or may not appear alone. In many cases, they appear in certain patterns, which may be symmetrical, antisymmetrical, cyclosymmetrical, or cycloantisymmetrical. Typical examples of such patterns, or load systems, are shown in Figure 2-7.

Loads acting on a beam produce reactions at the supports, stresses within the beam, and deformations in the beam geometry. The resulting reactions, stresses, and deformations are linear functions of the load: if load is increased by 30%, the reactions, stresses, and deformations increase by the same 30%; if loads are cut in half, the reactions, stresses, and deformations are cut in half, too. This direct linearity between the load and its effects is a very useful concept.

Further, several loads may be superimposed on each other without disturbing the linearity of their individual effects. The partial uniform load of Figure 2-8(a), for example, produces certain reactions, stresses, and deformations in the beam. If that load is removed and the concentrated load of Figure 2-8(b) is applied, the concentrated load produces a completely different set of reactions, stresses, and deformations. If the two sets of loads are applied successively, as in Figure 2-8(c), their combined effects are the direct sum of their individual effects, as shown. The loads and their effects are linearly additive in any order, as long as the material in the beam remains elastic.

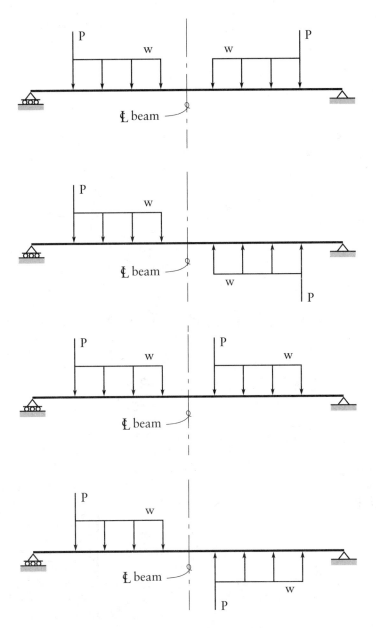

FIGURE 2-7 Systems of loads on a beam.

The linearity of loads is a simple but very important concept in structural analysis. It means that the load can often be factored out of the mathematics and used as a variable. It also means that an analysis can be performed for a 1-lb (unit) load, and the load can be multiplied later by one or more actual values of load; all results will then increase or decrease by the same multiplier. Such solutions, working from a 1-lb unit load, are commonly used in structural analysis.

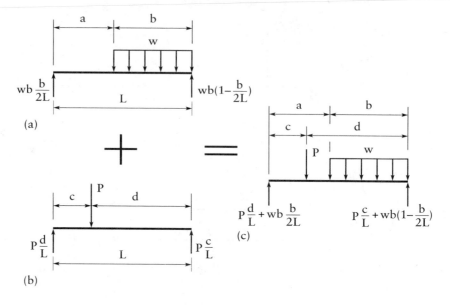

FIGURE 2-8 Linear superposition of loads.

The following examples demonstrate the use of a 1-lb unit load as one approach to the analysis of a simple beam.

Example 2-1   Determine the reactions at A and at B of the given beam when the load changes from 2340 lb progressively to 4120 lb, 5280 lb, and 1280 lb.

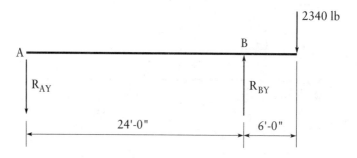

Solution   The reactions are initially found for a 1-lb load, rather than for the indicated 2340-lb load:

$$\sum M_A = 0 \qquad (-R_{BY} \times 24) + (1 \text{ lb} \times 30) = 0$$

$$R_{BY} = 1.25 \text{ lb} \quad (\text{upward})$$

$$\sum M_B = 0 \qquad (-R_{AY} \times 24) + (1\text{ lb} \times 6) = 0$$
$$R_{AY} = 0.25 \text{ lb} \quad \text{(downward)}$$

The units for the reactions are given as lb, but they might more realistically be given as lb of reaction per lb of load.

For each of the four loads of interest, the foregoing reactions are multiplied by the actual magnitude of the load. The results are summarized in the following table.

LOAD	REACTION	
	R_{AY}	R_{BY}
1 lb	0.25 lb	1.25 lb
2340 lb	585 lb	2925 lb
4120 lb	1030 lb	5150 lb
5280 lb	1320 lb	6600 lb
1280 lb	320 lb	1600 lb

Example 2-2 For the accompanying design, determine the reactions at A and B as the 1000-lb load increases incrementally to 2000 lb, 3000 lb, and 4000 lb, while (in the same increments of time) the 5000-lb load decreases to 4000 lb, 3000 lb, and 2000 lb.

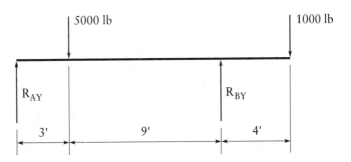

Solution The reactions are found first for a 1-lb load at the point where the 5000-lb load occurs (load #1):

$$\sum M_A = 0 \qquad (R_{B1} \times 12) - (1\text{ lb} \times 3) = 0$$
$$R_{B1} = 0.25 \text{ lb/lb of load}$$

$$\sum M_B = 0 \qquad (R_{A1} \times 12) - (1\ \text{lb} \times 9) = 0$$
$$R_{A1} = 0.75\ \text{lb/lb of load}$$

The reactions are again computed, this time for a 1-lb load at the point where the 1000-lb load occurs (load #2):

$$\sum M_A = 0 \qquad (R_{B2} \times 12) - (1\ \text{lb} \times 16) = 0$$
$$R_{B2} = 1.333\ \text{lb/lb of load}$$

$$\sum M_B = 0 \qquad (R_{A2} \times 12) + (1\ \text{lb} \times 4) = 0$$
$$R_{A2} = -0.333\ \text{lb/lb of load}$$

The total reaction R_{AY} is the sum of R_{A1} and R_{A2} for the various loads; R_{BY} is found similarly. The relevant results are summarized in the following table.

LOAD #1 (LB)	LOAD #2 (LB)	R_{A1} (LB)	R_{A2} (LB)	R_{AY} (LB)	R_{B1} (LB)	R_{B2} (LB)	R_{BY} (LB)
5000	1000	3750	−0333	3417	1250	1333	2583
4000	2000	3000	−0667	2333	1000	2667	3667
3000	3000	2250	−1000	1250	0750	4000	4750
2000	4000	1500	−1333	0167	0500	5333	5833

2.3 STATICALLY DETERMINATE REACTIONS

Beam reactions are said to be statically determinate if they can be computed entirely on the basis of the three conditions of equilibrium: $\sum F_X = 0$, $\sum F_Y = 0$, and $\sum M_O = 0$. Consequently, no more than three unknown reactions may appear in the beam supports of statically determinate beams. Designers may experience difficulty at times, however, in distinguishing what constitutes a beam support.

A beam support may be external or internal; typical external and internal supports are shown in Figure 2-9. In external supports, the beam is supported by some external and unyielding reaction. At an internal hinge point, one portion of the beam provides the support for an adjoining portion of the beam. (See the appendix for a brief review of the reactions at internal hinge points in beams and frames.)

Consider the cantilever beam of Figure 2-9(a). A total of three reactions occur at point B, the only support. Since three external unknown reactions and three equations of statics are involved, this cantilever beam is statically determinate.

A similar situation is presented by the simply supported beam of Figure 2-9(b). Simple beams may or may not have overhangs; either way, the total number of external unknown reactions for a simple beam is three. Since three external unknown reactions and three equations of statics are involved, the simply supported beam of Figure 2-9(b) is statically determinate.

Now consider the compound beam of Figure 2-9(c); this beam has four external reactions. Since there are only three equations of statics, the overall beam at first seems to be statically indeterminate. However, the intermediate internal hinge at point B produces an equivalent support for segment AB. Thus, segment AB, taken as a free body, has only three unknown reactions and is statically determinate. As a result, the reactions of segment AB can be found and then applied simply as known loads to the adjoining portion of the beam (segment BCD). Segment BCD in turn becomes a solvable simple beam that has only three unknown reactions at its external supports C and D. Segment BCD is therefore statically determinate, as is the overall system.

Similarly, the compound beam (or hinged beam) of Figure 2-9(d) has four unknown external reactions. The intermediate internal hinge at B, however, allows segment AB to be removed and solved as a simple beam. The reactions at B can then be applied as known loads to the adjoining portion of the beam (segment BC). Segment BC, initially unsolvable, then becomes a statically determinate cantilever beam. The overall system of beams of Figure 2-9(d) is therefore statically determinate.

The three-hinged arch of Figure 2-9(e) can be treated in the same way. It has four unknown external reactions, so the overall system is not immediately solvable. Both of the simple beams that make up the three-hinged arch can be removed and solved, however, since each beam has only three reactions. Consequently, the overall three-hinged arch is statically determinate.

The compound three-hinged arch shown in Figure 2-9(f) can be broken into four beams, two of which are solvable as statically determinate simple beams and two of which are initially unsolvable cantilevers. The computed reactions from the two simple beams become known loads on the adjoining cantilevers. The overall system is therefore statically determinate.

When separating compound systems of beams into their component beams, one must remember that a hinge can develop forces but no moment. Consequently, the only resistance that member CD in Figure 2-9(f) can develop is a compressive force along its axis, as shown. In contrast, the cantilever DE can develop resistance along its axis, and it can also develop resistance to lateral loads due to its moment-resistant base (at point E). In drawing the free body, one must carefully ensure that each support reflects *all* the forces that the particular support can develop, but *only* the forces that it can develop.

Even if no lateral load exists on a beam, one equation of statics must be used to obtain the trivial solution confirming that the horizontal reaction is in fact zero. For example, the beam of Figure 2-10 has only three reactions; the fourth reaction R_{BX} obviously does not exist. It *could* exist as shown, however, and proving that it is zero requires using the statics equation $\Sigma F_H = 0$. Because the beam of Figure 2-10 could develop four reactions, it is statically indeterminate.

(a) Cantilever beam   (b) Simple beam with overhang

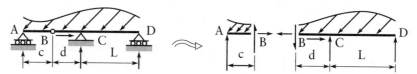

(c) Compound beam with hinged supports

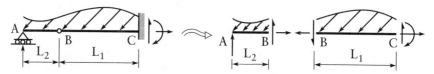

(d) Compound beam with fixed support

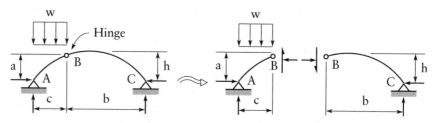

(e) Three-hinged arch on hinged supports

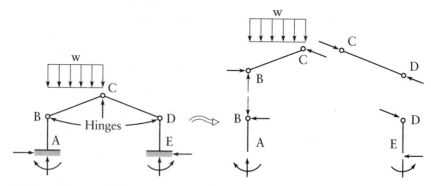

(f) Three-hinged arch on cantilevered supports

FIGURE 2-9 Statically determinate system of beams.

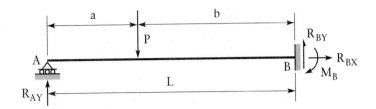

FIGURE 2-10 Beam with no horizontal load.

Example 2-3 Determine whether the given system of beams is statically determinate or statically indeterminate.

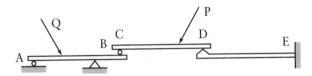

Solution The system is first broken into its three component beams, as shown in the accompanying figure.

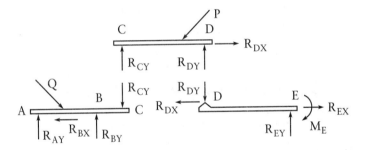

The beam CD has only three reactions and no unknown loads, so it is completely solvable. With its reactions R_{DX}, R_{DY} and R_{CY} now reduced to known loads, both of the remaining beams have only three unknowns and are therefore solvable.

This system of beams is statically determinate.

When the reactions are placed on the freebody sketch, as in Example 2-3, they need not be shown in their correct direction. It is important only that *every* reaction that a support can develop is included, and that *only* the reactions that a support can develop are included.

Example 2-4   Determine whether the given system of beams is statically determinate or statically indeterminate.

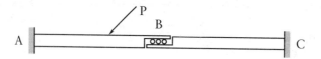

Solution   The system is first broken into its two component beams, as shown in the accompanying figure.

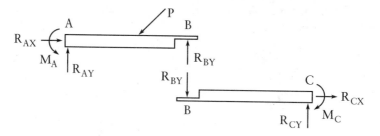

Each of the two component beams has only three external reactions. Both, however, have an additional unknown internal reaction R_{BY} that cannot be determined by statics; no individual beam in this system is completely solvable.

This system of beams is statically indeterminate.

Example 2-5   Determine whether the given system of beams is statically determinate or statically indeterminate.

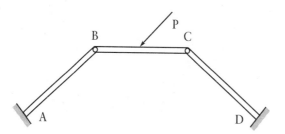

Solution   The system is first broken into its components, as shown in the accompanying figure.

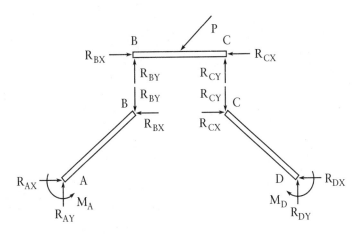

Each of the three component beams has more than three unknown forces. No single beam is statically determinate.

This system of beams is statically indeterminate.

Example 2-6   Determine whether the given system of beams is statically determinate or statically indeterminate.

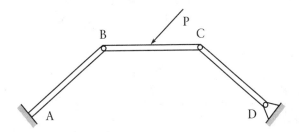

Solution   This beam system is the same as the one presented in Example 2-5, except that the support at D has been changed into a hinge. The system is broken into its three component parts, as shown in the accompanying figure. With pins at both ends, the member CD can develop only an axial force; transverse shear cannot develop in such a member.

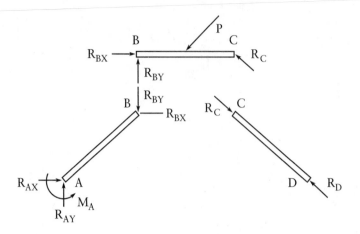

As a result, the component beam BC is statically determinate. Its reactions, when computed, become known loads on the other two beams, which in turn become statically determinate.

This system of beams is statically determinate.

Example 2-7   Determine whether the given system of beams is statically determinate or statically indeterminate. (Reactions may be directed either upward or downward.)

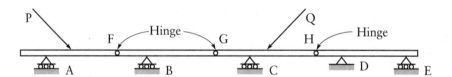

Solution   The system is first broken into its component parts, as shown in the accompanying figure.

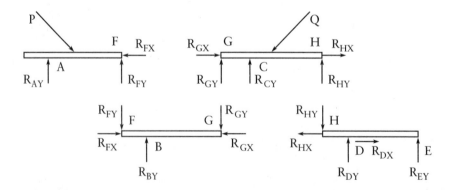

Of these four component beams, only segment *AF* is immediately solvable as a statically determinate beam. Its reactions, when known, reduce the adjoining segment *FBG* to a statically determinate beam. The reactions of segment *FBG*, in turn, when computed, reduce the adjoining segment *GCH* to a statically determinate beam. And finally, when R_{HX} and R_{HY} are known, beam segment *HDE* becomes statically determinate.

This system of beams is statically determinate.

Example 2-8 Determine whether the given system of beams is statically determinate or statically indeterminate.

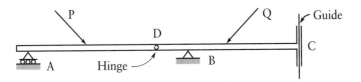

Solution The system is first broken into its component parts, as shown in the accompanying figure.

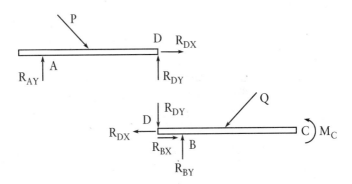

The segment *AD* is a completely solvable statically determinate beam. Its reactions, when known, become loads on the adjoining segment *DBC*. Segment *DBC* then has only three unknown reactions and is therefore statically determinate.

This system of beams is statically determinate.

The idea of a compound system of hinged beams can be overdone. For example, consider the hinged beams of Figure 2-11(a). A load placed anywhere on the system will cause the system to collapse. The system is not a stable arrangement and cannot be used as structure.

Similarly, the frame of Figure 2-11(b) is unstable. A load placed anywhere on the system (other than at a precarious point of balance) will cause the system to collapse. Systems of the type shown in Figure 2-11 are called *mechanisms* or *link mechanisms*.

A more subtle problem can occur when too many internal hinges occur in a straight line. Each of the two systems of Figure 2-12, for example, includes three internal hinges between the two exterior supports. The configuration of Figure 2-12(a) is unstable, while the configuration of Figure 2-12(b) is stable.

The instability of the configuration in Figure 2-12(a) may be shown by removing segment BC as a free body and trying to solve for reactions. With no vertical reaction possible at point C, the condition of moment equilibrium cannot be met. In contrast, the same procedure will show that the segment BC of Figure 2-12(b) is stable, since in this case the reaction at C can have a vertical component.

If more than two internal hinges occur between two points of exterior support, the hinges must form a three-hinged arch. Otherwise, the system will not be in moment equilibrium.

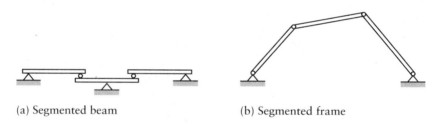

(a) Segmented beam   (b) Segmented frame

FIGURE 2-11 Unstable configurations.

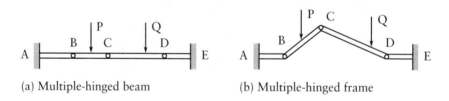

(a) Multiple-hinged beam   (b) Multiple-hinged frame

FIGURE 2-12 Multiple-hinged configurations.

2.4 GENERAL CONCLUSIONS AND RULES

At this point, some general conclusions may be drawn and some rules stated.

If a system of hinged beams can be separated into a set of component beams such that each component beam has no more than three external reactions and at least one of the component beams is completely solvable, the system of beams is statically determinate. The solution begins with one of the solvable beams and propagates into the adjoining beams.

These conclusions may also be summarized mathematically. In a system of hinged beams where r is the number of external reactions and f is the number of internal hinge points,

if $r - f > 3$, the system is statically indeterminate;

if $r - f = 3$, the system is statically determinate;

if $r - f < 3$, the system is an unstable mechanism.

Further, if more than two internal hinges occur between two external supports, either they must form three-hinged arches or the system will be unstable.

Some further examples will demonstrate the use of the foregoing equalities and inequalities.

Example 2-9   Determine whether the given system of beams is statically determinate or statically indeterminate.

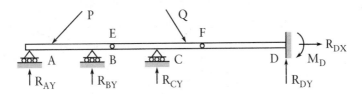

Solution   The external supports can develop the six reactions shown. With two internal hinges (at E and F), the excess number of unknown reactions is

$$r - f = 6 - 2 = 4$$

Hence,

$$r - f > 3$$

The system of beams is statically indeterminate.

Example 2-10 Determine whether the given system of beams is statically determinate or statically indeterminate.

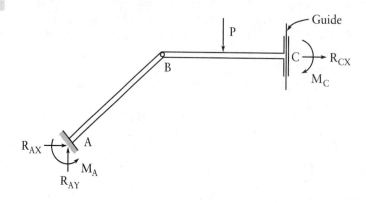

Solution The external supports can develop the five reactions shown. With one internal hinge (at B), the excess number of unknown reactions is

$$r - f = 5 - 1 = 4$$

Hence,

$$r - f > 3$$

The system of beams is statically indeterminate.

Example 2-11 Determine whether the given system of beams is statically determinate or statically indeterminate.

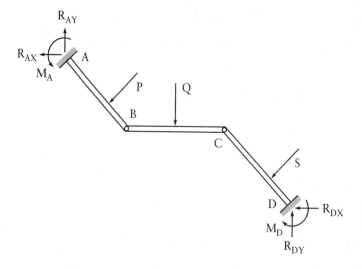

Solution The external supports can develop the six reactions shown. With two internal hinges (at B and C), the excess number of unknown reactions is

$$r - f = 6 - 2 = 4$$

Hence,

$$r - f > 3$$

The system of beams is statically indeterminate.

Example 2-12 Determine whether the system of beams in Example 2-11 would be statically determinate if both the fixed supports were changed to hinged supports.

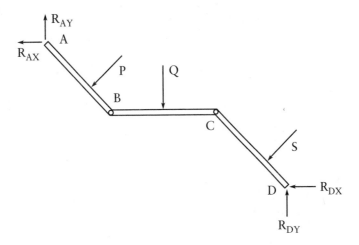

Solution The external reactions can now develop only four reactions, as shown in the preceding figure. With two internal hinges (at B and C), the number of unknown reactions is

$$r - f = 4 - 2 = 2$$

Hence,

$$r - f < 3$$

The system of beams is an unstable mechanism.

Example 2-13 Determine whether the given system of bent and straight beams is statically determinate or statically indeterminate.

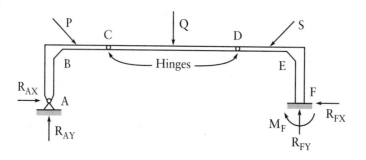

Solution The external supports can develop the five reactions shown in the preceding figure. With two internal hinges, the number of unknown reactions is

$$r - f = 5 - 2 = 3$$

Hence,

$$r - f = 3$$

The system of beams is statically determinate.

Example 2-14 Determine whether the given system of bent and straight beams is statically determinate or statically indeterminate.

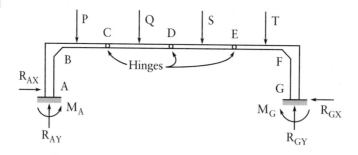

Solution The external supports can develop six reactions, as shown. With three internal hinges, the system seems to be statically determinate.

The system, however, has three hinges in one line between the two external supports. The system is therefore a mechanism of uncertain response to load. To produce stability, a vertical support (column) might be added at point D, or one hinge might be eliminated.

Outside Problems Determine whether the indicated system is statically determinate or statically indeterminate. If it is statically determinate, solve for the reactions. An open circle in the sketches denotes an interior hinge point.

Asterisks indicate problem is answered in the Answer Section at the back of the book.

Problem 2-1*

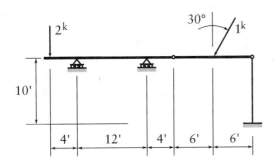

Problem 2-2

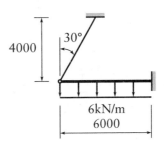

Problem 2-3*

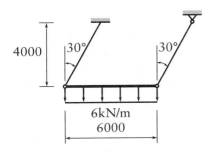

Problem 2-4

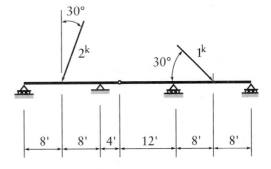

Problem 2-5*

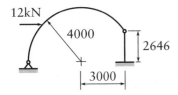

Problem 2-6

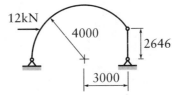

Problem 2-7*

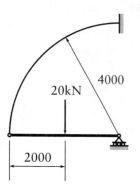

Problem 2-8

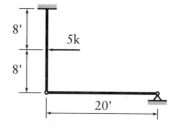

Problem 2-9*

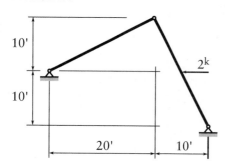

Problem 2-10

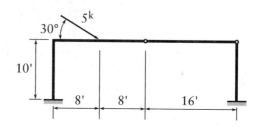

Problem 2-11*

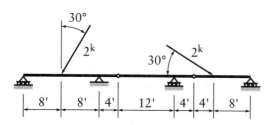

Problem 2-12

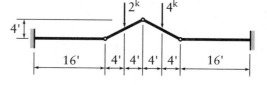

Problem 2-13*

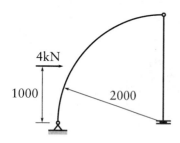

Problem 2-14

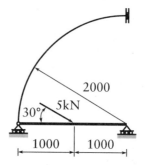

2.5 STATICALLY INDETERMINATE REACTIONS

The only distinctive feature of a statically indeterminate beam is the fact that the reactions at the supports cannot be computed by using static equilibrium alone; the size and stiffness of the beam must also be included in computations of its reactions. Once the reactions are found, by whatever means, there is no difference in any succeeding calculations between a beam that was initially statically indeterminate and a beam that was initially statically determinate. Stresses and deformations in later calculations are found in exactly the same way, using identical approaches and identical methods; the only difference between these two categories of beams lies in how the reactions at the supports were initially computed.

Consider, for example, the beam of Figure 2-13. Assume that the end reactions were computed earlier and that the beam has been taken from some larger structure as a free body, with its end reactions as shown.

At this point, relying entirely on the information just provided, there is no way to know whether this beam was taken from a continuous rigid frame (a highly indeterminate structure) or from a simple beam with two overhangs (a completely determinate structure). Nor does it matter. Selecting the size of the member, selecting reinforcement, computing deflections (if needed), and performing any other necessary calculations will proceed from this point in exactly the same way.

The methods of the preceding section enable the designer to determine whether the reactions for a particular beam are statically determinate or statically indeterminate. If the reactions are indeterminate, the designer might consult a handbook for the beam reactions for some of the more common cases. Or if necessary, the designer might proceed into the more time-consuming indeterminate analysis. Finally, if permissible, the beam supports may be redesigned in such a way that the beam becomes statically determinate.

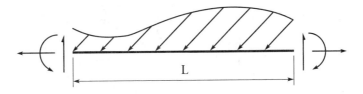

FIGURE 2-13 Simple beam with end reactions.

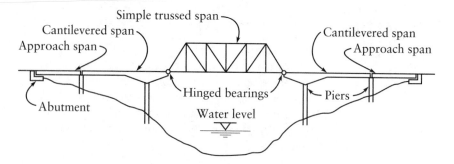

FIGURE 2-14 Typical double cantilever bridge.

It should not be inferred from foregoing discussions that larger structures are necessarily statically indeterminate. For example, double cantilever bridges, which are used to make hundreds of river crossings around the world, are completely statically determinate. A sketch of a typical bridge of this type is shown in Figure 2-14.

In routine construction, the two cantilevered spans of the bridge, with their overhangs (similar to the beam of Figure 2-9(b)) are built simultaneously from the two sides of the river. When they are complete, the simple center span, having been assembled upstream during this same period, is barged downstream into position and lifted into place. Regardless what the size of the final bridge may be, the entire primary structural system of this bridge is statically determinate. There is thus no correlation between the size of a structure and its static determinacy.

REVIEW QUESTIONS

Boldface Review Question numbers indicate that the question is answered in the Answer Section at the back of the book.

1. In a building design, how does one distinguish between the structural members and the nonstructural members?

2. Floor joists spaced at 2'-0" on center are supported by a beam. Is the beam considered to be loaded by a series of concentrated loads or by a uniform load?

3. Sketch a simply supported beam 20'-0" long, loaded antisymmetrically by two hydrostatic loads 10'-0" long that have their minimum values at the supports and that have a maximum value of 600 lb/ft.

4. Sketch a simply supported beam 20'-0" long, loaded cycloantisymmetrically by two hydrostatic loads 10'-0" long that have a maximum value of 600 lb/ft.

5. In sketches showing beam reactions, why is it advisable to include horizontal reactions at the hinged support even if there are no horizontal loads and it is obvious that the horizontal reaction is zero?

6. What is a link mechanism?

7. How is a link mechanism formed?

8. How is a three-hinged arch formed?

9. What effects would a change in temperature produce on the structure discussed in Example 2-5? On the structure discussed in Example 2-6?

10. What effects would a change in temperature produce on the structure discussed in Example 2-11? On the structure discussed in Example 2-13?

11. In view of the answers to questions 9 and 10, what conclusion may be drawn about the relationship between statical determinacy and temperature change?

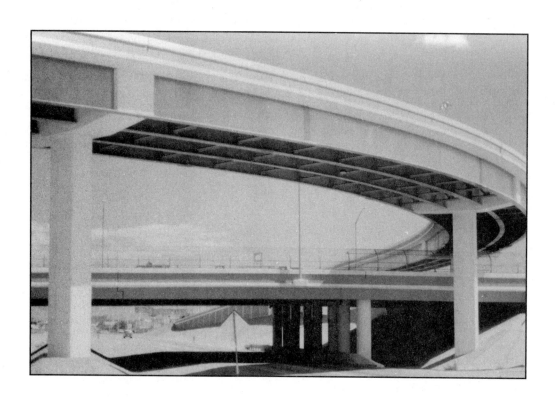

Elevated steel highway flyover, Las Vegas, Nevada.
(Photograph courtesy American Institute of Steel
Construction, reprinted by permission.)

Shear and Moment in Beams

The general topics of shear and moment in beams are the same ones introduced in courses on the elementary strength of materials. The coverage in strength of materials, however, is too superficial to be adequate for civil engineering practice; a much more thorough treatment is required. In this chapter, the study of shear and moment in beams is thoroughly and rigorously developed to include the definitions, nomenclature, and approaches commonly used in civil engineering practice. These symbols, methods, and practices will be used throughout the remainder of this text.

3.1 CROSS-SECTIONAL RESULTANTS OF LOAD

Cross-sectional resultants of load are the loads acting on a particular cross section of a loaded member. They are necessarily the loads used to compute the stresses on that cross section. For example, the flexural stress on a cross section is computed from the flexure formula:

$$f = Mc/I \tag{3.1}$$

where

f is the flexural stress normal to the cross section at a distance c from the neutral axis;

I is the moment of inertia of the cross-sectional area about the neutral axis;

M is the moment acting on that cross section.

The moment M in the flexure formula is a cross-sectional resultant of load. Because it varies throughout the length of the beam, it must be computed for each section where stress is sought.

As a point of review, a typical beam in flexure is shown in Figure 3-1. To find the flexural stress at some point in the beam, such as at midspan, it is necessary to compute the cross-sectional moment M at that point. The cross-sectional moment M at midspan is computed by summing all moments and moments due to forces that act to one side of that cross section. For example, the moment M at the centerline in Figure 3-1 is computed as

$$M = 10,000 \times 10 - (1000 \times 10)(10/2) = 50,000 \text{ lb-ft}$$

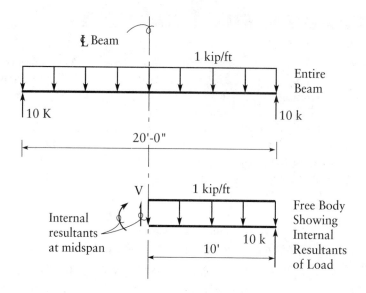

FIGURE 3-1 Typical beam in flexure.

In all cases, the moment acting on a cross section is found by summing moments to one side of the cross section. While it does not matter which side of the cross section is chosen for summing moments, the arithmetic can often be reduced considerably by choosing the side that has fewer forces acting on it.

Four such cross-sectional resultants of load appear in elementary strength of materials:

1. Moment M The moment M on a cross section is the sum of all moments and moments due to forces acting to one side of the cross section. A moment is positive if it causes the beam to cup upward (smile) with respect to a viewer whose shoulders are parallel to the beam.

2. Normal Force P The normal force P on a cross section is the sum of all forces or components of forces whose action lines are normal to the plane of the cross section. A normal force is positive if it causes tension on the cross section.

3. Shearing Force V The shearing force V on a cross section is the sum of all forces or components of forces whose action lines are parallel to the plane of the cross section; the sum is usually computed separately for the vertical and the horizontal components of these shearing forces. A shearing force is positive if it causes the left side of the beam to move upward with respect to the right side.

4. Torque T The torque T on a cross section is the sum of all torques and torque due to forces acting to one side of the cross section. A torque is positive if it is exerted clockwise to a viewer looking into the cross section along the remaining portion of the member.

The stresses associated with the foregoing resultants are given in standard textbooks in strength of materials; they are discussed more fully in Chapter 4, as Equations 4.4, 4.7, 4.10, and 4.14. For flexural stress:

$$f = Mc/I \tag{3.1}$$

For axial stress:

$$f = P/A \tag{3.2}$$

For beam shearing stress:

$$v = VQ/Ib \tag{3.3}$$

For torsional shear stress:

$$v = Tc/J \tag{3.4}$$

The foregoing equations should be familiar; if they are not, outside review of them is in order.

Some examples will illustrate the calculation of cross-sectional resultants of load.

Example 3-1   Determine the internal resultants of load that will occur at the base of the given lamppost (at section *A-A*) due to the dead load of the lights and ballast.

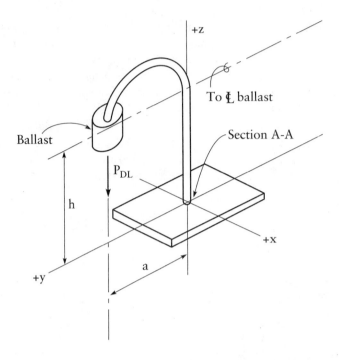

Solution   The sum of moments above section *A-A* provides the cross-sectional resultant of moment

$$M_{XX} = P_{DL}a$$

The sum of forces normal to the plane of the cross section provides the cross-sectional resultant of axial load

$$N_{ZZ} = -P_{DL} \qquad \text{(produces compression)}$$

The cross-sectional resultants acting at section *A-A* are shown in the following sketch.

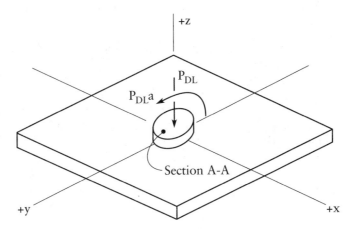

Example 3-2   Determine the internal resultants of load that will occur at the base of the given lamppost (at section *A-A*) due only to the wind load acting in the direction shown.

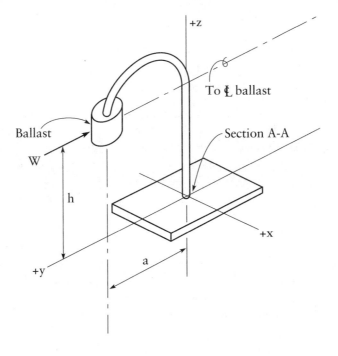

Solution   The sum of moments above section *A-A* provides the cross-sectional resultant of moment

$$M_{XX} = Wh$$

The sum of shearing forces above section *A-A* provides the cross-sectional resultant of shear

$$V_{YY} = W$$

The cross-sectional resultants acting at section *A-A* are shown in the following sketch.

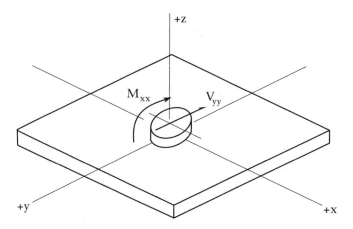

Example 3-3   Determine the internal resultants of load that will occur at the base of the given lamppost (at section *A-A*) due to the combined dead load and wind load, with wind acting in the direction shown.

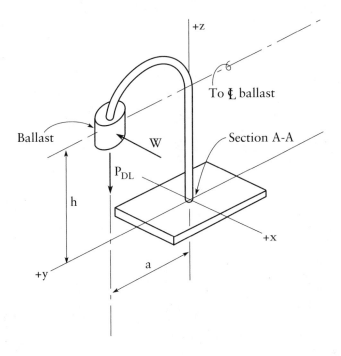

Solution   There are moments acting about both the *xx* and the *yy* axes, and there is a torque acting about the *zz* axis:

$$M_{XX} = P_{DL}a$$
$$M_{YY} = Wh$$
$$T_{ZZ} = Wa$$

There is a normal force acting on the plane of the cross section:

$$N_{ZZ} = -P_{DL} \qquad \text{(causing compression)}$$

There is a shearing force acting in the *xx* direction:

$$V_{XX} = W$$

The cross-sectional resultants acting at section *A-A* are shown in the following sketch.

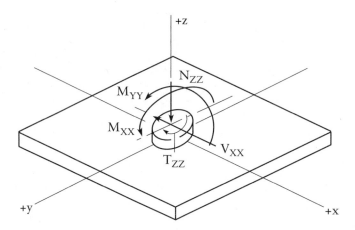

3.2 SHEAR AND MOMENT EQUATIONS AND DIAGRAMS

For computing stresses, the only cross-sectional resultants that are usually of interest are those that occur where the cross-sectional resultant reaches its maximum or minimum value. It is not always evident, however, where a cross-sectional resultant is going to reach its maximum or minimum value. Consequently, it has become standard practice to sketch a graph of the cross-sectional resultant and to identify visually the maximum or minimum value as desired. (In brittle materials, such as concrete or cast iron, the point where moment or shear reverses is also a critical point of interest to be found from such a graph.)

The uses of graphs of cross-sectional resultants extend far beyond just picturing the points where maxima and minima occur. Such graphs are also used for computing deflections, for varying the size of the cross section, and for optimizing spans and overhangs such that positive and negative resultants have roughly equal magnitudes. In concrete, the graphs indicate where particular kinds of reinforcement are needed; the graphs may even be drawn accurately to scale so that the reinforcement can be placed by scaling the graphs. Being able to make a quick sketch of these graphs is often a key to making a correct analysis.

In addition to sketching the graphs, designers frequently must determine the equations of the graphs, in order to find key values exactly. Further, the equations of the graphs are used in determining the deformations of the member. In all, the graphs and their equations are an important feature in structural analysis, and developing a reasonable skill in handling them is essential to anyone engaged in structural analysis at any level.

The graphs are commonly termed *shear and moment diagrams*, although they must include axial load and torsion (when these exist) in addition to shear and moment. In subsequent discussions, references to shear and moment diagrams should be understood to include axial load and torsion, if appropriate.

Certain relationships between load, shear, and moment resultants are useful for sketching the diagrams. These relationships are readily derived from the differential element of Figure 3-2. The resultants are shown in their positive sense on the differential element.

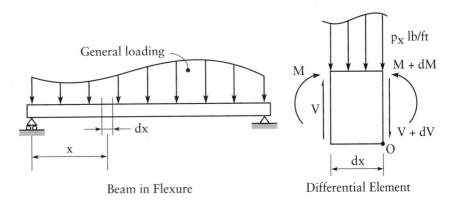

FIGURE 3-2 Beam in general flexure.

The sum of vertical forces on the differential element yields a relationship between the intensity of the load p and the shear:

$$\sum F_V = 0; \qquad V - p\,dx - (V + dV) = 0$$

$$dV/dx = -p_X \qquad (3.5)$$

The sum of moments about point 0 yields a relationship between shear V and moment M:

$$\sum M_0 = 0; \qquad M + V\,dx - p_X\,dx\,(dx/2) - (M + dM) = 0$$

Second-order terms are dropped, leaving

$$dM/dx = V \qquad (3.6)$$

The relationships defined by Equation 3.5 and Equation 3.6 can be stated verbally:

1. The rate of change of shear at any point x is equal to the negative intensity of load at that point.

2. The rate of change of moment at any point x is equal to the magnitude of shear at that point.

Alternatively, they can be stated in more graphic terms:

1. The slope of the shear diagram at any point x is $-p_X$.
2. The slope of the moment diagram at any point x is $+V_X$.

The following examples present several common techniques that are used for sketching shear and moment diagrams and for writing shear and moment equations. In these examples, the term *domain* is used to define the range of values of x within which the equation is valid.

Example 3-4 Write the shear and moment equations and sketch the shear and moment diagrams for the given cantilever.

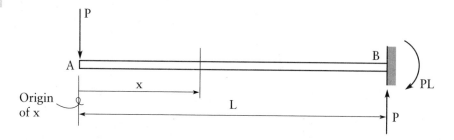

Solution To begin, it is noted that there are no discontinuities in load between $x = 0$ and $x = L$. Both the shear equation (and shear diagram) and the moment equation (and moment diagram) are therefore continuous throughout the domain $0 \le x \le L$.

A point x is chosen at some transient point somewhere within the domain $0 \le x \le L$. A free body is drawn to the left of point x, to include the origin of x. The following sketch represents the free body to the left of point x.

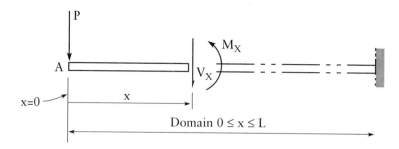

The sum of forces to the left of point x yields the shear equation at the point x:

$$0 \leq x \leq L; \qquad V_X = -P$$

The sum of all moments and moments due to forces to the left of point x yields the moment equation at the point x:

$$0 \leq x \leq L; \qquad M_X = -Px$$

As a boundary condition, the moment at $x = 0$ is zero.

The graphs of the equations for V_X and M_X are shown in the following sketches.

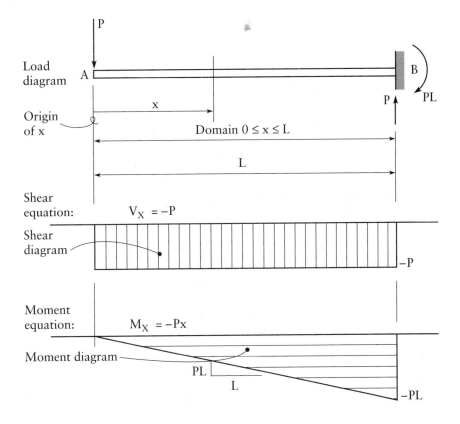

To construct the shear diagram:

1. Recognize from the shear equation that the shear is a constant; the shear diagram between points A and B is therefore a horizontal straight line.

2. Plot the values of shear at A and at B.

3. Connect the two values with a horizontal straight line.

To construct the moment diagram:

1. Recognize from the moment equation that the moment is linear in x; the moment diagram between points A and B is therefore a sloping straight line.
2. Plot the values of moment at A and at B.
3. Connect the two values with a sloping straight line.

The next problem is a bit more complex; the load is variable in x.

Example 3-5   Write the shear and moment equations and sketch the shear and moment diagrams for the given cantilever.

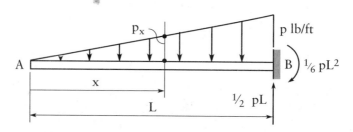

Solution   First, it is noted that there are no discontinuities in the load between $x = 0$ and $x = L$. The load is a linear function of x, however, varying from $p_x = 0$ at $x = 0$ to $p_x = p$ at $x = L$. As a ratio,

$$\frac{p_x}{x} = \frac{p}{L}; \quad p_x = p\left(\frac{x}{L}\right)$$

Since there are no discontinuities, both the shear equation (and the shear diagram) and the moment equation (and the moment diagram) will be continuous throughout the domain $0 \le x \le L$.

A point x is chosen at some transient point somewhere within the domain $0 \le x \le L$. A free body is drawn to the left of point x, to include the origin of x. The following sketch represents the free body to the left of point x.

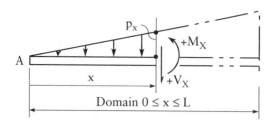

The sum of forces to the left of the point x yields the shear equation at point x:

$$0 \leq x \leq L; \quad V_X = -\left(\frac{1}{2}p_X x\right)$$

$$= \frac{-px^2}{2L}$$

The sum of moments to the left of the point x yields the moment equation at point x:

$$0 \leq x \leq L; \quad M_X = -\left(\frac{1}{2}p_X x\right)\left(\frac{x}{3}\right)$$

$$= \frac{-px^3}{6L}$$

Again, as a boundary condition, the moment at the free end of the cantilever is zero.

The graphs of the equations for V_X and M_X are shown in the following sketches:

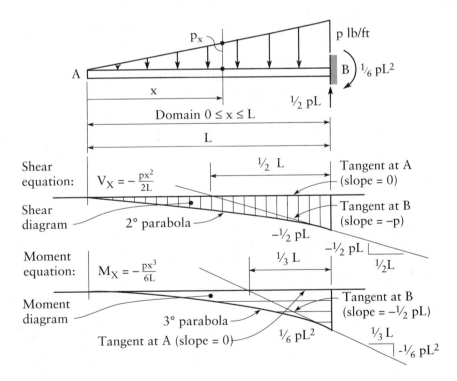

To construct the shear diagram:

1. Recognize from the shear equation that the shear is a function of x^2; the shear diagram between points A and B is therefore a 2° parabola.

2. Plot the values of shear at A and at B. At A, the shear is zero; and at B, the shear is $-^1/_2pL$.

3. Plot the slopes of the shear diagram at A and at B. At A, the load p has only one value and that value is zero; the slope of the shear diagram at A is therefore zero (horizontal). At B, the load has the value $+p$; a tangent is drawn through the point $^1/_2pL$ at the point B having a slope $-p$.

4. With a French curve, draw the 2° parabola through the two known values of shear, tangent to the two known slopes.

To construct the moment diagram:

1. Recognize from the moment equation that the moment is a function of x^3; the moment diagram between points A and B is therefore a 3° parabola.

2. Plot the values of moment at A and at B. At A, the moment is zero; and at B, the moment is $-^1/_6pL^2$.

3. Plot the slopes of the moment diagram at A and at B. At A, the shear has only one value and that value is zero; the slope of the moment diagram at A is therefore zero (horizontal). At B, the shear has a value $-^1/_2pL$; a tangent is drawn through the point $-^1/_6pL^2$ at point B having a slope $-^1/_2pL$.

4. With a French curve, draw the 3° parabola through the two known values of moment, tangent to the two known slopes.

Where loads are discontinuous, both the shear and the moment equations must reflect these points of discontinuity. Consequently, the equations have to be written in several parts in order to cover the entire span, with each part being valid only so long as there are no discontinuities in load. The next two examples illustrate the procedure where loading is discontinuous; they also introduce numerical loads rather than algebraic loads.

Example 3-6   Write the shear and moment equations and sketch the shear and moment diagrams for the given cantilever.

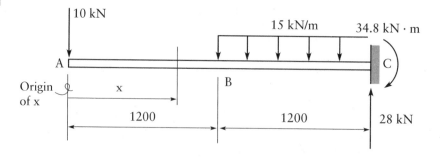

Solution There is a discontinuity in the load. Both the shear equation (and the shear diagram) and the moment equation (and the moment diagram) will have points of discontinuity at the same points where the load is discontinuous. Two domains of x can be recognized, however, over which the load is piecewise continuous: $0 \leq x \leq 1.2$ and $1.2 \leq x \leq 2.4$.

Within the domain $0 \leq x \leq 1.2$, a point x is chosen at some transient point between the limits 0 and 1.2 m. A free body is drawn to the left of point x to include the origin of x. The following sketch represents the free body to the left of point x.

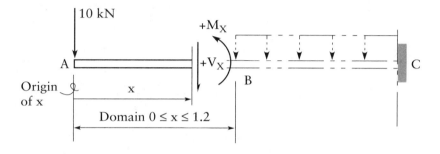

The sum of forces to the left of point x yields the shear equation at point x:

$$0 \leq x \leq 1.2; \qquad V_X = -10$$

The sum of moments to the left of point x yields the moment equation at point x:

$$0 \leq x \leq 1.2; \qquad M_X = -10x$$

The moment at $x = 0$ is therefore zero, and the moment at $x = 1.2$ m is therefore -12 kN·m.

Within the domain $1.2 \leq x \leq 2.4$, a point x is chosen at some transient point between the limits 1.2 m and 2.4 m. A free body is drawn to the left of point x to include the origin of x. The following sketch represents the free body to the left of point x.

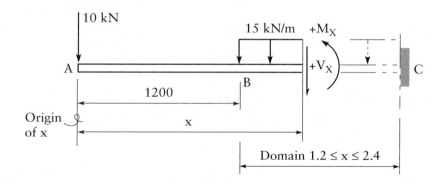

The sum of forces to the left of point x yields the shear equation at point x:

$$1.2 < x < 2.4; \qquad V_X = -10 - 15(x - 1.2)$$

The sum of moments to the left of point x yields the moment equation at point x:

$$1.2 < x < 2.4; \qquad M_X = -10x - \frac{1}{2}(15)(x - 1.2)^2$$

The graphs of these four equations for V_X and M_X are the shear and moment diagrams over the entire span, as shown in the following sketches.

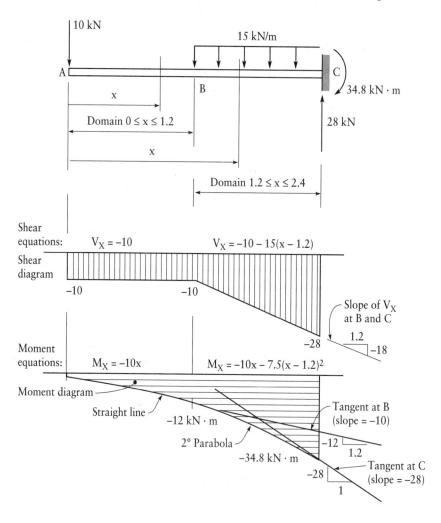

To construct the shear diagram:

1. Recognize from the shear equations that the shear is a constant for $0 \le x \le 1.2$; the shear diagram in the first domain of x is therefore a horizontal straight line. For the second domain, the shear diagram is linear in x and is therefore a sloping straight line.

2. Plot the values of shear at points A, B, and C. At the point A, $V = -10$ kN; at B, $V = -10$ kN; at C, $V = -28$ kN.

3. Connect the values of V with straight lines.

To construct the moment diagram:

1. Recognize from the moment equations that, in the first domain, the moment is linear in x and is therefore a sloping straight line. In the second domain, the moment varies as x^2 and is therefore a 2° parabola.

2. Plot the values of moment at points A, B, and C. At point A, $M = 0$; at B, $M = -12$ kN·m; at C, $M = -34.8$ kN·m.

3. Plot the slopes of the moment diagram through these moment values at points A, B, and C. At A, the shear is multivalued, but just to the right of point A, the value of the shear is -10 kN·m; the slope of the moment diagram just to the right of point A is therefore -10 kN·m/m. At point B, the value of shear is -10 kN·m; the slope of the moment diagram is therefore -10 kN·m/m at both sides of B. Just to the left of point C, the value of shear is -28 kN·m; the slope of the moment diagram just to the left of point C is therefore -28 kN·m/m.

4. Connect the points between A and B with a sloping straight line. With a French curve, draw the 2° parabola through the two known values of moment at B and C, tangent to the two known slopes.

Example 3-7 Write the shear and moment equations and sketch the shear and moment diagrams for the given simple beam.

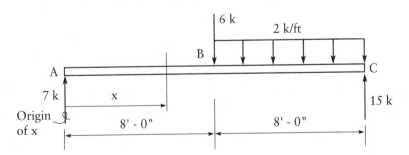

Solution It is noted that there is a discontinuity in the load. Over the two domains of x, however, the shear and moment equations (and diagrams) are piecewise continuous: $0 \le x \le 8'$ and $8' \le x \le 16'$.

A free body is drawn for some point x within the domain $0 \leq x \leq 8'$.

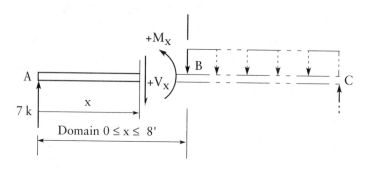

The sum of forces to the left of x yields the shear equation:

$$0 \leq x \leq 8'; \qquad V_X = +7$$

The sum of moments to the left of x yields the moment equation:

$$0 \leq x \leq 8'; \qquad M_X = +7x$$

A free body is drawn for some point x within the domain $8' \leq x \leq 16'$.

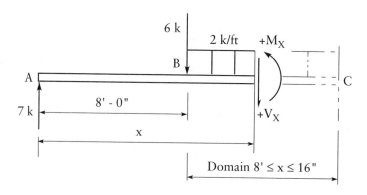

The sum of forces to the left of x yields the shear equation:

$$8' \leq x \leq 16'; \qquad V_X = 7 - 6 - 2(x - 8)$$
$$= 1 - 2(x - 8)$$

The sum of moments to the left of x yields the moment equation:

$$8' \leq x \leq 16'; \qquad M_X = 7x - 6(x - 8) - (x - 8)^2$$

The graphs of these four equations for V_X and M_X are the shear and moment diagrams, as shown in the following sketches.

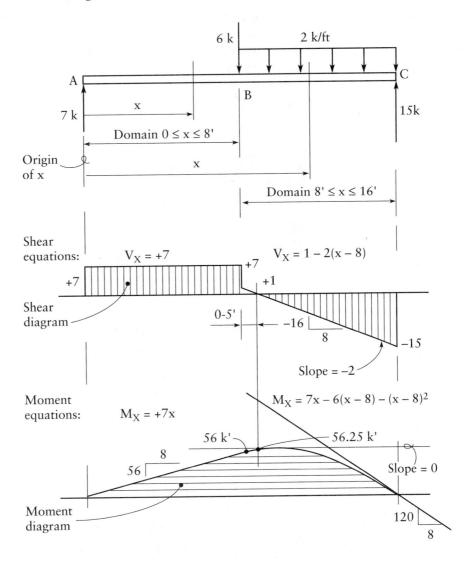

To construct the shear diagram:

1. Recognize that the shear diagram in the first domain is a horizontal straight line, and that the shear diagram in the second domain is a sloping straight line.
2. Plot the value of shear at each limit (endpoint) in the first domain, and connect them with a horizontal straight line.
3. Plot the value of shear at each limit (endpoint) in the second domain, and connect them with a sloping straight line.

To construct the moment diagram:

1. Recognize that the moment diagram in the first domain is a sloping straight line, and that the moment diagram in the second domain is a 2° parabola.
2. Plot the values of moment at A, B, and C.
3. Plot the slopes of the moment diagram through these values of M. At A, the slope is +7; at B, the slope is +1; at C, the slope is –15.
4. Connect the points between A and B with a sloping straight line. With a French curve, draw the 2° parabola through the two known values of moment at B and D, tangent to the two known slopes.

Additional points on the moment diagram can now be investigated. The absolute maximum value of moment occurs where shear is zero, at which point the slope of the moment diagram is zero. Shear is zero in the second domain. Thus, the shear equation for the second domain is set equal to zero and solved for x:

$$8 \leq x \leq 16; \qquad V_X = 0 = 1 - 2(x - 8)$$
$$x = 8.50 \text{ ft}$$

Maximum moment therefore occurs at $x = 8.5$ ft. The value of $x = 8.5$ ft is now substituted into the moment equation to obtain the maximum value of moment:

$$8 \leq x \leq 16; \qquad M_X = 7(8.5) - 6(8.5 - 8) - (8.5 - 8)^2$$
$$= 56.25 \text{ kip-ft}$$

These values for x and M_x have been entered on the preceding sketch.

The next example illustrates the procedure for analyzing a beam with an overhang.

Example 3-8   Write the shear and moment equations and sketch the shear and moment diagrams for the given simple beam with overhang.

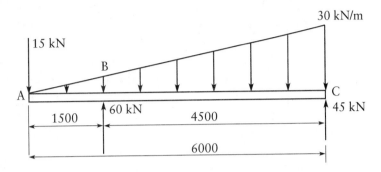

Solution   The discontinuity in the load diagram is noted. The two piecewise continuous domains of x are $0 \leq x \leq 1.5$ m and 1.5 m $\leq x \leq 6$ m.

The intensity of the load p_X at any point x is found by ratios:

$$\frac{p_X}{x} = \frac{30}{6}; \qquad p_X = 5x \text{ kN/m}$$

A free body is drawn, with x in the first domain.

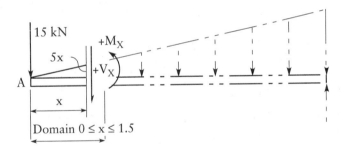

The sum of forces to the left of x yields the shear equation:

$$0 \leq x \leq 1.5; \qquad V_X = -15 - 5x\left(\frac{1}{2}x\right)$$

$$= -15 - 2.5x^2$$

The sum of moments to the left of x yields the moment equation:

$$0 \leq x \leq 1.5 ; \qquad M_x = -15 - 5x\left(\tfrac{1}{2}x\right)\left(\tfrac{1}{3}x\right)$$

$$= -15\,x - 0.8333x^3$$

A free body is drawn, with x in the second domain.

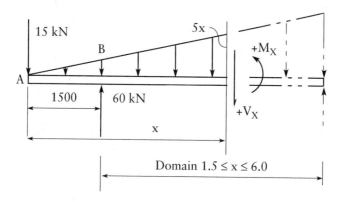

The sum of forces to the left of x yields the shear equation:

$$1.5 \leq x \leq 6 ; \qquad V_x = -15 + 60 - 5x\left(\tfrac{1}{2}x\right)$$

$$= 45 - 2.5x^2$$

The sum of moments to the left of x yields the moment equation:

$$1.5 \leq x \leq 6 ; \qquad M_x = -15x + 60\,(x - 1.5) - 5x\left(\tfrac{1}{2}x\right)\left(\tfrac{1}{3}x\right)$$

$$= -90 + 45x - 0.8333x^3$$

The graphs of these four equations are plotted as the following shear and moment diagrams.

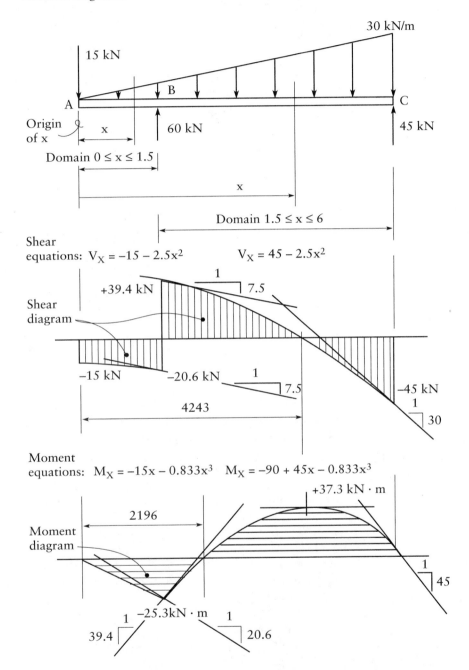

30 kN/m

15 kN

B

A   C

Origin of x   x   60 kN   45 kN

Domain $0 \leq x \leq 1.5$

x

Domain $1.5 \leq x \leq 6$

Shear equations: $V_X = -15 - 2.5x^2$ $V_X = 45 - 2.5x^2$

+39.4 kN

$\frac{1}{7.5}$

Shear diagram

−15 kN   −20.6 kN $\frac{1}{7.5}$

−45 kN

$\frac{1}{30}$

4243

Moment equations: $M_X = -15x - 0.833x^3$ $M_X = -90 + 45x - 0.833x^3$

+37.3 kN · m

2196

Moment diagram

$\frac{1}{45}$

$\frac{1}{39.4}$ −25.3kN · m $\frac{1}{20.6}$

To construct the shear diagram:

1. Recognize that the shear diagram is a 2° parabola throughout the beam.
2. Plot the value of shear at each limit (endpoint) of each of the two domains.
3. Plot the slopes of the shear diagram through each of these values of shear.
4. With a French curve, draw the 2° parabolas through these known values, tangent to the known slopes.
5. Compute the value of x where the shear becomes zero.

To construct the moment diagram:

1. Recognize that the moment diagram is a 3° parabola throughout the beam.
2. Plot the value of moment at each limit (endpoint) of each of the two domains.
3. Compute the value of maximum moment where the shear is zero, and plot this value.
4. Plot the slopes of the moment diagram at each of these known values of moment.
5. With a French curve, draw the 3° parabolas through these known values of moment, tangent to the known slopes.

Some notable observations can be made from the results of Example 3-8. For instance, the slope through the value of shear −20.6 kN at point B is plotted by dividing the shear of −20.6 kN by the intensity of load 7.5 kN/m; the result is a distance of 2.75 m, which is plotted to the left of B along the axis of the shear diagram. A line drawn through this point and the value of shear −20.6 kN at point B has the desired slope of −7.5 kN/m. All slopes in the two diagrams are plotted in this way.

A second observation involves the sharply pointed configuration of the two diagrams at point B. It has been noted, for example, that the slope of the moment diagram is equal to the value of shear; at point B, the value of shear is multivalued, varying from −20.6 kN to +39.4 kN. So, too, the slope of the moment diagram at point B is interpreted to be multivalued, consisting of a family of lines whose slopes vary from a minimum value of −20.6 kN·m/m to the left of point B to a maximum value of +39.4 kN·m/m to the right of point B.

A third observation relates to the point where moment reaches its maximum value, at a distance $x = 4243$ mm from the origin. At that point the shear has only one value, zero; the slope of the moment diagram therefore has only one value, zero.

A fourth observation involves the slope of the shear diagram at point A. Just to the right of the 15 kN load, the intensity of load p is zero. The slope of the shear diagram at that point is therefore zero, as shown. The slope of the moment diagram at that point, however, is not zero but is −15 kN; the slope is plotted on the moment diagram as shown.

As a final observation, this beam has an inflection point—that is, a point where moment goes to zero as it changes from tension on top to tension on bottom. The exact location of the inflection point is found by setting the moment equation for the appropriate domain to zero and solving for x:

Domain $1.5 \leq x \leq 6$

$$M_X = 0 = -90 + 45x - 0.8333x^3$$

This cubic equation is solved by trial and error to find

$$x = 2196 \text{ mm}$$

from the left end of the beam. This value for the inflection point has been included in the sketch of the moment equation. The location of the inflection point is an extremely important consideration in the design both of concrete beams and of steel beams; whenever an inflection point occurs in a beam, its location is automatically included in the moment diagram.

The following rather complex example contains only the briefest of explanations; it indicates how the equations and diagrams would likely be developed by a designer fully familiar with the procedures.

Example 3-9   Write the shear and moment equations and sketch the shear and moment diagrams for the given beam.

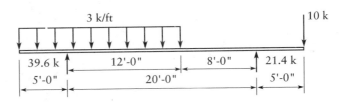

Solution   There are four domains of x where loads are piecewise continuous: $0 \leq x \leq 5'$, $5' \leq x \leq 17'$, $17' \leq x \leq 25'$, and $25' \leq x \leq 30'$.

A piece of scrap paper is held successively over the right portion of the beam from about the midpoint of each of the four domains. In this way, the four shear and moment equations can be written without requiring four additional free body sketches. The four shear equations from this procedure are

$$
\begin{aligned}
0 \leq x \leq 5'; & \quad V_X = -3x & = -3x \\
5' \leq x \leq 17'; & \quad V_X = -3x + 39.6 & = -3x + 39.6 \\
17' \leq x \leq 25'; & \quad V_X = -51 + 39.6 & = -11.4 \\
25' \leq x \leq 30'; & \quad V_X = -51 + 39.6 + 21.4 & = +10.0
\end{aligned}
$$

The same procedure is used for writing the moment equations:

$$0 \le x \le 5'; \quad M_X = -1.5x^2 \qquad\qquad\qquad\qquad = -1.5x^2$$
$$5' \le x \le 17'; \quad M_X = -1.5x^2 + 39.6(x - 5) \qquad = -1.5x^2 + 39.6(x - 5)$$
$$17' \le x \le 25'; \quad M_X = -10(30 - x) + 21.4(25 - x) \quad = -11.4x + 235$$
$$25' \le x \le 30'; \quad M_X = -10(30 - x) \qquad\qquad = +10x - 300$$

(For the two domains at the right, the moment equations were written from the right.)

The shear and moment diagrams are sketched by plotting the values of shear and moment at each end of each domain, and then plotting the slopes of the shear and moment through these values as required. The final curves are sketched to pass through these known values while staying tangent to these known slopes.

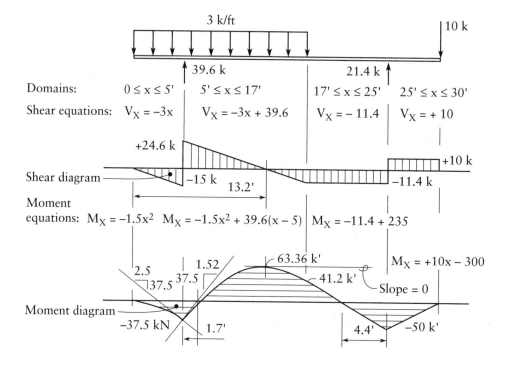

The exact locations of the two inflection points are found as before, by setting the moment diagram for the appropriate domain to zero and solving for x:

Domain $5' \le x \le 17'$

$$M_X = 0 = -1.5x^2 + 39.6(x - 5)$$

Solve by the quadratic formula to find:

$x = 6.7$ ft from the left end, and

$x = 19.7$ ft from the left end (outside the domain).

Domain $17' \leq x \leq 25'$

$M_X = 0 = -11.4x + 235$

$x = 20.6$ ft from the left end.

Outside Problems Write the shear and moment equations and sketch the shear and moment diagrams for the given cantilever beams.

Problem 3-1*

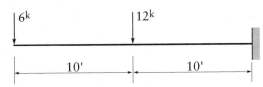

Problem 3-2

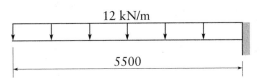

Problem 3-3*

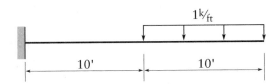

Problem 3-4

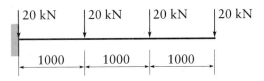

Problem 3-5*

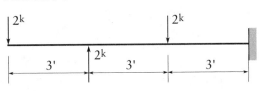

Problem 3-6

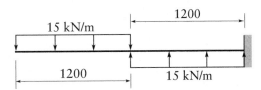

Problem 3-7*

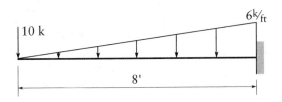

Problem 3-8

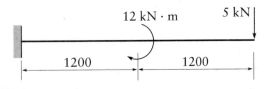

Problem 3-9*

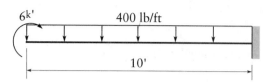

Problem 3-10

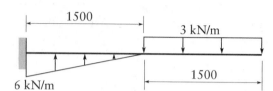

Problem 3-11*

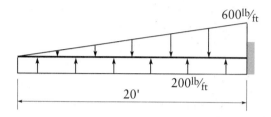

Problem 3-12

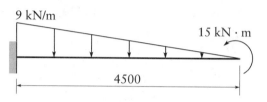

Write the shear and moment equations and sketch the shear and moment diagrams for the given simply supported beams.

Problem 3-13*

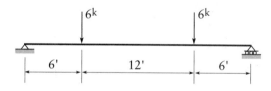

Problem 3-14

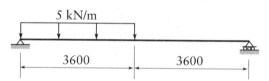

Problem 3-15*

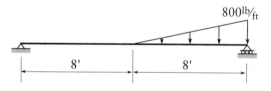

Problem 3-16

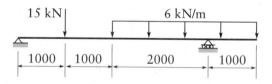

Problem 3-17*

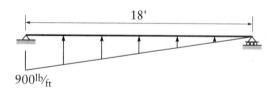

Problem 3-18

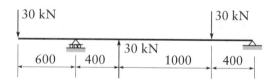

Problem 3-19*

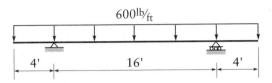

Problem 3-20

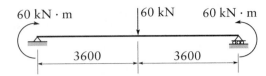

Problem 3-21*

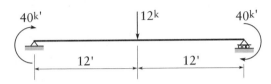

Problem 3-22

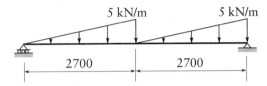

Problem 3-23*

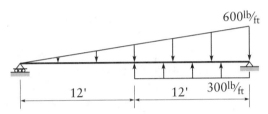

Problem 3-24

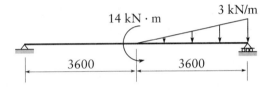

3.3 SHEAR AND MOMENT DIAGRAMS FOR HINGED BEAMS

It was noted earlier that a hinged beam can be broken into its components of simple beams and cantilevers. The shear and moment diagrams for these individual component beams are no different from those of other simple beams and cantilevers. Occasionally, however, the hinge point can create some uncertainties when the diagrams are being drawn. Some examples will demonstrate the appropriate procedures.

Example 3-10

Write the shear and moment equations and sketch the shear and moment diagrams for the given beam. Notice that reactions have already been computed.

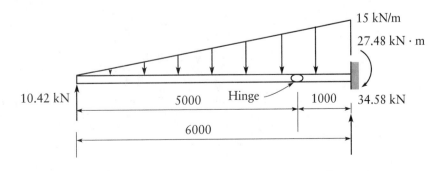

Solution   The intensity of load p_X at any point x is found by ratios:

$$\frac{p_X}{x} = \frac{15 \text{ kN/m}}{6 \text{ m}}; \qquad p_X = 2.5x$$

Since the loads are continuous, the shear and moment equations are continuous. Therefore, the shear and moment equations are

$$0 \le x \le 6; \qquad V_X = 10.42 - (2.5x)\left(\frac{1}{2}x\right)$$

$$= 10.42 - 1.25x^2$$

$$0 \le x \le 6; \qquad M_X = 10.42x - (2.5x)\left(\frac{1}{2}x\right)\left(\frac{1}{3}x\right)$$

$$= 10.42x - 0.4167x^3$$

The shear and moment diagrams are shown in the following sketches.

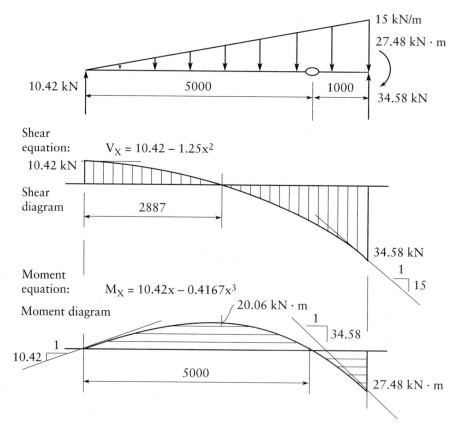

Notice that the moment at $x = 5000$ is zero, indicating that an inflection point (or mechanical hinge) occurs at that point.

Example 3-11   Write the shear and moment equations and sketch the shear and moment diagrams for the given beam. Notice that reactions have already been computed.

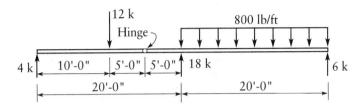

Solution   There are three domains of x over which the loads are continuous:

$$0 \leq x \leq 10', \ 10' \leq x \leq 20', \text{ and } 20' \leq x \leq 40'.$$

The shear equations are

$$
\begin{aligned}
0 \leq x \leq 10'; \quad & V_X = +4 \\
10' \leq x \leq 20'; \quad & V_X = -8 \\
20' \leq x \leq 40'; \quad & V_X = +4 - 12 + 18 - 0.8(x - 20) \\
& \quad = +26 - 0.8x
\end{aligned}
$$

The moment equations are

$$
\begin{aligned}
0 \leq x \leq 10'; \quad & M_X = +4 \\
10' \leq x \leq 20'; \quad & M_X = +4x - 12(x - 10) \\
& \quad = 120 - 8x \\
20' \leq x \leq 40'; \quad & M_X = +4x - 12(x - 10) + 18(x - 20) - 0.4(x - 20)^2 \\
& \quad = +10x - 240 - 0.4(x - 20)^2
\end{aligned}
$$

In the foregoing equations, the origin of x is taken at the left support of the left span and remains there for all equations. It might have been shifted to the center support for the right span, but in this particular problem there was little reason to do so. The choice of the origin is not a major issue; it is subject to the preferences of the individual designer.

Shear and moment diagrams are shown in the following sketches.

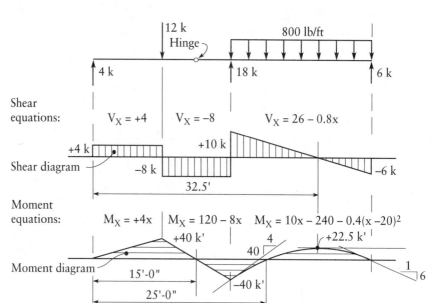

The exact locations of the two inflection points are found, as usual, by setting the moment equations for the appropriate domains to zero and solving for x:

Domain $10 \leq x \leq 20$

$M_X = 0 = 120 - 8x$

$x = 15$ ft from the left end.

Domain $20 \leq x \leq 40$

$M_X = 0 = 10x - 240 - 0.4(x - 20)^2$

$x = 25$ ft from the left end of the beam, and

$x = 40$ ft from the left end (not valid—out of domain).

The moment is thus seen to be zero at $x = 15$ ft and at $x = 25$ ft, indicating that an inflection point (or hinge) occurs at those points. In a typical moment diagram, there is no way to distinguish whether an inflection point occurs naturally or whether it occurs due to the insertion of a mechanical hinge; both produce the same end result.

Outside Problems Write the shear and moment equations and sketch the shear and moment diagrams for the given hinged beams.

Problem 3-25*

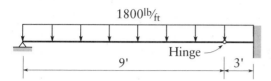

Problem 3-26

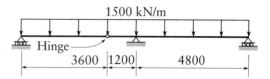

Problem 3-27*

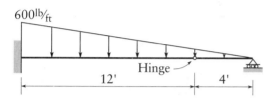

Problem 3-28

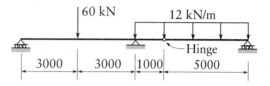

Problem 3-29*

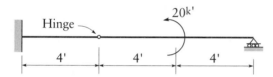

Problem 3-30

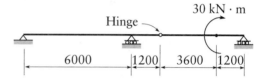

Problem 3-31*

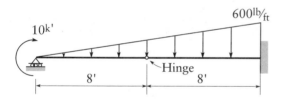

Problem 3-32

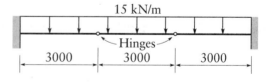

3.4 CROSS-SECTIONAL RESULTANTS FOR SLOPED, CURVED, OR BENT BEAMS

It was noted in Chapter 1 that, in the usual approach to structural analysis, lateral loads such as wind and earthquake are applied to the horizontal projection of the building. Similarly, dead and live loads are averaged over the horizontal projection of a roof rather than being applied over the actual sloping length of a roof beam. In such an approach, all loads are correct along the coordinate x- and y-axes and need not be adjusted at every change in roof slope or at every change in angle of a wall.

When it comes time to determine the cross-sectional resultants on a sloped or curved or bent member, however, the actual angle to the axis of the member must be accounted for. Such a case is shown in Figure 3-3, with all cross-sectional resultants represented in the positive sense. The angle α is assumed to be positive if counterclockwise, as shown.

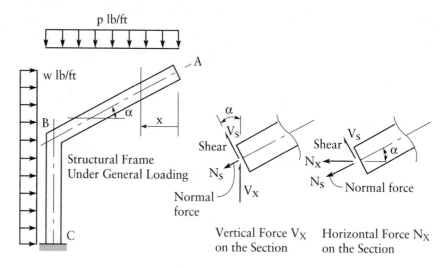

FIGURE 3-3 Rectangular resultants in a sloping section.

For the sloping roof member AB, the cross-sectional resultants are computed initially for a vertical section at x; then, when convenient, the resultants are conformed to the actual slope (angle α) of the member. At any point x on the coordinate axes, the total shear V_S on the sloping cross section due to the force V_X and the force N_X on the vertical cross section is

$$V_S = -V_X \cos \alpha + N_X \sin \alpha \qquad (3.7)$$

Similarly, the total normal force N_S on the sloping cross section due to the force V_X and the force N_X on the vertical cross section is

$$N_S = V_X \sin \alpha + N_X \cos \alpha \qquad (3.8)$$

The torque T_S on the sloping section follows the same pattern (when it occurs):

$$T_S = T_X \cos \alpha \qquad (3.9)$$

The moment M_S on the sloping section is the same as it is on the vertical section, since the moment lies in a plane perpendicular to both sections:

$$M_S = M_X \qquad (3.10)$$

For the vertical column BC of Figure 3-3, the equations and diagrams are best written for a horizontal section at y along the y-axis. In such an approach, point B becomes a point of discontinuity for all equations and diagrams. The final results obtained in this vertical column do not require corrections for slope or orientation.

Once the shear force V_S parallel to the sloping cross section at the point x has been determined, the shear diagram is drawn for this value of shear. The diagram is drawn on the sloping axis of the member, with V_S plotted perpendicular to the axis. Similarly, the normal force diagram and the torque diagram (when they occur) are drawn along the actual sloping axis of the member, rather than on the coordinate x- and y-axes. The moment M_S is also drawn along the actual sloping axis of the member; no correction need be applied to moments, however.

The key feature of this approach is that the cross-sectional resultants are defined as usual for some point (x, y) in the rectangular coordinate system, but the magnitudes of the resultants at point (x, y) have been corrected to suit the actual slope of the cross section. Some examples will illustrate the approach.

Example 3-12   Write the shear and moment equations and sketch the shear and moment diagrams for the given bent beam.

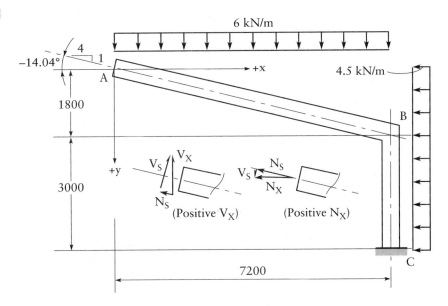

Solution   The origin of the coordinate axes is chosen at the free end of the bent canti-lever beam; positive y is directed downward. There are two domains of x and y in which loads are continuous: $0 \le x \le 7.2$ for $0 \le y \le 1.8$, and $1.8 \le y \le 4.8$ for $x = 7.2$ m.

For the roof member AB, the shear equation for a vertical section at x is

$$0 \leq x \leq 7.2; \qquad V_X = -6x$$

The equation for normal force on that same vertical section is

$$0 \leq x \leq 7.2; \qquad N_X = +4.5y$$

The equation for moment on that same vertical section is

$$0 \leq x \leq 7.2; \qquad M_X = -3x^2 - 2.25y^2$$

For the roof member, AB, the shear on a sloping cross section is, from Equation 3.7,

$$0 \leq x \leq 7.2; \qquad V_S = V_X \cos{(-14.04)} + N_X \sin{(-14.04)}$$
$$= -5.82x - 1.09y$$

The normal force on that same sloping cross section is, from Equation 3.8,

$$0 \leq x \leq 7.2; \qquad N_S = -V_X \sin{(-14.04)} + N_X \cos{(-14.04)}$$
$$= -1.46x + 4.37y$$

The moment acting on that same sloping cross section is unaffected:

$$0 \leq x \leq 7.2; \qquad M_S = -3x^2 - 2.25y^2$$

For the column member BC, the shear equation for a horizontal section at y is

$$1.8 \leq y \leq 4.8; \qquad V_Y = -4.5y$$

The equation for normal force on that same section is

$$1.8 \leq y \leq 4.8; \qquad N_Y = -(6)(7.2)$$
$$= -43.2 \text{ kN}$$

The equation for moment on that same section is

$$1.8 \leq y \leq 4.8; \qquad M_Y = -(6)(7.2)(3.6) - 2.25y^2$$
$$= -155.52 - 2.25y^2$$

The cross-sectional resultants need no corrections, since the column BC is vertical.

The normal, shear, and moment diagrams are shown in the following sketches.

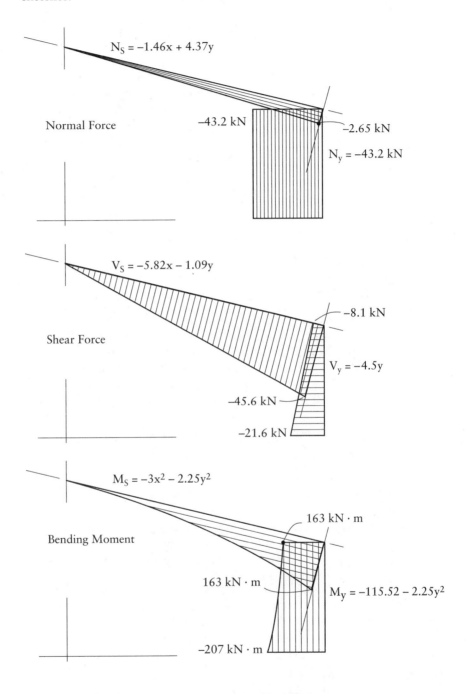

$N_S = -1.46x + 4.37y$

Normal Force

-43.2 kN

-2.65 kN

$N_y = -43.2$ kN

$V_S = -5.82x - 1.09y$

Shear Force

-8.1 kN

$V_y = -4.5y$

-45.6 kN

-21.6 kN

$M_S = -3x^2 - 2.25y^2$

Bending Moment

163 kN $\cdot$ m

163 kN $\cdot$ m

$M_y = -115.52 - 2.25y^2$

-207 kN $\cdot$ m

Example 3-13   Write the shear and moment equations and sketch the shear and moment diagrams for the given curved beam.

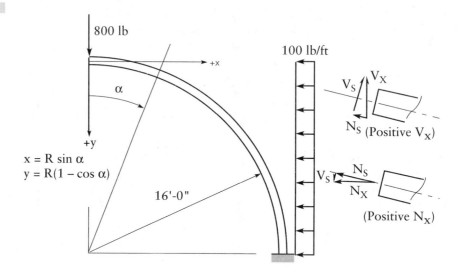

$x = R \sin \alpha$
$y = R(1 - \cos \alpha)$

Solution   The origin of the coordinate axes is chosen at the free end of the curved cantilever beam; positive y is directed downward. The loads are continuous throughout the entire length of the beam.

The shear equation for a vertical section at x is given by

$$0 \leq x \leq 16'; \qquad V_X = -800$$

The normal force on that same section is

$$0 \leq x \leq 16'; \qquad N_X = +100y$$

The moment on that same section is

$$0 \leq x \leq 16'; \qquad M_X = -800x - 50y^2$$

The shear on a section perpendicular to the axis of the curved beam is, from Equation 3.7,

$$0 \leq x \leq 16; \qquad V_S = +V_X \cos(-\alpha) + N_X \sin(-\alpha)$$
$$= -800 \cos \alpha - 100y \sin \alpha$$

The normal force on that same sloping section is, from Equation 3.8,

$$0 \le x \le 16; \qquad N_S = -V_X \sin(-\alpha) + N_X \cos(-\alpha)$$
$$= -800 \sin\alpha + 100y \cos\alpha$$

The moment on that same sloping section is unaffected:

$$0 \le x \le 16; \qquad M_S = -800x - 50y^2$$

For this particular beam, the cross-sectional resultants may also be stated entirely in terms of the angle α, where

$$x = 16 \sin\alpha; \qquad y = 16(1 - \cos\alpha)$$

The resultants are

$$0 \le \alpha \le \frac{1}{2}\pi; \qquad V_C = -800 \cos\alpha - 1600 \sin\alpha\,(1 - \cos\alpha)$$

$$0 \le \alpha \le \frac{1}{2}\pi; \qquad N_S = -800 \sin\alpha + 1600 \cos\alpha\,(1 - \cos\alpha)$$

$$0 \le \alpha \le \frac{1}{2}\pi; \qquad M_S = -12{,}800\,[\sin\alpha + (1 - \cos\alpha)^2]$$

The normal, shear, and moment diagrams are shown in the following sketches.

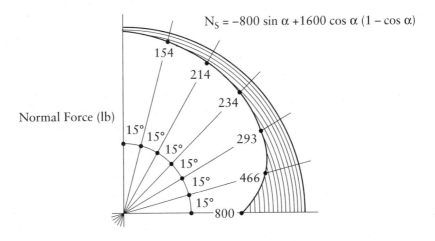

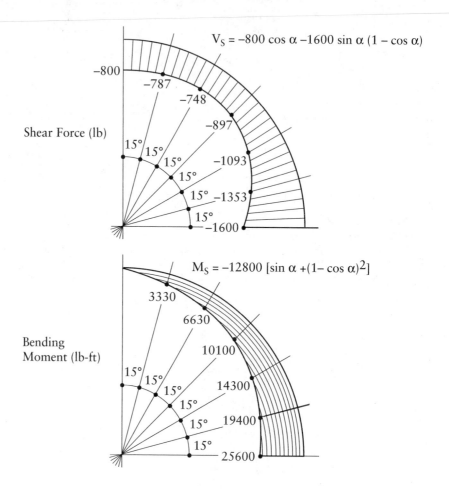

$$V_S = -800 \cos \alpha - 1600 \sin \alpha \, (1 - \cos \alpha)$$

Shear Force (lb)

−800
−787
−748
−897
−1093
−1353
−1600

15° 15° 15° 15° 15° 15°

$$M_S = -12800 \, [\sin \alpha + (1 - \cos \alpha)^2]$$

Bending
Moment (lb-ft)

3330
6630
10100
14300
19400
25600

15° 15° 15° 15° 15° 15°

**Outside
Problems** Write the shear, moment, and normal force equations and sketch the shear, moment, and normal force diagrams for the given bent or curved beams.

Problem 3-33*

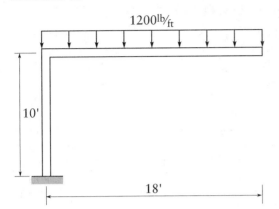

Problem 3-34

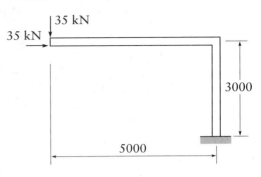

Problem 3-35*

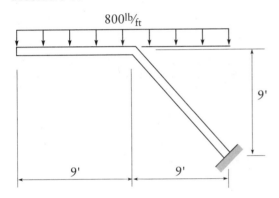

Problem 3-36

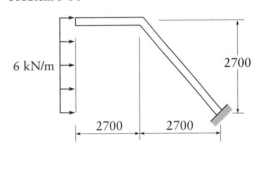

Problem 3-37*

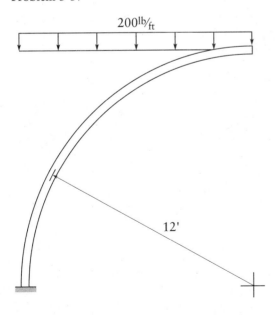

Problem 3-38

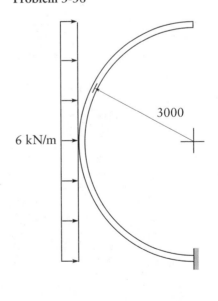

3.5 SHEAR AND MOMENT DIAGRAMS FOR THREE-HINGED ARCHES

The shear and moment diagrams for each individual beam in a three-hinged arch are no different from those for any other hinge-supported beam. The individual beams are typically sloped (possibly curved or bent), with reactions occurring at some angle to the member. When considered in their proper perspective, however, they fall into the same category as the sloped, curved, or bent beams of the preceding section.

In the analysis, all reactions should always be kept in their vertical and horizontal x and y components—never at some angle to the coordinate system. The reason for this precaution is that the cross-sectional elements are first computed in their x and y components and then corrected later to match the actual slopes or curvatures of the members; keeping all loads, reactions, and forces in their x and y components keeps the loads and their resultants consistent.

An example will illustrate the procedure.

Example 3-14   The bent cantilever equipment shed of Example 3-12 is made into a three-hinged arch as shown. Write the shear and moment equations, and sketch the shear and moment diagrams.

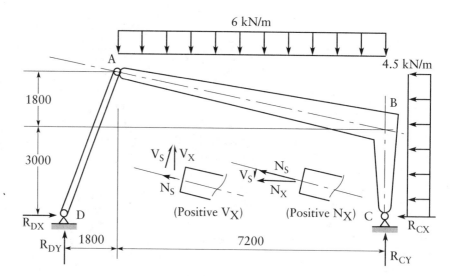

Solution   The member AD is a support for the bent beam ABC. The reactions for member AD are computed in their x-y-coordinate components:

$$\sum M_C = 0; \quad R_{DY}(9) - (6)(7.2)(3.6) - (4.5)(4.8)(2.4) = 0$$

$$R_{DY} = 23.04 \text{ kN}$$

Moments are taken about A for member AD only:

$$\sum M_A = 0; \quad R_{DY}(1.8) - R_{DX}(4.8) = 0$$

$$R_{DX} = 8.64 \text{ kN}$$

The free bodies of the two beams are shown in the following sketch.

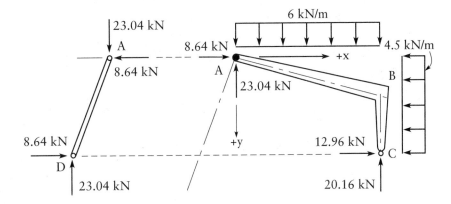

The member AD is seen to be subject to axial load only:

$$N_S = \sqrt{8.64^2 + 23.04^2} = 2461 \text{ kN}$$

Loads on member ABC are seen to be discontinuous at B. There are two continuous domains of x and y: $0 \le x \le 7.2$ for $0 \le y \le 1.8$, and $1.8 \le y \le 4.8$ for $x = 7.2$.

On a vertical section in leg AB,

$$0 \le x \le 7.2; \quad V_X = 23.04 - 6x$$

$$N_X = -8.64 + 4.5y$$

$$M_X = 23.04x + 8.64y - 3x^2 - 2.25y^2$$

On a horizontal section in leg BC,

$$1.8 \leq y \leq 4.8; \qquad V_Y = +8.64 - 4.5y$$

$$N_Y = -43.2 + 23.04 = -20.16$$

$$M_Y = 8.64y + 23.04(7.2) - 6(7.2)(3.6) - 2.25y^2$$
$$= 10.37 + 8.64y - 2.25y^2$$

At the sloping cross section of leg AB, from Equations 3.7, 3.8, and 3.10,

$$0 \leq x \leq 7.2; \qquad V_S = V_X \cos \alpha + N_X \sin \alpha$$
$$= (23.04 - 6x) \cos (-14.04) + (-8.64 + 4.5y) \sin (-14.04)$$
$$= 24.45 - 5.82x - 1.09y$$

$$N_S = -V_X \sin \alpha + N_X \cos \alpha$$
$$= -(23.04 - 6x) \sin (-14.04)$$
$$+ (-8.64 + 4.5y) \cos (-14.04)$$
$$= -13.79 - 1.46x + 4.37y$$

$$M_S = 23.04x + 8.64y - 3x^2 - 2.25y^2$$

Maximum moment occurs on leg AB when shear is zero. With $y = 1/4\,x$, the shear equation is set to zero and solved, yielding

$$V_S = 0 = 24.45 - 5.82x - 1.09\left(\frac{1}{4}\right)x$$

Hence,

$$x = 4.013 \text{ m}$$
$$y = \frac{1}{4}x = 1.003 \text{ m}$$

and at these values of x and y,

$$M_S = 23.04(4.013) + 8.64(1.003) - 3(4.013)^2 - 2.25(1.003)^2$$
$$= 50.5 \text{ kN·m}$$

The normal, shear, and moment diagrams are shown in the following sketches.

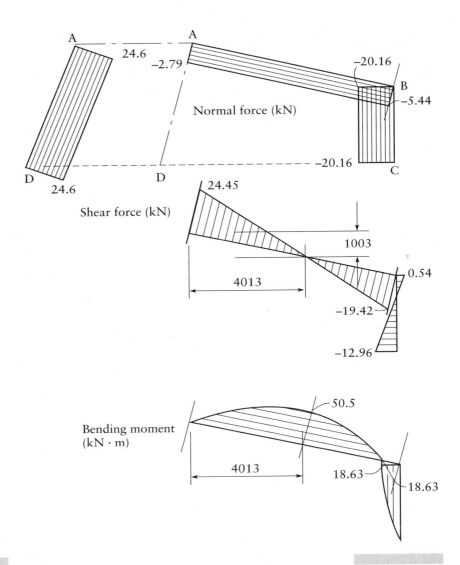

Outside Problems Write the shear and moment equations and sketch the shear and moment diagrams for the given three-hinged arches.

Problem 3-39*

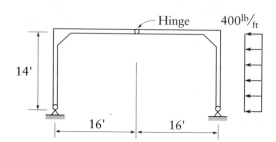

Problem 3-40

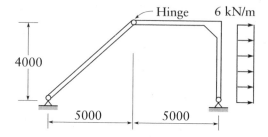

Problem 3-41*

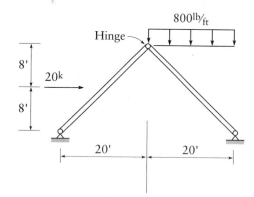

Problem 3-42

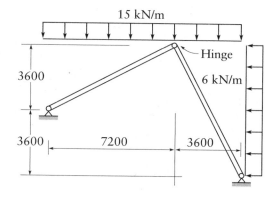

REVIEW QUESTIONS

A steel bar 2 inches in diameter is subjected first to a moment of 1500 lb·ft, second to a torque of 2000 lb·ft, third to a beam shearing force of 36,000 lb, and last to an axial force of 70,000 lb.

1. For the given data, determine the maximum flexural stress.

2. For the given data, determine the maximum torsional shear stress.

3. For the given data, determine the maximum beam shear stress.

4. For the given data, determine the maximum axial stress.

5. Name the four cross-sectional resultants of load commonly used in engineering mechanics.

6. How does one quickly find the slope of the shear diagram?

7. How does one quickly find the slope of the moment diagram?

8. What is meant by the phrase "domain of x"?

9. When the load at some point on a beam is a single concentrated load, what happens to the shear diagram at that point?

10. When the shear diagram at some point is multivalued—that is, when the shear diagram jumps from one value to the left of the point to a different value to the right of the point—what shape does the moment diagram take at that point?

11. When the shear diagram at some point has only one value and that value is zero, what happens to the moment diagram at that point?

12. When there is no load in a particular domain of x, what is the shape of the shear diagram?

13. What is an inflection point?

14. How does one distinguish between an inflection point produced as a natural consequence of loads and one caused by the deliberate insertion of a mechanical hinge?

15. What is a point of contraflexure?

Typical reinforced concrete bridge on a secondary road.
(Photograph courtesy of Portland Cement Association,
reprinted by permission.)

Equations of the Elastic Curve

This chapter is devoted to the method of double integration for finding deflections. It is one of the truly classical methods—a method that has formed a cornerstone of structural analysis for generations. In many schools, the method is included as an integral part of the coursework in mechanics of materials; in such a case, this chapter may be skipped with no loss of continuity.

For students who are not yet familiar with the method, it definitely should be included in their study of the fundamentals of structural analysis. Certainly, such study enables students to develop real skill in evaluating and matching the boundary conditions that occur in discontinuous functions. While this skill may be of minor importance in elementary analysis, it is of critical importance in advanced studies in structural dynamics, as well as in plates and shells. At that point in the study of structures, students have little time to go back and pick up a topic as fundamental as the evaluation of boundary conditions in a discontinuous function.

Two primary approaches are currently in use for computing deformations of structures. One approach utilizes the elastic curves formed by the structural members as they deform. This is the more widely used approach, and it is presented in this chapter. The second approach utilizes the energy stored in the structure through its deformations; energy methods are presented in Chapter 6. Together, these two methods for computing structural deformations have been found to be adequate for the analysis of most, if not all, routine structures. Analysis of more complicated structures such as plates and shells is based on these same concepts, but the applications become somewhat different; such applications are not treated in this text.

The language of modern structural engineering is calculus. A half-century ago, structures might have been designed (more or less) on the basis of empirical formulas and rules of thumb; but those days are gone forever. It would indeed be misleading to suggest that one can understand modern structural engineering without the concepts of calculus, particularly when the trends over the past 50 years indicate exactly the opposite. It is a very real fact that today's structures are designed, and that the language of structural design is calculus.

In keeping with the realities of the practice, the methods used in this chapter are calculus-based. These general methods in their classical form are simple and straightforward, although they do become somewhat tedious and laborious. Simplified methods (which are developed in the next chapter) can be used to perform limited parts of the general solutions. These simplified solutions—and not the classical methods—form the basis for much of contemporary structural analysis; they are the primary methods used throughout the later chapters of this text.

4.1 STRESS AND DEFORMATIONS IN BEAMS

Under load, a structural member changes shape. Such a change in shape is called *deformation*. The amount of displacement of any point in the member from its original unloaded position is termed its *deflection*. To simplify the calculations, the deflection of a point is usually broken into its x and y components when the methods of the elastic curve are applied.

The common assumptions concerning mechanical properties of materials that were introduced in coursework on elementary strength of materials remain valid for the methods of analysis that use the elastic curve. Materials are assumed to be linearly elastic and to conform to Hooke's Law—that is, if the load increases 50%, deformations increase 50%. Materials are assumed to be isotropic—that is, they have the same mechanical properties in all directions, for both tensile and compressive loads. Materials are also assumed to be homogeneous—that is, they possess no unpredictable discontinuities, variations, or interruptions in the mechanical properties of the material.

The definitions for stress, strain, and modulus of elasticity introduced in coursework on elementary strength of materials remain valid for the methods of the elastic curve. For immediate reference, a sketch showing the relationship between stress and strain is shown in Figure 4-1.

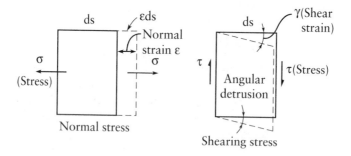

FIGURE 4-1 Stress and strain.

The relationships between stress (σ, τ) and strain (ε, γ) are given by Hooke's Law:

$$E = \frac{\sigma}{\varepsilon} \tag{4.1}$$

for normal stress, and

$$G = \frac{\tau}{\gamma} \tag{4.2}$$

for shear stress, where E is the modulus of elasticity of the material under normal stress, and G is the modulus of elasticity of the material under shearing stress. The relationship between the normal modulus of elasticity E and the shear modulus of elasticity G is given by

$$G = \frac{E}{2(1+\mu)} \tag{4.3}$$

where μ is Poisson's ratio for the material.

The common assumptions introduced in coursework on elementary strength of materials for deriving the various stress and deformation equations remain valid for the methods of the elastic curve. The cross section of a beam or column is assumed to be small compared to its length; the cross section is assumed to be a plane, both before and after deformation; and the geometry of the cross section undergoes no appreciable change in size or shape due to stresses and strains. The common equations derived in coursework on elementary strength of materials for computing stress and deformation will be used here without being rederived. For future reference, these basic equations are given in the following discussions.

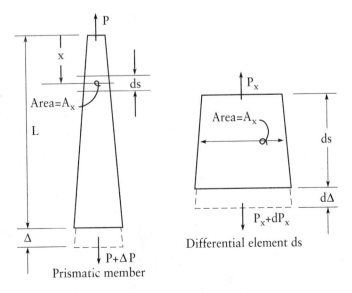

FIGURE 4-2 Axial deformations in a prismatic member.

The deformation of a member subject to axial loads is shown in Figure 4-2.

For axial stress, the general equation is

$$\sigma_x = \frac{P_x}{A_x} \tag{4.4}$$

where

σ_x is the uniform stress on the cross section at some distance x along the member;

P_x is the axial force normal to the section at the distance x, acting through its centroid;

A_x is the area of the cross section at the distance x.

The general solution for axial deformation is given by the line integral

$$\Delta = \int_0^L \frac{P_x ds}{A_x E_x} \tag{4.5}$$

where

Δ is the axial elongation of the prismatic member over its axial length L;

x is the coordinate distance to the differential element ds;

P_x is the axial force in the member at the distance x, expressed as a variable in x;

A_x is the cross-sectional area of the member at the distance x, expressed as a variable in x;

E_x is the modulus of elasticity of the material at the distance x, expressed as a variable in x;

ds is the differential length along the actual axis of the member, which, for curved or slanted members, may not be equal to dx.

For constant values of P, A, and E throughout the length L, Equation 4.5 degenerates into its more familiar form:

$$\Delta = \frac{PL}{AE} \tag{4.6}$$

The deformation of a member subject to torsion is shown in Figure 4-3.

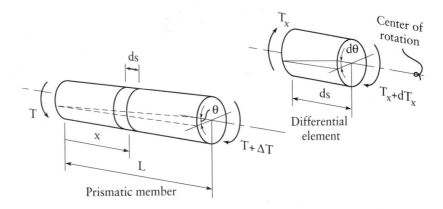

FIGURE 4-3 Torsional deformations in a prismatic member.

For torsional shearing stress, the general equation is

$$\tau_x = \frac{T_x c_x}{J_x} \tag{4.7}$$

where

τ_x is the torsional shearing stress on the section at some distance x along the member, located at a distance c_x from the center of rotation;

T_x is the torque acting on the section at the distance x;

J_x is the polar moment of inertia of the section at the distance x, taken about the center of rotation.

The general solution for torsional deformation is given by the line integral

$$\theta = \int_0^L \frac{T_x ds}{J_x G_x} \tag{4.8}$$

where

θ is the angular rotation of a prismatic (circular) member over its axial length L;

x is the coordinate distance to the differential element ds;

T_x is the torque acting on the section at the distance x, expressed as a variable in x;

J_x is the polar moment of inertia of the section at the distance x, expressed as a variable in x;

G_x is the shear modulus of elasticity of the material at the distance x, expressed as a variable in x;

ds is the differential length along the actual axis of the member, which, for curved or slanted members, may not be equal to *dx*.

For constant values of *T*, *J*, and *G* throughout the length *L*, Equation 4.8 degenerates into its more familiar form:

$$\theta = \frac{TL}{JG} \tag{4.9}$$

The deformation of a member subject to flexure is shown in Figure 4-4.

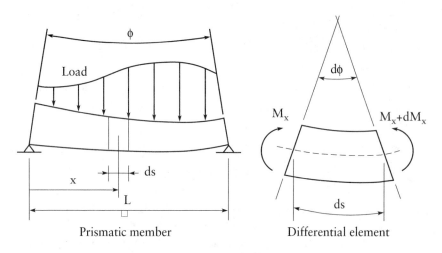

Prismatic member   Differential element

FIGURE 4-4 Flexural deformations in a prismatic member.

For beam flexural stress, the general equation is

$$\sigma_x = \frac{M_x c_x}{I_x} \tag{4.10}$$

where

σ_x is the flexural stress on a section at some distance *x* along the beam, located at a distance c_x from the neutral axis of bending;

M_x is the moment on the section at the distance *x*, taken about the neutral axis of bending;

I_x is the moment of inertia of the cross section at the distance *x*, taken about the neutral axis of bending.

The general solution for flexural deformation is given by the line integral

$$\phi = \int_0^L \frac{M_x ds}{E_x I_x} \tag{4.11}$$

where

ϕ is the angular rotation of a prismatic beam between two points spaced a distance L apart;

x is the coordinate distance to the differential element ds;

M_x is the moment acting on the section at the distance x, expressed as a variable in x;

I_x is the moment of inertia of the cross section at the distance x, expressed as a variable in x;

E_x is the modulus of elasticity of the material at the distance x, expressed as a variable in x;

ds is the differential length along the actual axis of the member, which, for curved or slanted members, may not be equal to dx.

For constant values of M, I, and E throughout the length L, Equation 4.11 degenerates into its more familiar form:

$$\phi = \frac{ML}{EI} \tag{4.12}$$

For beams, a more useful form of the deformation equation—the Bernoulli equation—is often used:

$$\frac{1}{\rho_x} = \frac{M_x}{E_x I_x} \tag{4.13}$$

where ρ_x is the radius of curvature of the beam at some point x, and the remaining symbols are those defined with Equation 4.8. The radius ρ_x is shown in Figure 4-5. The quantity $1/\rho_x$ is expressed in radians per unit of length and represents the instantaneous change in the angle of rotation of the cross section per unit of length; it is the *curvature* of the beam at the point x.

The deformation of a member subject to shear is shown in Figure 4-6.

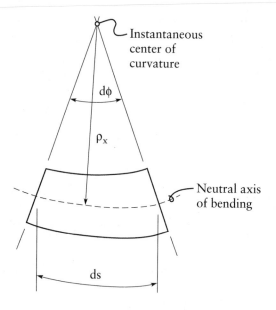

FIGURE 4-5 Flexural curvature in beams.

For beam shearing stress, the general equation is

$$\tau_x = \frac{V_x Q_x}{I_x t_x}$$ (4.14)

where

τ_x is the beam shearing stress at some point A on a cross section of the beam, taken at the distance x along the beam;

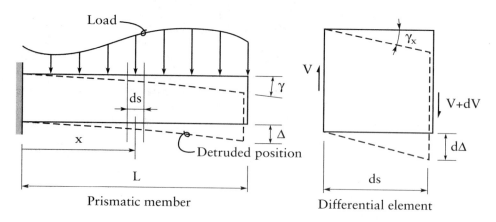

Prismatic member   Differential element

FIGURE 4-6 Shearing deformations in a prismatic member.

V_x is the shearing force acting across the section at the distance x along the beam;

Q_x is the moment of the portion of the cross section beyond point A, taken about the neutral axis of bending;

I_x is the moment of inertia in bending of the cross section;

t_x is the width of material that is subject to the shear stress τ_x.

The general solution for deflection due to shear detrusion is given by the line integral

$$\Delta = \int_0^L \frac{V_x ds}{A_x G_x} \qquad\qquad (4.15)$$

where

Δ is the deflection due to shear detrusion in a beam that is undergoing flexure over its axial length L;

x is the coordinate distance to the differential element ds;

V_x is the shearing force on the beam at the distance x, expressed as a variable in x;

A_x is the cross-sectional area of the web of the beam at the distance x, expressed as a variable in x;

G_x is the shear modulus of elasticity of the material at the distance x, expressed as a variable in x,

ds is the differential length along the actual axis of the member, which, for curved or slanted members, may not be equal to dx.

For constant values of V, A, and G throughout the length L, the deformation curve shown in Figure 4-6 becomes a straight-line parallelogram, and Equation 4.15 degenerates into its more familiar form:

$$\Delta = \frac{VL}{AG} \qquad\qquad (4.16a)$$

Hence,

$$\gamma = \frac{\Delta}{L} = \frac{V}{AG} \qquad\qquad (4.16b)$$

It is important to recognize that all of the integral forms given by Equations 4.5, 4.8, 4.11, and 4.15 are line integrals. In any line integral, the actual axial length s is assumed to be always increasing, in which case the differential length ds is positive. In later developments, it will occasionally prove convenient to take the integral limits backward; in such cases, the axial length will be decreasing, and the corresponding differential length ds must be given a negative sign.

Finally, it is assumed throughout all of structural analysis that deformations are small and that the geometry of the overall structure is essentially unchanged due to structural deformations. For example, a beam that is 20 feet long before loads are applied is assumed to remain 20 feet long after loads are applied; the change in its geometry due to the slight curvature of the beam is so insignificant that it may be ignored. Similarly, a column that is 10 feet long before loads are applied is assumed to remain 10 feet long after loads are applied; the change in length due to axial deformation of the column is so insignificant (compared to the original length) that it may be ignored.

Similarly, angular changes or rotations in a structure are always quite small, usually being measured in fractions of a degree. For such small angles, the angle α (in radians) may be assumed to be equal to its tangent or to its sine:

$$\tan \alpha = \sin \alpha = \alpha \qquad \text{(in radians)} \tag{4.17}$$

The proof of Equation 4.17 is given in elementary texts in calculus and is not repeated here. (The equation's validity may easily be verified with a hand calculator, however, simply by finding the tangent or sine of a few angles smaller than about $5°$.)

4.2 THE ELASTIC CURVE OF A BEAM

The elastic curve of a beam is the curve formed by the centerline of the beam as it deforms under load. Since torsion and axial loads do not affect the curvature of a beam (even if such loads were to exist on a beam), the only loads of interest in defining the elastic curve of a beam are the bending moments and shear forces. Further, in almost all applications in beams, the deformations produced by shear are negligible in comparison to those produced by bending; exceptions are very short beams that are loaded heavily in shear and lightly in bending.

A segment of a beam is shown in Figure 4-7, subject only to flexural rotations; shear detrusion will be considered in a separate discussion.

It has been noted that the quantity $1/\rho$ is the curvature of the elastic curve. The radius of curvature ρ is given in elementary mathematics handbooks; the exact value of curvature is given by

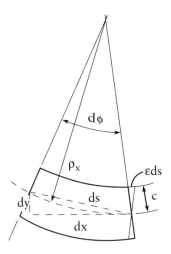

FIGURE 4-7 Segment of an elastic curve.

$$\frac{d^2y}{dx^2} = \frac{1}{\rho_x}\left[1 + \left(\frac{dy}{dx}\right)^2\right]^{\frac{3}{2}} \qquad\qquad (4.18)$$

where x and y are the rectilinear coordinates of the elastic curve.

It was noted earlier that angular changes in an elastic beam are quite small; hence the slope dy/dx is quite small and its square (in engineering analysis) is negligible. Equation 4.18 then degenerates to its more familiar form:

$$\frac{d^2y}{dx^2} = \frac{1}{\rho_x} \qquad\qquad (4.19)$$

When Equation 4.19 is substituted into the Bernoulli equation (Equation 4.13), the result is the differential equation of the elastic curve in flexure:

$$\frac{d^2y}{dx^2} = \frac{M_x}{E_x I_x} \qquad\qquad (4.20)$$

The solution of Equation 4.20 provides the slope and deflection at every point in a prismatic member subject to flexure. The classical solution of Equation 4.20, using ordinary integration methods is presented in the next section.

4.3 EQUATIONS OF THE ELASTIC CURVE FOR CANTILEVER BEAMS

As a first example in the use of Equation 4.20, consider the cantilever beam shown in Figure 4-8. Modulus of elasticity E and moment of inertia I are constant. The moment diagram and the moment equation are given; the moment diagram is negative since the top of the beam is in tension.

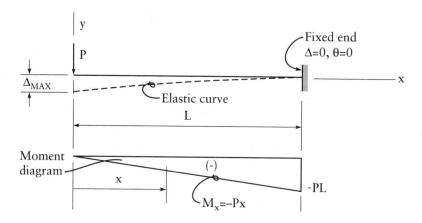

FIGURE 4-8 Cantilever with concentrated load at end.

The coordinate axes for x and y are arbitrarily chosen, with the origin at the free end of the unloaded cantilever; hence, Equation 4.20 becomes

$$EI\frac{d^2y}{dx^2} = -Px$$

Integrating once yields the slope of the beam at any point x:

$$EI\frac{dy}{dx} = -P\int x\,dx$$

$$= -\frac{Px^2}{2} + C_1$$

where C_1 is a constant of integration. C_1 may be evaluated for the boundary condition at $x = L$, at which point the slope of the beam is zero. Hence, at $x = L$,

$$EI\frac{dy}{dx} = 0 = -\frac{PL^2}{2} + C_1$$

and

$$C_1 = \frac{PL^2}{2}$$

The completed equation for the slope of the elastic curve at any point is then

$$\frac{dy}{dx} = \frac{PL^2}{2EI}\left[1-\left(\frac{x}{L}\right)^2\right] \tag{4.21}$$

Integrating again yields the equation of the elastic curve:

$$EIy = \frac{PL^2}{2}\int\left[1-\left(\frac{x}{L}\right)^2\right]dx$$
$$= \frac{PL^3}{2}\left[\frac{x}{L}-\frac{1}{3}\left(\frac{x}{L}\right)^3\right] + C_2$$

where C_2 is again a constant of integration. C_2 may be evaluated for the boundary condition at $x = L$, at which point $y = 0$. Hence, at $x = L$,

$$0 = \frac{PL^3}{2} - \frac{PL^3}{6} + C_2$$

and

$$C_2 = -\frac{PL^3}{3}$$

The completed general equation of the elastic curve is then

$$y = -\frac{PL^3}{6EI}\left[\left(\frac{x}{L}\right)^3 - 3\left(\frac{x}{L}\right) + 2\right] \tag{4.22}$$

For the cantilever beam, the maximum slope θ and the maximum deflection Δ will obviously occur at the free end, where, with $x = 0$,

$$\theta_{MAX} = \frac{dy}{dx}\bigg|_{x=0} = +\frac{PL^2}{2EI} \tag{4.23}$$

$$\Delta_{MAX} = y_{x=0} = -\frac{PL^3}{3EI} \tag{4.24}$$

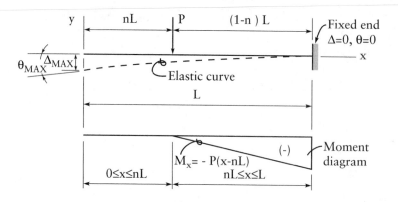

FIGURE 4-9   Cantilever with concentrated load in span.

The positive sign for θ_{MAX} means that the slope is positive or that a tangent to the elastic curve at $x = 0$ will point upward to the right. The negative sign for Δ_{MAX} means that y is negative at $x = 0$ or that the elastic curve has moved downward on the coordinate axes.

The foregoing solutions for slope (given by Equation 4.21) and deflection (given by Equation 4.22) are completely general. The slope or deflection at any point x along the beam may be found simply by substituting the desired value of x into these general solutions.

As a second example in defining the elastic curve of a beam, consider the cantilever beam shown in Figure 4-9. Modulus of elasticity E and moment of inertia I are constant. The load P has been moved to some distance nL from the end of the beam.

Again, coordinate axes are arbitrarily chosen, with the origin at the free end of the unloaded cantilever. In this example, the moment equation is discontinuous, requiring two equations to define the moment across the length of the beam. Equation 4.20 then becomes

$$0 \leq x \leq nL; \qquad EI\frac{d^2y}{dx^2} = 0$$

$$nL \leq x \leq L; \qquad EI\frac{d^2y}{dx^2} = -P\,(x - nL)$$

$$= -PL^2\left(\frac{x}{L} - n\right)\frac{1}{L}$$

The second equation is shown in the form $U^n du$ for direct integration. Integration of these two equations yields the slope of the beam at any point x:

$$0 \leq x \leq nL; \qquad EI\frac{dy}{dx} = C_1$$

$$nL \leq x \leq L; \qquad EI\frac{dy}{dx} = -\frac{PL^2}{2}\left(\frac{x}{L} - n\right)^2 + C_2$$

where C_1 and C_2 are constants of integration. In the domain of x between 0 and nL, there is no point at which the value of the slope dy/dx is known. The only certainty is that, at the point $x = nL$, the slope of the beam immediately to the left of the load must be equal to the slope immediately to the right of the load:

$$\left.\frac{dy}{dx}\right|_{LT} = \left.\frac{dy}{dx}\right|_{RT}$$

At this point, however, the slope to the right of the load is not known either, since that equation also contains an unknown constant, C_2. Since C_2 has not yet been evaluated, nothing further to the left of the load can be evaluated at this stage.

To the right of the load, in the domain $nL \leq x \leq L$, the slope of the beam at $x = L$ is zero. The constant C_2 can therefore be evaluated for this boundary condition:

$$EI\frac{dy}{dx} = 0 = -\frac{PL^2}{2}(1-n)^2 + C_2$$

Hence,

$$C_2 = \frac{PL^2}{2}(1-n)^2$$

The completed equation for slope for the portion of the beam between the load and the wall is then

$$nL \leq x \leq L; \qquad EI\frac{dy}{dx} = \frac{PL^2}{2}\left[(1-n)^2 - \left(\frac{x}{L}-n\right)^2\right]$$

Now C_1 can be evaluated at the point $x = nL$:

$$\left.\frac{dy}{dx}\right|_{LT}^{nL} = \left.\frac{dy}{dx}\right|_{RT}^{nL}$$

$$C_1 = -\frac{PL^2}{2}(1-n)^2 + C_2$$

Hence,

$$C_1 = C_2 = \frac{PL^2}{2}(1-n)^2$$

With C_1 known, the slopes both to the left of the load and to the right of the load have now been determined; the complete solution for the slope dy/dx is then

$$0 \leq x \leq nL; \qquad \frac{dy}{dx} = \frac{PL^2}{2EI}(1-n)^2 \qquad\qquad (4.25a)$$

$$nL \leq x \leq L; \qquad \frac{dy}{dx} = \frac{PL^2}{2EI}\left[(1-n)^2 - \left(\frac{x}{L}-n\right)^2\right] \qquad\qquad (4.25b)$$

The second equation is again put into the form $U^n du$. Integration of the two equations then yields the equation of the elastic curve across the entire length of the beam:

$$0 \leq x \leq nL; \qquad EIy = -\frac{PL^3}{2}(1-n)^2\left(\frac{x}{L}\right) + C_3$$

$$nL \leq x \leq L; \qquad EIy = \frac{PL^3}{2}(1-n)^2\left(\frac{x}{L}\right) - \frac{PL^3}{6}\left(\frac{x}{L}-n\right)^3 + C_4$$

As before, there is no point to the left of the load where y is known, so the constant C_3 in the domain $0 \leq x \leq nL$ cannot be evaluated. To the right of the load, however, the value of y at the point $x = L$ is known to be zero. Hence,

$$nL \leq x \leq L; \qquad EIy = 0 = \frac{PL^3}{2}(1-n)^2 - \frac{PL^3}{6}(1-n)^3 + C_4$$

Hence,

$$C_4 = \frac{PL^3}{6}\left[(1-n)^3 - 3(1-n)^2\right]$$

For the evaluation of C_3, it may be observed that, at the point $x = nL$, the value of y just to the left of the load must be equal to the value of y just to the right of the load. Thus, at $x = nL$,

$$EIy\big|_{LT}^{nL} = EIy\big|_{RT}^{nL}$$

Substitute $x = nL$, and solve for C_3 to find

$$C_3 = C_4 = \frac{PL^3}{6}[(1-n)^3 - 3(1-n)^2]$$

The final solution for the equation of the elastic curve is

$$0 \leq x \leq nL; \quad y = -\frac{PL^3}{6EI}\left[3(1-n)^2\left(1-\frac{x}{L}\right) - (1-n)^3\right] \quad (4.26a)$$

$$nL \leq x \leq L; \quad y = -\frac{PL^3}{6EI}\left[\left(\frac{x}{L}-n\right)^3\right.$$

$$\left. + 3(1-n)^2\left(1-\frac{x}{L}\right) - (1-n)^3\right] \quad (4.26b)$$

The maximum slope and deflection will occur at the free end of this beam, for which, at $x = 0$,

$$0 \leq x \leq nL; \quad \theta_{MAX} = \left.\frac{dy}{dx}\right|_{x=0} = \frac{PL^2}{2EI}(1-n)^2 \quad (4.27)$$

$$0 \leq x \leq nL; \quad \Delta_{MAX} = y_{x=0} = -\frac{PL^3}{6EI}[n^3 - 3n + 2] \quad (4.28)$$

The slope and the deflection at any other point, such as point nL, can be found simply by substituting the value of x into the set of equations. Since both sets of equations are valid at $x = nL$, substituting $x = nL$ into either set of equations yields

$$\theta_{nL} = \left.\frac{dy}{dx}\right|_{nL} = -\frac{PL^2}{2EI}(1-n)^2$$

$$\Delta_{nL} = y_{nL} = -\frac{PL^3}{3EI}(1-n)^3$$

For the next case in defining the elastic curve of a beam, consider a cantilever loaded by a uniform load, as shown in Figure 4-10. Modulus of elasticity E and moment of inertia I are constant.

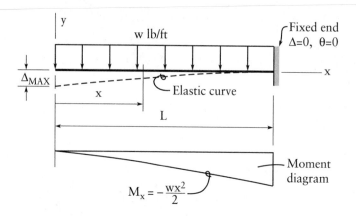

FIGURE 4-10 Cantilever with full uniform load.

The origin of the coordinate axes x and y is again chosen at the free end of the beam, before deformations occur. Equation 4.20 then becomes, for this load system,

$$EI\frac{d^2y}{dx^2} = -\frac{wx^2}{2}$$

Integrating once yields the slope of the beam at any point x:

$$EI\frac{dy}{dx} = -\frac{wx^3}{6} + C_1$$

where C_1 is a constant of integration to be evaluated for the boundary conditions. At $x = L$, the slope of the beam is zero; hence,

$$EI\frac{dy}{dx} = 0 = -\frac{wL^3}{6} + C_1$$

$$C_1 = \frac{wL^3}{6}$$

The final equation for the slope of the beam is therefore

$$\frac{dy}{dx} = \frac{wL^3}{6EI}\left[1 - \left(\frac{x}{L}\right)^3\right] \tag{4.29}$$

Integrating again yields the equation of the elastic curve:

$$EIy = \frac{wL^3}{6}x - \frac{wx^4}{24} + C_2$$

The constant of integration is evaluated for the boundary condition $y = 0$ at $x = L$:

$$EIy = 0 = \frac{wL^4}{6} - \frac{wL^4}{24} + C_2$$

$$C_2 = -\frac{wL^4}{8}$$

The final equation of the elastic curve is given by

$$y = -\frac{wL^4}{24EI}\left[\left(\frac{x}{L}\right)^4 - 4\left(\frac{x}{L}\right) + 3\right] \tag{4.30}$$

Maximum slope and deflection occur at the free end, for which case

$$\theta_{MAX} = \frac{dy}{dx}\bigg|_{x=0} = \frac{wL^3}{6EI} \tag{4.31}$$

$$y_{MAX} = y_{x=0} = -\frac{wL^4}{8EI} \tag{4.32}$$

Now consider a cantilever beam loaded by a partial uniform load, as shown in Figure 4-11. Modulus of elasticity E and moment of inertia I are constant. The origin of the coordinate axes is taken at the free end of the unloaded beam.

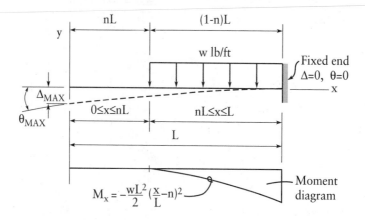

FIGURE 4-11 Cantilever with partial uniform load.

Since the moment diagram is discontinuous, two equations are needed to define the moment across the length of the beam:

$$0 \le x \le nL; \qquad EI\frac{d^2y}{dx^2} = 0$$

$$nL \le x \le L; \qquad EI\frac{d^2y}{dx^2} = -\frac{wL^3}{2}\left(\frac{x}{L} - n\right)^2\left(\frac{1}{L}\right)$$

The second equation is shown alternatively in the integrable form $U^n du$. Integrating once yields the equations for slope:

$$0 \le x \le nL; \qquad EI\frac{dy}{dx} = C_1$$

$$nL \le x \le L; \qquad EI\frac{dy}{dx} = -\frac{wL^3}{6}\left(\frac{x}{L} - n\right)^3 + C_2$$

As in previous cases, the constant of integration C_2 must be evaluated first, since there are no boundary points where C_1 is known.

At $x = L$, the slope is zero; hence,

$$nL \le x \le L; \qquad \frac{dy}{dx} = 0 = -\frac{wL^3}{6}(1-n)^3 + C_2$$

$$C_2 = \frac{wL^3}{6}(1-n)^3$$

At the point $x = nL$, the slope given by the equation to the left of the point must be equal to that given by the equation to the right of the point:

$$EI\frac{dy}{dx}\bigg|_{LT}^{nL} = EI\frac{dy}{dx}\bigg|_{RT}^{nL}$$

$$C_1 = -\frac{wL^3}{6}(0) + C_2$$

Hence,

$$C_1 = C_2 = \frac{wL^3}{6}(1-n)^3$$

The two final equations for slope are, therefore,

$$0 \leq x \leq nL; \qquad \frac{dy}{dx} = \frac{wL^3}{6EI}(1-n)^3 \qquad\qquad (4.33a)$$

$$nL \leq x \leq L; \qquad \frac{dy}{dx} = \frac{wL^3}{6EI}\left[(1-n)^3 - \left(\frac{x}{L}-n\right)^3\right] \qquad (4.33b)$$

A second integration yields the equations for the elastic curve:

$$0 \leq x \leq nL; \qquad EIy = \frac{wL^4}{6EI}(1-n)^3\left(\frac{x}{L}\right) + C_3$$

$$nL \leq x \leq L; \qquad EIy = \frac{wL^4}{24EI}\left[4(1-n)^3\left(\frac{x}{L}\right) - \left(\frac{x}{L}-n\right)^4\right] + C_4$$

The constant C_4 is evaluated for $y = 0$ at $x = L$, yielding

$$nL \leq x \leq L; \qquad EIy = 0 = \frac{wL^4}{24EI}[4(1-n)^3 - (1-n)^4] + C_4$$

$$C_4 = \frac{wL^4}{24EI}[(1-n)^4 - 4(1-n)^3]$$

The constant C_3 is evaluated for $y_{LT} = y_{RT}$ at $x = nL$, yielding

$$C_3 = C_4 = \frac{wL^4}{24EI}[(1-n)^4 - 4(1-n)^3]$$

Table 4-1 Equations of the Elastic Curve for Cantilevers

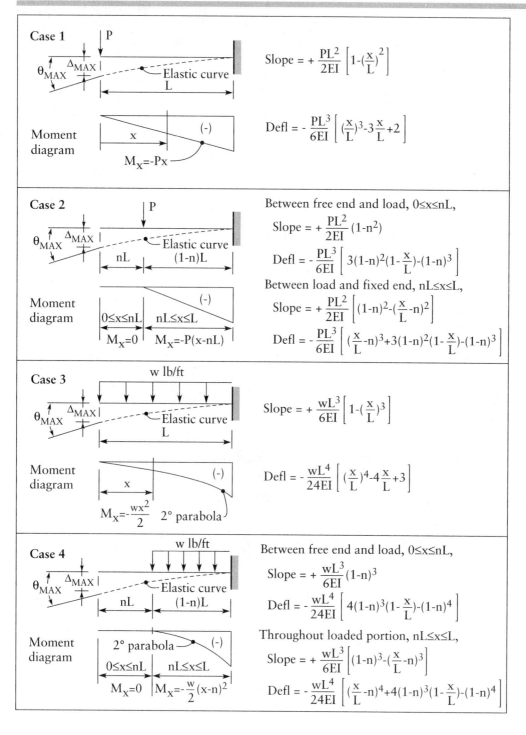

Case 1

$$\text{Slope} = + \frac{PL^2}{2EI}\left[1-\left(\frac{x}{L}\right)^2\right]$$

$$\text{Defl} = -\frac{PL^3}{6EI}\left[\left(\frac{x}{L}\right)^3-3\frac{x}{L}+2\right]$$

Moment diagram $M_x=-Px$

Case 2

Between free end and load, $0\leq x\leq nL$,

$$\text{Slope} = + \frac{PL^2}{2EI}(1-n^2)$$

$$\text{Defl} = -\frac{PL^3}{6EI}\left[3(1-n)^2(1-\frac{x}{L})-(1-n)^3\right]$$

Between load and fixed end, $nL\leq x\leq L$,

$$\text{Slope} = + \frac{PL^2}{2EI}\left[(1-n)^2-(\frac{x}{L}-n)^2\right]$$

$$\text{Defl} = -\frac{PL^3}{6EI}\left[(\frac{x}{L}-n)^3+3(1-n)^2(1-\frac{x}{L})-(1-n)^3\right]$$

Moment diagram $0\leq x\leq nL$ $M_x=0$ $nL\leq x\leq L$ $M_x=-P(x-nL)$

Case 3

w lb/ft

$$\text{Slope} = + \frac{wL^3}{6EI}\left[1-\left(\frac{x}{L}\right)^3\right]$$

$$\text{Defl} = -\frac{wL^4}{24EI}\left[\left(\frac{x}{L}\right)^4-4\frac{x}{L}+3\right]$$

Moment diagram $M_x=-\frac{wx^2}{2}$ 2° parabola

Case 4

w lb/ft

Between free end and load, $0\leq x\leq nL$,

$$\text{Slope} = + \frac{wL^3}{6EI}(1-n)^3$$

$$\text{Defl} = -\frac{wL^4}{24EI}\left[4(1-n)^3(1-\frac{x}{L})-(1-n)^4\right]$$

Throughout loaded portion, $nL\leq x\leq L$,

$$\text{Slope} = + \frac{wL^3}{6EI}\left[(1-n)^3-(\frac{x}{L}-n)^3\right]$$

$$\text{Defl} = -\frac{wL^4}{24EI}\left[(\frac{x}{L}-n)^4+4(1-n)^3(1-\frac{x}{L})-(1-n)^4\right]$$

Moment diagram   2° parabola $0\leq x\leq nL$ $M_x=0$ $nL\leq x\leq L$ $M_x=-\frac{w}{2}(x-n)^2$

Table 4-1 Equations of the Elastic Curve for Cantilevers (Continued)

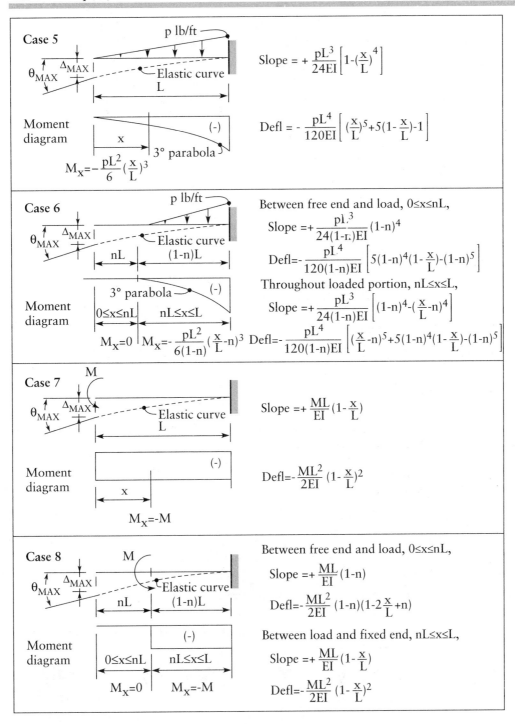

Case 5

$$\text{Slope} = +\frac{pL^3}{24EI}\left[1-\left(\frac{x}{L}\right)^4\right]$$

Moment diagram

$$\text{Defl} = -\frac{pL^4}{120EI}\left[\left(\frac{x}{L}\right)^5+5\left(1-\frac{x}{L}\right)-1\right]$$

$$M_x=-\frac{pL^2}{6}\left(\frac{x}{L}\right)^3$$

Case 6

Between free end and load, $0\leq x\leq nL$,

$$\text{Slope} =+\frac{pL^3}{24(1-n)EI}(1-n)^4$$

$$\text{Defl}=-\frac{pL^4}{120(1-n)EI}\left[5(1-n)^4\left(1-\frac{x}{L}\right)-(1-n)^5\right]$$

Throughout loaded portion, $nL\leq x\leq L$,

$$\text{Slope} =+\frac{pL^3}{24(1-n)EI}\left[(1-n)^4-\left(\frac{x}{L}-n\right)^4\right]$$

Moment diagram

$$M_x=0 \quad M_x=-\frac{pL^2}{6(1-n)}\left(\frac{x}{L}-n\right)^3 \quad \text{Defl}=-\frac{pL^4}{120(1-n)EI}\left[\left(\frac{x}{L}-n\right)^5+5(1-n)^4\left(1-\frac{x}{L}\right)-(1-n)^5\right]$$

Case 7

$$\text{Slope} =+\frac{ML}{EI}\left(1-\frac{x}{L}\right)$$

Moment diagram

$$\text{Defl}=-\frac{ML^2}{2EI}\left(1-\frac{x}{L}\right)^2$$

$$M_x=-M$$

Case 8

Between free end and load, $0\leq x\leq nL$,

$$\text{Slope} =+\frac{ML}{EI}(1-n)$$

$$\text{Defl}=-\frac{ML^2}{2EI}(1-n)\left(1-2\frac{x}{L}+n\right)$$

Between load and fixed end, $nL\leq x\leq L$,

$$\text{Slope} =+\frac{ML}{EI}\left(1-\frac{x}{L}\right)$$

Moment diagram

$$M_x=0 \quad M_x=-M$$

$$\text{Defl}=-\frac{ML^2}{2EI}\left(1-\frac{x}{L}\right)^2$$

The final equations for the elastic curve are

$$0 \le x \le nL; \qquad y = -\frac{wL^4}{24EI}\left[4(1-n)^3\left(1-\frac{x}{L}\right) - (1-n)^4\right] \qquad (4.34a)$$

$$nL \le x \le L; \qquad y = -\frac{wL^4}{24EI}\left[\left(\frac{x}{L}-n\right)^4\right.$$
$$\left. + 4(1-n)^3\left(1-\frac{x}{L}\right) - (1-n)^4\right] \qquad (4.34b)$$

Maximum slope and deflection occur at the free end, $x = 0$:

$$0 \le x \le nL; \qquad \theta_{MAX} = \left.\frac{dy}{dx}\right|_{MAX} = \frac{wL^3}{6EI}(1-n)^3 \qquad (4.35)$$

$$0 \le x \le nL; \qquad \Delta_{MAX} = y_{MAX} = \frac{wL^4}{24EI}[4(1-n)^3 - (1-n)^4] \qquad (4.36)$$

At $x = nL$, the slopes and deflections are

$$\theta_{nL} = \frac{wL^3}{6EI}(1-n)^3$$

$$\Delta_{nL} = -\frac{wL^4}{8EI}(1-n)^4$$

Other cases of loading on a cantilever may be solved similarly. A summary of the preceding load cases is given in Table 4-1, along with a hydrostatic (triangular) load case and an applied moment. Detailed solutions for these additional load cases are included with the following assigned problems.

Outside Problems

Problem 4-1 Develop the equations for the slope and deflection of load case 5 in Table 4-1.

Problem 4-2 Develop the equations for the slope and deflection of load case 7 in Table 4-1.

Problem 4-3 Develop the equations for the slope and deflection of load case 6 in Table 4-1.

Problem 4-4 Develop the equations for the slope and deflection of load case 8 in Table 4-1.

4.4 SUPERPOSITION OF LOAD CASES ON CANTILEVER BEAMS

The simple load cases of Table 4-1 may be combined to produce other, more complex load cases. Superpositioning one simple load case on another to produce a more complex load case is very common in structural analysis and will be used extensively throughout this text. Superpositioning is valid for all cases of loading—assuming, of course, that the material remains within its elastic range. Some examples will illustrate the concept.

Example 4-1   Determine the equations for the slope and deflection of the given cantilever beam.

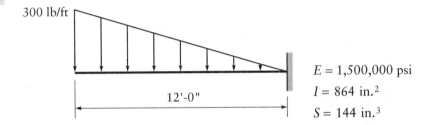

$E = 1,500,000$ psi

$I = 864$ in.^{2}

$S = 144$ in.^{3}

Solution   The given load case can be produced by combining load case 3 of Table 4–1 with load case 5, as indicated in the following sketch.

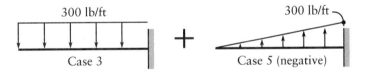

The resultant equations for the slope and deflection of the combined case are found by substitution into the equations of load case 3 and load case 5 of Table 4-1:

$$\text{Slope} = \frac{wL^3}{6EI}\left[1 - \left(\frac{x}{L}\right)^3\right] - \frac{pL^3}{24EI}\left[1 - \left(\frac{x}{L}\right)^4\right]$$

$$= \frac{\left(\frac{300}{12}\right)(12 \times 12)^3}{(24)(1.5)(10^6)(864)}\left[4\left(1 - \frac{x}{144}\right)^3 - \left(1 - \frac{x}{144}\right)^4\right]$$

$$= 0.0024\left[4\left(1 - \frac{x}{144}\right)^3 - \left(1 - \frac{x}{144}\right)^4\right] \text{ radians}$$

$$\text{Deflection} = \frac{wL^4}{24EI}\left[\left(\frac{x}{L}\right)^4 - 4\left(\frac{x}{L}\right) + 3\right] + \frac{pL^4}{120EI}\left[\left(\frac{x}{L}\right)^5 + 5\left(1 - \frac{x}{L}\right) - 1\right]$$

$$= \frac{\left(\frac{300}{12}\right)(12 \times 12)^4}{(120)\,(1.5)\,(10^6)\,(864)}\left[16 - 15\left(\frac{x}{144}\right)\right.$$

$$\left. + 5\left(\frac{x}{144}\right)^4 - \left(\frac{x}{144}\right)^5\right]$$

$$= -0.0691\left[16 - 15\left(\frac{x}{144}\right) + 5\left(\frac{x}{144}\right)^4 - \left(\frac{x}{144}\right)^5\right]$$

At $x = 0$ (free end):

$$\text{Slope} = 0.0024 \times 4 = 0.0096 \text{ radians} = 0.55°$$

$$\text{Deflection} = -0.0691 \times 16 = 1.11 \text{ in.}$$

Example 4-2   Determine the equations for the slope and deflection of the given cantilever beam.

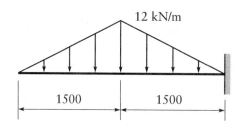

$E = 200,000$ psi
$I = 15.3 \times 10^6$ mm^4
$S = 172 \times 10^3$ mm^3

Solution   The given load case can be produced by combining load case 6 of Table 4-1 with load case 5. It is recognized that a discontinuity occurs at a point 1.5 m into the span.

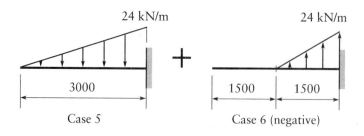

The resultant equations for the slope and deflection of the combined case can be found, for $n = 1/2$, with x in mm and p in N/mm.

For $0 \leq x \leq 1500$,

$$
\begin{aligned}
\text{Slope} &= \frac{pL^3}{24EI}\left[1 - \left(\frac{x}{L}\right)^4\right] - \frac{pL^3}{24EI(1-n)}(1-n)^4 \\
&= \frac{(24)(3000)^3}{(24)(200,000)(15.3 \times 10^6)}\left[1 - \left(\frac{x}{3000}\right)^4 - \left(1 - \frac{1}{2}\right)^3\right] \\
&= 0.0088235\left[\left(\frac{7}{8}\right) - \left(\frac{x}{3000}\right)^4\right]
\end{aligned}
$$

$$
\begin{aligned}
\text{Deflection} &= -\frac{pL^4}{120EI}\left[\left(\frac{x}{L}\right)^5 + 5\left(1 - \frac{x}{L}\right) - 1\right] \\
&\quad + \frac{pL^4}{120EI(1-n)}\left[5(1-n)^4\left(1 - \frac{x}{L}\right) - (1-n)^5\right] \\
&= -\frac{(24)(3000)^4}{(120)(200,000)(15.3 \times 10^6)} \\
&\quad \left[\left(\frac{x}{3000}\right)^5 + 3\frac{5}{8}\left(1 - \frac{x}{3000}\right) - \left(\frac{15}{16}\right)\right] \\
&= -5.2941\left[\left(\frac{x}{3000}\right)^5 + \left(\frac{35}{8}\right)\left(1 - \frac{x}{3000}\right) - \left(\frac{15}{16}\right)\right]
\end{aligned}
$$

For $1500 \leq x \leq 3000$,

$$
\begin{aligned}
\text{Slope} &= \frac{pL^3}{24EI}\left[1 - \left(\frac{x}{L}\right)^4\right] - \frac{pL^3}{24EI(1-n)}\left[(1-n)^4 - \left(\frac{x}{L} - n\right)^4\right] \\
&= \frac{(24)(3000)^3}{(24)(200,000)(15.3 \times 10^6)} \\
&\quad \left[1 - \left(\frac{x}{3000}\right)^4 - \left(1 - \frac{1}{2}\right)^3 + 2\left(\frac{x}{3000} - \frac{1}{2}\right)^4\right] \\
&= 0.0088235\left[\left(\frac{7}{8}\right) - \left(\frac{x}{3000}\right)^4 + 2\left(\frac{x}{3000} - \frac{1}{2}\right)^4\right]
\end{aligned}
$$

$$
\begin{aligned}
\text{Deflection} &= -\frac{pL^4}{120EI}\left[\left(\frac{x}{L}\right)^5 + 5\left(1 - \frac{x}{L}\right) - 1\right] + \frac{pL^4}{120EI(1-n)} \\
&\quad \left[\left(\frac{x}{L} - n\right)^5 + 5(1-n)^4\left(1 - \frac{x}{L}\right) - (1-n)^5\right] \\
&= -\frac{(24)(3000)^4}{(120)(200,000)(15.3 \times 10^6)} \\
&\quad \left[\left(\frac{x}{3000}\right)^5 - 2\left(\frac{x}{3000} - \frac{1}{2}\right)^5 + \left(\frac{35}{8}\right)\left(1 - \frac{x}{3000}\right) - \left(\frac{15}{16}\right)\right]
\end{aligned}
$$

$$= -5.2941\left[\left(\frac{x}{3000}\right)^5 - 2\left(\frac{x}{3000} - \frac{1}{2}\right)^5\right.$$
$$\left. + \left(\frac{35}{8}\right)\left(1 - \frac{x}{3000}\right) - \left(\frac{15}{16}\right)\right]$$

At $x = 0$ (free end):

$$\text{Slope} = 0.0088235\left(\frac{7}{8}\right) = 0.00772 \text{ radians} = 0.442°$$

$$\text{Deflection} = -5.2941\left(\frac{35}{8} - \frac{15}{16}\right) = -18.20 \text{ mm}$$

Other load combinations can be treated in the same way as the preceding examples. A few examples of such combinations follow, in which it is required only to find the load combination; the equations for slope and deflection are not required.

Example 4-3   Determine a combination of load cases from those given in Table 4-1 that will produce the given load case.

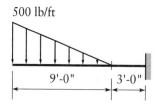

500 lb/ft

9'-0"   3'-0"

Solution   The given load case can be produced by the sum of three load cases, as shown in the following sketch.

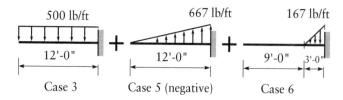

500 lb/ft   667 lb/ft   167 lb/ft

12'-0"   12'-0"   9'-0"   3'-0"

Case 3   Case 5 (negative)   Case 6

Example 4-4   Determine a combination of load cases from those given in Table 4-1 that will produce the given load case.

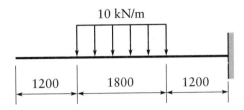

Solution   The given load case can be produced by the sum of two load cases, as shown in the following sketch.

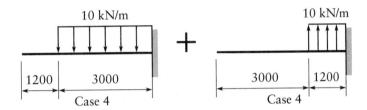

In Example 4-4, there are three discontinuities in loading. Consequently, three sets of equations are needed to define the slope and deflection across the full length of the beam. In millimeters, one equation is valid for the domain $0 \leq x \leq 1200$, another for the domain $1200 \leq x \leq 3000$, and a third for the domain $3000 \leq x \leq 4200$.

Example 4-5   Determine a combination of load cases from those given in Table 4-1 that will produce the given load case.

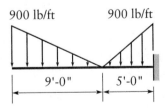

Solution   The given load case can be produced by the sum of three load cases, as shown in the following sketch.

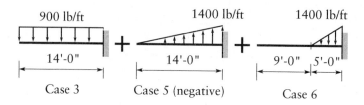

Case 3 + Case 5 (negative) + Case 6

Example 4-6   Determine a combination of load cases from those given in Table 4-1 that will produce the given load case.

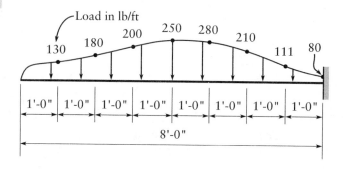

Solution   The loading is approximated as a series of concentrated loads taken at the middle of each 1'–0" length of beam, as shown in the following sketch.

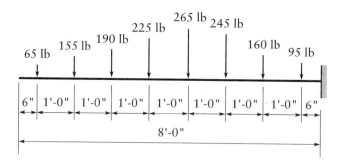

The load case of Example 4-6 is typical of loadings developed by wind tunnel experimentation. The loads (or pressures) may be given at closely spaced intervals (such as the 1'–0" interval shown in Example 4-6) or, on larger structures, at longer intervals or even at irregular intervals. In all such cases, the loading may be approximated by a series of concentrated loads and then solved by repeated applications of case 2 of Table 4-1. In Example 4-6, there are nine such applications, requiring nine sets of equations to define the slope and deflection of the beam across its full length; such computations are well-suited for solution by a programmable calculator using nine subroutine calculations.

Outside Problems Determine the equations for the slope and deflection of the given steel cantilever beams.

Problems 4-5 & 4-6*

400 lb/ft

5'   5'

I=32 in.⁴

Problems 4-7 & 4-8

12 kN/m

2400   2400

I=20x10⁶mm⁴

Problems 4-9 & 4-10*

4k

4k

4'   4'

I=22in.⁴

Problems 4-11 & 4-12

9 kN/m   18 kN

2000   2000

I=22x10⁶mm⁴

Determine a combination of load cases from Table 4-1 that will yield the slope and deflection of the given steel cantilever beams. Actual calculation of deflection is not required.

Problem 4-13*

2k   2k

I=60 in.⁴

2k   2k

3'   3'   3'   3'

Problem 4-14

15 kN/m

1500   1500

I=22x10⁶mm⁴

Problem 4-15*

300 lb/ft

6'

I=26 in.^{4}

6'

300 lb/ft

Problem 4-16

12 kN/m   12 kN/m

1200   1200   1200

I=15×10^{6}mm^4

Problem 4-17*

800 lb/ft

4'

I=41 in.^{4}

4'   4'

800 lb/ft

Problem 4-18

6 kN/m   2400

2400

6 kN/m

I=24×10^{6}mm^4

Problem 4-19*

800 lb/ft   800 lb/ft

I=54 in.^{4}

4'   4'   4'

Problem 4-20

4.5 kN/m   1800

1800   1800   4.5 kN/m

I=11×10^{6}mm^4

4.5 BEAMS HAVING A VARIABLE MOMENT OF INERTIA

All of the foregoing discussions were concerned with beams that had a constant cross section, where the moment of inertia I was a constant. But while such cases form the great majority of cases encountered in practice, in many cases the cross section is not a constant. The means to treat such a feature is just a variation of the methods already discussed; the only disadvantage is that the calculations become somewhat more involved.

Where a beam section is stepped to a larger size, the step simply introduces one more discontinuity into the integration. It is handled in the same way as any other discontinuity. An example will illustrate.

Example 4-7 Determine the equations for slope and deflection of the given cantilever. Moments of inertia of the two segments are shown in the sketch.

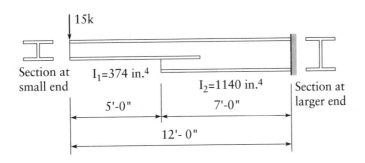

$$E = 30,000,000 \text{ psi}$$

Solution The coordinate axes are chosen with the origin at the free end of the cantilever. Equation 4.20 becomes

$$0 \le x \le 60''; \qquad \frac{d^2y}{dx^2} = \frac{M_x}{EI_1} = \frac{15,000x}{(30,000,000)(374)}$$

$$60 \le x \le 144''; \qquad \frac{d^2y}{dx^2} = \frac{M_x}{EI_2} = \frac{15,000x}{(30,000,000)(1140)}$$

The first integration yields the slope of the beam at any point x:

$$0 \le x \le 60''; \qquad \frac{dy}{dx} = -(0.668)(10^{-6})x^2 + C_1$$

$$60 \le x \le 144''; \qquad \frac{dy}{dx} = -(0.219)(10^{-6})x^2 + C_2$$

At $x = 60''$, the two slopes must be equal; hence,

$$C_1 - C_2 = 0.001616$$

At $x = 144''$, the slope of the second equation is zero:

$$0 = -(0.219)(10^{-6})(144)^2 + C_2$$

Hence,

$$C_2 = 0.00454$$

$$C_1 = 0.00616$$

The second integration yields the deflection of the beam at any point x:

$$0 \leq x \leq 60\text{''}; \qquad y = -(0.223)(10^{-6})x^3 + 0.00616x + C_3$$

$$60\text{''} \leq x \leq 144\text{''}; \qquad y = -(0.073)(10^{-6})x^3 + 0.00454x + C_4$$

At $x = 144$, $y = 0$, the value of C_4 can be identified:

$$0 = -(0.073)(10^{-6})(144)^3 + 0.00454(144) + C_4$$
$$C_4 = -0.436$$

At $x = 60\text{''}$, the value of y must be the same for both equations:

$$C_3 = -0.065 + C_4 = -0.501$$

The final equations can now be calculated.

For $0 \leq x \leq 60$, the results are

$$\text{Slope} = -(0.668)(10^{-6})x^2 + 0.00616$$

$$\text{Deflection} = -(0.223)(10^{-6})x^3 + 0.00616x - 0.501$$

For $60 \leq x \leq 144$, the results are

$$\text{Slope} = -(0.219)(10^{-6})x^2 + 0.00454$$

$$\text{Deflection} = -(0.073)(10^{-6})x^3 + 0.00454x - 0.436$$

As a matter of curiosity, the deflection at the end of the beam, where $x = 0$, is found to be

$$\Delta_{MAX} = -0.501 \text{ in.}$$

Outside Problems   Determine the equations for the slope and deflection of the given steel cantilever beams.

Problem 4-21*

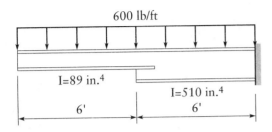

Problem 4-22

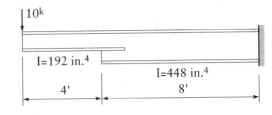

Problem 4-23*

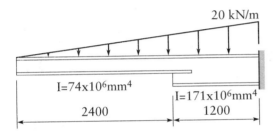

Problem 4-24

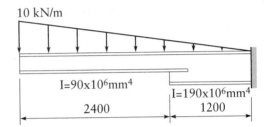

4.6 EQUATIONS OF THE ELASTIC CURVE FOR SIMPLE BEAMS

Equation 4.20 can also be applied to simple beams; the procedures involved are very similar to those used for cantilevers. For the first case, consider the uniformly loaded beam shown in Figure 4-12. Modulus of elasticity E and moment of inertia I are constant. The origin of the coordinate axes is arbitrarily chosen at the left support.

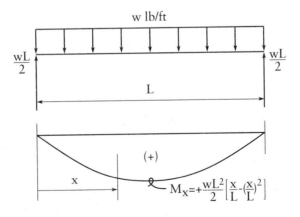

FIGURE 4-12 Simple beam with full uniform load.

For the load case of Figure 4–12, Equation 4.20 becomes

$$EI\frac{dy^2}{dx^2} = \frac{wL^2}{2}\left[\frac{x}{L} - \left(\frac{x}{L}\right)^2\right]$$

Integrating once yields the slope of the beam at any point x:

$$EI\frac{dy}{dx} = \frac{wL^3}{2}\left[\frac{1}{2}\left(\frac{x}{L}\right)^2 - \frac{1}{3}\left(\frac{x}{L}\right)^3\right] + C_1$$

For evaluating the constant of integration C_1, it is noted that the slope at midspan of a symmetrically loaded beam is zero. Hence, for $x = L/2$,

$$0 = EI\frac{dy}{dx} = \frac{wL^3}{2}\left[\frac{1}{2}\left(\frac{1}{4}\right) - \frac{1}{3}\left(\frac{1}{8}\right)\right] + C_1$$

$$= \frac{wL^3}{24} + C_1$$

$$C_1 = -\frac{wL^3}{24}$$

The complete equation for the slope at any point x is then

$$\frac{dy}{dx} = -\frac{wL^3}{24EI}\left[4\left(\frac{x}{L}\right)^3 - 6\left(\frac{x}{L}\right)^2 + 1\right] \tag{4.37}$$

A second integration yields the equation of the elastic curve,

$$EIy = -\frac{wL^4}{24}\left[\left(\frac{x}{L}\right)^4 - 2\left(\frac{x}{L}\right)^3 + \frac{x}{L}\right] + C_2$$

For evaluating the constant of integration C_2, it is noted that, at $x = 0$, $y = 0$; hence,

$$0 = EIy = -\frac{wL^4}{24}[0] + C_2$$

$$C_2 = 0$$

The final equation of the elastic curve is then

$$y = -\frac{wL^4}{24EI}\left[\left(\frac{x}{L}\right)^4 - 2\left(\frac{x}{L}\right)^3 + \frac{x}{L}\right] \tag{4.38}$$

For a symmetrically loaded simple span, the maximum deflection occurs at midspan, Hence, with $x = 1/2\,L$,

$$\Delta_{\text{MAX}} = -\frac{5wL^4}{384EI} \qquad\qquad (4.39)$$

The negative sign for Δ_{MAX} indicates that the neutral axis of the beam at midspan is below that at the supports.

For a second case, consider the simple beam shown in Figure 4-13, having a concentrated load at midspan. As before, E and I are constant, and the origin of the coordinate axes is at the left support.

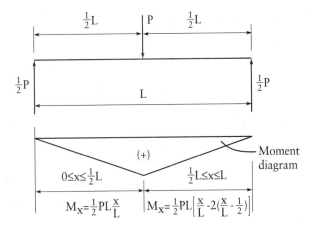

FIGURE 4-13 Simple beam with concentrated load at center.

For the load case of Figure 4-13, with its discontinuous moment equation, Equation 4.20 becomes

$$0 \le x \le \frac{1}{2}L; \qquad EI\frac{d^2y}{dx^2} = \frac{PL}{2}\left(\frac{x}{L}\right)$$

$$\frac{1}{2}L \le x \le L; \qquad EI\frac{d^2y}{dx^2} = \frac{PL}{2}\left[\frac{x}{L} - 2\left(\frac{x}{L} - \frac{1}{2}\right)\right]$$

The first integration yields the equations for slope:

$$0 \le x \le \frac{1}{2}L; \qquad EI\frac{dy}{dx} = \frac{PL^2}{2}\left[\frac{1}{2}\left(\frac{x}{L}\right)^2\right] + C_1$$

$$\frac{1}{2}L \le x \le L; \qquad EI\frac{dy}{dx} = \frac{PL^2}{2}\left[\frac{1}{2}\left(\frac{x}{L}\right)^2 - \left(\frac{x}{L} - \frac{1}{2}\right)^2\right] + C_2$$

The constants of integration C_1 and C_2 may be evaluated at midspan, where the slope is zero at $x = 1/2\,L$,

$$x = \frac{1}{2}L; \qquad 0 = \frac{PL^2}{4}\left(\frac{1}{4}\right) + C_1$$

$$C_1 = -\frac{PL^2}{16}$$

$$x = \frac{1}{2}L; \qquad 0 = \frac{PL^2}{4}\left[\left(\frac{1}{4}\right) - 0\right] + C_2$$

$$C_2 = -\frac{PL^2}{16}$$

The final equations for slope are then

$$0 \le x \le \frac{1}{2}L; \qquad \frac{dy}{dx} = -\frac{PL^2}{16EI}\left[1 - 4\left(\frac{x}{L}\right)^2\right] \tag{4.40}$$

$$\frac{1}{2}L \le x \le L; \qquad \frac{dy}{dx} = -\frac{PL^2}{16EI}\left[1 - 4\left(\frac{x}{L}\right)^2 + 8\left(\frac{x}{L} - \frac{1}{2}\right)^2\right] \tag{4.41}$$

A second integration yields the equations for deflection:

$$0 \le x \le \frac{1}{2}L; \qquad EIy = -\frac{PL^3}{16}\left[\frac{x}{L} - \frac{4}{3}\left(\frac{x}{L}\right)^3\right] + C_3$$

$$\frac{1}{2}L \le x \le L; \qquad EIy = -\frac{PL^3}{16}\left[\frac{x}{L} - \frac{4}{3}\left(\frac{x}{L}\right)^3 + \frac{8}{3}\left(\frac{x}{L} - \frac{1}{2}\right)^3\right] + C_4$$

The constants of integration C_3 and C_4 are evaluated at the two supports, where $y = 0$ when $x = 0$ and $y = 0$ when $x = L$:

$$x = 0, \qquad C_3 = 0$$

$$x = L, \qquad C_4 = 0$$

The final equations for deflection are

$$0 \le x \le \frac{1}{2}L; \qquad y = -\frac{PL^3}{48EI}\left[3\left(\frac{x}{L}\right) - 4\left(\frac{x}{L}\right)^3\right] \tag{4.42}$$

$$\frac{1}{2}L \le x \le L; \qquad y = -\frac{PL^3}{48EI}\left[3\frac{x}{L} - 4\left(\frac{x}{L}\right)^3 + 8\left(\frac{x}{L} - \frac{1}{2}\right)^3\right] \tag{4.43}$$

At midspan, either equation provides the maximum deflection:

$$\Delta_{MAX} = \frac{PL^3}{48EI} \tag{4.44}$$

A third case involves a concentrated load, unsymmetrically placed, as shown in Figure 4-14. As before, E and I are constant, and the origin of the coordinate axes is at the left support.

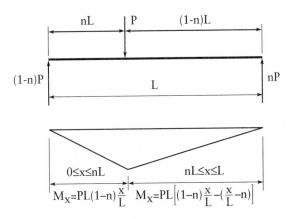

FIGURE 4-14 Simple beam with concentrated load at any point.

For the load case of Figure 4-14, Equation 4.20 becomes, for the discontinuous moment equation,

$$0 \le x \le nL; \qquad EI\frac{d^2y}{dx^2} = PL(1-n)\left(\frac{x}{L}\right)$$

$$nL \le x \le L; \qquad EI\frac{d^2y}{dx^2} = PL\left[(1-n)\left(\frac{x}{L}\right) - \left(\frac{x}{L} - n\right)\right]$$

The first integration yields the equations for slope across the entire span:

$$0 \le x \le nL; \qquad EI\frac{dy}{dx} = \frac{1}{2}PL^2\left[(1-n)\left(\frac{x}{L}\right)^2\right] + C_1$$

$$nL \le x \le L; \qquad EI\frac{dy}{dx} = \frac{1}{2}PL^2\left[(1-n)\left(\frac{x}{L}\right)^2 - \left(\frac{x}{L} - n\right)^2\right] + C_2$$

For the evaluation of C_1 and C_2, there is no point anywhere along the span where the slope is known. The evaluation of C_1 and C_2 must therefore be undertaken later.

The second integration yields the equations for deflection:

$$0 \leq x \leq nL; \quad EIy = \frac{1}{6}PL^3(1-n)\left(\frac{x}{L}\right)^3 + C_1L\left(\frac{x}{L}\right) + C_3$$

$$nL \leq x \leq L; \quad EIy = \frac{1}{6}PL^3\left[(1-n)\left(\frac{x}{L}\right)^3 - \left(\frac{x}{L}-n\right)^3\right]$$

$$+ C_2L\left(\frac{x}{L}\right) + C_4$$

There are four boundary conditions for the slopes and deflections. At $x = nL$,

$$\left.\frac{dy}{dx}\right|_{LT} = \left.\frac{dy}{dx}\right|_{RT}$$

At $x = nL$,

$$y_{LT} = y_{RT}$$

At $x = 0$,

$$y = 0$$

At $x = L$,

$$y = 0$$

The equations for slopes and deflections are substituted into these boundary conditions, and the results are solved simultaneously for C_1, C_2, C_3, and C_4:

$$C_1 = C_2 = -\frac{1}{6}PL^3n(1-n)(2-n)$$

$$C_3 = C_4 = 0$$

With the foregoing constants, the final equations for slopes are

$$0 \leq x \leq nL; \quad \frac{dy}{dx} = -\frac{PL^2}{6EI}\left[n(1-n)(2-n) - 3(1-n)\left(\frac{x}{L}\right)^2\right] \quad (4.45)$$

$$nL \leq x \leq L; \quad \frac{dy}{dx} = -\frac{PL^2}{6EI}\left[n(1-n)(2-n) - 3(1-n)\left(\frac{x}{L}\right)^2\right.$$

$$\left. + 3\left(\frac{x}{L}-n\right)^2\right] \quad (4.46)$$

Similarly, the final equations for deflection are

$$0 \leq x \leq nL; \qquad y = -\frac{PL^3}{6EI}\left[n(1-n)(2-n)\frac{x}{L} - (1-n)\left(\frac{x}{L}\right)^3\right] \qquad (4.47)$$

$$nL \leq x \leq L; \qquad y = -\frac{PL^3}{6EI}\left[n(1-n)(2-n)\frac{x}{L}\right.$$
$$\left. - (1-n)\left(\frac{x}{L}\right)^3 + \left(\frac{x}{L} - n\right)^3\right] \qquad (4.48)$$

The next case is that of a partial uniform load, as shown in Figure 4-15. The origin of the coordinate axes is again taken at the left support, with E and I constant. The moment at point x is somewhat simpler in this case if it is taken to the right of point x, rather than to the left.

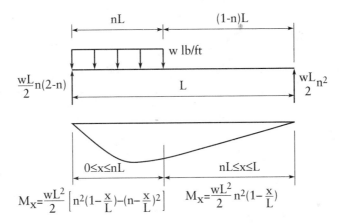

FIGURE 4-15 Simple beam with partial uniform load.

For the load case of Figure 4-15, Equation 4.20 becomes, for the discontinuous moment equation,

$$0 \leq x \leq nL; \qquad EI\frac{d^2y}{dx^2} = \frac{wL^2}{2}\left[n^2\left(1 - \frac{x}{L}\right) - \left(n - \frac{x}{L}\right)^2\right]$$

$$nL \leq x \leq L; \qquad EI\frac{d^2y}{dx^2} = \frac{wL^2}{2}\left[n^2\left(1 - \frac{x}{L}\right)\right]$$

The first integration yields the equations for slope:

$$0 \leq x \leq nL; \qquad EI\frac{dy}{dx} = -\frac{wL^3}{2}\left[\frac{n^2}{2}\left(1 - \frac{x}{L}\right)^2 - \frac{1}{3}\left(n - \frac{x}{L}\right)^3\right] + C_1$$

$$nL \le x \le L; \qquad EI\frac{dy}{dx} = -\frac{wL^3}{2}\left[\frac{n^2}{2}\left(1-\frac{x}{L}\right)^2\right] + C_2$$

A second integration yields the equations for deflection:

$$0 \le x \le nL; \qquad EIy = \frac{wL^4}{2}\left[\frac{1}{6}n^2\left(1-\frac{x}{L}\right)^3 - \frac{1}{12}\left(n-\frac{x}{L}\right)^4\right]$$
$$+ C_1 L\left(\frac{x}{L}\right) + C_3$$

$$nL \le x \le L; \qquad EIy = \frac{wL^4}{2}\left[\frac{1}{6}n^2\left(1-\frac{x}{L}\right)^3\right] + C_2 L\left(\frac{x}{L}\right) + C_4$$

There are four boundary conditions for the slopes and deflections. At $x = nL$,

$$\left.\frac{dy}{dx}\right|_{LT} = \left.\frac{dy}{dx}\right|_{RT}$$

At $x = nL$,

$$y_{LT} = y_{RT}$$

At $x = 0$,

$$y = 0$$

At $x = L$,

$$y = 0$$

The equations for slopes and deflections are substituted into these boundary conditions, and the results are solved simultaneously for the constants of integration C_1, C_2, C_3, and C_4:

$$C_1 = C_2 = -\frac{wL^3}{24}(n^4 - 2n^2)$$

$$C_3 = C_4 = \frac{wL^4}{24}(n^4 - 2n^2)$$

With these constants, the equations for slopes are

$$0 \le x \le nL; \qquad \frac{dy}{dx} = -\frac{wL^3}{24EI}\left[n^4 - 2n^2 + 6n^2\left(1-\frac{x}{L}\right)^2\right]$$

$$-4\left(n-\frac{x}{L}\right)^3\,\Bigg] \tag{4.49}$$

$$nL \le x \le L\,; \qquad \frac{dy}{dx} = -\frac{wL^3}{24EI}\left[n^4 - 2n^2 + 6n^2\left(1 - \frac{x}{L}\right)^2\right] \tag{4.50}$$

The equations for deflections are

$$0 \le x \le nL\,; \qquad y = -\frac{wL^4}{24EI}\left[(2n^2 - n^4)\left(1 - \frac{x}{L}\right)\right.$$

$$\left. - 2n^2\left(1 - \frac{x}{L}\right)^3 + \left(n - \frac{x}{L}\right)^4\right] \tag{4.51}$$

$$nL \le x \le L\,; \qquad y = -\frac{wL^4}{24EI}\left[(2n^2 - n^4)\left(1 - \frac{x}{L}\right) - 2n^2\left(1 - \frac{x}{L}\right)^3\right] \tag{4.52}$$

A final example involving simple beams is shown in Figure 4-16, where the load is a partial hydrostatic load. As in the other examples, the origin of the coordinate axes is taken at the left support, and E and I are constant. The moment equations are again written by taking moments to the right of x.

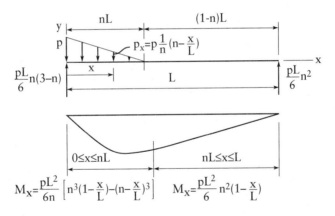

FIGURE 4-16 Simple beam with partial hydrostatic load.

For the load case of Figure 4-16, Equation 4.20 becomes

$$0 \le x \le nL\,; \qquad EI\frac{d^2y}{dx^2} = \frac{pL^2}{6n}\left[n^3\left(1 - \frac{x}{L}\right) - \left(n - \frac{x}{L}\right)^3\right]$$

$$nL \le x \le L\,; \qquad EI\frac{d^2y}{dx^2} = \frac{pL^2}{6}n^2\left(1 - \frac{x}{L}\right)$$

The first integration yields the equations for slope:

$$0 \le x \le L; \qquad EI\frac{dy}{dx} = -\frac{pL^3}{6n}\left[\frac{1}{2}(n^3)\left(1-\frac{x}{L}\right)^2 - \frac{1}{4}\left(n-\frac{x}{L}\right)^4\right] + C_1$$

$$nL \le x \le L; \qquad EI\frac{dy}{dx} = -\frac{pL^3}{6n}\left[\frac{1}{2}(n^3)\left(1-\frac{x}{L}\right)^2\right] + C_2$$

The second integration yields the equations for deflection:

$$0 \le x \le nL; \qquad EIy = \frac{pL^4}{6n}\left[\frac{1}{6}(n^3)\left(1-\frac{x}{L}\right)^3 - \frac{1}{20}\left(n-\frac{x}{L}\right)^5\right]$$
$$+ C_1 L\left(\frac{x}{L}\right) + C_3$$

$$nL \le x \le L; \qquad EIy = \frac{pL^4}{6n}\left[\frac{1}{6}(n^3)\left(1-\frac{x}{L}\right)^3\right] + C_2 L\frac{x}{L} + C_4$$

There are four boundary conditions for the slopes and deflections. At $x = nL$,

$$\left.\frac{dy}{dx}\right|_{LT} = \left.\frac{dy}{dx}\right|_{RT}$$

At $x = nL$,

$$y_{LT} = y_{RT}$$

At $x = 0$,

$$y = 0$$

At $x = L$,

$$y = 0$$

The equations for slopes and deflections are substituted into these boundary conditions, and the results are solved simultaneously for the constants of integration C_1, C_2, C_3, and C_4:

$$C_1 = C_2 = \frac{pL^2}{360n}(10n^3 - 3n^5)$$

$$C_3 = C_4 = -\frac{pL^3}{360n}(10n^3 - 3n^5)$$

With the foregoing constants, the final equations for the slopes are

$$0 \le x \le nL; \quad \frac{dy}{dx} = -\frac{pL^3}{360nEI}\left[(3n^5 - 10n^3) + 30n^3\left(1 - \frac{x}{L}\right)^2 \right.$$
$$\left. -15\left(n - \frac{x}{L}\right)^4 \right] \tag{4.53}$$

$$nL \le x \le L; \quad \frac{dy}{dx} = -\frac{pL^3}{360nEI}\left[3n^5 - 10n^3 + 30n^3\left(1 - \frac{x}{L}\right)^2 \right] \tag{4.54}$$

The final equations for deflections are

$$0 \le x \le nL; \quad y = -\frac{pL^4}{360nEI}\left[(10n^3 - 3n^5)\left(1 - \frac{x}{L}\right) \right.$$
$$\left. - 10n^3\left(1 - \frac{x}{L}\right)^3 + 3\left(n - \frac{x}{L}\right)^5 \right] \tag{4.55}$$

$$nL \le x \le L; \quad y = -\frac{pL^4}{360nEI}\left[(10n^3 - 3n^5)\left(1 - \frac{x}{L}\right) \right.$$
$$\left. - 10n^3\left(1 - \frac{x}{L}\right)^3 \right] \tag{4.56}$$

Other common cases of loading may be treated in the same way as the foregoing cases. A summary of several such load cases is presented in Table 4-2, including coverage of the load cases just derived.

Outside Problems

Problems 4-25 & 4-26 Determine the equations for the slope and deflection of load case 3 in Table 4-2.

Problems 4-27 & 4-28 Determine the equations for the slope and deflection of load case 5 in Table 4-2.

TABLE 4-2 Equations of the Elastic Curve for Simple Beams

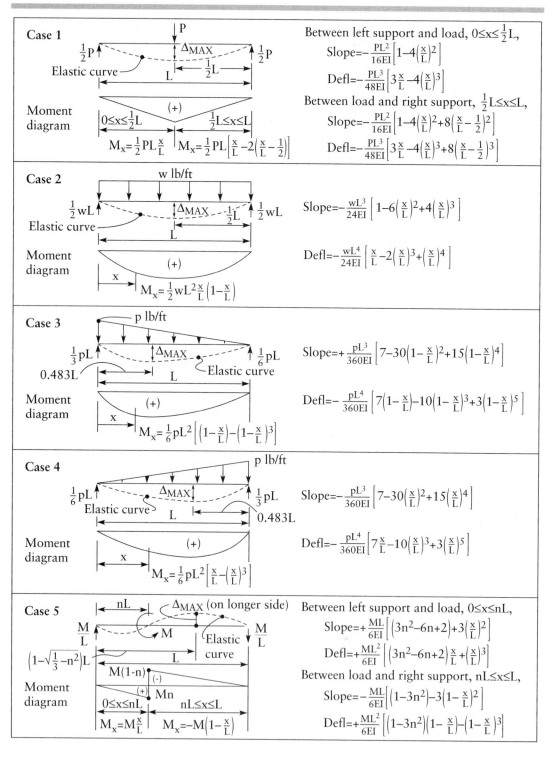

Case 1

Between left support and load, $0 \leq x \leq \frac{1}{2}L$,

$$\text{Slope} = -\frac{PL^2}{16EI}\left[1 - 4\left(\frac{x}{L}\right)^2\right]$$

$$\text{Defl} = -\frac{PL^3}{48EI}\left[3\frac{x}{L} - 4\left(\frac{x}{L}\right)^3\right]$$

Between load and right support, $\frac{1}{2}L \leq x \leq L$,

$$\text{Slope} = -\frac{PL^2}{16EI}\left[1 - 4\left(\frac{x}{L}\right)^2 + 8\left(\frac{x}{L} - \frac{1}{2}\right)^2\right]$$

$$\text{Defl} = -\frac{PL^3}{48EI}\left[3\frac{x}{L} - 4\left(\frac{x}{L}\right)^3 + 8\left(\frac{x}{L} - \frac{1}{2}\right)^3\right]$$

Moment diagram

$$0 \leq x \leq \tfrac{1}{2}L \qquad M_x = \tfrac{1}{2}PL\frac{x}{L} \qquad M_x = \tfrac{1}{2}PL\left[\frac{x}{L} - 2\left(\frac{x}{L} - \frac{1}{2}\right)\right] \qquad \tfrac{1}{2}L \leq x \leq L$$

Case 2

w lb/ft

$$\text{Slope} = -\frac{wL^3}{24EI}\left[1 - 6\left(\frac{x}{L}\right)^2 + 4\left(\frac{x}{L}\right)^3\right]$$

$$\text{Defl} = -\frac{wL^4}{24EI}\left[\frac{x}{L} - 2\left(\frac{x}{L}\right)^3 + \left(\frac{x}{L}\right)^4\right]$$

Moment diagram

$$M_x = \tfrac{1}{2}wL^2\frac{x}{L}\left(1 - \frac{x}{L}\right)$$

Case 3

p lb/ft

$$\text{Slope} = +\frac{pL^3}{360EI}\left[7 - 30\left(1 - \frac{x}{L}\right)^2 + 15\left(1 - \frac{x}{L}\right)^4\right]$$

$$\text{Defl} = -\frac{pL^4}{360EI}\left[7\left(1 - \frac{x}{L}\right) - 10\left(1 - \frac{x}{L}\right)^3 + 3\left(1 - \frac{x}{L}\right)^5\right]$$

Moment diagram

$$M_x = \tfrac{1}{6}pL^2\left[\left(1 - \frac{x}{L}\right) - \left(1 - \frac{x}{L}\right)^3\right]$$

Case 4

p lb/ft

$$\text{Slope} = -\frac{pL^3}{360EI}\left[7 - 30\left(\frac{x}{L}\right)^2 + 15\left(\frac{x}{L}\right)^4\right]$$

$$\text{Defl} = -\frac{pL^4}{360EI}\left[7\frac{x}{L} - 10\left(\frac{x}{L}\right)^3 + 3\left(\frac{x}{L}\right)^5\right]$$

Moment diagram

$$M_x = \tfrac{1}{6}pL^2\left[\frac{x}{L} - \left(\frac{x}{L}\right)^3\right]$$

Case 5

Between left support and load, $0 \leq x \leq nL$,

$$\text{Slope} = +\frac{ML}{6EI}\left[(3n^2 - 6n + 2) + 3\left(\frac{x}{L}\right)^2\right]$$

$$\text{Defl} = +\frac{ML^2}{6EI}\left[(3n^2 - 6n + 2)\frac{x}{L} + \left(\frac{x}{L}\right)^3\right]$$

Between load and right support, $nL \leq x \leq L$,

$$\text{Slope} = -\frac{ML}{6EI}\left[(1 - 3n^2) - 3\left(1 - \frac{x}{L}\right)^2\right]$$

$$\text{Defl} = +\frac{ML^2}{6EI}\left[(1 - 3n^2)\left(1 - \frac{x}{L}\right) - \left(1 - \frac{x}{L}\right)^3\right]$$

Moment diagram

$$0 \leq x \leq nL \qquad M_x = M\frac{x}{L} \qquad M_x = -M\left(1 - \frac{x}{L}\right) \qquad nL \leq x \leq L$$

TABLE 4-2 Equations of the Elastic Curve for Simple Beams *(Continued)*

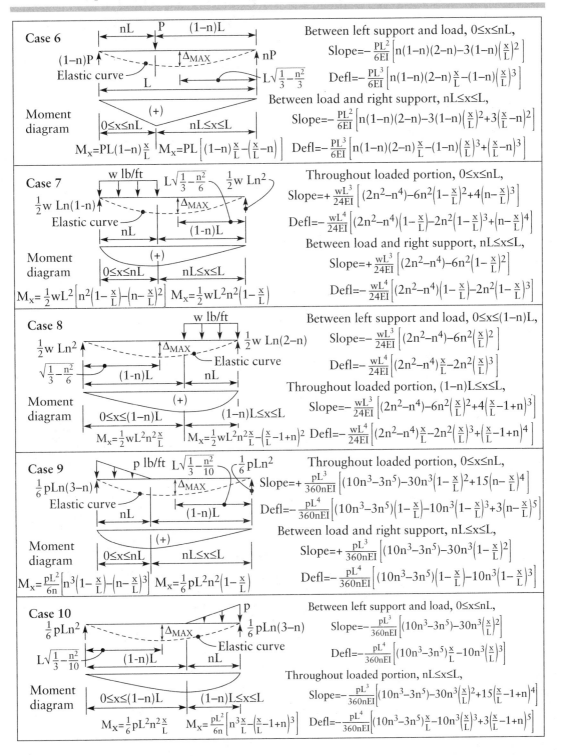

Case 6

Between left support and load, $0 \le x \le nL$,

$$\text{Slope} = -\frac{PL^2}{6EI}\left[n(1-n)(2-n)-3(1-n)\left(\frac{x}{L}\right)^2\right]$$

$$\text{Defl} = -\frac{PL^3}{6EI}\left[n(1-n)(2-n)\frac{x}{L}-(1-n)\left(\frac{x}{L}\right)^3\right]$$

Between load and right support, $nL \le x \le L$,

$$\text{Slope} = -\frac{PL^2}{6EI}\left[n(1-n)(2-n)-3(1-n)\left(\frac{x}{L}\right)^2+3\left(\frac{x}{L}-n\right)^2\right]$$

$$\text{Defl} = -\frac{PL^3}{6EI}\left[n(1-n)(2-n)\frac{x}{L}-(1-n)\left(\frac{x}{L}\right)^3+\left(\frac{x}{L}-n\right)^3\right]$$

$$M_x = PL(1-n)\frac{x}{L} \qquad M_x = PL\left[(1-n)\frac{x}{L}-\left(\frac{x}{L}-n\right)\right]$$

Case 7

Throughout loaded portion, $0 \le x \le nL$,

$$\text{Slope} = +\frac{wL^3}{24EI}\left[(2n^2-n^4)-6n^2\left(1-\frac{x}{L}\right)^2+4\left(n-\frac{x}{L}\right)^3\right]$$

$$\text{Defl} = -\frac{wL^4}{24EI}\left[(2n^2-n^4)\left(1-\frac{x}{L}\right)-2n^2\left(1-\frac{x}{L}\right)^3+\left(n-\frac{x}{L}\right)^4\right]$$

Between load and right support, $nL \le x \le L$,

$$\text{Slope} = +\frac{wL^3}{24EI}\left[(2n^2-n^4)-6n^2\left(1-\frac{x}{L}\right)^2\right]$$

$$\text{Defl} = -\frac{wL^4}{24EI}\left[(2n^2-n^4)\left(1-\frac{x}{L}\right)-2n^2\left(1-\frac{x}{L}\right)^3\right]$$

$$M_x = \frac{1}{2}wL^2\left[n^2\left(1-\frac{x}{L}\right)-\left(n-\frac{x}{L}\right)^2\right] \qquad M_x = \frac{1}{2}wL^2 n^2\left(1-\frac{x}{L}\right)$$

Case 8

Between left support and load, $0 \le x \le (1-n)L$,

$$\text{Slope} = -\frac{wL^3}{24EI}\left[(2n^2-n^4)-6n^2\left(\frac{x}{L}\right)^2\right]$$

$$\text{Defl} = -\frac{wL^4}{24EI}\left[(2n^2-n^4)\frac{x}{L}-2n^2\left(\frac{x}{L}\right)^3\right]$$

Throughout loaded portion, $(1-n)L \le x \le L$,

$$\text{Slope} = -\frac{wL^3}{24EI}\left[(2n^2-n^4)-6n^2\left(\frac{x}{L}\right)^2+4\left(\frac{x}{L}-1+n\right)^3\right]$$

$$\text{Defl} = -\frac{wL^4}{24EI}\left[(2n^2-n^4)\frac{x}{L}-2n^2\left(\frac{x}{L}\right)^3+\left(\frac{x}{L}-1+n\right)^4\right]$$

$$M_x = \frac{1}{2}wL^2 n^2\frac{x}{L} \qquad M_x = \frac{1}{2}wL^2 n^2\frac{x}{L}-\left(\frac{x}{L}-1+n\right)^2$$

Case 9

Throughout loaded portion, $0 \le x \le nL$,

$$\text{Slope} = +\frac{pL^3}{360EI}\left[(10n^3-3n^5)-30n^3\left(1-\frac{x}{L}\right)^2+15\left(n-\frac{x}{L}\right)^4\right]$$

$$\text{Defl} = -\frac{pL^4}{360nEI}\left[(10n^3-3n^5)\left(1-\frac{x}{L}\right)-10n^3\left(1-\frac{x}{L}\right)^3+3\left(n-\frac{x}{L}\right)^5\right]$$

Between load and right support, $nL \le x \le L$,

$$\text{Slope} = +\frac{pL^3}{360nEI}\left[(10n^3-3n^5)-30n^3\left(1-\frac{x}{L}\right)^2\right]$$

$$\text{Defl} = -\frac{pL^4}{360nEI}\left[(10n^3-3n^5)\left(1-\frac{x}{L}\right)-10n^3\left(1-\frac{x}{L}\right)^3\right]$$

$$M_x = \frac{pL^2}{6n}\left[n^3\left(1-\frac{x}{L}\right)-\left(n-\frac{x}{L}\right)^3\right] \qquad M_x = \frac{1}{6}pL^2 n^2\left(1-\frac{x}{L}\right)$$

Case 10

Between left support and load, $0 \le x \le nL$,

$$\text{Slope} = -\frac{pL^3}{360nEI}\left[(10n^3-3n^5)-30n^3\left(\frac{x}{L}\right)^2\right]$$

$$\text{Defl} = -\frac{pL^4}{360nEI}\left[(10n^3-3n^5)\frac{x}{L}-10n^3\left(\frac{x}{L}\right)^3\right]$$

Throughout loaded portion, $nL \le x \le L$,

$$\text{Slope} = -\frac{pL^3}{360nEI}\left[(10n^3-3n^5)-30n^3\left(\frac{x}{L}\right)^2+15\left(\frac{x}{L}-1+n\right)^4\right]$$

$$\text{Defl} = -\frac{pL^4}{360nEI}\left[(10n^3-3n^5)\frac{x}{L}-10n^3\left(\frac{x}{L}\right)^3+3\left(\frac{x}{L}-1+n\right)^5\right]$$

$$M_x = \frac{1}{6}pL^2 n^2\frac{x}{L} \qquad M_x = \frac{pL^2}{6n}\left[n^3\frac{x}{L}-\left(\frac{x}{L}-1+n\right)^3\right]$$

4.7 SUPERPOSITION OF LOAD CASES ON SIMPLE BEAMS

The simple load cases of Table 4-2 may be superimposed on each other to provide more complex load cases on simple beams; the concepts are the same as those developed earlier for cantilever beams. A few examples will illustrate the technique for simple beams.

Example 4-8   Determine the equations for the slope and deflection of the given simple beam.

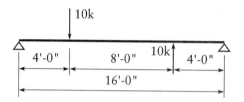

$$E = 30 \times 10^6 \text{ psi}$$
$$I = 198 \text{ in.}^4$$

Solution   The sum of the two load cases shown in the following sketch will produce the given load case.

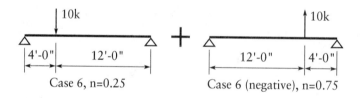

From the equations given for load case 6 of Table 4-2, the equations for slope (with x in inches) can be calculated.

For $0 \le x \le 4'$, the results are

$$\text{Slope} = -\frac{10{,}000\,(16 \times 12)^2}{(6)(30)(10^6)(198)}\left[\left(\frac{1}{4}\right)\left(\frac{3}{4}\right)\left(\frac{7}{4}\right) - 3\left(\frac{3}{4}\right)\left(\frac{x}{192}\right)^2\right]$$

$$-\frac{10{,}000\,(16 \times 12)^2}{(6)(30)(10^6)(198)}\left[\left(-\frac{3}{4}\right)\left(\frac{1}{4}\right)\left(\frac{5}{4}\right) + 3\left(\frac{1}{4}\right)\left(\frac{x}{192}\right)^2\right]$$

$$= -0.0009697 + 0.015515\left(\frac{x}{192}\right)^2$$

For $4' \leq x \leq 12'$, the results are

$$\text{Slope} = -\frac{10{,}000\,(16 \times 12)^2}{(6)(30)(10^6)(198)}\left[\left(\frac{1}{4}\right)\left(\frac{3}{4}\right)\left(\frac{7}{4}\right) - 3\left(\frac{3}{4}\right)\left(\frac{x}{192}\right)^2\right.$$

$$\left. + 3\left(\frac{x}{192} - \frac{1}{4}\right)^2\right] - \frac{10{,}000\,(16 \times 12)^2}{(6)(30)(10^6)(198)}\left[\left(-\frac{3}{4}\right)\left(\frac{1}{4}\right)\left(\frac{5}{4}\right)\right.$$

$$\left. + 3\left(\frac{1}{4}\right)\left(\frac{x}{192}\right)^2\right]$$

$$= -0.0009697 + 0.015515\left(\frac{x}{192}\right)^2 - 0.0310303\left[\frac{(x-48)}{192}\right]^2$$

For $12' \leq x \leq 16'$, the results are

$$\text{Slope} = -\frac{10{,}000\,(16 \times 12)^2}{(6)(30)(10^6)(198)}\left[\left(\frac{1}{4}\right)\left(\frac{3}{4}\right)\left(\frac{7}{4}\right) - 3\left(\frac{3}{4}\right)\left(\frac{x}{192}\right)^2\right.$$

$$\left. + 3\left(\frac{x}{192} - \frac{1}{4}\right)^2\right] - \frac{10{,}000\,(16 \times 12)^2}{(6)(30)(10^6)(198)}\left[\left(-\frac{3}{4}\right)\left(\frac{1}{4}\right)\left(\frac{5}{4}\right)\right.$$

$$\left. + 3\left(\frac{1}{4}\right)\left(\frac{x}{192}\right)^2 - 3\left(\frac{x}{192} - \frac{3}{4}\right)^2\right]$$

$$= -0.0009697 + 0.015515\left(\frac{x}{192}\right)^2$$

$$+ 0.0310303\left[\frac{(x-48)}{192}\right]^2 + 0.0310303\left[\frac{(x-144)}{192}\right]^2$$

Deflection equations are found similarly.

For $0 \leq x \leq 4'$,

$$\text{Deflection} = -0.18618\left(\frac{x}{192}\right) + 0.99297\left(\frac{x}{192}\right)^3$$

For $4' \leq x \leq 12'$,

$$\text{Deflection} = -0.18618\left(\frac{x}{192}\right) + 0.99297\left(\frac{x}{192}\right)^3$$

$$- 1.98594\left[\frac{(x-48)}{192}\right]^3$$

For $12' \leq x \leq 16'$,

$$\text{Deflection} = -0.18618\left(\frac{x}{192}\right) + 0.99297\left(\frac{x}{3}\right)^3$$
$$- 1.98594\left[\frac{(x-48)}{192}\right]^3 + 1.98594\left[\frac{(x-144)}{192}\right]^3$$

Example 4-9   Determine the equations for the slope and deflection of the given simple beam.

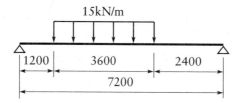

$E = 200,000 \text{ N/mm}^2$

$I = 215 \times 10^6 \text{ mm}^4$

Solution   The given load case may be reproduced by two simpler cases, as shown in the following sketch.

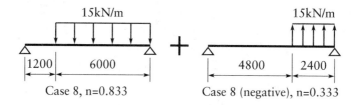

The equations for slope and deflection are the sum of these two cases. There are, however, three points of discontinuity in the loads; a total of three equations are needed to cover the span.

Slope equations are found from load case 8 of Table 4-2, with x in millimeters.

For $0 \leq x \leq 1200$, the results are

$$\text{Slope} = \frac{(15)(7200)^3}{(24)(200,000)(215 \times 10^6)}\left[2\,(0.833)^2 - (0.833)^4\right.$$
$$\left. -6\,(0.833)^2\left(\frac{x}{7200}\right)^2\right]$$

$$-\frac{(15)(7200)^3}{(24)(200{,}000)(215\times10^6)}\Big[-2\,(0.333)^2+(0.333)^4$$

$$+6\,(0.333)^2\Big(\frac{x}{7200}\Big)^2\Big]$$

$$=-0.00378+0.01899\Big(\frac{x}{7200}\Big)^2$$

$$+0.00653-0.02620\Big(\frac{x}{7200}\Big)^2$$

For $1200\le x\le4800$, the results are

$$\text{Slope}=-\frac{(15)(7200)^3}{(24)(200{,}000)(215\times10^6)}\Big[2\,(0.833)^2-(0.833)^4$$

$$-6\,(0.833)^2\Big(\frac{x}{7200}\Big)^2-4\Big(\frac{x}{7200}-0.167\Big)^3\Big]$$

$$-\frac{(15)(7200)^3}{(24)(200{,}000)(215\times10^6)}\Big[-2\,(0.333)^2+(0.333)^4$$

$$+6\,(0.333)^2\Big(\frac{x}{7200}\Big)^2+0.6653\Big(\frac{x}{7200}\Big)^2\Big]$$

$$=-0.00378+0.6843\Big(\frac{x}{7200}\Big)^2+0.0217\Big[\frac{(x-1200)}{7200}\Big]^3$$

For $4800\le x\le7200$, the results are

$$\text{Slope}=-\frac{(15)(7200)^3}{(24)(200{,}000)(215\times10^6)}\Big[2\,(0.833)^2-(0.833)^4$$

$$-6\,(0.833)^2\Big(\frac{x}{7200}\Big)^2+4\Big(\frac{x}{7200}-0.167\Big)^3\Big]$$

$$-\frac{(15)(7200)^3}{(24)(200{,}000)(215\times10^6)}\Big[-2\,(0.333)^2+(0.333)^4$$

$$+6\,(0.333)^2\Big(\frac{x}{7200}\Big)^2-4\Big(\frac{x}{7200}-0.667\Big)^3\Big]$$

$$=-0.00378+0.01899\Big(\frac{x}{7200}\Big)^2-0.02170\Big[\frac{(x-1200)}{7200}\Big]^3$$

$$+0.02154\Big[\frac{(x-4800)}{7200}\Big]^3$$

$$=0.006053-0.02620\Big(\frac{x}{7200}\Big)^2+0.217\Big(\frac{x-1200}{7200}\Big)^3$$

$$+0.217\Big(\frac{x-4800}{7200}\Big)^3$$

Deflection equations are developed similarly.

For $0 \leq x \leq 1200$,

$$\text{Deflection} = -27.2156\left(\frac{x}{7200}\right) + 45.5710\left(\frac{x}{7200}\right)^3$$

For $1200 \leq x \leq 4800$,

$$\text{Deflection} = -27.2156\left(\frac{x}{7200}\right) + 45.5170\left(\frac{x}{7200}\right)^3$$
$$- 39.0608\left[\frac{(x-1200)}{7200}\right]^4$$

For $4800 \leq x \leq 7200$,

$$\text{Deflection} = -27.2156\left(\frac{x}{7200}\right) + 45.5170\left(\frac{x}{7200}\right)^3$$
$$- 39.0608\left[\frac{(x-1200)}{7200}\right]^4 + 39.0608\left[\frac{(x-4800)}{7200}\right]^4$$

Example 4-10 Determine the equations for the slope and deflection of the given simple beam.

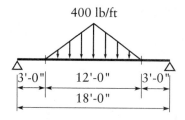

400 lb/ft

3'-0"   12'-0"   3'-0"
18'-0"

$E = 30,000,000$ psi
$I = 1152$ in.^{4}

Solution The given load may be reproduced from three simpler cases, as shown in the following sketch.

1040 lb/ft   1280 lb/ft   240 lb/ft

3'-0" 15'-0"   +   9'-0" 9'-0"   +   15'-0" 3'-0"

Case 10, n=0.833   Case 10(negative),   Case 10, n=0.167
                      n=0.50

Since the beam is symmetrical, the equations can focus on the left half of the beam. The equations for the right half can then be found (if needed) simply by substituting $(L - x)$ for x.

Slope equations are found from load case 10 of Table 4-2, with x in inches.

For $0 \le x \le 3'$, the calculations are

$$\text{Slope} = -\frac{\left(\frac{1040}{12}\right)(18 \times 12)^3}{(360)(0.833)(30)(10^6)(1152)}\left[4.58140\right.$$

$$\left. - 17.36109\left(\frac{x}{216}\right)^2\right]$$

$$-\frac{\left(\frac{1280}{12}\right)(18 \times 12)^3}{(360)(0.50)(30)(10^6)(1152)}\left[- 1.15625\right.$$

$$\left. +3.75000\left(\frac{x}{216}\right)^2\right]$$

$$-\frac{\left(\frac{240}{12}\right)(18 \times 12)^3}{(360)(0.167)(30)(10^6)(1152)}\left[0.04591\right.$$

$$\left. - 0.13889\left(\frac{x}{216}\right)^2\right]$$

$$= - 0.0001906 + 0.0008280\left(\frac{x}{216}\right)^2$$

For $3 \le x \le 9'$, the calculations are

$$\text{Slope} = -0.00008424\left[4.58140 - 17.36109\left(\frac{x}{216}\right)^2 + 15\left(\frac{(x-36)}{216}\right)^4\right]$$

$$- 0.00017280\left[- 1.15625 + 3.75000\left(\frac{x}{216}\right)^2\right]$$

$$- 0.00009720\left[0.04591 - 0.13889\left(\frac{x}{216}\right)^2\right]$$

$$= - 0.0001906 + 0.0008280\left(\frac{x}{216}\right)^2 - 0.0012636\left[\frac{(x-36)}{216}\right]^4$$

Deflections are found similarly.

For $0 \le x \le 3'$,

$$\text{Deflection} = - 0.041169\left(\frac{x}{216}\right) + 0.059615\left(\frac{x}{216}\right)^3$$

For $3 \le x \le 9'$,

$$\text{Deflection} = -0.041169\left(\frac{x}{216}\right) + 0.059615\left(\frac{x}{216}\right)^3$$
$$-0.054588\left[\frac{(x-36)}{216}\right]^5$$

For the right side of the beam, substitute $216 - x$ wherever x occurs. For $9 \le x \le 12'$, the results are

$$\text{Slope} = -0.0001906 + 0.0008280\left(1 - \frac{x}{216}\right)^2$$
$$-0.0012636\left[1 - \frac{(x+36)}{216}\right]^4$$

$$\text{Deflection} = -0.041169\left(1 - \frac{x}{216}\right) + 0.059615\left(1 - \frac{x}{216}\right)^3$$
$$-0.054588\left[1 - \frac{(x+36)}{216}\right]^5$$

For $12 \le x \le 16'$, the results are

$$\text{Slope} = -0.0001906 + 0.0008280\left(1 - \frac{x}{216}\right)^2$$

$$\text{Deflection} = -0.041169\left(1 - \frac{x}{216}\right) + 0.059615\left(1 - \frac{x}{216}\right)^3$$

The foregoing examples illustrate rather clearly that the sheer volume of arithmetic can sometimes be a serious obstacle in computing the equations for slopes and deflections. Fortunately, it is often unnecessary to determine these equations. In most cases, it is only necessary to find a particular value of slope or deflection at a single point or (at most) at two points. A faster means to determine such individual solutions is presented in the next chapter.

In recent years, the use of the digital computer, with its commercial software and graphically displayed solutions, has increased the use of these general equations for slope and deflection. Such solutions are likely to remain popular in computer applications. In manual applications, however, they will probably continue to be used only as a method of last resort.

Outside Problems Determine the equations for the slope and the deflection of the given simply supported steel beams. For all beams, $E = 30,000,000$ lb/in.^{2}.

Problems 4-29 & 4-30*

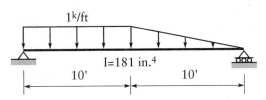

Problems 4-31 & 4-32

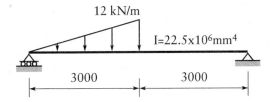

Problems 4-33 & 4-34*

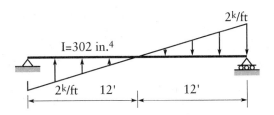

Problems 4-35 & 4-36

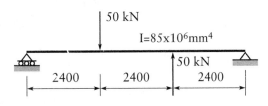

Determine a combination of load cases from Table 4-2 that will yield the slope and the deflection of the given simply supported beams. Actual calculation of deflections is not required.

Problem 4-37*

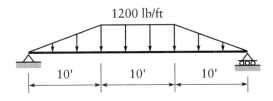

Problem 4-38

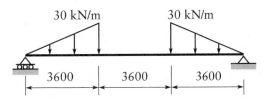

Problem 4-39*

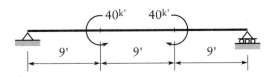

Problem 4-40

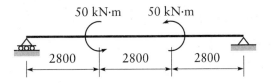

Problem 4-41*

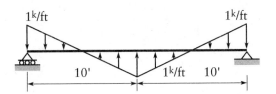

Problem 4-42

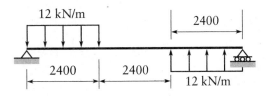

Problem 4-43*   **Problem 4-44**

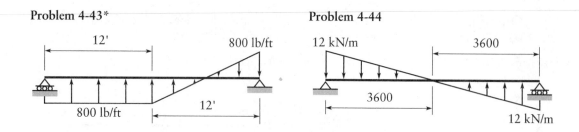

4.8 MAXIMUM DEFLECTION OF SIMPLE BEAMS

The maximum deflection of an unsymmetrically loaded beam occurs somewhere off the center of the beam. The point where this maximum deflection occurs can be found quite readily by setting the equation for slope equal to zero and solving the result for x. A typical case is shown in Figure 4-17.

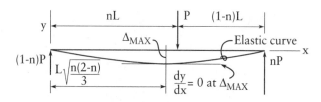

FIGURE 4-17 Maximum deflection for an unsymmetrical load.

The load case of Figure 4-17 corresponds to load case 6 of Table 4-2. When the equation for slope is set to zero and solved, the result is the one shown in Figure 4-17, where, for $n \geq 1/2L$, Δ_{MAX} occurs at

$$\frac{x}{L} = \sqrt{\frac{n(2-n)}{3}} \qquad (4.57)$$

For the worst possible case of eccentric loading in Figure 4-17—the case where n approaches 1—the maximum deflection Δ_{MAX} will occur at the point

$$\frac{x}{L} = \sqrt{\frac{1}{3}} = 0.57735 \qquad (4.58)$$

Maximum deflection will therefore occur within a distance of $0.07735L$ on either side of the centerline. It is concluded that no matter where the concentrated load is placed, the maximum deflection of the simple beam will occur within the middle 15.47% of the span.

At the value of x/L given by Equation 4.57, the maximum deflection Δ_{MAX} is, as given by Equation 4.47,

$$\Delta_{MAX} = -\frac{PL^3}{EI}\left(\frac{1-n}{9\sqrt{3}}\right)[n(2-n)]^{\frac{3}{2}} \tag{4.59}$$

This value of Δ_{MAX}, which occurs off-center, can now be compared to the deflection at the center. The deflection at the center of the span is also given by Equation 4.47. For $x = L/2$,

$$\Delta_{CTR} = -\frac{PL^3}{EI}\left(\frac{1-n}{48}\right)[4n(2-n)-1] \tag{4.60}$$

The ratio of Equations 4.60 and 4.59 yields the ratio of the two deflections:

$$\frac{\Delta_{CTR}}{\Delta_{MAX}} = -\frac{3\sqrt{3}}{16}\left[\frac{4n(2-n)-1}{(n[2-n])^{\frac{3}{2}}}\right] \tag{4.61}$$

At the worst possible case of eccentricity—that is, as n approaches 1—the ratio of deflections given by Equation 4.61 becomes

$$\frac{\Delta_{CTR}}{\Delta_{MAX}} = \frac{9\sqrt{3}}{16} = 0.9743 \tag{4.62}$$

or

$$\Delta_{CTR} = 0.9743\Delta_{MAX} \tag{4.63}$$

It is concluded that no matter where the concentrated load is placed, the deflection at the center of the simple beam will always be within 2.57% of the maximum deflection.

Other cases of loading shown in Table 4-2 can be analyzed similarly and yield the same results. The exception is load case 5, where the deflection does not fit the same pattern. Even in load case 5, however, when the moment is located at the end of the span (with $n = 0$), the deflections do follow this same general rule.

As a practical matter, a maximum error in the range of 2.57% in computing the deflections is well within the range of accuracy usually ascribed to the analysis itself. For example, the modulus of elasticity E for even the best materials can be found only to about 5% accuracy. In addition, the manufacturing process for making beams produces misalignments and slight variations in the cross section that can easily cause an error of 2.57% in any calculations involving deflections. Hence, it is common practice to compute the deflection at midspan of a simple beam and to assume that this is equivalent to the maximum deflection. In subsequent discussions, such an assumption will be shown to simplify calculations considerably.

REVIEW QUESTIONS

1. State mathematically the Bernoulli equation for curvatures, and define each term.
2. Define the term *homogeneous*.
3. Define the term *isotropic*.
4. Define the term *elastic*.
5. Give the mathematical relationship between linear modulus of elasticity and shear modulus of elasticity.
6. How are constants of integration evaluated?
7. Give the general differential equation for the elastic curve of a beam.
8. Given a simple beam loaded by a single set of loads, within what portion of the beam will the maximum deflection occur?

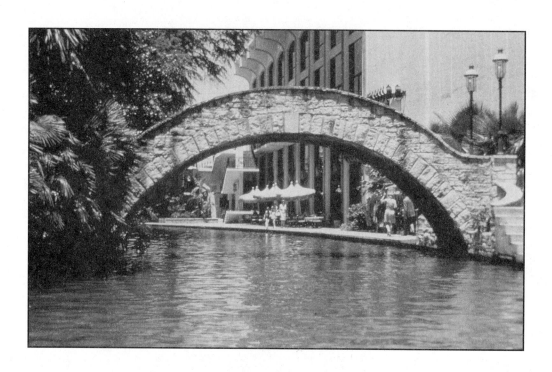

Arch bridge of reinforced concrete, faced with
natural stone. (Photograph courtesy of Portland Cement
Association, reprinted by permission.)

Area Moment Methods in Beams

The preceding classical methods for finding the equations of the slope and deflection of a beam by double integration are completely general. The actual values of the slope and deflection at any point along the beam are found simply by substituting the appropriate value of x into these general equations and solving for the values of slope and deflection at that point. As a practical matter, however, the solutions for these equations are tedious and cumbersome; except in connection with computer applications, such a detailed solution is rarely feasible.

It was noted earlier that a general solution is often unnecessary. Frequently, the only deformation that is of interest is the maximum deflection or, on occasion, the slope of the beam at a particular point. In these cases, a fast, simple solution for computing the slope or the deflection at a particular point is enough. A method for finding such a particular solution is presented in this chapter; it is called the method of area moment. Along with its many variations, the area moment method is widely used as a basic method of structural analysis.

5.1 AREA MOMENT THEOREMS FOR DEFORMATION AT A POINT

Consider the portion AB of an elastic beam in flexure shown in Figure 5-1. The coordinate x- and y-axes are horizontal and vertical; but as before, the slopes are so small that $\sin \phi = \tan \phi = \phi$ (in radians).

Further, for small angles, $dx = ds$. Hence, with $ds = dx$,

$$ds = \rho d\phi \, ,$$

and

$$\frac{d\phi}{dx} = \frac{1}{\rho} \tag{5.1}$$

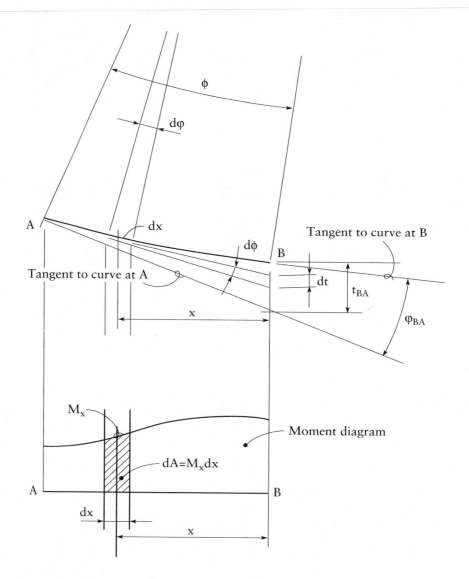

FIGURE 5-1 Beam in flexural curvature.

The Bernoulli equation (Equation 4.13) is substituted:

$$d\phi = \frac{M_x dx}{E_x I_x} \tag{5.2}$$

Integration between the points A and B yields ϕ:

$$\phi_{BA} = \int_A^B \frac{M_x d_x}{E_x I_x} \tag{5.3}$$

Physically, the definite integral given in Equation 5.3 is seen to be the area of the moment diagram between points A and B, divided by EI. This notable property constitutes the first area moment theorem.

Area Moment Theorem I

Given two points A and B on the elastic curve of a beam, the angular change in radians from the tangent at A to the tangent at B can be computed as the area of the bending moment diagram between A and B, divided by EI. If the sign of the angular change is positive, the elastic curve cups upward.

The distance dt in Figure 5-1 can be computed for small values of ϕ as

$$dt = x d\phi \tag{5.4}$$

The angle $d\phi$ is given by Equation 5.2; hence,

$$dt = \frac{M_x x dx}{E_x I_x} \tag{5.5}$$

Integration between the points A and B yields the distance t_{BA}:

$$t_{BA} = \int_A^B \frac{M_x x dx}{E_x I_x} \tag{5.6}$$

Physically, the definite integral given by Equation 5.6 is the moment of the moment diagram between A and B, with the moments taken about the deviation line at B. This property constitutes the second area moment theorem.

Area Moment Theorem II

Given two points A and B on the elastic curve of a beam, the vertical deviation of the point B from the tangent to the elastic curve at point A can be computed as the moment about B of the area of the bending moment diagram between A and B, divided by EI. If the sign of the deviation is positive, the tangent to the point A lies below the elastic curve at the point B.

The foregoing two theorems provide a means to compute changes in slopes and deflections in the elastic curve of a beam. The computations are not always straightforward, however, and some manipulation is sometimes necessary. Examples of typical computations are presented in the following section.

It is important to recognize that the method of area moment is simply a way to evaluate graphically the integrals given by Equations 5.3 and 5.6. The method is used so universally and has been used for so long, however, that it is included here as a "classical" method. Occasionally in the following examples, the integral will be evaluated directly as well as by area moment; the duplication will serve to emphasize the point that area moment is nothing more than a graphical means of evaluating the integral.

5.2 APPLICATIONS OF THE AREA MOMENT THEOREMS

A cantilever beam having a concentrated load at its free end is taken as a first example. Such a beam is shown in Figure 5-2. The moment diagram is a single triangle having a length L and an altitude PL, as shown.

A cantilever beam has a feature that simplifies calculations considerably: a tangent to the beam at B is horizontal. Calculations can therefore be referenced to this horizontal line, and results automatically represent absolute values for slopes and deflections.

For the beam of Figure 5-2, the maximum slope and the maximum deflection occur at the free end of the beam, as shown. The slope at that point is the angle θ_{MAX}, measured as the angle between the tangent to the elastic curve at A and the tangent to the elastic curve at B. The angle is given by the first area moment theorem:

$$\theta_{MAX} = \int_A^B \frac{M_x d_x}{E_x I_x} = \frac{A_M}{EI} \qquad (5.7)$$

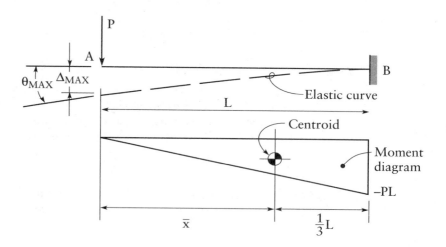

FIGURE 5-2 Cantilever with concentrated load at end.

where A_M is the area of the bending moment diagram between points A and B. The slope therefore becomes

$$\theta_{MAX} = \frac{-\left(\frac{1}{2}PL\right)(L)}{EI} = -\frac{PL^2}{2EI} \qquad (5.8)$$

and the negative sign indicates that the two tangents cross at a point above the elastic curve. This result for the slope at the end of the beam agrees with the result found earlier using double integration (Equation 4.23), but the two methods use different sign conventions for slope.

The maximum deflection Δ_{MAX} shown in Figure 5-2 is, in this case, the deviation of point A from the tangent at point B; the existence of the horizontal tangent at point B thus helps to simplify calculations. The deflection at the free end is given by the second area moment theorem:

$$t_{AB} = \Delta_{MAX} = \int_A^B \frac{M_x x \, dx}{EI} = \frac{A_M \bar{x}}{EI} \qquad (5.9)$$

where A_M is the area of the bending moment diagram between A and B, and $\bar{x}$ is the distance to its centroid, measured from the deviation line at A. The deflection at the free end is then

$$\Delta_{MAX} = \frac{-\left(\frac{1}{2}PL\right)(L)\left(\frac{2}{3}L\right)}{EI} = -\frac{PL^3}{3EI} \qquad (5.10)$$

where the negative sign indicates that the tangent from B lies above the point A (after deflection). This result agrees with the maximum deflection found earlier using double integration (Equation 4.24); in this case, the two methods yield the same algebraic signs.

A second example in cantilever beams is shown in Figure 5-3, where a concentrated load is located at some interior point along the beam. The moment diagram is again a single triangle, but it begins at the point of loading, as shown.

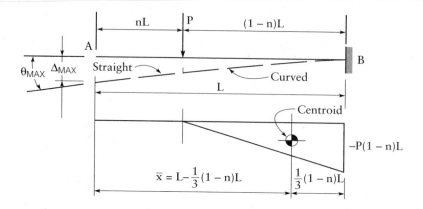

FIGURE 5-3 Cantilever with concentrated load at interior.

The maximum slope occurs anywhere along the straight portion of the beam, taken in this instance at point A:

$$\theta_{MAX} = \int_A^B \frac{M_x dx}{E_x I_x} = \frac{A_M}{EI} \tag{5.11}$$

The area of the moment diagram is substituted, yielding

$$\theta_{MAX} = \frac{-\frac{1}{2} P (1-n)(L)(1-n)(L)}{EI} = -\frac{PL^2}{2EI}(1-n)^2 \tag{5.12}$$

This result agrees with that given by double integration (Equation 4.25a); again, however, the sign conventions for the two methods may yield different algebraic signs.

The maximum deflection occurs at the free end of the beam:

$$\Delta_{MAX} = \int_A^B \frac{M_x dx}{EI} = \frac{A_M \bar{x}}{EI} \tag{5.13}$$

where $\bar{x}$ is again the distance from the deviation line at A to the centroid of the bending moment diagram. The values for A_M and $\bar{x}$ are substituted, yielding

$$\Delta_{MAX} = \frac{-\frac{1}{2} P (1-n) L (1-n) L \left[L - \frac{1}{3}(1-n) L \right]}{EI}$$

$$= -\frac{PL^3}{6EI}[3(1-n)^2 - (1-n)^3] \qquad (5.14)$$

This value of Δ_{MAX} agrees with that found by double integration, given by Equation 4.28.

A third example is shown in Figure 5-4, where a simple beam is loaded symmetrically by a single concentrated load.

The maximum deflection occurs at midspan, as indicated. Here again, there is a known horizontal tangent; this time, it is the tangent to the point C. The deviation at A, t_{AC}, is thus equal to the deflection Δ_{MAX}:

$$\Delta_{MAX} = t_{AC} = \int_A^C \frac{M_x x\,dx}{E_x I_x} = \frac{A_M \bar{x}}{EI} \qquad (5.15)$$

In this case the value of A_M is the area of the moment diagram between the points A and C, and the arm $\bar{x}$ is the distance from the deviation line at A to the centroid of A_M. These values are substituted, yielding

$$\Delta_{MAX} = t_{AC} = \frac{+\frac{1}{2}\left(\frac{1}{4}PL\right)\left(\frac{1}{2}L\right)\left(\frac{2}{3}\right)\frac{1}{2}L}{EI}$$

$$\Delta_{MAX} = \frac{PL^3}{48EI} \qquad (5.16)$$

In Equation 5.16, the value of t_{AC} is positive, indicating that the point A lies above the tangent line. This solution agrees with the result of the general solution (given by Equation 4.44), except, of course, that the sign conventions produce different signs.

Some numerical examples will further illustrate the procedure.

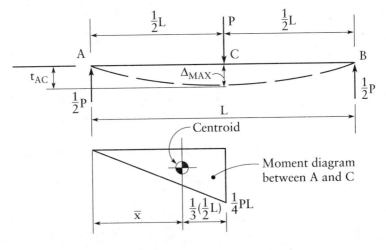

FIGURE 5-4 Simple beam with concentrated load.

Example 5-1   For the given beam and loads, determine the slope of the elastic curve at both ends of the beam and the deflection at midspan.

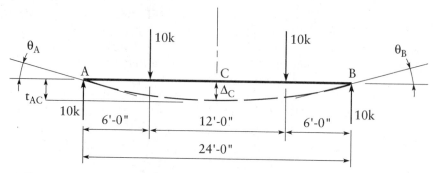

$E = 30,000,000$ psi

$I = 244$ in.^{4}

Solution   The moment diagram is shown below, divided into four component parts.

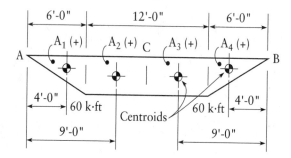

The slope at A is given by the area of the moment diagram between A and C, divided by EI:

$$\theta_A = \frac{A_M}{EI} = \frac{A_1 + A_2}{EI}$$

$$= \frac{\frac{1}{2}(60,000 \times 12)(6 \times 12) + (60,000 \times 12)(6 \times 12)}{30,000,000 \times 244}$$

$$= 0.0106 \text{ radians} = 0.60°$$

At the other end of the beam, the solution for θ_B is identical, yielding

$$\theta_B = 0.0106 \text{ radians}$$

The positive sign for both slopes indicates that, at both ends, the elastic curve cups upward; that is, the top of the beam is in compression.

The deflection at midspan is equal to the deviation of the point A above a line that is tangent to point C. Moments are therefore taken about the deviation line at A:

$$\Delta_C = t_{AC} = \frac{A_M \bar{x}}{EI} = \frac{A_1 \times 4' + A_2 \times 9'}{EI}$$

$$= \frac{\frac{1}{2}(60{,}000 \times 12)(72)(48) + (60{,}000 \times 12)(72)(108)}{300{,}000{,}000 \times 244}$$

$$= 0.935 \text{ in.}$$

Alternatively, the value of t_{AC} can be found by evaluating the integral directly. The integral form is given by

$$t_{AC} = \int_A^C \frac{M_x x_A dx}{EI_x}$$

The moment and moment arm are given by

$$0 \le x \le 72; \qquad M_x = 10{,}000x; \qquad x_A = x$$

$$72 \le x \le 144; \qquad M_x = 10{,}000\,(72)\,x; \qquad x_A = x$$

$$t_{AC} = \int_0^{72} \frac{(10{,}000x)(x)\,dx}{(30 \times 10^6)(244)} + \int_{72}^{144} \frac{10{,}000\,(72)(x)\,dx}{(30 \times 10^6)(244)}$$

$$= 0.935 \text{ in.}$$

The result, of course, is the same as that found by area moment, since the integral has simply been evaluated by using two different techniques.

Example 5-2   For the given beam and loads, find the slope of the beam at the left end.

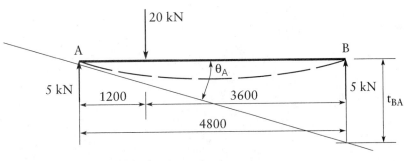

$$E = 10{,}000 \text{ N/mm}^2$$

$$I = 208 \times 10^6 \text{ mm}^2$$

Solution   Since there is no known point in this unsymmetrical system where the slope is known to be zero, the slope at the left end cannot be found in the usual way. Instead, for small angles, where L is the span length of 4800,

$$\theta_A = \tan\theta_A = \frac{t_{BA}}{L}$$

The unknown in this case becomes the deviation t_{BA} in millimeters. The moment diagram is shown next, divided into two component parts.

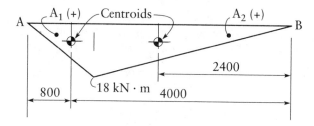

The deviation t_{BA} is at the point B; hence, moments are taken about point B:

$$t_{BA} = \frac{A_M\bar{x}}{EI} = \frac{A_1\bar{x}_2 + A_2\bar{x}_2}{EI}$$

$$= \frac{\frac{1}{2}(18 \times 10^6)(1200)(4000) + \frac{1}{2}(18 \times 10^6)(3600)(2400)}{(10,000)(208 \times 10^6)}$$

$$= 58.15 \text{ mm}$$

The slope at A is then

$$\theta_A = \frac{t_{BA}}{L} = \frac{58.15}{4800} = 0.01212 \text{ radians} = 0.69°$$

Example 5-3   Determine the deflection at the center of the given beam.

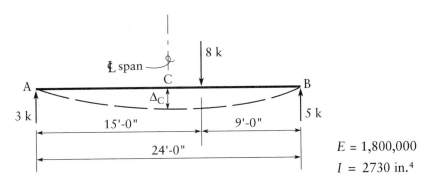

$E = 1,800,000$

$I = 2730$ in.[4]

Solution   Since there is no known point in this unsymmetrical system where the slope is known to be zero, the deflection cannot be found in the usual way. Two alternative solutions for Δ_C are indicated in the following sketches.

Solution No. 1

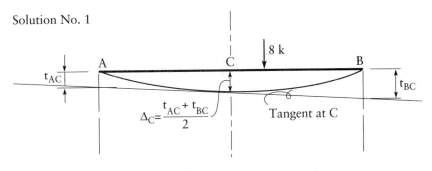

Solution No. 2

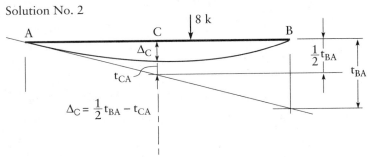

For either of the two solutions, it is necessary to find the deviation at two points, so neither solution has any particular advantage over the other.

Solution No. 2 is chosen for this particular problem. The moment diagram between points B and A is shown in the following sketch.

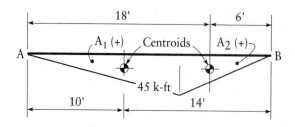

The deviation at B with respect to the tangent at A is found by taking moments about the deviation line at B:

$$t_{BA} = \frac{A_M \bar{x}}{EI} = \frac{(A_1 \times 14) + (A_2 \times 6)}{EI}$$

$$= \frac{\left[\frac{1}{2}(45,000 \times 12)(15 \times 12)(14 \times 12) + \frac{1}{2}(45,000 \times 12)(9 \times 12)(6 \times 12) \right]}{(1,800,000 \times 2730)}$$

$$= 2.089 \text{ in.}$$

The moment diagram between points A and C is shown in the following sketch.

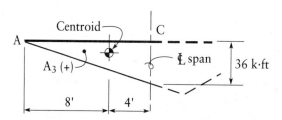

The deviation at C with respect to the tangent at A is found by taking moments about the deviation line at C:

$$t_{CA} = \frac{A_M \bar{x}}{EI} = \frac{A_3 \times 4}{EI}$$

$$= \frac{\frac{1}{2}(3600 \times 12)(12 \times 12)(4 \times 12)}{1,800,000 \times 2730}$$

$$= 0.03038 \text{ in.}$$

The deflection at midspan is then

$$\Delta_C = \frac{1}{2}t_{BA} - t_{CA} = \frac{1}{2}(2.089) - 0.03038$$

$$= 1.014 \text{ in.}$$

The foregoing examples demonstrate that the area moment solution can be fast and convenient, so long as the moment diagram is not a complex shape and so long as a horizontal tangent occurs at some known point in the span. Where these conditions do not exist, the method can become quite intricate and tedious. A simplified (and commonly used) approach to the computations involves breaking the moment diagram into its component parts; this extraneous simplification is presented in the next section for use in all subsequent examples.

Outside Problems Using the completed moment diagrams, determine the indicated slopes and deflections for the given load cases. Verify your results using Tables 4-1 and 4-2.

Problem 5-1 Find slope at free end.*
Problem 5-2 Find deflection at free end.*

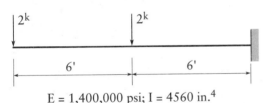

E = 1,400,000 psi; I = 4560 in.⁴

Problem 5-3 Find slope at free end.
Problem 5-4 Find deflection at free end.

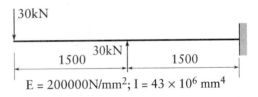

E = 200000N/mm²; I = 43 × 10⁶ mm⁴

Problem 5-5 Find slope at free end.*
Problem 5-6 Find deflection at free end.*

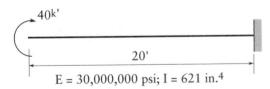

E = 30,000,000 psi; I = 621 in.⁴

Problem 5-7 Find slope at end.
Problem 5-8 Find deflection at center.

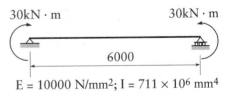

E = 10000 N/mm²; I = 711 × 10⁶ mm⁴

Problem 5-9 Find slope at end.*
Problem 5-10 Find deflection at center.*

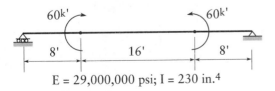

E = 29,000,000 psi; I = 230 in.⁴

Problem 5-11 Find slope at end.
Problem 5-12 Find deflection at center.

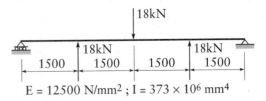

E = 12500 N/mm² ; I = 373 × 10⁶ mm⁴

5.3 AREA MOMENT USING MOMENT DIAGRAMS BY PARTS

A completed moment diagram may be treated as a scalar sum of the various parts of the moment equation. To illustrate this point, the moment diagram for a cantilever beam is shown in Figure 5-5, along with the moment diagrams that are produced by each load.

As indicated in Figure 5-5, the composite moment diagram is the scalar sum of the individual terms of the moment equation. Each term may, in fact, be drawn separately, as shown in the moment diagram by parts. The sum of the three simple shapes of course produces the composite, or complete, moment diagram.

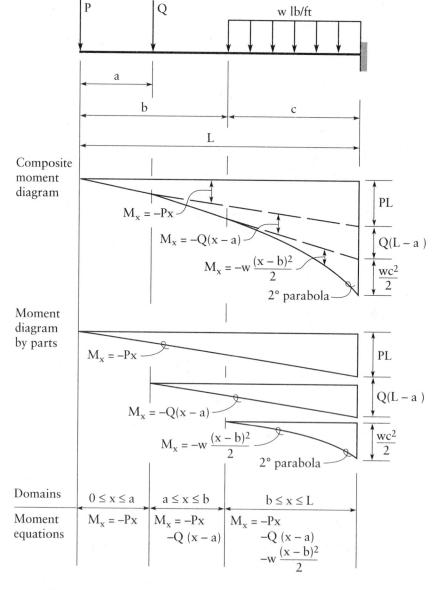

FIGURE 5-5 Cantilever bending moment by parts.

Another example is shown in the simple beam of Figure 5-6. As indicated here, the composite diagram may become quite complex, but it is still simply the sum of the moment diagrams produced by the individual loads. The moment equations again verify that the composite moment diagram is the scalar sum of these component parts.

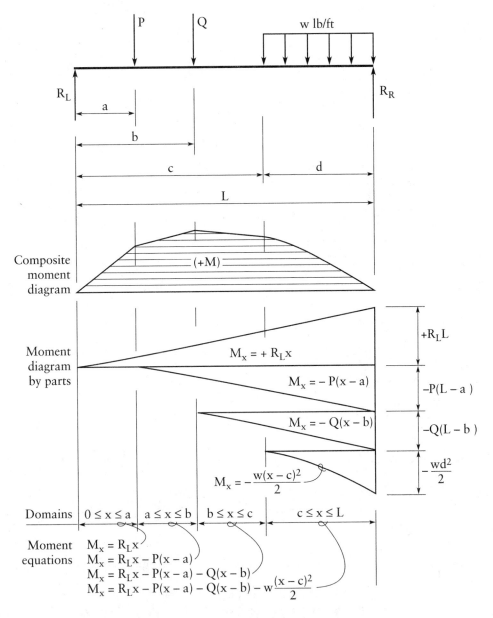

FIGURE 5-6 Simple beam bending moment diagram by parts.

As indicated in Figures 5-5 and 5-6, the moment diagram for each individual load has a relatively simple and familiar shape. The areas and centroids of these shapes are given in standard handbooks; a table of the more common loads and shapes is presented in Table 5-1, for immediate reference.

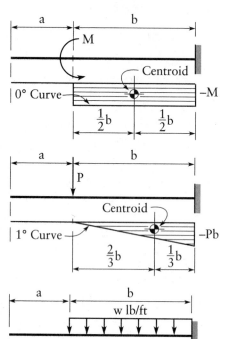

APPLIED MOMENT

$A_M = 1 \times$ the area of the circumscribing rectangle

$A_M = 1\,(-M)(b) = -Mb$

CONCENTRATED LOAD

$A_M = \dfrac{1}{2}$ the area of the circumscribing rectangle

$A_M = \dfrac{1}{2}\,(-Pb)(b) = -\dfrac{1}{2}pb^2$

UNIFORM LOAD

$A_M = \dfrac{1}{3}$ the area of the circumscribing rectangle

$A_M = \dfrac{1}{3}\left(-\dfrac{1}{2}wb^2\right)(b) = -\dfrac{1}{6}wb^3$

HYDROSTATIC LOAD

$A_M = \dfrac{1}{4}$ the area of the circumscribing rectangle

$A_M = \dfrac{1}{4}\left(-\dfrac{1}{6}pb^2\right)(b) = -\dfrac{1}{24}pb^3$

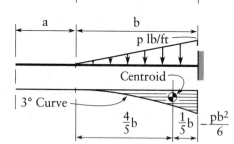

Table 5-1 Geometric Properties of Moment Diagrams

The simple shapes shown in Table 5-1 can be combined to produce the moment diagrams for more complex loads. Typical examples of such combinations follow.

Example 5-4   Determine the deflection at the free end of the given cantilever beam.

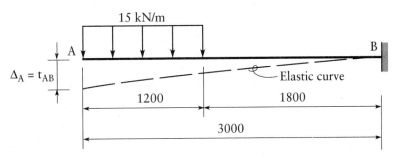

$E = 200,000$ N/mm^2

$I = 40 \times 10^6$ mm^4

Solution   The given loading may be shown as a combination of two loads, as indicated in the following sketch. The moment diagrams for these two loads are shown below immediately below the load diagrams.

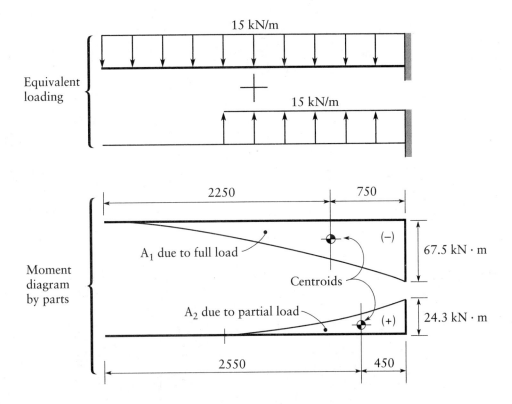

The deflection at the free end is equal to the deviation t_{AB}. For Δ expressed in mm,

$$\Delta = t_{AB} = \frac{A_M \bar{x}}{EI} = \frac{-A_1 \bar{x}_1 + A_2 \bar{x}_2}{EI}$$

$$= \frac{-\frac{1}{3}(67.5 \times 10^6)(3000)(2250) + \frac{1}{3}(24.3 \times 10^6)(1800)(2550)}{(200,000)(40 \times 10^6)}$$

$$= -14.34 \text{ mm}$$

Alternatively, the deflection can be found by evaluating the integral form of the area moment solution.

$$0 \le x \le 1200; \qquad M_x = -7.5x^2; \qquad x_A = x$$

$$1200 \le x \le 3000; \qquad M_x = -18,000\,(x - 600); \qquad x_A = x$$

$$t_{AB} = \int_A^B \frac{M_x x_A dx}{EI_x}$$

$$= \int_0^{1200} \frac{(-7.5x^2)(x)dx}{(200,000)(40 \times 10^6)} + \int_{1200}^{3000} \frac{(-18,000)(x - 600)(x)dx}{(200,000)(40 \times 10^6)}$$

$$=$$

$$-(9.375)(10^{-13})\frac{x^4}{4}\bigg|_0^{1200} - (2.25)(10^{-9})\frac{x^3}{3}\bigg|_{1200}^{3000} + (1.35)(10^{-6})\frac{x^2}{2}\bigg|_{1200}^{3000}$$

$$= -14.34 \text{ mm}$$

This result, of course, is the same as that found by the graphic techniques of area moment.

Example 5-5　　Determine the slope at the left end of the given simple beam.

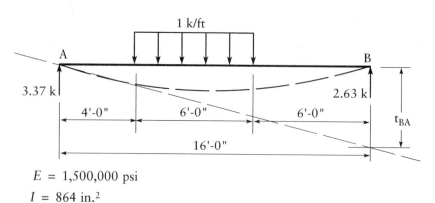

$$E = 1,500,000 \text{ psi}$$
$$I = 864 \text{ in.}^2$$

Solution   Since the system is unsymmetrical, there is no reference point at which the slope is known to be zero; the slope at A must therefore be solved as the tangent of the angle

$$\theta_A = \tan\theta_A = \frac{t_{BA}}{L}$$

The load and the moment diagrams can be reproduced as the sum of the individual loads, as shown in the following sketches.

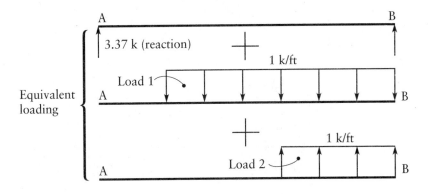

Equivalent loading

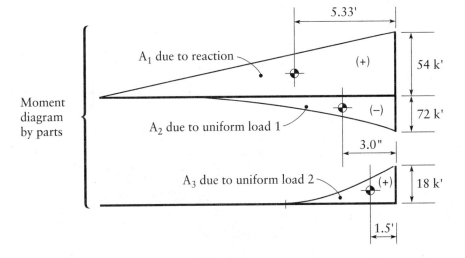

Moment diagram by parts

The deviation t_{BA} is found by taking the moment of the moment diagrams about the deviation line at B:

$$t_{BA} = \frac{A_M \bar{x}}{EI} = \frac{(A_1)(5.33') - (A_2)(3.0') + (A_3)(1.5')}{EI}$$

$$\frac{\frac{1}{2}(54,000 \times 12)(16 \times 12)(5.33 \times 12)}{-\frac{1}{3}(72,000 \times 12)(12 \times 12)(3 \times 12)}$$

$$\frac{+\frac{1}{3}(18,000 \times 12)(6 \times 12)(1.5 \times 12)}{1,500,000 \times 864}$$

$$= 1.99 \text{ in.}$$

Solve for slope θ_A:

$$\theta_A = \frac{t_{BA}}{L} = \frac{1.99}{16 \times 12} = 0.0104 \text{ radians} = 0.59°$$

Example 5-6   Determine the deflection at the center of the given simple beam.

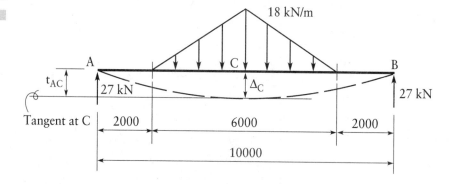

$E = 200,000 \text{ N/mm}^2$

$I = 156 \times 10^6 \text{ mm}^4$

Solution   Since this beam is symmetrical, the deflection at its center is equal to the deviation t_{AC}, as shown. For computing t_{AC}, it is only necessary to sketch the portion of the moment diagram between A and C, as indicated in the following sketch.

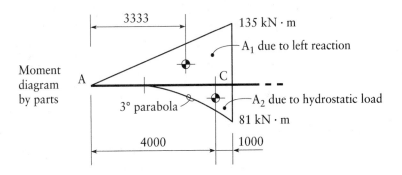

The deviation t_{AC} (in mm) is found by taking moments about the deviation line at A:

$$t_{AC} = \frac{A_M \bar{x}}{EI} = \frac{A_1 \bar{x}_1 - A_2 \bar{x}_2}{EI}$$

$$= \frac{\frac{1}{2}(135 \times 10^6)(5000)(3333) - \frac{1}{4}(81 \times 10^6)(3000)(4000)}{(200{,}000)(156 \times 10^6)}$$

$$\Delta = 28.27 \text{ mm}$$

Many innovations are possible in the use of the moment diagrams by parts. For example, it may sometimes be simpler to draw the diagram from right to left, as shown in Figure 5-7. Since the area moment method uses absolute values for area and for distance, the origin of x for sketching the diagrams is rarely a major concern.

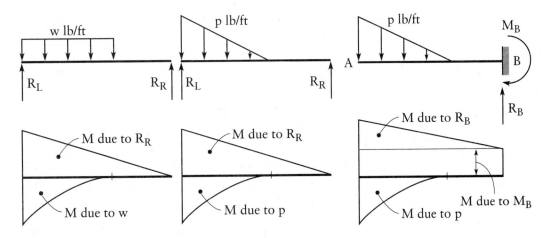

FIGURE 5-7 Moment diagrams with origin of x at right.

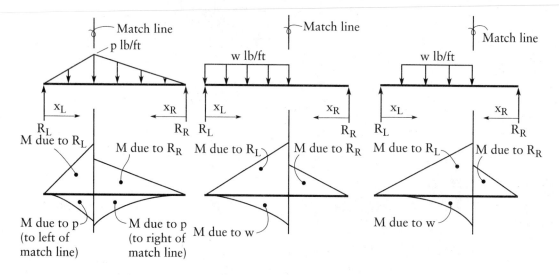

FIGURE 5-8 Moment diagrams with two origins of x.

Further, it is possible to sketch the left portion of the moment diagram while using the origin of x at the left side and to sketch the right portion of the moment diagram while using the origin of x at the right side. Typical examples of this technique are shown in Figure 5-8. Notice that the technique requires establishing a match line, at which the two sets of moment diagrams must terminate. (For a numerical check, the two sides must also produce the same numerical value for moment at this match line.)

With the foregoing innovations, the use of area moment as a method of analysis can be expanded considerably over the examples given earlier. Complex loadings and unsymmetrical cases may be solved relatively easily, although at times the numerical calculations do become tedious. Some examples of such complex cases of loads and deformations can now be considered.

Outside Problems

Draw the moment diagrams by parts for the given load cases.

Problem 5-13*

Problem 5-14

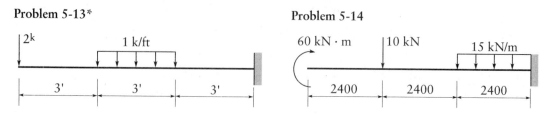

Problem 5-15*

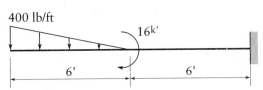

400 lb/ft

16$^{k'}$

6'   6'

Problem 5-16

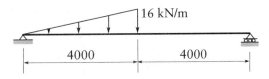

16 kN/m

4000   4000

Problem 5-17*

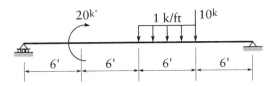

20$^{k'}$ 1 k/ft   10^k

6'   6'   6'   6'

Problem 5-18

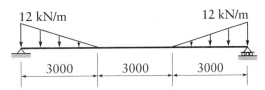

12 kN/m   12 kN/m

3000   3000   3000

5.4 APPLICATIONS OF AREA MOMENT TO GENERAL CASES

Area moment solutions can now be applied to more general cases of loading and to more general cases of supports. Some examples will illustrate the solutions for these general cases.

Example 5-7   Determine the deflection at the end of the given cantilever beam.

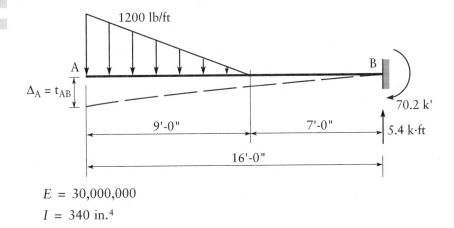

1200 lb/ft

A   B

$\Delta_A = t_{AB}$

9'-0"   7'-0"

70.2 k'

5.4 k·ft

16'-0"

$E = 30,000,000$

$I = 340 \text{ in.}^4$

Solution   Reactions at the fixed end of the cantilever have been computed and entered on the preceding sketch. They may be treated in the same way as any other loads on the beam. The moment diagram is drawn from the right to the left, as shown in the following sketch.

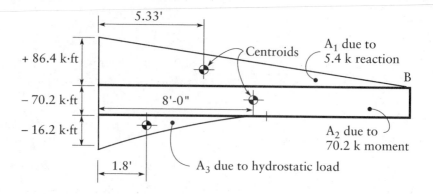

The deflection at the free end is equal to the deviation t_{AB}; the moment of the area of the moment diagram is therefore taken about the deviation line at A:

$$\Delta = t_{AB} = \frac{A_M \bar{x}}{EI} = \frac{(A_1)(5.33) - (A_2)(8.0') - (A_3)(1.8)}{EI}$$

$$= \frac{\begin{array}{l} \frac{1}{2}(86{,}400 \times 12)(16 \times 12)(5.33 \times 12) \\[6pt] - (70{,}200 \times 12)(16 \times 12)(8.0 \times 12) \\[6pt] - \frac{1}{4}(16{,}200 \times 12)(8 \times 12)(1.8 \times 12) \end{array}}{30{,}000{,}000 \times 340}$$

$$= -0.91 \text{ in.}$$

The negative sign indicates that the elastic curve at A falls below the tangent line drawn from B.

Example 5-8   Determine the deflection at the center of the given simple beam.

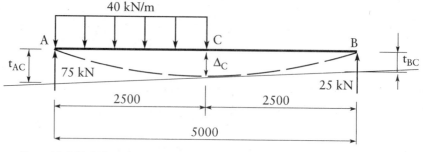

$E = 12{,}000$ N/mm²

$I = 1705 \times 10^6$ mm⁴

Solution   The deflection at the center is the average of t_{AC} and t_{BC}. The deviation t_{AC} is found by using only the left half of the moment diagram, while t_{BC} is found by using only the right half. The moment diagram by parts can therefore be drawn from both ends toward the middle, as shown in the following sketch.

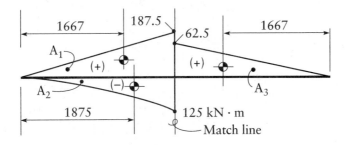

The deviation t_{AC} (in millimeters) is found by computing the moment of the left half of the bending moment diagram about A:

$$t_{AC} = \frac{A_M \bar{x}}{EI} = \frac{A_1 \bar{x}_1 - A_2 \bar{x}_2}{EI}$$

$$= \frac{\frac{1}{2}(187.5 \times 10^6)(2500)(1667) - \frac{1}{3}(125 \times 10^6)(2500)(1875)}{(12,000)(1705 \times 10^6)}$$

$$= 9.55 \text{ mm}$$

The deviation t_{BC} is found similarly, by computing the moment of the right half of the bending moment diagram about the deviation line at B:

$$t_{BC} = \frac{A_M \bar{x}}{EI} = \frac{A_3 \bar{x}}{EI}$$

$$= \frac{\frac{1}{2}(62.5 \times 10^6)(2500)(1667)}{(12,000)(1705 \times 10^6)}$$

$$= 6.37 \text{ mm}$$

The deflection at the center is the average of these:

$$\Delta = \frac{1}{2}(t_{AC} + t_{BC}) = 7.96 \text{ mm}$$

It is interesting to compare this solution to that of a fully loaded beam. If this beam were to be loaded on both sides, the deflection at the center would be doubled, to 15.9 mm. The general solution for the deflection at the center of a fully loaded span was determined earlier, and the result given by Equation 3.39 was

$$\Delta_{MAX} = -\frac{5wL^4}{384EI}$$

As a check, this general solution gives a numerical deflection of

$$\Delta_{MAX} = -\frac{5(40)(5000)^4}{384\,(12,000)(1705 \times 10^6)} = -15.9 \text{ mm}$$

The general solution therefore agrees with the solution obtained here.

Example 5-9   Determine the approximate maximum deflection of the given simple beam.

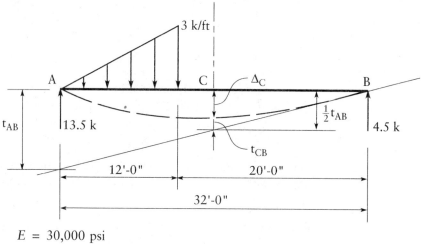

$E = 30,000$ psi

$I = 517$ in.^{2}

Solution   The deflection at centerline is taken to be approximately equal to the maximum deflection. The deflection at centerline is given by

$$\Delta_C = \frac{1}{2}t_{AB} - t_{CB}$$

For purposes of sketching the moment diagram by parts, the match line is chosen at the end of the hydrostatic load, as shown in the following diagram.

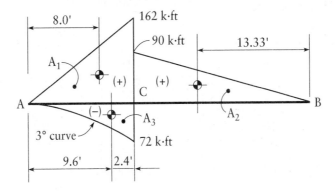

The deviation at A, t_{AB}, is the moment of the entire bending moment diagram about A, divided by EI:

$$t_{AB} = \frac{A_M \bar{x}}{EI} = \frac{(A_1)(8) + (A_2)(18.67) - (A_3)(9.6)}{EI}$$

$$\frac{\left[\frac{1}{2}(162{,}000 \times 12)(12 \times 12)(8 \times 12)\right.}{}$$

$$+ \frac{1}{2}(90{,}000 \times 12)(20 \times 12)(18.67 \times 12)$$

$$\frac{\left. - \frac{1}{4}(72{,}000 \times 12)(12 \times 12)(9.6 \times 12)\right]}{30{,}000{,}000 \times 517}$$

$$= 2.51 \text{ in.}$$

The deviation at C, t_{CB}, is found by taking the moment of that portion of the bending moment diagram between C and B, about the deviation line at C. For clarity, that portion of the moment diagram is redrawn below.

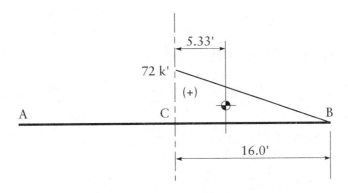

The deviation t_{CB} is then

$$t_{CB} = \frac{A_M \bar{x}}{EI}$$

$$= \frac{\frac{1}{2}(72{,}000 \times 12)(16 \times 12)(5.33 \times 12)}{30{,}000{,}000 \times 517}$$

$$= 0.31 \text{ in.}$$

The deflection at midspan can now be computed:

$$\Delta = \frac{1}{2}t_{AB} - t_{CB} = \frac{1}{2} \times 2.51 - 0.34$$

$$= 0.92 \text{ in.}$$

Example 5-10   Determine the deflection at the free end of the given overhang.

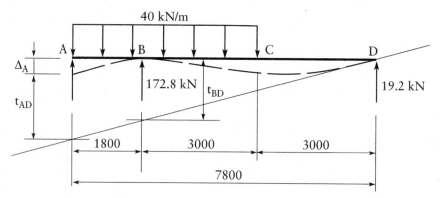

$$E = 200{,}000 \text{ N/mm}^2$$
$$I = 52 \times 10^6 \text{ mm}^4$$

Solution   The geometry of the deflections is found by means of simple ratios:

$$\frac{\Delta + t_{AD}}{7800} = \frac{t_{BD}}{6000}$$

$$\Delta = \left(\frac{7800}{6000}\right)t_{BD} - t_{AD} = 1.30 t_{BD} - t_{AD}$$

For this case, the moment diagram by parts is somewhat simpler if drawn from right to left, as shown in the following sketch.

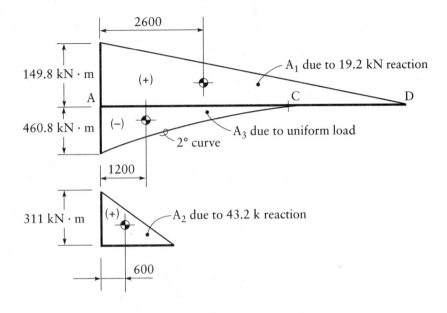

For t_{AD}, moments are taken about A:

$$t_{AD} = \frac{A_M \bar{x}}{EI} = \frac{A_1 \bar{x}_1 + A_2 \bar{x}_2 - A_3 \bar{x}_3}{EI}$$

$$\frac{\left[\frac{1}{2}(149.8 \times 10^6)(7800)(2600) + \frac{1}{2}(311 \times 10^6)(1800)(600) - \frac{1}{3}(460.8 \times 10^6)(4800)(1200)\right]}{(200{,}000)(52 \times 10^6)}$$

$$= 77.13 \text{ mm}$$

For t_{BD}, only the portion of the moment diagram between B and D is used, with moments taken about B. The moment diagram by parts is redrawn below for clarity.

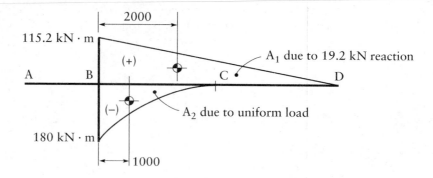

The deviation t_{BD} is now computed, with moments taken about the deviation line at B:

$$t_{BD} = \frac{A_M}{EI} = \frac{A_1 \bar{x}_1 - A_2 \bar{x}_2}{EI}$$

$$= \frac{\frac{1}{2}(115.2 \times 10^6)(6000)(2000) - \frac{1}{3}(180 \times 10^6)(3000)(1000)}{(200,000)(52 \times 10^6)}$$

$$= 49.15 \text{ mm}$$

The deflection at the end of the overhang is then

$$\Delta = 1.3 t_{BD} - t_{AD}$$
$$= (1.3)(49.15) - (77.13)$$
$$= -13.24 \text{ mm}$$

The negative sign indicates only that the deflection is upward.

Outside Problems   Determine the indicated slopes and deflections for the given load cases.

Problem 5-19 Find slope at free end.*
Problem 5-20 Find deflection at free end.*

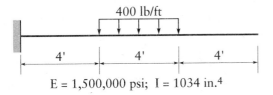

E = 1,500,000 psi; I = 1034 in.^{4}

Problem 5-21 Find slope at free end.
Problem 5-22 Find deflection at free end.

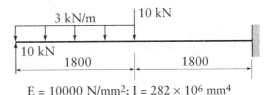

E = 10000 N/mm^2; I = 282 × 10^6 mm^4

Problem 5-23 Find slope at free end.*
Problem 5-24 Find deflection at free end.*

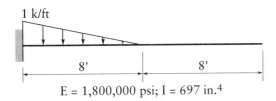

E = 1,800,000 psi; I = 697 in.^{4}

Problem 5-25 Find slope at end.
Problem 5-26 Find deflection at center.

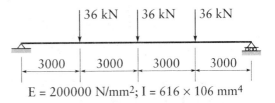

E = 200000 N/mm^2; I = 616 × 106 mm^4

Problem 5-27 Find slope at left end.*
Problem 5-28 Find deflection at center.*

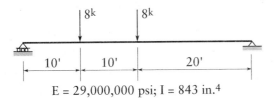

E = 29,000,000 psi; I = 843 in.^{4}

Problem 5-29 Find slope at end.
Problem 5-30 Find deflection at center.

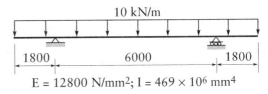

E = 12800 N/mm^2; I = 469 × 10^6 mm^4

Problem 5-31 Find slope at left end.*
Problem 5-32 Find deflection at left end.*

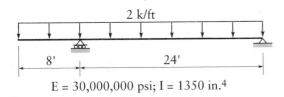

E = 30,000,000 psi; I = 1350 in.^{4}

Problem 5-33 Find slope at end.
Problem 5-34 Find deflection at center.

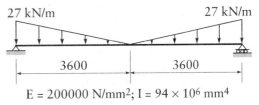

E = 200000 N/mm^2; I = 94 × 10^6 mm^4

Problem 5-35 Find slope at center.*
Problem 5-36 Find deflection at right end.*

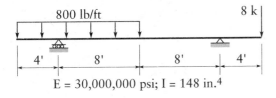

E = 30,000,000 psi; I = 148 in.^{4}

Problem 5-37 Find slope at end.
Problem 5-38 Find deflection at end.

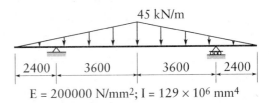

E = 200000 N/mm^2; I = 129 × 10^6 mm^4

Problem 5-39 Find slope at end.*
Problem 5-40 Find deflection at center.*

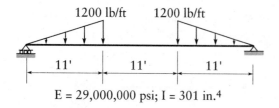

1200 lb/ft   1200 lb/ft

11'   11'   11'

E = 29,000,000 psi; I = 301 in.^{4}

5.5 BEAMS WITH VARIABLE CROSS SECTIONS

The area moment theorems remain valid when the beam contains variations in its cross section. The solution requires that the changes (or discontinuities) must be recognized when the area moment theorems are applied. An example will illustrate the procedure for a simple load system.

Example 5-11   Determine the deflection at the center of the given beam.

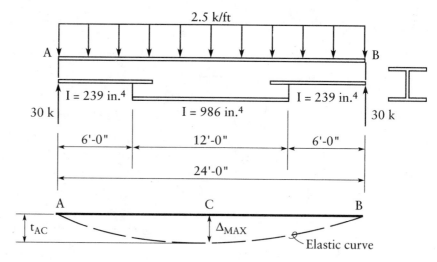

2.5 k/ft

A   B

I = 239 in.^{4} I = 986 in.^{4} I = 239 in.^{4}

30 k   30 k

6'-0"   12'-0"   6'-0"

24'-0"

A   C   B

t_{AC} Δ_{MAX}

Elastic curve

E = 30,000,000 psi

Solution   The deflection at midspan is equal to the deviation t_{AC}, as shown. Therefore, only the portion of the moment diagram between A and C is needed, with the first 6 ft having $I = 239$ in.^{4} and the next 6 ft having $I = 986$ in.^{2}. The two segments are shown in the following sketches.

For the first 6 feet, the moment of the bending moment diagram about A is to be divided by an I of 239 in.[4].

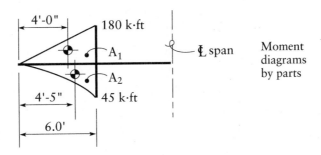

For the next 6 feet, the moment of the bending moment diagram about A is to be divided by an I of 986 in.[4].

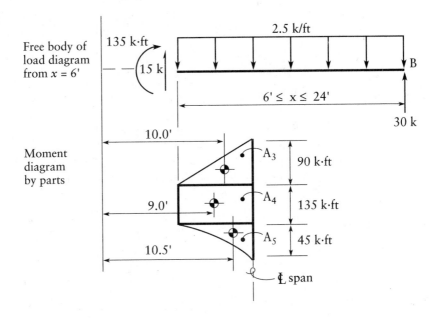

The deviation t_{AC} can now be computed, using both of the foregoing moment diagrams:

$$t_{AC} = \frac{A_M \bar{x}}{EI} = \frac{(A_1)(3) - (A_2)(4.5)}{(E)(239)}$$

$$+ \frac{(A_3)(10) + (A_4)(9) - (A_5)(10.5)}{(E)(986)}$$

$$\frac{\frac{1}{2}(180,000 \times 12)(6 \times 12)(4 \times 12)}{30,000,000 \times 239}$$
$$\frac{-\frac{1}{3}(45,000 \times 12)(6 \times 12)(4.5 \times 12)}{30,000,000 \times 239}$$

$$+ \frac{\frac{1}{2}(90,000 \times 12)(6 \times 12)(10 \times 12)}{30,000,000 \times 986}$$
$$\frac{+ (135,000 \times 12)(6 \times 12)(9 \times 12)}{30,000,000 \times 986}$$
$$\frac{-\frac{1}{3}(45,000 \times 12)(6 \times 12)(10.5 \times 12)}{30,000,000 \times 986}$$

$$= 0.95 \text{ in.}$$

The area moment theorems may also be applied to beams for which the moment of inertia I is continuously changing. In such cases, it is usually simpler to perform the integration numerically than to attempt any form of exact solution. An example will illustrate such an integration.

Example 5-12 Determine the deflection at the center of the given tapered steel girder.

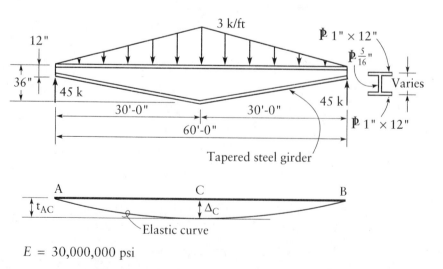

Tapered steel girder

$E = 30,000,000$ psi

Solution   The deflection at the center is equal to the deviation at *A* with respect to the tangent at *C*, as shown. The deviation t_{AC} is given by the second area moment theorem (Equation 3.69):

$$t_{AC} = \int_A^C \frac{M_x x \, dx}{E_x I_x}$$

The integral form is written as a finite summation of *m* elements of length Δx:

$$t_{AC} = \sum_{i=1}^{m} \frac{M_x x \, (\Delta x)}{E_x I_x}$$

The beam is now broken into a series of 20 strips of 3 ft each, as shown in the following sketch, and the finite summation is evaluated numerically for this approximation.

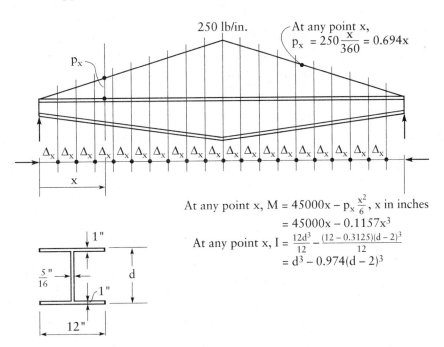

250 lb/in.

At any point x,
$p_x = 250 \dfrac{x}{360} = 0.694x$

At any point x, $M = 45000x - p_x \dfrac{x^2}{6}$, x in inches
$$= 45000x - 0.1157x^3$$
At any point x, $I = \dfrac{12d^3}{12} - \dfrac{(12 - 0.3125)(d - 2)^3}{12}$
$$= d^3 - 0.974(d - 2)^3$$

The finite summation is given in the following table, with *x* taken to the center of each element Δx.

Strip	Δx (in.)	x (in.)	d (in.)	I_x (in.^{4})	M_x (kip·in.)	$\dfrac{M_x x\,(\Delta x)}{I_x}$
01	36	018	13.2	932	810	563
02	36	054	15.6	1346	2412	3484
03	36	090	18.0	1842	3966	6976
04	36	126	20.4	2422	5438	10,184
05	36	162	22.8	3087	6798	12,843
06	36	198	25.2	3841	8012	14,868
07	36	234	27.6	4684	9047	16,271
08	36	270	30.0	5619	9872	17,077
09	36	306	32.4	6648	10,454	17,323
10	36	342	34.8	7774	10,760	17,041

$$\Sigma = \overline{116,600}$$

The result is divided by E_x, which is a constant for all values of x. The final result is then the deflection at midspan:

$$\Delta = \sum_{i=1}^{m} \frac{M_x x\,(\Delta x)}{E_x I_x} = \frac{116,600,000}{30,000,000}$$
$$= 3.89 \text{ in.}$$

Alternatively, this deflection can be found by evaluating the integral form of the area moment solution:

$$0 \le x \le 360; \qquad M_x = 45,000\,(x) - 0.1157\,(x^3); \qquad x_A = x$$

$$I_x = d^3 - 0.974\,(d-2)^3 \qquad \text{where} \qquad d = 12 + 0.06667x$$

$$t_{AC} = \int_A^C \frac{M_x x_A dx}{EI}$$
$$= \int_0^{360} \frac{(45,000x - 0.1157x^3)(x)\,dx}{(30)(10^6)\,[d^3 - 0.974\,(d-2)^3]}$$

The integral is evaluated by computer software to find

$$t_{AC} = 3.886 \text{ in.}$$

Interestingly, the manual solution based on only 20 elements is as accurate as the machine solution.

Outside Problems For the given load cases, find the slope at the end and the deflection at the center.

Problems 5-41 & 5-42

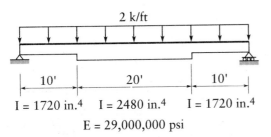

| 10' | 20' | 10' |

I = 1720 in.^{4} I = 2480 in.^{4} I = 1720 in.^{4}

E = 29,000,000 psi

Problems 5-43* & 5-44*

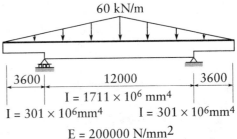

60 kN/m

| 3600 | 12000 | 3600 |

I = 1711 × 10^6 mm^4

I = 301 × 10^{6}mm^4 I = 301 × 10^{6}mm^4

E = 200000 N/mm^2

REVIEW QUESTIONS

1. State the first area moment theorem verbally.

2. State the second area moment theorem verbally.

3. What does it mean if the algebraic sign of the angle computed by the first area moment theorem is negative?

4. What does it mean if the algebraic sign of the deviation computed by the second area moment theorem is negative?

5. In the first area moment theorem, if the tangents cross above the elastic curve, will the algebraic sign of the solution be positive or negative?

6. In the text, the area moment solution is called a "particular" solution of the differential equation of the elastic curve. Is this terminology mathematically correct?

High clearance steel bridge at Lawyer's Canyon, Idaho.
(Photograph courtesy American Institute of Steel
Construction, reprinted by permission.)

Classical Energy Methods in Beams and Frames

When external loads are applied to an elastic structure, the structure deforms, much as an elastic spring deforms under load. The external loads therefore undergo a small movement; work has been done. The structural members, through their associated stress and deformation, store the energy thus generated. By the law of conservation of energy, the work W that is done by the small movements of the external loads must be equal to the potential energy U that is stored in the deformed members. Stated as an equality,

External work done = Internal energy stored

or symbolically,

$$W = U \tag{6.1}$$

When the external loads are removed, the structure rebounds elastically, and the stored potential energy drops back to zero.

The concept of having energy stored within a structure, like a deformed spring, provides a second means of investigating the deformations of a structure under external loads. These methods, generically called *energy methods*, are completely independent of the methods of the elastic curve developed earlier. It is therefore possible (although not always practical) to obtain an independent check on one's numerical calculations by using one method to corroborate the other.

The energy methods are developed in this chapter. These methods are based on the Castigliano theorem, which is probably the best-known and most widely used of the energy methods. A few other specialized methods that can be directly derived from the Castigliano theorem are also introduced, but they are not pursued further; a clutter of such specialized methods exists.

Like the area moment methods, the energy methods provide a means of finding only a particular deformation at a particular point; they do not provide general equations for deformation at every point, comparable to those given by the method of double integration. But in defense of the energy methods, the same argument used earlier still applies: the particular solution is often the only information needed. The energy methods are a powerful tool in finding these particular solutions.

Although not specifically discussed in Chapters 4 and 5, application of the methods of the elastic curve is limited to prismatic members that have a smooth and continuous elastic curve; these methods are not appropriate for segmental members such as trusses. The energy methods, by contrast, can be applied with equal validity to prismatic members and to trusses. Further, the energy methods are well-suited for applications by computers and require no graphic interpretations of moment diagrams such as those used in the area moment methods. The energy methods thus constitute a useful adjunct method in contemporary structural analysis.

The energy methods require evaluation of a definite integral, which can sometimes become quite tedious to perform. The evaluation may be performed manually or by standard computer software. In the examples of this chapter, manual evaluation is included in the text only for the simpler cases; when manual methods are clearly impractical, the computer evaluation is given.

6.1 ELASTIC STRAIN ENERGY

Consider an elastic body acted upon by some system of externally applied loads, as indicated in Figure 6-1(a). The work done by any external load P_1 is equal to the force times the displacement δ_1, but the force P_1 begins with its initial value of zero and increases linearly to its final value of P_1, as shown in Figure 6-1(b). The work done by any one of the external forces is then its average value $1/2\,P_1$ times the displacement δ_1. The total work done by all external forces, denoted here as W, is the sum of the individual increments:

$$W = \frac{1}{2}P_1\delta_1 + \frac{1}{2}P_2\delta_2 + \frac{1}{2}P_3\delta_3 + \ldots + \frac{1}{2}P_n\delta_n \qquad (6.2)$$

If any one of the external forces (such as P_1) is increased by a small amount ΔP_1, the displacement δ_1 will increase correspondingly by its inverse spring constant $\partial\delta_1/\partial P_1$ inches per pound; or

$$\Delta\delta_1 = \frac{\partial\delta_1}{\partial P_1}\Delta P_1, \quad \Delta\delta_2 = \frac{\partial\delta_2}{\partial P_1}\Delta P_1, \quad \Delta\delta_3 = \frac{\partial\delta_3}{\partial P_1}\Delta P_1,$$

$$\ldots\Delta\delta_n = \frac{\partial\delta_n}{\partial P_1}\Delta P_1 \qquad (6.3)$$

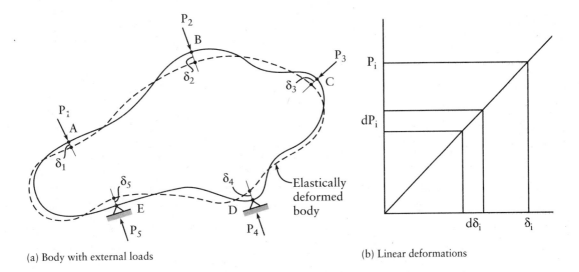

(a) Body with external loads

(b) Linear deformations

FIGURE 6-1 Elastic body under external load.

Implicitly, the load P_1 has now taken on the character of a variable. The corresponding change in work W is given by

$$\frac{\partial W}{\partial P_1}\Delta P_1 = P_1\Delta\delta_1 + P_2\Delta\delta_2 + P_3\Delta\delta_3 + \ldots + P_n\Delta\delta_n$$

The terms of Equation 6.3 are substituted, yielding

$$\frac{\partial W}{\partial P_1}\Delta P_1 = P_1\frac{\partial\delta_1}{\partial P_1}\Delta P_1 + P_2\frac{\partial\delta_2}{\partial P_1}\Delta P_1 + P_3\frac{\partial\delta_3}{\partial P_1}\Delta P_1 + \ldots + P_n\frac{\partial\delta_n}{\partial P_1}\Delta P_1 \quad (6.4)$$

When simplified, Equation 6.4 becomes

$$\frac{\partial W}{\partial P_1} = P_1\frac{\partial\delta_1}{\partial P_1} + P_2\frac{\partial\delta_2}{\partial P_1} + P_3\frac{\partial\delta_3}{\partial P_1} + \ldots + P_n\frac{\partial\delta_n}{\partial P_1} \quad (6.5)$$

The partial derivative of Equation 6.2 gives a second expression for $\partial W/\partial P_1$;

$$2\frac{\partial W}{\partial P_1} = \delta_1 + P_1\frac{\partial\delta_1}{\partial P_1} + P_2\frac{\partial\delta_2}{\partial P_1} + P_3\frac{\partial\delta_3}{\partial P_1} + \ldots + P_n\frac{\partial\delta_n}{\partial P_1} \quad (6.6)$$

Equation 6.5 is subtracted from Equation 6.6, yielding the Castigliano theorem in its general mathematical form:

$$\frac{\partial W}{\partial P_1} = \delta_1 \qquad (6.7)$$

The Castigliano theorem may be stated verbally as follows:

Castigliano Theorem

In an elastic body under a general system of external loads, the first partial derivative of the energy equation with respect to any one of the concentrated loads gives the displacement of that load along its line of action. The sign of the displacement is positive if the displacement is in the same direction as the load.

The result given by Equation 6.7 is completely general; it applies to the work done by a moment M acting through a rotation θ, as well as to the work done by a force P acting through a distance δ:

$$\frac{\partial W}{\partial M_1} = \theta_1 \qquad (6.8)$$

The proof of Equation 6.8 parallels that of Equation 6.7, where work is computed as $M\theta$; the proof of Equation 6.8 is assigned as one of the outside problems included at the end of this chapter.

In the Castigliano theorem, it is not necessary that the variable load P_1 or the variable moment M_1 have magnitude. After the partial derivative has been taken, the variable load P_1 or moment M_1 may take on any value, including zero. In such a case, the Castigliano theorem simply yields the deflection or rotation that occurs at that particular point when P_1 or $M_1 = 0$.

Consequently, if a concentrated variable load P_1 does not happen to exist at a point where a deflection is sought, a concentrated variable load Z may be added at that point. After the partial derivatives due to this variable "null" load Z have been found, the null load Z is assigned a value of zero. The Castigliano theorem then yields the deflection along the action line of Z produced by the remaining nonzero loads.

The same technique may be used to solve for rotations at a point where no moment M_1 actually occurs. A null moment Q is added; then, after the partial derivatives are found, the null moment Q is assigned a value of zero. The Castigliano theorem then yields the rotation at Q due to the remaining nonzero loads.

The energy equation used in the Castigliano theorem (Equations 6.7 and 6.8) need not be written in terms of the external forces; it may also be written equivalently in terms of the energy U that is stored within the deformed members. The energy stored in the deformed members consists of four possible components: the average axial force $1/2\,P$ times its related deformation $d\Delta$; the average flexural moment $1/2\,M$ times its related rotation $d\phi$;

the average shearing force $1/2\,V$ times its related deflection $d\Delta$; and the average torque $1/2\,T$ times its related torsional rotation $d\theta$. The deformations in the foregoing relationships are given by the derivatives of the line integrals of Equations 4.5, 4.8, 4.11, and 4.15.

In mathematical form, the differential energy stored in a member may therefore be stated as

$$dU = \frac{P^2 ds}{2E_x A_x} + \frac{M^2 ds}{2E_x I_x} + \frac{V^2 ds}{2G_x A_x} + \frac{T^2 ds}{2G_x J_x} \tag{6.9}$$

The total energy stored in the member (or structure) is the integral of Equation 6.9:

$$U = \int_0^L \frac{P^2 ds}{2E_x A_x} + \int_0^L \frac{M^2 ds}{2E_x I_x} + \int_0^L \frac{V^2 ds}{2G_x A_x} + \int_0^L \frac{T^2 ds}{2G_x J_x} \tag{6.10}$$

By the Castigliano theorem, the deflection at some point i is given by the first partial derivative of the energy equation with respect to the force P_i. Hence, since $W = U$,

$$\delta_i = \frac{\partial U}{\partial P_i} = \int_0^L \frac{P\left(\dfrac{\partial P}{\partial P_i}\right) ds}{E_x A_x} + \int_0^L \frac{M\left(\dfrac{\partial M}{\partial P_i}\right) ds}{E_x I_x}$$
$$+ \int_0^L \frac{V\left(\dfrac{\partial V}{\partial P_i}\right) ds}{G_x A_x} + \int_0^L \frac{T\left(\dfrac{\partial V}{\partial P_i}\right) ds}{G_x J_x} \tag{6.11}$$

Similarly, the rotation at some point i is given by the first partial derivative of Equation 6.10 with respect to a moment M_i:

$$\theta_i = \frac{\partial U}{\partial M_i} = \int_0^L \frac{P\left(\dfrac{\partial P}{\partial M_i}\right) ds}{E_x A_x} + \int_0^L \frac{M\left(\dfrac{\partial M}{\partial M_i}\right) ds}{E_x I_x}$$
$$+ \int_0^L \frac{V\left(\dfrac{\partial V}{\partial M_i}\right) ds}{G_x A_x} + \int_0^L \frac{T\left(\dfrac{\partial T}{\partial M_i}\right) ds}{G_x J_x} \tag{6.12}$$

In beams, the most significant deformation is due to flexure (shear deformation is generally negligible), for which case Equations 6.11 and 6.12 degenerate to

$$\delta_i = \int_0^L \frac{M\left(\dfrac{\partial M}{\partial P_i}\right) ds}{E_x I_x} \tag{6.13a}$$

and

$$\theta_i = \int_0^L \frac{M\left(\frac{\partial M}{\partial M_i}\right)ds}{E_x I_x} \qquad (6.13b)$$

Similarly in trusses, where the only force in a truss member is the axial load P, Equations 6.11 and 6.12 degenerate to a single equation for δ_i:

$$\delta_i = \int_0^L \frac{P\left(\frac{\partial P}{\partial P_i}\right)ds}{E_x A_x} \qquad (6.14)$$

The line integrals given by Equations 6.13 and 6.14 will be used throughout subsequent discussions to determine displacements and rotations. In Equation 6.13, for example, the moment equation for each member is written in the same manner as before; its first partial derivative is then taken with respect to one of the loads (either P_i or M_i), the results are substituted into Equation 6.13, and the integral is evaluated. The result is the deflection at the point where P_i or M_i occurs.

The signs to be used in writing the moment equation are the same ones used previously: for all flexural members, moment is positive when it causes tension on the bottom of the member. If the member is sloping or vertical, the viewer turns either left or right such that the positive direction of x (if the differential being used is dx) or of y (if the differential being used is dy) increases algebraically toward the viewer's right; the top and bottom of the beam then correspond to this orientation of the viewer. (For sloping members, the choice whether the moment equation should be written along the x-axis or along the y-axis depends on the choice of dx or dy to be used for the integration; the two must correspond.) For all members, the differential length ds along the axis of the member is positive if the limits of the line integral are chosen to increase algebraically, and it is negative if the limits of the line integral are chosen to decrease algebraically.

In evaluations of the integrals in the energy method, discontinuities in the moment equation or in the beam cross section are treated as they were treated earlier. After all, they are simply discontinuities in the integration; the only effect such discontinuities have is to increase the volume of arithmetic calculations. Some examples will illustrate the procedures.

6.2 APPLICATIONS OF ENERGY METHODS TO BEAMS

As a first example in applying the energy methods, a beam with no discontinuities—neither in load or in cross section—is chosen.

Example 6-1   Determine the slope and the deflection at the free end of the given cantilever beam.

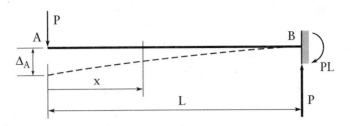

Solution   The origin of x is chosen at the left end of the unloaded beam. The slope and the deflection will then be found at $x = 0$. The deflection in the direction of the load P is given by the Castigliano theorem, where, with $ds = dx$,

$$\Delta_A = \int_0^L \frac{M_x \left(\frac{\partial M_x}{\partial P} \right) dx}{E_x I_x}$$

The moment at x is given by

$$M_x = -Px$$

and the partial derivative is

$$\frac{\partial M_x}{\partial P} = -x$$

Hence,

$$\Delta_A = \int_0^L \frac{Px^2 dx}{EI}$$

$$= \frac{Px^3}{3EI} \Big|_0^L$$

$$= \frac{PL^3}{3EI}$$

This solution agrees with the solution found in Chapter 4, given by Equation 4.24. The positive sign in the solution indicates that the displacement is in the same direction as the load P (the work done is positive).

For computing the slope at the end of the beam, no applied moment is conveniently located where one is needed. A null moment Q is therefore applied, as shown in the following sketch; later its value will be allowed to decrease to zero.

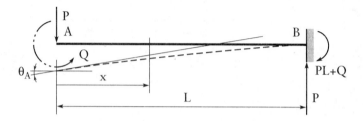

The angle of rotation at the end of the beam in the direction of Q is given by the Castigliano theorem, where, with $ds = dx$,

$$\theta_A = \int_0^L \frac{M_x\left(\dfrac{\partial M_x}{\partial Q}\right)dx}{E_x I_x}$$

The moment at x is given by

$$M_x = -Px - Q$$

and the partial derivative is

$$\frac{\partial M}{\partial Q} = -1$$

The null moment Q is now assigned a value of zero:

$$\theta_A = \int_0^L \frac{(-Px)(-1)dx}{E_x I_x}$$

$$= \left.\frac{Px^2}{2EI}\right|_0^L$$

$$= \frac{PL^2}{2EI}$$

Again, this solution agrees with the one found in Chapter 4, given by Equation 4.23. The positive sign indicates that the rotation θ occurs in the same direction as the null moment Q.

In Example 6-1, the reactions at point B include the effects of the null moment. In this particular problem, the reaction at B is not used; but the null moment does affect reactions, and it must be included when the reactions are used.

The next two examples illustrate further the use of the null load in computing deflections. In these examples, neither a force nor a moment exists at the point where the displacement is sought; both a null force and a null moment must be added.

Example 6-2   Determine the slope and the deflection at the free end of the given cantilever beam.

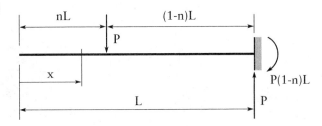

Solution   In this case, it is desirable to find both the slope and the deflection where no loads occur. Consequently, a null force Z and a null moment Q must be added at the point where these deformations are to be found.

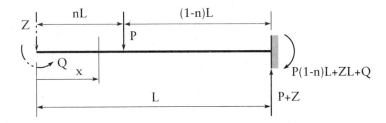

The slope and the deflection are given by the Castigliano theorem, where, with $ds = dx$,

$$\theta_A = \int_0^L \frac{M_x\left(\dfrac{\partial M_x}{\partial Q}\right)dx}{E_x I_x}$$

$$\Delta_A = \int_0^L \frac{M_x\left(\dfrac{\partial M_x}{\partial Z}\right)dx}{E_x I_x}$$

A discontinuity occurs at the load P; the moment equation must therefore be written in two parts. The origin of x is chosen at the left end of the unloaded beam. The moment equations and partial derivatives then become

$$0 \le x \le nL; \qquad M_x = -Q - Zx; \qquad \frac{\partial M_x}{\partial Z} = -x; \qquad \frac{\partial M_x}{\partial Q} = -1$$

$$nL \le x \le L; \qquad M_x = -Q - Zx - P(x - nL); \qquad \frac{\partial M_x}{\partial Z} = -x;$$

$$\frac{\partial M_x}{\partial Q} = -1$$

The slope is found by integration over the full length L, with the null loads Z and Q now assigned a value of zero:

$$\theta_A = \int_0^{nL} \frac{(0)(-1)dx}{EI} + \int_{nL}^{L} \frac{-P(x-nL)(-1)}{EI}$$

$$= \frac{Px^2}{2EI}\Big|_{nL}^{L} - \frac{PnLx}{EI}\Big|_{nL}^{L}$$

$$= \frac{PL^2}{2EI}(1-n)^2$$

The deflection is found similarly:

$$\Delta_A = \int_0^{nL} \frac{(0)(-x)dx}{EI} + \int_{nL}^{L} \frac{-P(x-nL)(-x)}{EI}$$

$$= \frac{Px^3}{3EI}\Big|_{nL}^{L} - \frac{PnLx^2}{EI}\Big|_{nL}^{L}$$

$$= \frac{PL^3}{6EI}(n^3 - 3n + 2)$$

The solutions for θ_A and Δ_A found here are the same as those found by the method of the elastic curve, using Equations 4.27 and 4.28.

Example 6-3 Determine the slope and the deflection at the free end of the given cantilever beam.

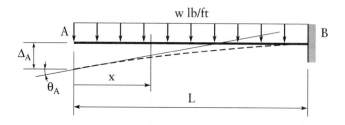

Solution Again, since no loads occur where the deformations are to be determined, it is necessary to add the null loads Z and Q at that point, as shown in the following sketch.

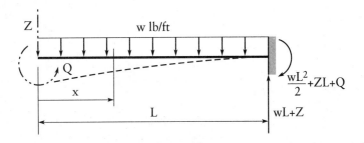

The slope and the deflection are given by the Castigliano theorem, where, with $ds = dx$,

$$\theta_A = \int_0^L \frac{M\left(\dfrac{\partial M}{\partial Q}\right)dx}{EI}$$

$$\Delta_A = \int_0^L \frac{M_x\left(\dfrac{\partial M_x}{\partial Z}\right)dx}{EI}$$

The moment equation is continuous over the entire span. With the origin of x at the free end, the moment equation and the partial derivatives are

$$M_x = -Q - Zx - \frac{1}{2}wx^2; \qquad \frac{\partial M_x}{\partial Q} = -1; \qquad \frac{\partial M_x}{\partial Z} = -x$$

The slope at the free end, with the null loads Q and Z now assigned a value of zero, is

$$\theta_A = \int_0^L \frac{\left(-\dfrac{1}{2}wx^2\right)(-1)\,dx}{EI}$$

$$= \left.\frac{wx^3}{6EI}\right|_0^L$$

$$= \frac{wL^3}{6EI}$$

The deflection is found similarly:

$$\Delta_A = \int_0^L \frac{\left(-\frac{1}{2}wx^2\right)(-x)dx}{EI}$$

$$= \frac{wx^4}{8EI}\Big|_0^L$$

$$= \frac{wL^4}{8EI}$$

The solutions found here for θ_A and Δ_A agree with those found earlier by the method of the elastic curve (Equations 4.31 and 4.32).

Again, the null loads Z and Q must be treated as actual loads when the moment equations are written. For the cantilever beams used in the foregoing examples, the effects of Z and Q on the reactions did not enter the moment equations, which simplified matters somewhat. In succeeding examples, simple beams are used; the effects of the null loads at the beam reactions must be included.

Example 6-4   For the simple beam in the accompanying drawing, determine the deflection at the center of the span.

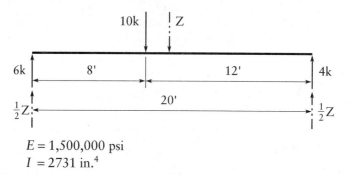

$E = 1,500,000$ psi
$I = 2731$ in.^{4}

Solution   Since no load occurs at the center of the span, a null load Z is added. The deflection at midspan is then found by application of the Castigliano theorem, where, with $ds = dx$,

$$\Delta = \int_0^L \frac{M_x\left(\frac{\partial M}{\partial Z}\right)dx}{EI}$$

$$EI\Delta = \int_0^L M_x\frac{\partial M_x}{\partial Z}dx$$

The origin of x is chosen at the left support. The moment equations and the partial derivatives, over the entire span, are

$$0 \leq x \leq 96"; \qquad M_x = \left(6000 + \frac{1}{2}Z\right)x; \qquad \frac{\partial M_x}{\partial Z} = \frac{1}{2}x$$

$$96" \leq x \leq 120"; \qquad M_x = \left(6000 + \frac{1}{2}Z\right)x - 10000\,(x - 96);$$

$$\frac{\partial M_x}{\partial Z} = \frac{1}{2}x$$

$$120" \leq x \leq 240"; \qquad M_x = \left(4000 + \frac{1}{2}Z\right)(240 - x);$$

$$\frac{\partial M_x}{\partial Z} = \frac{1}{2}(240 - x)$$

The null load Z is now assigned a value of zero and the integration is then carried out over the entire span,

$$EI\Delta = \int_0^{96} (6000x)\left(\frac{1}{2}x\right)dx + \int_{96}^{120} [6000x - 10000\,(x - 96)]\left(\frac{1}{2}x\right)dx$$

$$+ \int_{120}^{240} (4000)(240 - x)^2\left(\frac{1}{2}\right)dx$$

$$= 1000x^3\big|_0^{96} - 667x^3\big|_{96}^{120} + 240{,}000x^2\big|_{96}^{120} - 667(240 - x)^3\big|_{120}^{240}$$

$$\Delta = \frac{2719 \times 10^6}{1{,}500{,}000 \times 2731} = 0.664"$$

Wherever an applied load P can be expressed algebraically, it retains its character as a variable; the partial derivatives can then be taken with respect to this variable load P. When actual numerical values (rather than algebraic symbols) are used, the partial derivative cannot be taken with respect to these constant numerical values. In such cases, the simplest remedy is to use the null loads at all points where displacements are sought. An example will illustrate the point.

Example 6-5   Determine the deflection under the 10–k load of Example 6-4.

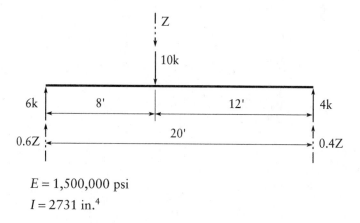

$$E = 1,500,000 \text{ psi}$$
$$I = 2731 \text{ in.}^4$$

Solution   Since the only load at the desired point is a constant, a variable null load Z must be introduced for the sake of the partial derivatives. The deflection can then be found by the Castigliano theorem, where, with $ds = dx$,

$$\Delta = \int_0^L \frac{M_x\left(\dfrac{\partial M_x}{\partial Z}\right)dx}{E_x I_x}$$

$$EI\Delta = \int_0^L M_x \frac{\partial M_x}{\partial Z} dx$$

The moment equations and partial derivatives over the entire span are then

$$0 \le x \le 96''; \qquad M_x = (6000 + 0.6Z)\,x\,; \qquad \frac{\partial M_x}{\partial Z} = 0.6x$$

$$96'' \le x \le 240''; \qquad M_x = (4000 + 0.4Z)(240 - x);$$

$$\frac{\partial M_x}{\partial Z} = 0.4(240 - x)$$

The null load Z is now allowed to decrease to zero, and the integration is carried out:

$$EI\Delta = \int_0^{96} (6000x)(0.6x)(dx) + \int_{96}^{240} (4000)(240 - x)^2(0.4)dx$$

$$= 1200x^3 \big|_0^{96} - 533(240 - x\,)^3 \big|_{96}^{240}$$

$$\Delta = \frac{2652 \times 10^6}{1,500,000 \times 2731} = 0.65 \text{ in.}$$

Outside Problems Determine the slopes and deflections of the given beams as indicated.

Problem 6-1 Find slope at free end.*
Problem 6-2 Find deflection at free end.*

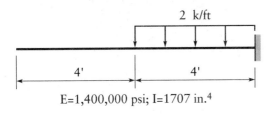

E=1,400,000 psi; I=1707 in.^{4}

Problem 6-3 Find slope at free end.
Problem 6-4 Find deflection at free end.

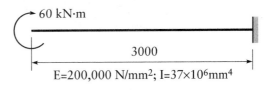

E=200,000 N/mm^2; I=37×10^{6}mm^4

Problem 6-5 Find slope at midpoint.*
Problem 6-6 Find deflection at midpoint.*

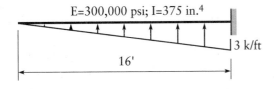

Problem 6-7 Find slope at left end.
Problem 6-8 Find deflection at left end.

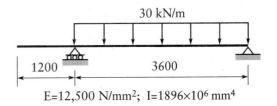

E=12,500 N/mm^2; I=1896×10^6 mm^4

Problem 6-9 Find slope at end.*
Problem 6-10 Find deflection at end.*

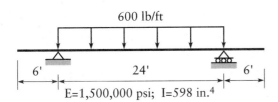

E=1,500,000 psi; I=598 in.^{4}

Problem 6-11 Find slope at end.
Problem 6-12 Find deflection at center.

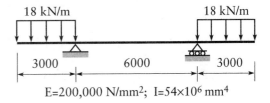

E=200,000 N/mm^2; I=54×10^6 mm^4

6.3 BEAMS HAVING STEPPED CROSS SECTIONS

The Castigliano theorem is readily applicable to beams of variable cross section. Where the size of the beam is stepped, such that the moment of inertia is constant over short segments of the beam, the step simply creates yet another discontinuity in the integration. Such circumstances are encountered in the next two examples.

Example 6-6   Determine the deflection at the free end of the given cantilever. Moments of inertia of the two segments are shown in the accompanying sketch.

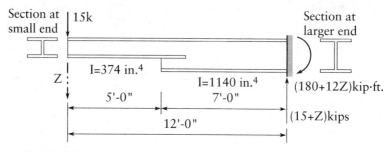

$$E = 30,000,000 \text{ psi}$$

Solution   For the sake of the derivatives at the free end, the null load Z has been added. The deflection at the free end is given by the Castigliano theorem, where, with $ds = dx$,

$$\Delta = \int_0^L \frac{M_x\left(\frac{\partial M_x}{\partial Z}\right)dx}{EI_x}$$

Again, the integration must be made over the full length L. The moment equation is continuous over the entire span:

$$0 \leq x \leq 144''; \qquad M_x = -15,000x - Zx; \qquad \frac{\partial M_x}{\partial Z} = -x$$

The moment of inertia is discontinuous at $x = 60''$:

$$0 \leq x \leq 60''; \qquad I = 374$$

$$60'' \leq x \leq 144''; \qquad I = 1140$$

The integration is made over the entire length L to include the discontinuity in I, with Z now going to zero:

$$\Delta = \int_0^{60} \frac{-(15,000x)(-x)dx}{(30,000,000)(374)} + \int_{60}^{144} \frac{(-15,000x)(-x)\,dx}{(30,000,000)(1140)}$$

$$= (0.446)(10^{-6})\,x^3\big|_0^{60} + (0.146)(10^{-6})\,x^3\big|_{60}^{144}$$

$$= 0.501 \text{ in.}$$

The solution here is the same as for Example 4-7. The general solution of Example 4-7, however, permits the deflection to be found at any point, while the particular solution found here provides only the deflection at a single point.

Earlier, the derivation of the Castigliano theorem required that the integration be carried out over the full length of the beam. It was not necessary, however, to carry out the integration with only one origin of x. If convenient, more than one origin of x might be used, so long as the entire length of the beam is covered.

Consider, for example, the symmetrical beam of Figure 6-2. Due to symmetry, the moment equations, partial derivatives, and moments of inertia are identical on the two ends of the system.

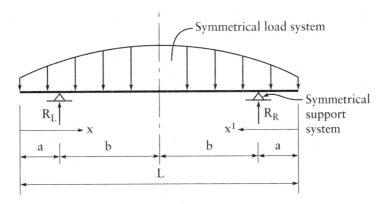

FIGURE 6-2 Symmetrical system.

Moreover, due to the symmetry, an equation written from the left in terms of x will be identical to an equation written from the right in terms of x'. The Castigliano theorem then appears as

$$\Delta = \int_0^{\frac{L}{2}} \frac{M_x \frac{\partial M_x}{\partial Z} ds}{E_x I_x} + \int_0^{\frac{L}{2}} \frac{M_{x'} \frac{\partial M_{x'}}{\partial Z} ds}{E_{x'} I_{x'}} \tag{6.15}$$

Alternatively, since the two integrals must be equal in a symmetrical system,

$$\Delta = 2\int_0^{\frac{L}{2}} \frac{M_x \frac{\partial M_x}{\partial Z} ds}{E_x I_x} \tag{6.16}$$

The integration can therefore be performed on half the beam, and the result doubled, greatly simplifying the algebra. This simplifying property of symmetrical systems will be used wherever appropriate in subsequent examples.

Example 6-7   Determine the deflection at the center of the given beam.

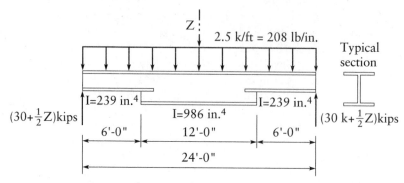

Solution   A null load Z has been added at the centerline to permit computation of the deflection at that point. For this symmetrical system, therefore, with $ds = dx$,

$$\Delta_C = \int_0^L \frac{M_x \dfrac{\partial M_x}{\partial Z} dx}{EI_x} = 2\int_0^{\frac{L}{2}} \frac{M_x \dfrac{\partial M_x}{\partial Z} dx}{EI_x}$$

The moment equations and partial derivatives over the entire span, where $x' = L - x$, are

$$0 \le x \le \frac{1}{2}L; \qquad M_x = \left(30,000 + \frac{1}{2}Z\right)x - 104x^2; \qquad \frac{\partial M_x}{\partial Z} = \frac{1}{2}x$$

$$0 \le x' \le \frac{1}{2}L; \qquad M_x = \left(30,000 + \frac{1}{2}Z\right)x' - 104\,(x')^2; \qquad \frac{\partial M_x}{\partial Z} = \frac{1}{2}x'$$

The moment of inertia is discontinuous at $x = 6$ ft and at $x' = 6$ ft:

$$0 \le x \le 72; \quad I = 239 \quad 0 \le x' \le 72; \quad I = 239$$

$$72 \le x \le 144; \quad I = 986 \quad 72 \le x' \le 144; \quad I = 986$$

The integration is carried out only over the left half of the symmetrical span, to include the discontinuities in I. With Z going to zero,

$$
\Delta = 2\int_0^{72} \frac{(30{,}000x - 104x^2)\left(\frac{1}{2}x\right)}{30{,}000{,}000 \times 239} + 2\int_{72}^{144} \frac{(30{,}000x - 104x^2)\left(\frac{1}{2}x\right)dx}{30{,}000{,}000 \times 986}
$$

$$
= (1.39)(10^{-6})\,x^3\big|_0^{72} - (0.00363)(10^{-6})\,x^4\big|_0^{72}
$$

$$
+ (0.338)\,(10^{-6})\,x^3\big|_{72}^{144} - (0.000879)(10^{-6})\,x^4\big|_{72}^{144}
$$

$$
= 0.95 \text{ in.}
$$

This solution verifies the result obtained in Example 5-11.

Whenever an unsymmetrical null load is introduced into a symmetrical system, the system becomes unsymmetrical. In some cases, however, it is still possible to preserve the symmetry of the system by using two symmetrical null loads. The next example demonstrates this use of a symmetrical arrangement of null loads.

Example 6-8   Determine the deflection at the end of the given overhang.

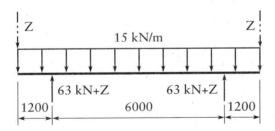

$$E = 200{,}000 \text{ N/mm}^2$$
$$I = 82 \times 10^6 \text{ mm}^4$$

Solution   To preserve the symmetry, a null load Z has been added at each overhang of the symmetrical system. The total external work $Z\delta_1$ (and the corresponding deflection) produced by these two equal and symmetrical loads is twice that produced by one load. Hence, by Equations 6.7 and 6.13a,

$$
2EI\Delta = \int_0^L M_x \frac{\partial M_x}{\partial Z} dx
$$

where the right side of the equation represents the total energy stored internally, including the effects of both null loads. Since the symmetrical system as shown in the sketch includes the effects of both null loads, the moment equations can be written for the load system as it appears in the sketch.

The moment equations and partial derivatives over the left half of the span can now be evaluated.

For $0 \leq x \leq 1200$,

$$M_x = -Zx - 7.5x^2; \qquad \frac{\partial M_x}{\partial Z} = -x$$

For $1200 \leq x \leq 4200$,

$$M_x = -Zx - 7.5x^2 + (63{,}000 + Z)(x - 1200);$$

$$\frac{\partial M_x}{\partial Z} = -x + (x - 1200) = -1200$$

As in the previous example, the integration of the symmetrical system can be carried out over half the span and then doubled. The integration with $Z = 0$, becomes

$$2EI\Delta = 2\int_0^{1200} (-7.5x^2)(-x)\,dx$$

$$+ 2\int_{1200}^{4200} [-7.5x^2 + 63{,}000(x - 1200)](-1200)\,dx$$

$$= 3.75x^4\big|_0^{1200} + 4500x^3\big|_{1200}^{4200} - (75.6)(10^6)\,x^2\big|_{1200}^{4200}$$

$$+ (1.8141)(10^{11})\,x\big|_{1200}^{4200}$$

$$\Delta = \frac{(-236)(10^{12})}{(2)(200{,}000)(82 \times 10^6)} = -7.20 \text{ mm}$$

The negative sign indicates that the deflection occurs in the direction opposite to Z; the deflection is therefore upward.

Example 6-8 can also be solved by using only one null load, placed at the end of the overhang; but in that case the system ceases to be symmetrical. For such a case, the integration must be carried out over the entire length of the beam, rather than over half the length, as was done for the fully symmetrical beam of the example.

Outside Problems

Problem 6-13 Find slope at free end.*
Problem 6-14 Find deflection at free end.*

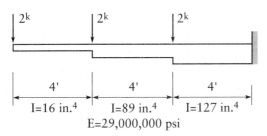

Problem 6-15 Find slope at end.
Problem 6-16 Find deflection at center.

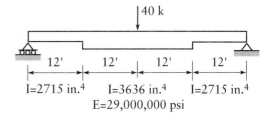

Problem 6-17 Find slope at midpoint.*
Problem 6-18 Find deflection at midpoint.*

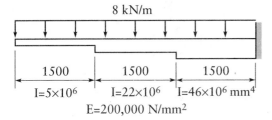

Problem 6-19 Find slope at step A.
Problem 6-20 Find deflection at step A.

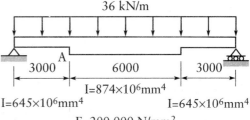

6.4 APPLICATIONS TO CURVED OR BENT MEMBERS

The Castigliano theorem applies equally well to members whose geometry includes a curve or a bend. A curve may or may not introduce discontinuities into the integration. In the first of the following examples, the integration can be simplified considerably if a change in variables, from rectangular coordinates to polar coordinates, is introduced.

In the derivation of the Castigliano theorem, the deformations given by Equations 4.5, 4.8, 4.11, and 4.15 were used to compute the energy. Those defining equations impose no requirement that the axis of the member remain straight; the distance ds is simply taken as some differential distance along the axis of the member, whatever its direction. In contrast, however, the moment M_x, shear V_x, torque T_x, and axial force P_x must be computed at some point (x, y) in a rectangular coordinate system. These distinctions must be preserved when the integration is made on a curved or bent member. The next few examples illustrate this point.

Example 6-9

A lamppost is made from a section of 8" diameter steel pipe, curved as shown. The ballast, light, and fixture at the free end of the post weigh 1000 lb. Determine the deflection at the free end of the lamppost.

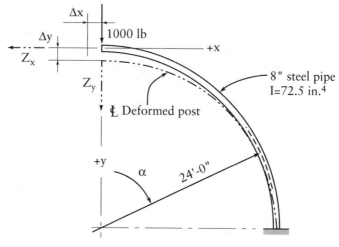

$$I = 72.5 \text{ in.}^4$$

Solution

The deflection at the free end of the post has two components—one in the x direction, and one in the y direction. The null loads Z_x and Z_y have been added to permit computation of these two deflections. The deflections are found by application of the Castigliano theorem:

$$EI\Delta_x = \int_0^L M_s \frac{\partial M_s}{\partial Z_x} ds$$

$$EI\Delta_y = \int_0^L M_s \frac{\partial M_s}{\partial Z_y} ds$$

where M_s is the moment at some distance s along the axis of the post.

After some false starts, the integration was found to be simpler in this case if all variables are expressed in terms of the differential $d\alpha$. The moment equation is written first in terms of x and y, with the origin of the coordinate axes being taken at the free end of the unloaded lamppost, with positive y downward. Positive moment is therefore computed with the viewer turned 90° to the right. In terms of both x and y, the moment equation is given by

$$M_s = -1000x - Z_x y - Z_y x$$

where

$$x = 288 \sin \alpha$$

$$y = 288(1 - \cos \alpha)$$

Hence, in terms of R and α, the moment equation is

$$M_s = (-1000)(288 \sin \alpha) - Z_y(288 \sin \alpha) - Z_x[288(1 - \cos \alpha)]$$

The partial derivatives and differential element are

$$\frac{\partial M_s}{\partial Z_x} = -288(1 - \cos \alpha); \qquad \frac{\partial M_s}{\partial Z_y} = -288 \sin \alpha; \qquad ds = 288 d\alpha$$

The null loads Z_x and Z_y are allowed to go to zero. The integrals then become

$$EI\Delta_x = \int_0^{\frac{\pi}{2}} (-1000)(288 \sin \alpha)[-288(1 - \cos \alpha)](288 d\alpha)$$

$$EI\Delta_y = \int_0^{\frac{\pi}{2}} (-1000)(288 \sin \alpha)[-288 \sin \alpha](288 d\alpha)$$

The deflection Δ_x is given by

$$EI\Delta_x = (2.389)(10^{10})\int_0^{\frac{\pi}{2}} (1 - \cos \alpha) \sin \alpha d\alpha$$

$$= (2.389)(10^{10}) \frac{(1 - \cos \alpha)^2}{2}\Big|_0^{\frac{\pi}{2}}$$

$$\Delta_x = \frac{(1.195)(10^{10})}{(30,000,000)(72.5)} = 5.49 \text{ in.}$$

The deflection Δ_y is found similarly:

$$EI\Delta_y = (2.389)(10^{10})\int_0^{\frac{\pi}{2}}\sin^2 \alpha d\alpha = (2.389)(10^{10})\left[\frac{\alpha}{2} - \frac{\sin 2\alpha}{4}\right]\Big|_0^{\frac{\pi}{2}}$$

$$= \frac{(1.876)(10^{10})}{(30,000,000)(72.5)} = 8.63 \text{ in.}$$

The end of the lamppost will therefore deflect downward 8.63 inches and outward 5.49 inches.

Example 6-10   An equipment shed is built with one side open; one of the structural frames is shown in the accompanying sketch. Determine the deflection at the free end of the frame.

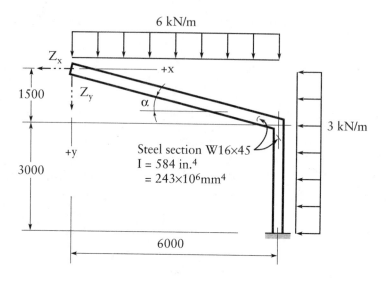

Solution   The deflection at the free end of the frame has two components—one in the x direction and one in the y direction. The null loads Z_x and Z_y have been added to permit computation of these two deflections. The deflections are found by application of the Castigliano theorem:

$$EI\Delta_x = \int_0^L M_s \frac{\partial M_s}{\partial Z_x} ds$$

$$EI\Delta_y = \int_0^L M_s \frac{\partial M_s}{\partial Z_y} ds$$

where M_s is the moment at some distance s along the axis of the frame.

All variables will be expressed in terms of x and y; hence, for the roof portion,

$$ds = (dx)(\sec \alpha) = 1.03dx$$

Notice that positive y has been taken as downward; positive moment on the vertical member is therefore found with the viewer turned 90° to the right. The moments and partial derivatives, over the full length of the frame, can now be calculated.

For $0 \leq x \leq 6000$,

$$M_s = -Z_x y - Z_y x - 3x^2 - 1.5y^2; \qquad \frac{\partial M_s}{\partial Z_x} = -y; \qquad \frac{\partial M_s}{\partial Z_y} = -x;$$

$$ds = 1.03dx$$

For $1500 \leq y \leq 4500$,

$$M_s = -Z_x y - Z_y (6000) - (108)(10^6) - 1.5y^2; \qquad \frac{\partial M_s}{\partial Z_x} = -y;$$

$$\frac{\partial M_s}{\partial Z_y} = -6000; \qquad ds = dy$$

The null loads Z_x and Z_y are now allowed to go to zero. At the roof line, $y = 0.25x$; hence, with E and I constant,

$$EI\Delta_x = \int_0^{6000} (-3.094x^2)(-0.25x)(1.03dx)$$

$$+ \int_{1500}^{4500} [-(108)(10^6) - 1.50y^2](-y)dy$$

$$EI\Delta_y = \int_0^{6000} (-3.094x^2)(-x)(1.03dx)$$

$$+ \int_{1500}^{4500} [-(108)(10^6) - 1.5y^2](-6000)dy$$

Since these limits are always increasing, ds is always positive.
The deflection Δ_x is given by

$$EI\Delta_x = 0.1992x^4\big|_0^{6000} + (54)(10^6)y^2\big|_{1500}^{4500} + 0.375y^4\big|_{1500}^{4500}$$

$$\Delta_x = \frac{(1382)(10^{12})}{(200,000)(243 \times 10^6)} = 28.44 \text{ mm}$$

The deflection Δ_y is given by

$$EI\Delta_y = 0.7967x^4\big|_0^{6000} + (0.648)(10^{12})y\big|_{1500}^{4500} + 3000y^3\big|_{1500}^{4500}$$

$$\Delta_y = \frac{(3239)(10^{12})}{(200,000)(243 \times 10^6)} = 66.65 \text{ mm}$$

The free end of the frame will therefore deflect downward 66.7 mm and outward 28.4 mm.

For the sake of illustration, the next two examples are computed in kips and feet rather than in pounds and inches. For the final conversions, the modulus of elasticity of steel in kips per square foot is 4,176,000 ksf. Similarly, the moment of inertia I in ft^4 is found by dividing I (in inches^4) by 12^4. These next two examples illustrate how the limits of integration can be set to keep the differential ds positive.

Example 6-11   Determine the deflection at point B of the given frame.

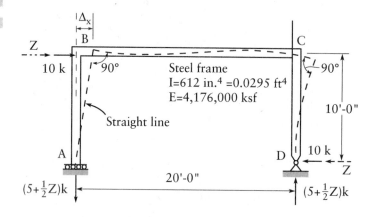

Solution   The vertical deflection at point B is the axial compression in the column AB and is assumed to be negligible. The lateral deflection Δ_x is shown on the sketch. The null load Z has been added to the sketch to permit computation of the deflection with the Castigliano theorem. Thus,

$$EI\Delta_x = \int_0^L M_s \frac{\partial M_s}{\partial Z} ds$$

where M_s is the moment at some distance s along the axis of the frame.

The moment equation is written for each of the three domains of x and y; the origin of x and y is taken at point A, with x increasing to the right and y increasing upward. Along the left column, with the viewer turned 90° to the left and with $0 \le y \le 10$ (y increasing),

$$M_s = 0; \qquad \frac{\partial M_s}{\partial Z} = 0; \qquad ds = +dy$$

Along the top member, with the viewer upright and with $0 \le x \le 20$ (x increasing),

$$M_s = -\left(5 + \frac{1}{2}Z\right)x; \qquad \frac{\partial M_s}{\partial Z} = -\frac{1}{2}x; \qquad ds = dx$$

Along the right column, with the viewer turned 90° to the left and with $10 \geq y \geq 0$ (y decreasing),

$$M_s = +\left(5 + \frac{1}{2}Z\right)20 - (10 + Z)(10 - y);$$

$$\frac{\partial M_s}{\partial Z} = 10 - (10 - y) = +y; \qquad ds = \pm dy$$

(The sign of dy has yet to be decided.)

The null loads are now assigned a value of zero, and the integrals are evaluated. Along the right column, either the limits of the integral must be set to increase algebraically or the differential dy must be assigned a negative value. In this example, the limits have been set such that dy remains positive. The final evaluation of the integrals produces

$$EI\Delta_x = \int_0^{10} (0)\, dy + \int_0^{20} (-5x)\left(-\frac{1}{2}x\right)dx + \int_0^{10} (+10y)(+y)dy$$

$$= 0 + \left.\frac{5x^3}{6}\right|_0^{20} + \left.\frac{10y^3}{3}\right|_0^{10} = 10{,}000$$

$$\Delta_x = \frac{10{,}000}{(4{,}176{,}000)(0.0295)} = 0.0812 \text{ ft} = 0.974 \text{ in.}$$

Example 6-12 Determine the deflection at the free end of the given frame.

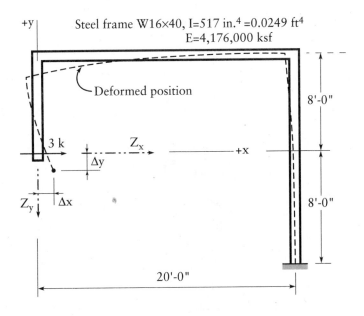

Steel frame W16×40, I=517 in.^{4} =0.0249 ft^4
E=4,176,000 ksf

Solution   The deflection has two components—Δ_x and Δ_y, as shown on the sketch. The variable null loads Z_x and Z_y have been added to permit computation of these deflections. The deflections are found by application of the Castigliano theorem:

$$EI\Delta_x = \int_0^L M_s \frac{\partial M_s}{\partial Z_x} ds$$

$$EI\Delta_y = \int_0^L M_s \frac{\partial M_s}{\partial Z_y} ds$$

where M_s is the moment at some distance s along the axis of the frame.

The moment equation is written to include the three domains of the variables x and y. In this case, $+y$ has been taken upward. The positive moment on the vertical members is therefore found with the viewer turned 90° to the left.

For $0 \le y \le +8'$ (y increasing),

$$M_s = -3y - Z_x y + Z_y(0); \qquad \frac{\partial M_s}{\partial Z_x} = -y; \qquad \frac{\partial M_s}{\partial Z_y} = 0;$$

$$ds = +dy$$

For $0 \le x \le +20'$ (x increasing),

$$M_s = -3(8) - Z_x(8) - Z_y x; \qquad \frac{\partial M_s}{\partial Z_x} = -8; \qquad \frac{\partial M_s}{\partial Z_y} = -x;$$

$$ds = +dx$$

For $+8 \le y < -8$ (y decreasing),

$$M_s = +3y + Z_x y + Z_y(20); \qquad \frac{\partial M_s}{\partial Z_x} = +y; \qquad \frac{\partial M_s}{\partial Z_y} = +20;$$

$$ds = \pm dy$$

(The sign of dy still must be decided.)

In the third domain, the signs for the moment equation are best found by taking a free body to the left of the section, with both x and y having positive values. The following sketch illustrates such a free body.

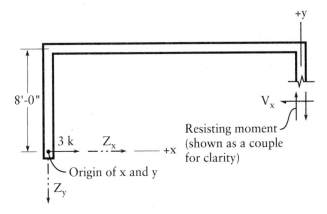

In the free body, all of the given forces produce tension on the bottom of the cut section (producing positive moment) when the viewer is positioned with y increasing to the right. The limits of the line integral in this domain will be set to increase algebraically; otherwise, a negative dy would have to be used.

The null loads are now allowed to go to zero. The integrals and their limits then become

$$EI\Delta_x = \int_0^8 (-3y)(-y)\,dy + \int_0^{20} (-24)(-8)\,dx + \int_{-8}^8 (3y)(y)(+dy)$$

$$EI\Delta_y = \int_0^8 (-3y)(0)\,dy + \int_0^{20} (-24)(-x)\,dx + \int_{-8}^8 (3y)(20)(+dy)$$

The final solution, with $E = 4{,}176{,}000$ ksf and $I = 0.0249$ ft^4, is

$$\Delta_x = 0.052 \text{ ft} = 0.62 \text{ in.} \qquad \text{(to the right)}$$

$$\Delta_y = 0.046 \text{ ft} = 0.55 \text{ in.} \qquad \text{(downward)}$$

6.5 THREE-HINGED ARCHES

It has been observed elsewhere that a three-hinged arch is nothing more than two beams—straight, curved, or bent—joined together such that their hinged supports form a triangle. Either of the two beams, taken as a free body, can be treated as a simple beam. Consequently, the individual beams that form the three-hinged arch do not warrant any further special attention insofar as beam deflections are concerned; but the overall deflection of the movable hinge point merits further examination.

The Castigliano theorem may be applied to the overall three-hinged arch in the same way it is applied to any other structure. The solutions for three-hinged arches do tend to become quite long and tedious, however. An example will illustrate the procedure for one relatively simple case.

Example 6-13   Determine the lateral deflection of the top hinge of the steel three-hinged arch under the indicated wind load. Moments of inertia are given on the sketch.

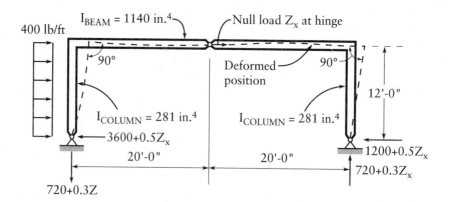

Solution   A null load Z_x has been added at the upper hinge point to permit computation of the lateral deflection at that point. Reactions have been computed to include Z_x, and the results have been entered on the sketch. The deflection at the hinge point is given by application of the Castigliano theorem:

$$\Delta_x = \int_0^L \frac{M_s\left(\dfrac{\partial M_s}{\partial Z_x}\right) ds}{E_s I_s}$$

where M_s is the moment at some distance s along the axis of the member.

The moment equations and the partial derivatives are found as usual.

For $0 \le y \le 144"$ and $x = 0$,

$$M_s = (3600 + 0.5 Z_x)\, y - 16.67 y^2 ; \qquad \frac{\partial M_s}{\partial Z_x} = 0.5 y; \qquad ds = dy$$

For $0 \le x \le 480"$ and $y = 144"$,

$$M_s = -(1200 + 0.5 Z_x)\, 144 + (720 + 0.3 Z_x)(480 - x);$$

$$\frac{\partial M_s}{\partial Z_x} = -0.5\,(144) + 0.3\,(480 - x) = 72 - 0.3 x; \qquad ds = dx$$

For $0 \leq y \leq 144$ and $x = 480"$,

$$M_s = (1200 + 0.5Z_x)\,y; \qquad \frac{\partial M_s}{\partial Z_x} = 0.5y; \qquad ds = dy$$

For the right leg, the moment equation has been written from the right support; for this orientation, y increases from 0 to 144", and M_x is positive. (The change in origin was done primarily to eliminate a messy moment equation and partial derivative along the right leg, but it also keeps the variable y and the differential ds increasing in value over the limits of the integral.)

The null load Z_x is now allowed to decrease to zero. With the indicated values for I,

$$\Delta = \int_0^{144} \frac{(3600y - 16.67y^2)(0.5y)dy}{(30,000,000)(281)}$$
$$+ \int_0^{480} \frac{(172,800 - 720x)(72 - 0.3x)dx}{(30,000,000)(1140)}$$
$$+ \int_0^{144} \frac{(1200y)(0.5y)dy}{(30,000,000)(281)}$$

After evaluation,

$$\Delta = 0.237 \text{ in.} \qquad \text{(to the right)}$$

Whenever a deflection problem involving a three-hinged arch is encountered, the solution can be expected to be quite tedious. Even for the relatively simple load case in Example 6-13, the evaluation of the integral was rather long and tedious. In fact, the exact evaluation of such integrals can become complex to the point of being hopeless. For such cases, evaluation of the integral might best be turned over to the computer.

6.6 BEAMS HAVING A VARIABLE MOMENT OF INERTIA

The Castigliano theorem may also be applied to beams that have a variable moment of inertia. The application to beams that have a stepped section was treated earlier, in Examples 6-6 and 6-7, but the theory may also be extended to members that have a continuously variable moment of inertia. In such cases, the denominator of the Castigliano integral almost always becomes so complex that the task of performing an exact integration becomes hopeless; substituting a numerical evaluation of the integral is usually the most sensible course. An example will demonstrate such a numerical evaluation.

Example 6-14   The frame of the equipment shed of Example 6-10 is to be built of 10 mm steel plate, as shown in the accompanying sketch. Determine the deflection at the free end of this frame.

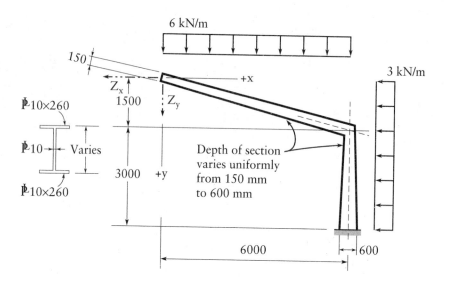

Solution   The deflection at the free end of the frame has two components—one in the x direction, and one in the y direction. The null loads Z_x and Z_y have been added to permit computation of these two deflections. The deflections are found by application of the Castigliano theorem:

$$\Delta_x = \int_0^L \frac{M_s \dfrac{\partial M_s}{\partial Z_x} ds}{E_s I_s}$$

$$\Delta_y = \int_0^L \frac{M_s \dfrac{\partial M_s}{\partial Z_y} ds}{E_s I_s}$$

where M_s is the moment at some distance s along the axis of the frame.

When the moment of inertia I_s is a variable, as in this case, an exact integration is not usually feasible. The alternative is to make a numerical evaluation of the foregoing integrals, as shown in the accompanying tabulation, where, for a finite summation of m elements of length Δx, the integrals become

$$\Delta_x = \sum_{i=1}^{m} \frac{M_s \dfrac{\partial M_s}{\partial Z_x} \Delta s}{E_s I_s}$$

$$\Delta_y = \sum_{i=1}^{m} \frac{M_s \dfrac{\partial M_s}{\partial Z_y} \Delta s}{E_s I_s}$$

For the tabulation, the moment equations and the partial derivatives are the same as in Example 6-10. With x and y in millimeters, the equations can now be calculated.

For $0 \le x \le 6000$,

$$M_s = -Z_x y - Z_y x - 3x^2 - 1.5y^2; \qquad \frac{\partial M_s}{\partial Z_x} = -y; \qquad \frac{\partial M_s}{\partial Z_y} = -x$$

For $1500 \le y \le 3000$,

$$M_s = -Z_x y - 6000 Z_y - (108)(10^6) - 1.5y^2; \qquad \frac{\partial M_s}{\partial Z_x} = -y;$$

$$\frac{\partial M_s}{\partial Z_y} = -6000$$

with x and y in mm.

The depth of the section is assumed to vary uniformly over the length of the frame. The length of the frame is found to be

$$L = \sqrt{1500^2 + 6000^2} + 3000 = 9184.66 \text{ mm}$$

For the tabulation, the frame is divided into 15 segments as shown in the following sketch, 10 at 618.466 mm along the roof beam, plus 5 at 600 mm along the column. The distances x and y to the center of each segment are computed and entered in the table.

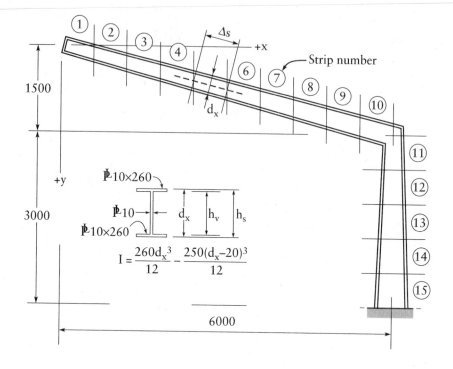

The two Castigliano integrals are expressed in the form of finite summations:

$$E_s \Delta_{yi} = \frac{M_s \dfrac{\partial M_s}{\partial Z_y} \Delta s}{I_s}$$

$$E_s \Delta_{xi} = \frac{M_s \dfrac{\partial M_s}{\partial Z_x} \Delta s}{I_s}$$

They are then evaluated in the following tabulation.

The depth of the section is assumed to vary uniformly from 150 mm to 600 mm along the entire length of 9184.66 mm. The depth d_x at the center of each segment is then

$$d_x = 165.15 + 0.049s$$

where s is the distance along the axis from the free end to the center of the segment. With this value of d_x, the moment of inertia I_x at the center of each segment is

$$I_x = \frac{260 d_x^3}{12} - \frac{250(d_x - 20)^3}{12}$$

The values of I_x thus computed are the ones entered in the table.

STRIP	Δs mm	x mm	y mm	d_x mm	I_s mm^4	M_s N·mm	$\dfrac{\partial M_s}{\partial Z_y}$	$\dfrac{\partial M_s}{\partial Z_x}$	Δ_{yi} mm	Δ_{xi} mm
1	618.5	300	75	165	34×10^6	—	−300	−75	—	—
2	618.5	700	225	195	49	− 3×10^6	−900	−225	+0.14	+0.04
3	618.5	1500	375	226	68	− 7	−1500	−375	+0.48	+0.12
4	618.5	2100	525	256	90	− 14	−2100	−525	+0.99	+0.25
5	618.5	2700	675	286	115	− 23	−2700	−675	+1.64	+0.41
6	618.5	3300	825	317	144	− 34	−3300	−825	+2.39	+0.60
7	618.5	3900	975	347	177	− 47	−3900	−975	+3.21	+0.80
8	618.5	4500	1125	377	213	− 63	−4500	−1125	+4.09	+1.02
9	618.5	5100	1275	408	254	− 81	−5100	−1275	+5.00	+1.25
10	618.5	5700	1425	438	299	−101	−5700	−1425	+5.93	+1.48
11	600.0	6000	1800	468	347	−113	−6000	−1800	+5.85	+1.76
12	600.0	6000	2400	497	399	−117	−6000	−2400	+5.26	+2.10
13	600.0	6000	3000	526	455	−121	−6000	−3000	+4.81	+2.40
14	600.0	6000	3600	555	513	−127	−6000	−3600	+4.45	+2.67
15	600.0	6000	4200	580	568×10^6	$−134 \times 10^6$	−6000	−4200	+4.22	+2.95

$$\Sigma \quad +48.4 \quad +17.8$$

Based on the results of the tabulation, the final values of Δ_x and Δ_y are

$$\Delta_x = \sum_{i=1}^{m} \frac{M_s \dfrac{\partial M_s}{\partial Z_x}\Delta s}{E_s I_s} = \sum_{i=1}^{m} \frac{E_s \Delta_{xi}}{E_s} = 18 \text{ mm} \qquad \text{(to the left)}$$

$$\Delta_y = \sum_{i=1}^{m} \frac{M_s \dfrac{\partial M_s}{\partial Z_y}\Delta s}{E_s I_s} = \sum_{i=1}^{m} \frac{E_s \Delta_{yi}}{E_s} = 48 \text{ mm} \qquad \text{(downward)}$$

Alternatively, the integral form of the Castigliano equation in this example can be evaluated by computer software. In fact, however, the computer program evaluates the integral by using discrete elements in exactly the same way as does the manual tabulation. The only difference between the computer evaluation and the manual evaluation is that the computer uses many more elements.

For the computer evaluation, the moment of inertia must be expressed in terms of x or y, as appropriate:

$$I = \left.\frac{bh_s^{\ 3}}{12}\right|_{\text{SOLID}} - \left.\frac{bh_v^{\ 3}}{12}\right|_{\text{VOID}}$$

where, at $x = 6000$,

$$h_s = \frac{6185}{9185}(600 - 150) + 150 = 453 \text{ mm}$$

and at $x = 6000$,

$$h_v = \frac{6185}{9185}(580 - 130) + 130 = 433 \text{ mm}$$

The equations for the moments of inertia I_x and I_y are given as follows. For $0 \le x \le 6000$,

$$h_s = 150 + \frac{x}{6000}(453 - 150)$$

$$h_v = 130 + \frac{x}{6000}(433 - 130) \ .$$

$$I_x = \left(\frac{260}{12}\right)(h_s)^3 - \left(\frac{250}{12}\right)(h_v)^3$$

For $1500 \le y \le 4500$,

$$h_s = 453 + \frac{y - 1500}{3000}(600 - 453)$$

$$h_v = 433 + \frac{y - 1500}{6000}(580 - 433)$$

$$I_y = \left(\frac{260}{12}\right)(h_s)^3 - \left(\frac{250}{12}\right)(h_v)^3$$

The integral forms then become identifiable.

For $0 \le x \le 6000$ and $y = 0.25x$,

$$\Delta_x = \int_0^{6000} \frac{[-3x^2 - 1.5\,(0.25x)^2]\,(-0.25x)\,dx}{200{,}000I_x}$$

$$\Delta_y = \int_0^{6000} \frac{[-3x^2 - 1.5\,(0.25x)^2]\,(-x)\,dx}{200{,}000I_x}$$

For $1500 \le y \le 4500$,

$$\Delta_x = \int_{1500}^{4500} \frac{[-(108)(10^6) - 1.5y^2]\,(-y)\,dy}{200{,}000I_y}$$

$$\Delta_y = \int_{1500}^{4500} \frac{[-(108)(10^6) - 1.5y^2]\,(-6000)\,dy}{200{,}000I_y}$$

The evaluation of the integrals yields the more exact solution:

$\Delta_x = 17.64$ mm   (to the left)

$\Delta_y = 47.74$ mm   (downward)

These results compare to 17.8 mm and 48.4 mm, respectively, obtained by the manual tabulation using 15 discrete elements.

In addition to solving problems involving regular geometric shapes (like those used in the preceding examples), the Castigliano theorem may be applied to members that have no geometrically defined shape. Such free-form members can result from a wind tunnel design or some other empirical design where the configuration of a member is developed experimentally to suit certain requirements for fluid flow. Or a free-form sculpture may take such a shape that it cannot be defined by the more common equations from analytic geometry. For such members, there is no possibility of making an exact integration; a numerical evaluation of the integral is the only possible solution. An example will illustrate the procedure.

Example 6-15   A free-form steel frame is to carry a load of 1000 lb from its free end, as shown in the accompanying drawing. The layout of the frame is shown in a following sketch at larger scale. Determine the deflection at the free end of the frame.

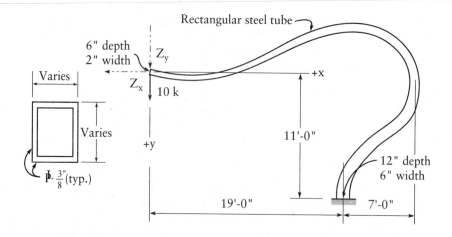

Solution The deflection at the free end of the frame has two components—one in the x direction, and one in the y direction. The null loads Z_x and Z_y have been added to permit computation of these two deflections. The deflections are found by application of the Castigliano theorem:

$$\Delta_x = \int_0^L \frac{M_s \dfrac{\partial M_s}{\partial Z_x} ds}{E_s I_s}$$

$$\Delta_y = \int_0^L \frac{M_s \dfrac{\partial M_s}{\partial Z_y} ds}{E_s I_s}$$

where M_s is the moment at some distance s along the axis of the frame.

In this case, the centerline of the frame cannot be defined by a geometric equation, so an exact integration is not possible under any circumstances. Instead, a numerical integration is performed, as given in the accompanying tabulation, where, for a summation of m elements of length Δs,

$$\Delta_x = \sum_{i=1}^{m} \frac{M_s \dfrac{\partial M_s}{\partial Z_x} \Delta s}{E_s I_s}$$

$$\Delta_y = \sum_{i=1}^{m} \frac{M_s \dfrac{\partial M_s}{\partial Z_y} \Delta s}{E_s I_s}$$

For the tabulation, the moment equation and partial derivatives are given by

$$M_s = -1000x - Z_y x - Z_x y; \qquad \frac{\partial M_s}{\partial Z_x} = -y; \qquad \frac{\partial M_s}{\partial Z_y} = -x$$

These equations need not be expressed in terms of a single variable. The tabulation can be made with both x and y being used in the computations.

POINT	b_x (in.)	b_x (in.)	I_x (in.⁴)	ΔS (in.)	x (in.)	y (in.)	M_s (lb.–in.)	$\frac{\partial M_s}{\partial Z_y}$	$\frac{\partial M_s}{\partial Z_x}$	$M_s \frac{\partial M_s}{\partial Z_y} \frac{\Delta S}{I}$	$M_s \frac{\partial M_s}{\partial Z_x} \frac{\Delta s}{I}$
01	06.142	2.047	022.6	24"	012	+003	−012,000	−012	−003	00,153,000	+0,038,000
02	06.426	2.142	026.2	24"	034	+005	−034,000	−034	−005	01,059,000	+0,156,000
03	06.710	2.237	030.1	24"	058	+006	−058,000	−058	−006	02,682,000	+0,277,000
04	06.994	2.331	034.4	24"	082	+004	−082,000	−082	−004	04,691,000	+0,229,000
05	07.278	2.426	039.1	24"	105	−002	−105,000	−105	+002	06,767,000	−0,129,000
06	07.562	2.521	044.2	24"	127	−011	−127,000	−127	+011	08,758,000	−0,759,000
07	07.846	2.615	049.7	24"	148	−022	−148,000	−148	+022	10,577,000	−1,572,000
08	08.130	2.710	055.7	24"	170	−032	−170,000	−170	+032	12,452,000	−2,344,000
09	08.414	2.805	062.1	24"	192	−040	−192,000	−192	+040	14,247,000	−2,968,000
10	08.698	2.900	069.1	24"	215	−046	−215,000	−215	+046	16,055,000	−3,435,000
11	08.982	2.994	076.5	24"	239	−047	−239,000	−239	+047	17,920,000	−3,524,000
12	09.266	3.089	084.4	24"	263	−043	−263,000	−263	+043	19,669,000	−3,216,000
13	09.550	3.183	092.9	24"	284	−031	−284,000	−284	+031	20,837,000	−2,274,000
14	09.834	3.278	101.9	24"	301	−014	−301,000	−301	+014	21,339,000	−0,993,000
15	10.118	3.373	111.4	24"	310	+007	−310,000	−310	−007	20,704,000	+0,468,000
16	10.402	3.467	121.6	24"	310	+031	−310,000	−310	−031	18,967,000	+1,897,000
17	10.686	3.562	132.3	24"	298	+052	−298,000	−298	−052	16,110,000	+2,811,000
18	10.970	3.657	143.7	24"	281	+067	−281,000	−281	−067	13,188,000	+3,144,000
19	11.254	3.751	155.7	24"	261	+081	−261,000	−261	−081	10,500,000	+3,259,000
20	11.538	3.846	168.4	24"	243	+097	−243,000	−243	−097	08,416,000	+3,359,000
21	11.822	3.941	181.7	27"	230	+117	−230,000	−230	−117	06,987,000	+3,554,000

$$\Sigma \quad 252,078,000 \quad -2,022,000$$

For the tabulation, the distance $\Delta s = 24$ in. per increment is laid out graphically along the centerline of the frame, as indicated in the sketch. The distances x and y to the center of each 24" increment are then scaled. The total length of the frame (at its centerline) is also scaled and found to be 42'-3" or 507 inches.

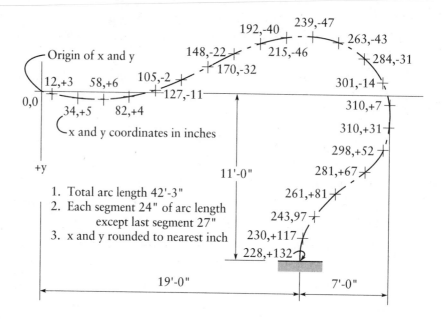

The height of the section is assumed to vary uniformly from 6" to 12" over the total length of 507 inches. The depth at the center of each 24" increment is given by

$$h_x = 6.142 + (n-1)(0.284)$$

where n is the number of the strip. Similarly, the width increases uniformly from 2" to 4" over the total length of 507 inches. Hence,

$$b_x = 2.047 + (n-1)(0.0947)$$

The moment of inertia given in the tabulation is then computed by

$$I_x = \frac{b_x h_x^3}{12} - \frac{(b_x - 0.75)\,(h_x - 0.75)^3}{12}$$

The final values for Δ_x and Δ_y are found by dividing the tabulated sums by the modulus of elasticity, a constant, taken in this case as 30,000,000 psi.

$$\Delta_x = \frac{2{,}022{,}000}{30{,}000{,}000} = -0.67 \text{ in.}$$

$$\Delta_y = \frac{+252{,}078{,}000}{30{,}000{,}000} = +8.40 \text{ in.}$$

The foregoing examples, even if somewhat contrived, serve to illustrate the versatility of the Castigliano solution in its applications to statically determinate structures. A free-form shape similar to that of Example 6-13 in combination with a free-form load such as that of Example 4-6 might at first glance seem to present an impossibly complex problem, yet such a problem can be handled routinely by use of the Castigliano theorem and the numerical methods of Example 6-15.

The Castigliano theorem may also be extended into three dimensions. For such problems, deformations due both to torque and to moment usually exist and have to be included, and the deflection in the z direction must also be added; the form of such solutions closely follows the patterns that have been presented in this chapter. Such problems are beyond the scope of an elementary text such as this—not due to any unusual level of difficulty, but simply due to lack of space.

In summary, the Castigliano theorem is one of the most powerful tools in all of structural analysis; anyone engaged in structural design at any level should maintain intimate familiarity with its use.

Outside Problems   Determine the indicated slopes and deflections.

Problem 6-21 Find rotation at *C*.*
Problem 6-22 Find deflections at *C*.*

Problem 6-23 Find rotation at *A*.
Problem 6-24 Find deflections at *A*.

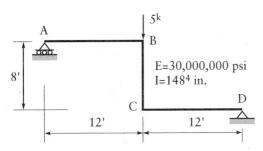

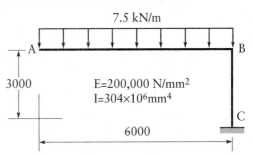

Problem 6-25 Find rotation at *C*.*
Problem 6-26 Find deflections at *C*.*

Problem 6-27 Find rotation at *B*.
Problem 6-28 Find deflections at *B*.

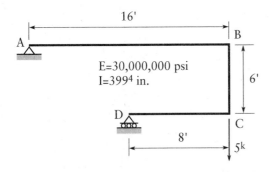

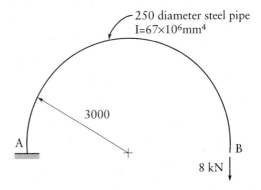

Problem 6-29 Find rotation at *B*.*
Problem 6-30 Find deflections at *B*.*

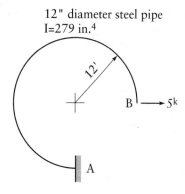

12" diameter steel pipe
I=279 in.⁴
12'
B → 5ᵏ
A

Problem 6-31 Find rotation at *B*.
Problem 6-32 Find deflections at *B*.

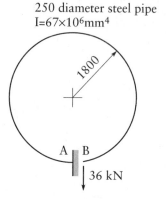

250 diameter steel pipe
I=67×10⁶mm⁴
1800
A B
36 kN

Problem 6-33 Find rotation at *A*.*
Problem 6-34 Find deflection at *A*.*

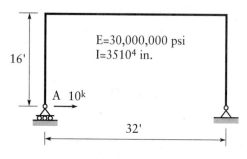

E=30,000,000 psi
I=35104 in.
16'
A 10ᵏ
32'

Problem 6-35 Find rotation at *A*.
Problem 6-36 Find deflection at *A*.

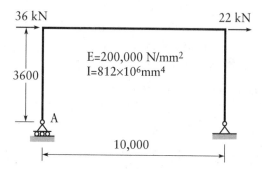

36 kN   22 kN
E=200,000 N/mm²
I=812×10⁶mm⁴
3600
A
10,000

Problem 6-37 Find rotation at *C*.*
Problem 6-38 Find deflection at *C*.*

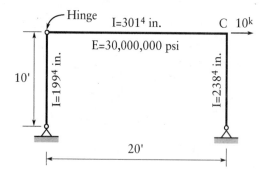

Hinge   I=3014 in.   C 10ᵏ
E=30,000,000 psi
10'   I=1994 in.   I=2384 in.
20'

Problem 6-39 Find rotation at *C*.
Problem 6-40 Find deflection at *C*.

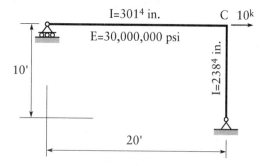

I=3014 in.   C 10ᵏ
E=30,000,000 psi
10'   I=2384 in.
20'

Problem 6-41 Find rotation at free end.*
Problem 6-42 Find deflection at free end.*

Problem 6-43 Find rotation at free end.
Problem 6-44 Find deflections at free end.

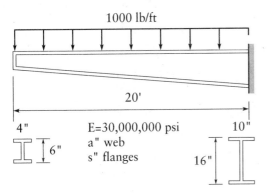

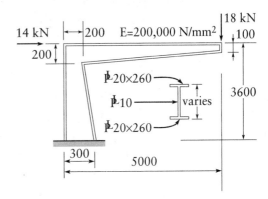

6.7 VIRTUAL WORK AND RELATED CONCEPTS

The study of mechanics in today's practice is centered primarily on equilibrium of forces. In the evolution of the study of mechanics, however, a second approach developed concurrently with that of force equilibrium. This alternative approach, called *virtual work*, is a completely developed approach to structural analysis.

The method of virtual work is based on the principle of conservation of energy. The basic logic behind the method of virtual work is given in the first paragraph of this chapter. The resulting equation, Equation 6.1, constitutes the basic relationship for all energy methods; it is equivalent to the laws of equilibrium ($\Sigma F_x = 0$, $\Sigma F_y = 0$, and $\Sigma M_o = 0$) in the equilibrium method.

In applications of the Castigliano theorem, it was not necessary to have a real load at the exact point where one was calculating a deflection. Rather, a null (and imaginary) load could be added that would later be assigned a value of zero. The deflection could then be found at the point where the null load had been placed.

Similarly, it is not necessary to have a real displacement in order to apply the method of virtual work. A *virtual displacement* can be imposed on the system, and the energy (or work) associated with this imaginary (but possible) displacement can be computed. The result permits computation of the real forces acting on the system.

It is appropriate at this point to state specifically the principles of virtual work, both for rigid-body mechanics (statics) and deformable-body mechanics (strength).

Principles of Rigid-body Mechanics

If a rigid body under a system of external loads is given a virtual displacement, and if the sum of all work done by the external loads is zero, the rigid body is in equilibrium.

Conversely, if a rigid body under a system of loads is in equilibrium, and if the rigid body is given a virtual displacement, the sum of all work done by the external loads is zero.

Principles of Deformable-body Mechanics

If the work done by a system of external loads acting on a deformable body is equal to the energy stored in the deformed body, the deformable body is in equilibrium.

Conversely, if a deformable body under a system of loads is in equilibrium, the sum of all work done by the system of external loads is equal to the energy stored in the deformed body.

A first example will illustrate the use of the foregoing principles of rigid-body mechanics.

Example 6-16   Determine the reactions at the supports of the given simple beam.

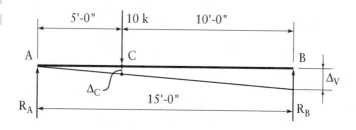

Solution   The rigid body is given a virtual displacement Δ_v at point B. By ratio,

$$\frac{\Delta_v}{15} = \frac{\Delta_c}{5}$$

$$\Delta_c = \frac{1}{3}\Delta_v$$

The work done by the external forces must be zero if the body is to be in equilibrium:

$$10,000\Delta_c - R_B\Delta_v = 0$$

where the term $R_B\Delta_v$ is negative, since Δ_v lies in a direction opposite to R_B. The value of Δ_c is substituted, yielding

$$R_B = \frac{1}{3}(10,000) = 3333 \text{ lb}$$

Similarly, the rigid body can be given a virtual displacement Δ_v at point A, in which case

$$\frac{\Delta_v}{15} = \frac{\Delta_c}{10}$$

$$\Delta_c = \frac{2}{3}\Delta_v$$

Again, the work done must be zero if the body is to be in equilibrium:

$$10,000\Delta_c = R_A\Delta_v$$

and

$$R_A = \frac{2}{3}(10,000) = 6667 \text{ lb}$$

This result can readily be verified by the usual methods of equilibrium.

A second example will illustrate the computation of reactions where moments are involved, such as in a cantilever.

Example 6-17 Determine the reactions on the given cantilever.

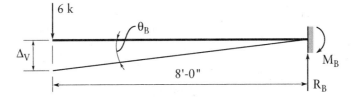

Solution The rigid body is given a virtual displacement Δ_v at point A, resulting in an angle θ at point B. For small angles,

$$\Delta_v = L\theta_B = 8\theta_B$$

The work done is then equated to zero,

$$6000 \, \Delta_v - M_B\theta_B = 0$$

$$M_B = 48,000 \text{ lb-ft}$$

Similarly, a virtual displacement Δ_v may be imposed at point B, resulting in formation of an angle θ_A at point A:

$$\Delta_v = L\theta_A = 8\theta_A$$

The work done is then equated to zero, yielding

$$M_B\theta_A - R_B\Delta_v = 0$$

$$R_B = 6000 \text{ lb}$$

Again, the result may be verified by the laws of static equilibrium.

It should be apparent that, in rigid-body mechanics, the virtual work solutions have no particular advantage over those obtained by the equilibrium method. Consequently, the method of virtual work is only rarely undertaken in rigid-body mechanics in today's practice. Nonetheless, it is a viable and sound approach to mechanics.

Virtual work is more widely used in deformable-body mechanics than in rigid-body mechanics; in fact, virtual work actually predates the Castigliano theorem. Probably the best-known application of virtual work in deformable-body mechanics is the *unit load method*. This method is usually classified as a form of virtual work, but it may also be derived and applied as a variation of the Castigliano theorem. It is also called the Maxwell–Mohr method, although the original applications of the Maxwell–Mohr method were limited to trusses. The method of unit load (or unit dummy load) is presented in detail in Chapter 7.

6.8 LEAST WORK AND REAL WORK

Another concept in energy solutions is that of *least work* and *real work*. These concepts are used primarily to describe an approach to analyzing statically indeterminate structures. Statically indeterminate structures are presented in detail later in this book; the brief description presented here of these analytical methods is essentially a preview.

Consider the statically indeterminate propped beam shown in Figure 6-3. There are a total of four unknown reactions on this beam, but there are only three equations of equilibrium; the solution is therefore one degree indeterminate. A fourth equation must be found if the reactions are to be found. It is evident, however, that the deflection of the beam at the point A is zero. Consequently,

$$\frac{\partial U}{\partial R_A} = 0 \tag{6.17}$$

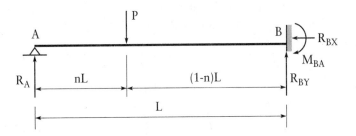

FIGURE 6-3 Propped-end beam.

This equation supplies the fourth equation needed for a solution. The fact that the derivative of the energy equation is zero indicates that the energy equation reaches a maximum/minimum point at the support A. Equation 6.17 thus constitutes a mathematical statement of the principle of *least work*.

The moment equations for the propped beam can now be written for the entire span.

For $0 \leq x \leq nL$,

$$M_x = R_A x; \qquad \frac{\partial M_x}{\partial R_A} = x$$

For $nL \leq x \leq L$,

$$M_x = R_A x - P(x - nL); \qquad \frac{\partial M_x}{\partial R_A} = x$$

The solution for Δ_A, for constant E and I, is therefore,

$$\Delta_A = 0 = \int_0^{nL} (R_A x)(x)dx + \int_{nL}^{L} [R_A x - P(x - nL)](x)dx$$

$$R_A = \frac{1}{2}P(n^3 - 3n + 2)$$

With this solution for R_A, the remaining three reactions can readily be found by applying the three equilibrium equations of simple statics, yielding the following final result:

$$R_{Bx} = 0; \qquad R_{By} = \frac{1}{2}Pn(3 - n^2); \qquad M_{BA} = \frac{1}{2}PLn(1 - n^2)$$

The concept of least work—that is, that the slope of the energy equation is known to be zero at a particular point—is thus simply a way of viewing the energy in a system.

If the deflection at the unknown reaction is not zero but takes on a known or allowable amount of deflection (such as a foundation settlement), the deflection becomes a fixed (nonzero) number. In this case, real work occurs at the support, rather than minimal or least work. A solution for a real (and unknown) reaction that is made possible by the fact that its deflection is real (and known) is termed a solution by the method of *real work*. An example will demonstrate the approach.

Consider the propped end beam shown in Figure 6-4, in which the end support is supported by an elastic spring that has an inverse spring constant of k inches of deflection per pound of load.

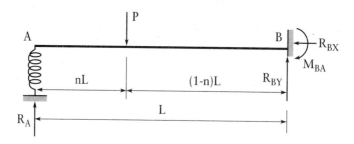

FIGURE 6-4 Propped-end beam with elastic support.

Four reactions are involved, so the beam is still one degree statically indeterminate. As before, the deflection at point A affords the one additional equation required for the solution.

The deflection Δ_A at the point A is found by the Castigliano theorem (termed *real work* in this application):

$$\frac{\partial U}{\partial R_A} = \Delta_A = -R_A k$$

where the negative sign indicates that the deflection Δ_A is assumed to occur in a direction opposite to the reaction R_A, and the constant k is known in lb/in.

The moment equations remain the same.

For $0 \leq x \leq nL$,

$$M_x = R_A x; \qquad \frac{\partial M_x}{\partial R_A} = x$$

For $nL \leq x \leq L$,

$$M_x = R_A x - P(x - nL); \qquad \frac{\partial M_x}{\partial R_A} = x$$

The solution for Δ_A for constant E and I, is therefore

$$\frac{\partial U}{\partial R_A} = \Delta_A = -R_A k = \int_0^{nL} \frac{(R_A x)\, x\, dx}{EI} + \int_{nL}^{L} \frac{[R_A x - P(x - nL)]\, x\, dx}{EI}$$

$$R_A = \frac{\frac{1}{2} P(n^3 - 3n + 2)}{1 + k \dfrac{3EI}{L^3}}$$

As before, the remaining reactions can be found by using this solution for R_A.

The methods of least work and real work thus provide a way of viewing the energy in a statically indeterminate system. The terms *least work* and *real work* are quite well known and widely used in the practice; nonetheless, they may be treated simply as a special form of the Castigliano solution.

In summary, the concepts of virtual work, least work, and real work in statically determinate systems may be regarded as specialty items. In circumstances where solutions requiring such measures are encountered frequently, maintaining familiarity with the rules of these specialized items may be worthwhile. Otherwise, they offer no particular improvements to the Castigliano solution.

6.9 THE MAXWELL THEOREM OF RECIPROCAL DISPLACEMENTS

An important theorem involving the deformations of structures can now be derived. For simplicity, the following derivation will use only the flexural energy $M\theta$ stored in a system, but it is valid for all the forms of energy listed in Equation 6.10.

Consider an elastic body acted upon only by the load P_B, as shown in Figure 6-5(a), with a null load Z_A at point A.

The deflection Δ_{AB} at point A due to the load P_B is found by the Castigliano theorem:

$$\Delta_{AB} = \int_0^L \frac{M_x \left(\dfrac{\partial M_x}{\partial Z_A} \right) ds}{EI} \tag{6.18}$$

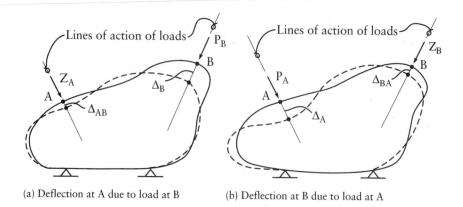

(a) Deflection at A due to load at B   (b) Deflection at B due to load at A

FIGURE 6-5 Reciprocal loads and deformations.

In any linear elastic system, the concentrated loads P_B and Z_A may be factored out of the moment equation, leaving the equation in the form

$$M_x = P_B f_B(x) + Z_A f_A(x) \qquad (6.19)$$

The deflection Δ_{AB} is therefore given by

$$\Delta_{AB} = \int_0^L \frac{P_B f_B(x) f_A(x)\, ds}{EI} \qquad (6.20)$$

Consider now the same elastic body loaded as shown in Figure 6-5(b). The deflection Δ_{BA} at point B due to the load P_A at point A is found similarly by the Castigliano theorem (with a null load N_B at point B):

$$\Delta_{BA} = \int_0^L \frac{M_x \left(\dfrac{\partial M_x}{\partial Z_B} \right) ds}{EI} \qquad (6.21)$$

Again, for a linearly elastic system, the moment equation may be stated in the form

$$M_x = P_A f_A(x) + Z_B f_B(x) \qquad (6.22)$$

Consequently, the deflection Δ_{BA} is given by

$$\Delta_{BA} = \int_0^L \frac{P_A f_A(x) f_B(x)\, ds}{EI} \qquad (6.23)$$

Equation 6.23 can be compared to Equation 6.20 to confirm that, for equal loads P_A and P_B,

$$\Delta_{BA} = \Delta_{BA} \tag{6.24}$$

Stated verbally, Equation 6.24 is the Maxwell Theorem of Reciprocal Displacements.

Maxwell Theorem of Reciprocal Displacements

Given the lines of action for a load P acting either through point A or through point B in an elastic structural system, the displacement of point A when the load is located at point B is equal to the displacement of point B when the load is located at point A, where the displacements are measured along the given lines of action.

In the foregoing statement of the Maxwell theorem, the term *displacement* is used rather than the term *deflection*, since the theorem is true for rotations as well as for deflection. The proof of the foregoing statement is left to the student; it is included as one of the review questions at the end of the chapter.

The Maxwell theorem is very useful for finding the deflections of a structure when the structure is subject to moving loads or to a varying arrangement of load. In general, its applications in beams are somewhat limited, but its applications in the deflection of trusses (discussed in Chapter 10) are quite useful.

REVIEW QUESTIONS

1. In the derivation of the energy methods, how is the external work generated?

2. In the derivation of the energy methods, how is the internal energy generated?

3. State the Castigliano theorem.

4. How is a null (zero) force or moment used in the Castigliano solution to compute a deflection or a rotation?

5. What is the effect of a stepped cross section (variable I) on the Castigliano solution?

6. What is the effect of a continuously varying cross section (tapered section) on the Castigliano solution?

7. Give two examples of structures for which a numerical integration of the Castigliano equation becomes necessary.

8. Develop the proof that the Castigliano theorem is true for externally applied moments and their corresponding angular rotations, as well as for externally applied loads and their linear displacements.

9. State the Maxwell Theorem of Reciprocal Displacements.

10. Develop the proof that the Maxwell theorem is true for moments and their corresponding angular rotations, as well as for concentrated loads and their linear deflections.

Monumental reinforced concrete architecture in the Atlanta
Central Library, Atlanta, Georgia. (Photograph courtesy
Portland Cement Association, reprinted by permission.)

Unit Load Method in Beams and Frames

In any method of analysis used as frequently as the Castigliano method, simplifications and shortcuts inevitably develop; the Castigliano method is no exception. One of the more useful simplifications is the unit load concept for finding the partial derivatives. The unit load (or "dummy load") concept is presented in this chapter.

The method of unit load has frequently been presented in years past as an independent method of analysis, but it need not be isolated in that way. It can be regarded entirely appropriately as a simple but worthwhile variation in the classical Castigliano method. The method of unit load is applicable wherever the classical methods are applicable; if the problem is solvable by the Castigliano method, it is solvable by the unit load method. The examples presented in this chapter show how the unit load method can be applied to beams and frames. Applications to trusses are presented in a later chapter.

In the examples of this chapter, the practice of giving the manual integration in the text is followed for the simpler cases. When manual integration becomes impractical, the solution obtained by computer software is given.

7.1 DEVELOPMENT OF THE UNIT LOAD METHOD

As was noted in Chapter 6, the unit load method is demonstrably a variation of the Castigliano solution. Consider, for example, the beam of Figure 7-1, where the deflection at midspan is to be found. The beam is shown twice—once with only the real loads shown, and once with only the null loads shown.

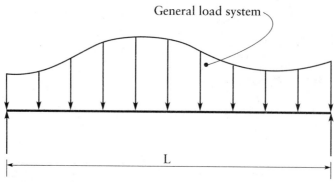

(a) Beam with real loads

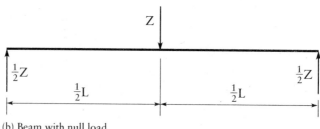

(b) Beam with null load

FIGURE 7-1 Real and null loads on a simple span.

Since the real loads on a beam are customarily given as numerical values, a variable null load Z is added, as shown—in this case, as a separate load system. The deflection of the beam at midspan is given by the Castigliano equation, with $ds = dx$;

$$\Delta_c = \int_0^L \frac{M_x\left(\dfrac{\partial M_x}{\partial Z}\right)dx}{EI}$$

The moment equation may be written in two parts—one for the real loads, and one for the null load Z—with the total moment being the sum of the two parts. The first part consists of moment and derivatives due only to real loads:

$$0 \le x \le L; \qquad M_x = \text{Moment equation due to real loads;}$$

$$\frac{\partial M_x}{\partial Z} = 0$$

for all cases of load.

The second part consists of moment and derivatives due only to null loads:

$$0 \leq x \leq \frac{1}{2}L; \qquad M_x = +\frac{1}{2}Zx; \qquad \frac{\partial M_x}{\partial Z} = m_x = \frac{1}{2}x$$

$$\frac{1}{2}L \leq x \leq L; \qquad M_x = +\frac{1}{2}Z(L-x); \qquad \frac{\partial M_x}{\partial Z} = m_x = \frac{1}{2}(L-x)$$

For the null loads, the two partial derivatives simply degenerate into the moment equations due to Z, with the load Z set equal to 1; a moment's reflection will affirm that this relationship is true for any equation linear in Z.

When these moment equations and derivatives are summed and the results are substituted into the Castigliano equation, the moments due to the null load Z go to zero and the result is

$$\Delta_c = \int_0^{\frac{L}{2}} \frac{M_x m_x dx}{EI} + \int_{\frac{L}{2}}^{L} \frac{M_x m_x dx}{EI}$$

where

M_x is the moment equation due only to real loads;

m_x is the moment equation due to a null load Z placed in the proper direction at the place where deflection is sought, with Z assigned a magnitude of 1;

dx is the incremental length;

E is elastic modulus;

I is moment of inertia.

It is concluded that no matter what the real loads may be, the partial derivative $\partial M_x/\partial Z$ is identical to the moment equation for a 1-lb load (unit load) placed in the proper direction at the point where the deflection is sought. In its generalized form, the deflection of a beam at a point A, according to the unit load method, is given by

$$\Delta_A = \int_0^L \frac{M_x m_x dx}{E_x I_x} \tag{7.1}$$

where m_x is the moment equation for a unit load placed in the proper direction at the point A.

It is important to realize that the 1-lb unit load does not exist. It simply provides a direct but clever means to obtain the partial derivative due to the null load Z. It has no other function, and it does not contribute to the moment equation for real loads.

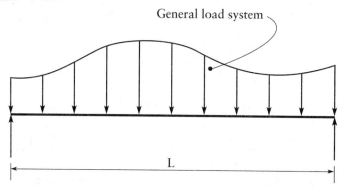

(a) Beam with real loads

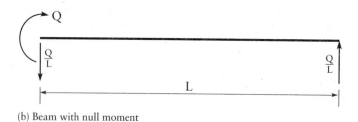

(b) Beam with null moment

FIGURE 7-2 Null moment on a beam.

By the same logic, the rotation θ at any point in a structure may also be found by the unit load method, simply by using a unit moment rather than a unit force. Consider, for example, the beam and loads of Figure 7-2, where the rotation at one end of the beam is to be found; as before, the loads have been separated into real loads and null loads.

The rotation at the end of the beam is given by the Castigliano equation, with $ds = dx$:

$$\theta_A = \int_0^L \frac{M_x\left(\dfrac{\partial M_x}{\partial Q}\right)dx}{EI}$$

The moment equation is again written in two parts—one for the real loads, and one for the null loads—and the total moment equation is the sum of the two. The first part consists of the moment equation due only to real loads:

$$0 \le x \le L; \qquad M_x = \text{Moment due to real loads}; \qquad \frac{\partial M_x}{\partial Q} = 0$$

The second part consists of moment and derivatives due only to null loads:

$$0 \le x \le L; \qquad M_x = Q - \left(\frac{Q}{L}\right)x = Q\left(1 - \frac{x}{L}\right); \qquad \frac{\partial M_x}{\partial Q} = \left(1 - \frac{x}{L}\right)$$

As before, the two partial derivatives with respect to Q simply degenerate into the moment equation for the null moment Q, with Q set equal to 1; a moment's reflection will affirm that this relationship is true for any equation linear in Q.

The conclusion is again drawn that no matter what the real loads may be, the partial derivative of the moment equation with respect to a null moment Q at point A is identical to the moment equation for a unit moment placed at the same point. In its generalized form, the rotation θ_A at any point A in a beam, according to the unit load method, is therefore given by

$$\theta_A = \int_0^L \frac{M_x m_x dx}{E_x I_x} \tag{7.2}$$

where m_x is the moment equation for a unit moment placed in the proper direction at A.

7.2 APPLICATION OF THE UNIT LOAD METHOD TO BEAMS

In its applications to beams, the unit load method is quite similar to the Castigliano method. Some examples will illustrate the use of the unit load method as it applies to cantilever beams and simply supported beams.

Example 7-1   Determine the deflection at the free end of the given cantilever.

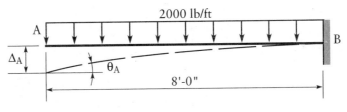

$E = 30,000,000$ psi

$I = 239$ in.^{4}

Solution   To find the deflection at the free end of the beam, using the unit load method, a unit load is placed at the point where deflection is sought. The deflection is then computed by evaluating the integral

$$\Delta_{CTR} = \int_0^L \frac{M_x m_x dx}{E_x I_x}$$

The two moment equations M_x and m_x, with x in inches, can now be calculated.

For the moment due only to real loads,

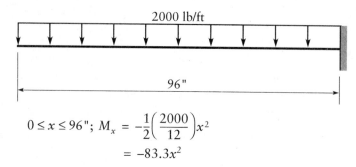

$$0 \leq x \leq 96"; \quad M_x = -\frac{1}{2}\left(\frac{2000}{12}\right)x^2$$
$$= -83.3x^2$$

For the moment due only to unit load

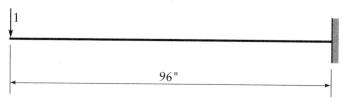

$$0 \leq x \leq 96"; \quad m_x = -x$$

The integral is evaluated, yielding

$$\Delta_{CTR} = \int_0^{96} \frac{(-83.3x^2)\,(-x)\,dx}{(30,000,000)\,(239)}$$
$$= (2.906 \times 10^{-9})\,x^4\big|_0^{96}$$
$$= 0.25 \text{ in.}$$

This result can be readily verified by checking the results of Example 6-3.

It should be immediately apparent in Example 7-1 that the execution of the unit load method is identical to that of the Castigliano solution. The unit load provides nothing more than an alternative (but a very convenient) way to obtain the partial derivative.

In the unit load method, the two moment equations M_x and m_x must be written in the same units. Had the moment equation for real loads M_x been written in kips and feet (with conversion to be done at some later point in the solution), the unit load would also have had to be 1 kip so that the moment equation m_x would be in kips and feet, consistent with M_x.

Example 7-2 Determine the slope (rotation) at the free end of the cantilever beam.

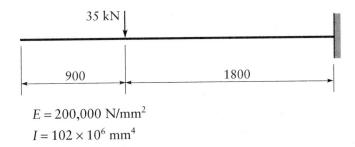

$E = 200,000 \text{ N/mm}^2$

$I = 102 \times 10^6 \text{ mm}^4$

Solution To determine the slope at point A, using the unit load method, a unit moment is applied at A. The rotation of the unit moment is then computed by using the two moment equations M_x and m_x:

$$\theta_A = \int_0^L \frac{M_x m_x \, dx}{E_x I_x}$$

The two moment equations, with x in millimeters, can now be calculated. For the moment due only to real loads,

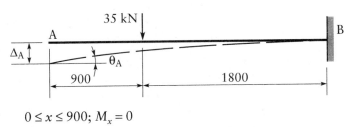

$0 \leq x \leq 900; \; M_x = 0$

$900 \leq x \leq 2700; \; M_x = 35,000(x - 900)$

For the moment due only to unit load,

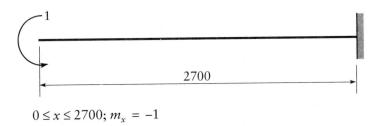

$0 \leq x \leq 2700; \; m_x = -1$

The integral is evaluated, yielding

$$\theta_A = \int_0^{900} \frac{(0)(-1)dx}{(200,000)(102 \times 10^6)} + \int_{900}^{2700} \frac{-35,000(x-900)(-1)dx}{(200,000)(102 \times 10^6)}$$

$$= 0 + \frac{35,000}{(200,000)(102 \times 10^6)} \left(\frac{1}{2}\right)(x-900)^2 \Big|_{900}^{2700}$$

$$= 0.00278 \text{ radians}$$

This result can be readily verified by checking the results of Example 6-2.

Example 7-3   Determine the deflection at the 10 kip load using the unit load method.

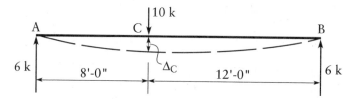

$E = 1,500,000$ psi

$I = 2731$ in.^{4}

Solution   To find the deflection at point C using the unit load method, a unit concentrated load is applied at C. The deflection of the unit concentrated load is then computed from the equation

$$\Delta_A = \int_0^L \frac{M_x m_x dx}{E_x I_x}$$

The two moment equations, with x in inches, can now be calculated. For the moment due only to real loads,

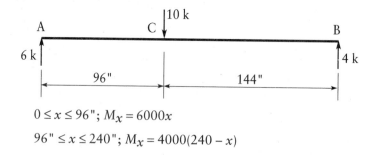

$0 \leq x \leq 96"; \ M_x = 6000x$

$96" \leq x \leq 240"; \ M_x = 4000(240 - x)$

For the moment due only to unit loads,

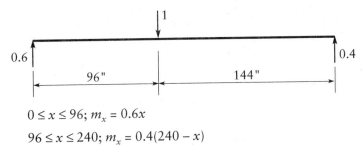

$0 \leq x \leq 96;\ m_x = 0.6x$

$96 \leq x \leq 240;\ m_x = 0.4(240 - x)$

The integral is evaluated, yielding

$$\Delta = \int_0^{96} \frac{(6000x)(0.6x)\,dx}{(1,500,000)(2731)}$$

$$+ \int_{96}^{240} \frac{(4000)(240 - x)(0.4)(240 - x)\,dx}{(1,500,000)(2731)}$$

$$= 0.648 \text{ in.}$$

This result can be verified by comparing it to Example 6-5.

7.3 BEAMS HAVING STEPPED CROSS SECTIONS

The unit load method is readily applicable to beams having nonuniform cross sections or stepped cross sections. In the case of stepped cross sections, the step simply creates another discontinuity in the integration. Some examples will illustrate the procedure.

Example 7-4   Determine the slope (rotation) at the free end of the stepped cantilever. Moments of inertia of the two segments are shown in the sketch.

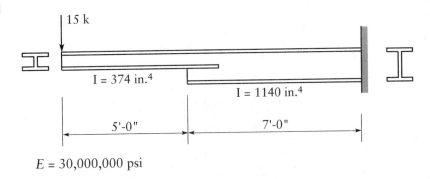

$E = 30,000,000$ psi

Solution   To find the rotation at point A using the unit load method, a unit moment is applied at A. The rotation of the unit moment is then computed from the equation

$$\theta_A = \int_0^L \frac{M_x m_x dx}{EI_x}$$

where m_x is the moment equation of a unit moment at A, and I_x is also variable.

The two moment equations, with x in inches, can now be calculated.

For the moment due only to real loads,

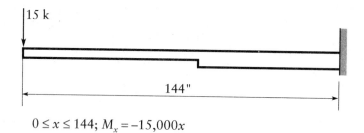

$0 \le x \le 144;\ M_x = -15{,}000x$

For the moment due only to unit load,

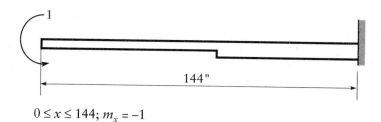

$0 \le x \le 144;\ m_x = -1$

I_x is also discontinuous. The equations for moment of inertia, with x in inches, are

$$0 \le x \le 60";\qquad I_x = 374$$

$$60" \le x \le 144";\qquad I_x = 1140$$

The variables are substituted into the integral form of the solution, yielding

$$\theta_A = \int_0^{60} \frac{(-15{,}000x)(-1)dx}{(30{,}000{,}000)(374)} + \int_{60}^{144} \frac{(15{,}000x)(-1)dx}{(30{,}000{,}000)(1140)}$$

$$= 0.00616 \text{ radians}$$

Example 7-5   Determine the deflection at the center of the given beam.

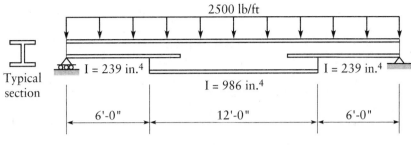

$E = 30,000,000$ psi

Solution   To find the deflection at the center of the beam, a concentrated unit load is applied at that point. The symmetry of the system permits the integral to be taken over half the span, after which the result is doubled. The deflection of the unit concentrated load is then computed from the integral solution, with $ds = dx$:

$$\Delta_c = 2\int_0^{\frac{L}{2}} \frac{M_x m_x dx}{EI_x}$$

where m_x is the moment equation of the unit concentrated load, and I_x is a variable.

The two moment equations, with x in inches, can now be calculated. For the moment due only to real loads,

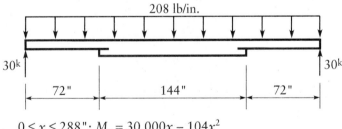

$0 \le x \le 288"$; $M_x = 30,000x - 104x^2$

For the moment due only to unit load,

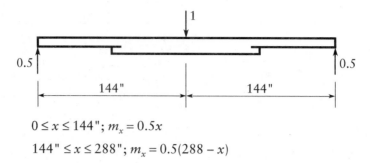

$$0 \leq x \leq 144"; \; m_x = 0.5x$$

$$144" \leq x \leq 288"; \; m_x = 0.5(288 - x)$$

The equations for the variable moment of inertia, with x in inches, are

$$0 \leq x \leq 72"; \qquad I_x = 239 \text{ in.}^4$$

$$72" \leq x \leq 216"; \qquad I_x = 986 \text{ in.}^4$$

$$216" \leq x \leq 288"; \qquad I_x = 239 \text{ in.}^4$$

The variables are substituted into the integral form, yielding

$$\Delta_c = 2 \left[\int_0^{72} \frac{(30{,}000x - 104x^2)(0.5x)\,dx}{(30{,}000{,}000)(239)} \right.$$
$$\left. + \int_{72}^{144} \frac{(30{,}000x - 104x^2)\,[0.50\,(240 - x)]\,dx}{(30{,}000{,}000)(986)} \right]$$
$$= 0.95 \text{ in.}$$

7.4 APPLICATION OF THE UNIT LOAD METHOD TO BENT OR CURVED BEAMS

The unit load method may also be applied directly to bent or curved beams. In such applications, however, deflections of the beam can occur in both the x and the y directions; special attention must therefore be paid to the way in which the two unit loads are used. Some examples will illustrate the procedure.

Example 7-6 Determine the deflection at the free end of the given bent beam.

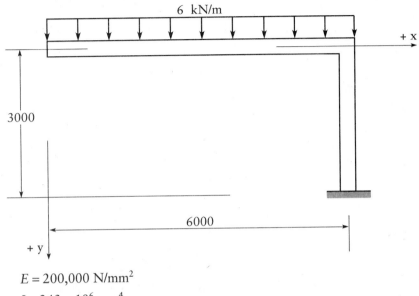

$$E = 200,000 \text{ N/mm}^2$$
$$I = 243 \times 10^6 \text{ mm}^4$$

Solution To find the vertical deflection at the end of the beam, a unit load is applied vertically; the moment produced by this unit load is denoted m_v. To find the horizontal deflection of the beam, a unit load is applied horizontally; the moment produced by this unit load is denoted m_h. The two deflections are then computed, using two separate integrations:

$$\Delta_y = \int_0^L \frac{M_s m_v ds}{E_x I_x}$$

$$\Delta_x = \int_0^L \frac{M_s m_h ds}{E_x I_x}$$

where M_s is the moment at any point s along the axis of the beam. The differential element ds may become either dx or dy, depending on the orientation of the element ds. For this beam, the coordinate axes have been chosen at the free end, with x increasing to the right and y increasing downward.

The three moment equations, with x and y in inches, can now be calculated.

For the moment due only to real loads,

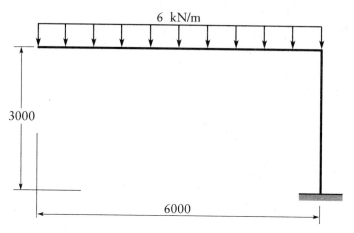

$$0 \le x \le 6000; \; M_s = -3x^2$$
$$0 \le y \le 3000; \; M_s = -108 \times 10^6 \; \text{N·mm}$$

For the moment due only to vertical unit load,

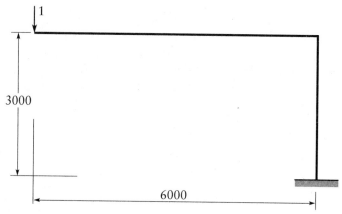

$$0 \le x \le 6000; \; m_v = -x$$
$$0 \le y \le 3000; \; m_v = -6000$$

For the moment due only to horizontal unit load,

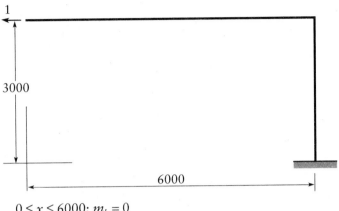

$0 \le x \le 6000$; $m_h = 0$

$0 \le y \le 3000$; $m_h = -y$

These moments are substituted into the integral form, yielding

$$\Delta_y = \int_0^{6000} \frac{-3x^2\,(-x)\,dx}{(200{,}000)(243)(10^6)} + \int_0^{3000} \frac{-(108)(10^6)(-6000)dy}{(200{,}000)(10)(10^6)}$$

$$= 60.0 \text{ mm}$$

$$\Delta_x = \int_0^{6000} \frac{-3x^2\,(0)\,dx}{(200{,}000)(243)(10^6)} + \int_0^{3000} \frac{-(108)(10^6)(-y)\,dy}{(200{,}000)(243)(10^6)}$$

$$= 10.0 \text{ mm}$$

Under the given uniform load, the end of the bent beam moves downward 60 mm as it moves 10 mm to the left.

Example 7-7   Use the unit load method to determine the deflection at the free end of the steel lamppost described in Example 6-9.

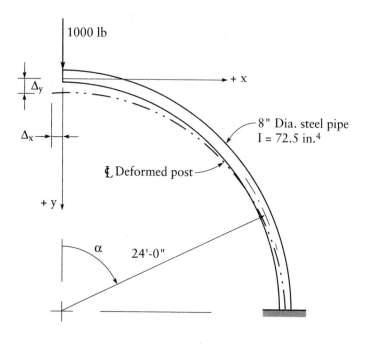

Solution   To find the vertical deflection at the end of the beam, a unit load is applied vertically; the moment produced by this unit load is denoted m_v. To find the horizontal deflection of the beam, a unit load is applied horizontally; the moment produced by this unit load is denoted m_h. The two deflections are then computed, using two separate integrations:

$$\Delta_y = \int_0^L \frac{M_s m_v \, ds}{E_x I_x}$$

$$\Delta_x = \int_0^L \frac{M_s m_h \, ds}{E_x I_x}$$

where M_s is the moment at any point s along the axis of the beam. For this beam, the coordinate axes have been chosen at the free end, with x increasing to the right and y increasing downward.

The three moment equations, with x and y in inches, can now be calculated.

For the moment due only to real loads,

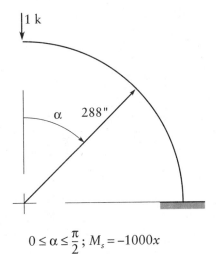

$$0 \le \alpha \le \frac{\pi}{2}; \ M_s = -1000x$$

For the moment due only to vertical unit load,

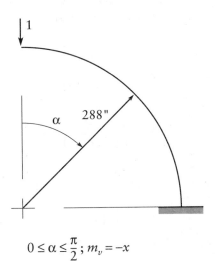

$$0 \le \alpha \le \frac{\pi}{2}; \ m_v = -x$$

For the moment due only to horizontal unit load,

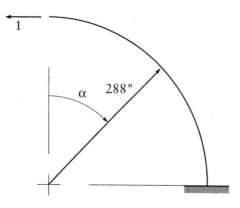

$$0 \le \alpha \le \frac{\pi}{2}\,; \; m_h = -y$$

The integration can be simplified by a change of variables to R and α, where

$$x = 288 \sin \alpha; \qquad y = 288\,(1 - \cos \alpha); \qquad ds = 288\,d\alpha$$

The equations for M_s, m_v, and m_h are expressed in terms of R and α, and then substituted into the integral form of the solution.

The deflections Δ_x and Δ_y are given by

$$\Delta_x = \int_0^{\frac{\pi}{2}} \frac{(-1000)(288 \sin \alpha)[-288\,(1 - \cos \alpha)\,](288\,d\alpha)}{(30{,}000{,}000)(72.5)}$$

$$\Delta_y = \int_0^{\frac{\pi}{2}} \frac{(-1000)(288 \sin \alpha)(-288 \sin \alpha)(288\,d\alpha)}{(30{,}000{,}000)(72.5)}$$

The solution at this point becomes identical to that of Example 6-9:

$$\Delta_x = 5.49 \text{ in.}$$

$$\Delta_y = 8.63 \text{ in.}$$

Example 7-8   Determine the deflection at the free end of the bent beam described in Example 6-10.

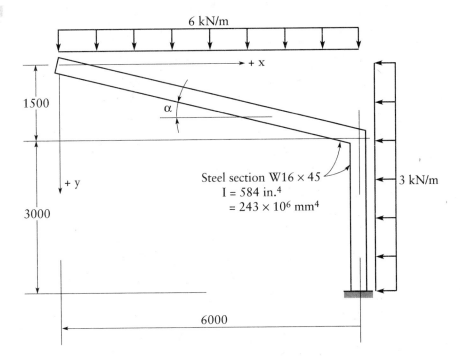

Solution   To find the vertical deflection at the end of the beam, a unit load is applied vertically; the moment produced by this unit load is denoted m_v. To find the horizontal deflection of the beam, a unit load is applied horizontally; the moment produced by this unit load is denoted m_h. The two deflections are then computed, using two separate integrations:

$$\Delta_y = \int_0^L \frac{M_s m_v\, ds}{E_x I_x}$$

$$\Delta_x = \int_0^L \frac{M_s m_h\, ds}{E_x I_x}$$

where M_s is the moment at any point s along the axis of the beam. For this beam, the coordinate axes have been chosen at the free end, with x increasing to the right and y increasing downward.

   The three moment equations, with x and y in millimeters, can now be calculated.

For the moment due only to real loads,

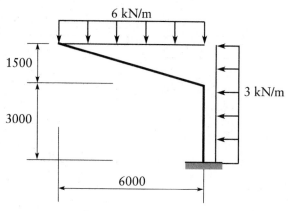

$0 \leq x \leq 6000;$

$M_s = -3x^2 - 1.5y^2$

$ds = 1.03dx$

$1500 \leq y \leq 4500;$

$M_s = -(108)(10^6) - 1.5y^2$

$ds = dy$

For the moment due only to vertical unit load,

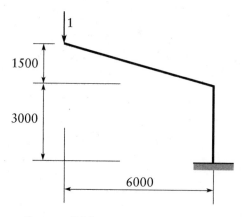

$0 \leq x \leq 6000;$

$m_v = -x$

$1500 \leq y \leq 4500;$

$m_v = -240$

For the moment due only to horizontal unit load,

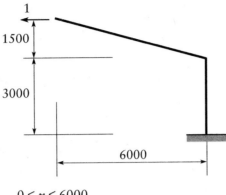

$0 \le x \le 6000$

$m_h = -y$

$1500 \le y \le 4500$

$m_h = -y$

Along the roof (when $0 \le x \le 6000$), $ds = 1.03dx$ and $y = 0.25x$. With these substitutions, the integral forms become

$$\Delta_y = \int_0^{6000} \frac{[-3x^2 - 1.5\,(0.25x)^2](-x)(1.03dx)}{(200{,}000)(243)(10^6)}$$

$$+ \int_{1500}^{4500} \frac{[-(108)(10^6) - 1.5y^2](-6000)\,dy}{(200{,}000)(243)(10^6)}$$

$$\Delta_x = \int_0^{6000} \frac{[-3x^2 - 1.5\,(0.25x^2)](-0.25x)(1.03dx)}{(200{,}000)(243)(10^6)}$$

$$+ \int_{1500}^{4500} \frac{[-(108)(10^6) - 1.5y^2](-y)dy}{(200{,}000)(243)(10^6)}$$

The evaluation of these integrals yields the value of the two components:

$\Delta_y = +66.7$ mm   (downward)

$\Delta_x = +28.4$ mm   (outward)

The sign of the components is positive, indicating that they occur in the same direction as that assumed for the unit loads.

Example 7-9   Determine the rotation of leg AB of the given frame.

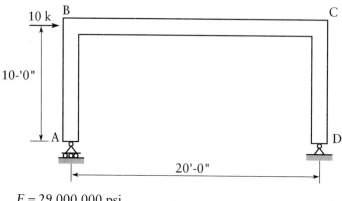

$E = 29,000,000$ psi
$I = 612$ in.^{4}

Solution   The moment on leg AB is zero; hence, the leg will remain straight under the given load case. The rotation of the leg may therefore be found by applying a unit moment at A. The rotation of point A (and consequently of leg AB) is given by

$$\theta_A = \int_0^L \frac{M_s m_s ds}{EI}$$

where M_s is the moment due to real loads along the axis of the beam, and m_s is the moment due to a unit moment at point A.

The coordinate axes are arbitrarily chosen with origin at point A, with x increasing to the right and y increasing upward. The moment equations, with x and y in inches, can now be calculated.

For the moment due only to real loads,

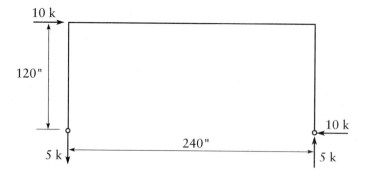

$0 \leq y \leq 120"; \; M_s = 0$

$$ds = dy$$

$0 \leq x \leq 240"; \; M_s = -5000x$

$$ds = dx$$

$120" \leq y \leq 0; \; M_s = 1,200,000 - 10,000(120 - y)$

$$= 10,000y$$
$$ds = -dy$$

For the moment due only to unit moment,

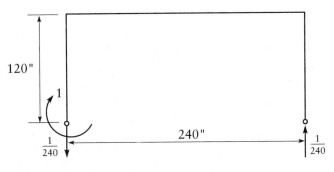

$0 \leq y \leq 120"; \; m_s = 1$

$0 \leq x \leq 240"; \; m_s = 1 - \dfrac{x}{240}$

$120" \leq y \leq 0; \; m_s = 0$

The integral form becomes

$$\theta_A = \int_0^{120} \frac{(0)(1)dy}{(29,000,000)(612)} + \int_0^{240} \frac{(-5000x)\left(1 - \dfrac{x}{240}\right)dx}{(29,000,000)(612)}$$

$$- \int_{120}^{0} \frac{(10,000y)(0)(-dy)}{(29,000,000)(612)}$$

$$= -0.002704 \text{ radians} \qquad \text{(opposite to direction assumed)}$$

It is concluded that the frame will deform as shown in the following sketch.

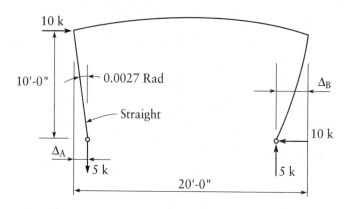

Example 7-10

Determine the lateral deflection of point B of the frame described in Example 7-9.

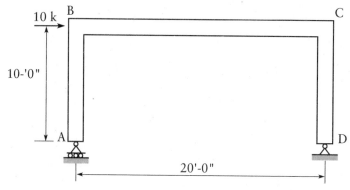

$E = 29,000,000$ psi

$I = 612$ in.^{4}

Solution

To find the lateral deflection of point B, a unit load is added at point B. The lateral deflection of the unit load is then given by

$$\Delta_B = \int_0^L \frac{\tilde{M}_s m_h \, ds}{EI}$$

where M_s is the moment at any point s along the frame due only to real loads, and m_h is the moment at any point s along the frame due only to the horizontal unit load at B.

The coordinate axes are arbitrarily chosen with origin at A, with x increasing to the right and y increasing upward. The moment equations, with x and y in inches, can now be calculated.

For the moment due only to real loads,

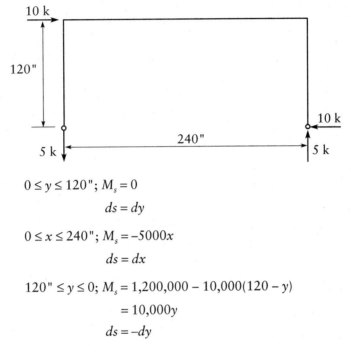

$0 \leq y \leq 120"; \ M_s = 0$

$$ds = dy$$

$0 \leq x \leq 240"; \ M_s = -5000x$

$$ds = dx$$

$120" \leq y \leq 0; \ M_s = 1{,}200{,}000 - 10{,}000(120 - y)$

$$= 10{,}000y$$

$$ds = -dy$$

For the moment due only to unit load,

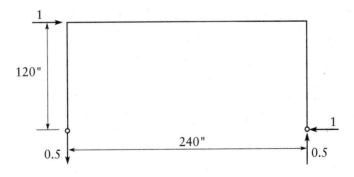

$0 \leq y \leq 120"; \ m_h = 0$

$0 \leq x \leq 240"; \ m_h = -0.5x$

$120" \leq y \leq 0; \ m_h = 120 - 1(120 - y)$

$$= +y$$

The integral form becomes

$$\Delta_x = \int_0^{120} \frac{(0)(0)dy}{(29,000,000)(612)} + \int_0^{240} \frac{(-5000x)(-0.5x)dx}{(29,000,000)(612)}$$

$$+ \int_{120}^{0} \frac{(10,000y)(+y)(-dy)}{(29,000,000)(612)}$$

$$= +0.973 \ in. \qquad (in \ the \ direction \ shown)$$

Outside Problems   Problems 7-1 through 7-36. For the corresponding Problems 6-1 through 6–36, solve the problems again, this time using the method of unit load. Compare these new solutions step-by-step with the solutions made earlier using the classical Castigliano method.

REVIEW QUESTIONS

1. What does the unit load concept contribute to the Castigliano solution?

2. Can the unit load method be used where the cross section is stepped?

3. Can the unit load method be used where the cross section is continuously variable?

4. Can the unit load method be used where the axis of the member is experimentally rather than geometrically defined (as in Example 6–15)?

5. How are rotations computed in the unit load method?

6. When both the x and the y components of a deflection are to be computed by the unit load method, why can't both the horizontal and the vertical unit loads be applied at the same time, similar to the way in which the null loads are applied in the Castigliano method?

7. Can both the unit moment and a unit load be applied at the same time in the unit load method?

8. Can the unit load method be used to find joint deflections in a three-hinged arch?

Short span concrete bridge, Greenville, Wisconsin.
(Photograph courtesy of Portland Cement Association,
reprinted by permission.)

8

Simple Trusses

The term *simple truss* is used here to describe a truss that is statically determinate both externally and internally. Simple trusses constitute the overwhelming majority of all trusses used in the industry, although at times they may be difficult to recognize as trusses. For such trusses, both the external reactions and the forces in every internal member can be found by simple statics; only the laws of equilibrium are needed in performing the analysis.

A truss is a structural system that derives its structural stability and strength from the triangulation of its members. The triangulation of many light, slender members permits maximum strength to be developed with a minimum of materials. Configurations can be deliberately arranged to ensure maximum utilization of materials, with stress in every member maintained at its highest, most efficient level. Triangulation also permits large spans to be bridged entirely by a network of short pieces of material—one of the more attractive features of trusses over the centuries.

The advantages of high stress levels and light weight come only with a penalty: trusses have little lateral stability, and the compression chord (indicated in Figure 8–1) tends to "roll" sideways under load. A system of lateral bracing on the compression chord is almost always necessary. Flooring, decking, or other such features in the structure can often be located along the compression chord in order to provide this lateral bracing as a secondary function. Where such bracing does not appear naturally in the design, some sort of independent (and expensive) bracing system will probably have to be provided at the compression chord.

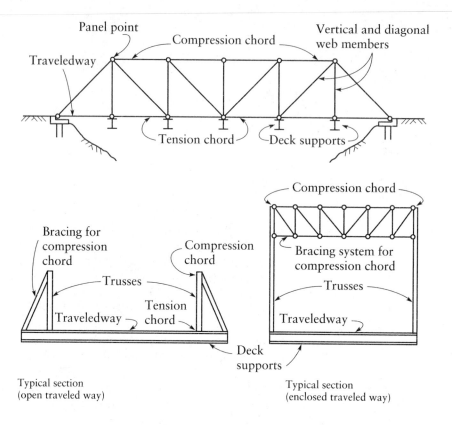

FIGURE 8-1 Typical truss.

Another disadvantage of trusses is that they are generally considered to be ugly. Their lack of definition of solid bold lines, their seeming tangle of members, and their high depth-to-span ratio often makes them undesirable in settings where appearance is a primary concern. In cases where the low cost of trusses necessitates their use in spite of their appearance, designers often choose to cover them rather than to attempt to deal with the issue of appearance.

Regardless what disadvantages trusses may possess, the appeal of their light weight and economy of materials assures them of a secure place among structural designers. Among builders, their ease of construction, reliability, and adaptability makes them a highly competitive alternative to solid beams. A thorough familiarity with the analysis and design of trusses is therefore essential to anyone involved in today's construction industry.

8.1 TRUSS GEOMETRY AND NOTATIONS

A properly formed simple truss begins with a base triangle such as those indicated in Figure 8-2; additional triangles are then produced by successively adding two members and their included hinge point. In Figure 8-2(b), for example, the truss is formed by starting with triangle 1, then adding pairs of members and their included hinge to form successively triangles 2, 3, 4, and 5. Ideally, no truss member is in flexure; truss members carry only axial loads.

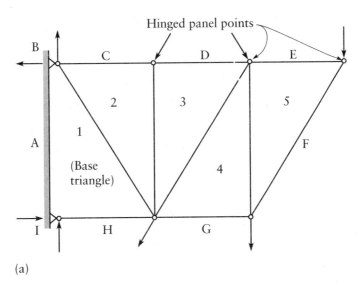

(a)

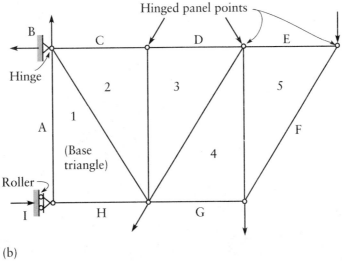

(b)

FIGURE 8-2 Bow's notation in truss formation.

The base triangle may have one of its three sides formed by a support system that has two hinged supports, as shown in Figure 8-2(a); alternatively, the third side may be another truss member that has one hinged support and one roller, as shown in Figure 8-2(b). For purposes of identification, the interior of both base triangles in Figure 8-2 is assigned the number 1, and all succeeding triangles are numbered sequentially. The interior of each triangle is thus identified by a number.

Loads may be applied only at a hinge point, as indicated in Figure 8-2. Around the perimeter of the truss, the space between hinge points (and therefore potential load points) is identified by a letter. Each load can then be identified by two letters; the load DE, for example, is the load occurring between letters D and E.

Perimeter members of the trusses in Figure 8-2 can be identified by a number and a letter. Member C2, for example, is the member occurring between the letter C and the number 2. Interior members of the truss are similarly identified, but by two numbers; member 23 is thus the member between the numbers 2 and 3.

The notation of members that has just been described is called *Bow's notation*. In some cases, only letters are used to identify the spaces inside the triangles and the space between the loads, but the end result is still called Bow's notation.

An alternative notation is shown in Figure 8-3. The upper hinge points are given sequential symbols U_0, U_1, U_2, and so on, and the lower hinge points are given sequential symbols L_0, L_1, L_2 and so on. Each member is then identified by its hinge points, such as L_2U_1, or U_1U_2. When additional lines of hinge points occur—for instance, the hinge points I_1 and I_2 in the triangular truss of Figure 8-3—the system proves to be less orderly.

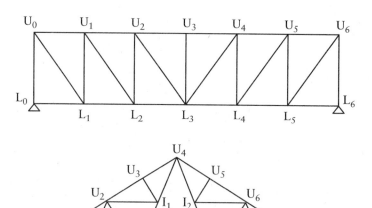

FIGURE 8-3 Hinge point notation.

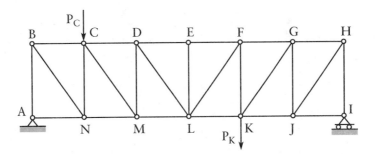

FIGURE 8-4 Sequential alphabetic notation.

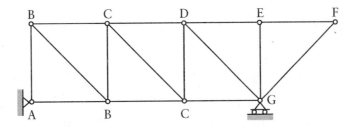

FIGURE 8-5 Properly formed truss.

A third alternative is widely used, particularly for computer applications. Each hinge point is simply given an identifying letter, as shown in Figure 8-4. Each member is then identified by the two hinge points at its ends, such as member CD for the member connecting hinges C and D. In this system, loads are identified by the same letter as the hinge point, such as P_C for a load occurring at hinge point C.

The choice of a notation system depends on the personal preference of the individual designer. For the sake of uniformity, only the sequential alphabetic notation is used in subsequent discussions in this text.

As stated earlier, a properly formed truss begins with a base triangle, and then is extended by the addition of two members and their included hinge until the desired configuration is complete. An example of such a properly formed truss is shown in Figure 8-5.

The base triangle may be any one of the three-sided triangles that form the truss; but if the support conditions include two adjacent hinges (such as those of Figure 8-2(a), the base triangle must be the one that includes those two hinges.

For the truss of Figure 8-5, the truss is assumed to start with triangle ABC. To this triangle, Members CI and IA are added, along with their included hinge at I. To this assembly, members CD and DI are added, with their included hinge at D. Next, members DH and HI are added, with their included hinge at H. This procedure is followed until the entire truss is formed, ending with members EF and FG, with their included hinge at F. Notice that the last hinge need not occur at a support point.

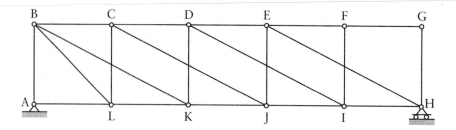

FIGURE 8-6 Properly formed truss with passing members.

A truss may sometimes appear unfamiliar and yet still be a properly formed stable truss. Consider, for example, the truss of Figure 8-6. Hinges are shown as circles; if no hinge is shown where two members cross, the members are continuous and pass each other freely.

The truss of Figure 8-6 may be checked for proper formation by beginning with the base triangle *ABL*. To this base triangle, members *BC* and *CL* and their included joint *C* are added. Next, members *BK* and *KL* and their included joint *K* are added; then members *CD* and *DK* and their included joint *D*; then members *CJ* and *JK* and their included joint *J*; and so on to the end of the truss. The truss is thus seen to be a properly formed simple truss; it is therefore statically determinate and it will be stable under load.

8.2 LOADING OF TRUSSES

Trusses are loaded only at hinge points. Only in this way can flexure be avoided in the slender truss members. Separate beams are used to deliver the loads to the hinge points, as indicated in Figure 8-7(a); these beams may be either conventional solid beams or small standard commercially fabricated trusses, as shown in Figure 8-7(b).

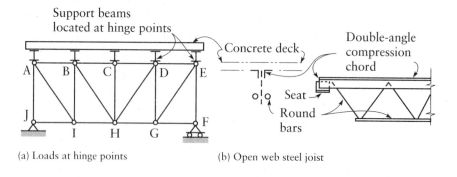

(a) Loads at hinge points   (b) Open web steel joist

FIGURE 8-7 Loads delivered to hinge points.

It should be apparent that casting a concrete deck on open-web steel joists, as shown in Figure 8-7(b), violates the rule that truss members may not be loaded in flexure. These standard commercially built trusses are specially built for such applications, however, and the compression chord is designed to carry such flexure in addition to its usual axial load. As a matter of interest, these standard joists have been extensively tested to failure under full-scale conditions; loading and load tables have been developed and published for the various sizes and spans in view of these full-scale tests.

Except in the case of these special trusses, ordinary truss members that are loaded in compression are designed as slender columns. The theory of slender (Euler) columns is introduced in coursework on elementary strength of materials, where it is shown that the allowable load decreases with the square of the length; if the length of a slender column is doubled, the column can carry only one-fourth as much load. It is obviously good design practice to keep compression members in trusses as short as is reasonably possible in order to maintain the highest possible level of loading.

In contrast, load in tension members is not affected by the length of the member. A truss member in tension can carry as much load over a long length as it can over a short length. It is good design practice, therefore, to arrange the truss configuration such that longer members are loaded in tension and shorter members are loaded in compression.

Load reversals can occur in a truss member. Under one condition of loading a member may be loaded in tension but under another condition of loading that member may go into compression. Since every member in a truss is deliberately designed to be heavily loaded, the failure of a single member due to an unsuspected load reversal can be disastrous. Load reversals in truss members are therefore quite serious; they are discussed more fully later in the next chapter.

8.3 HINGE POINTS IN TRUSSES

All members in a truss are assumed to be joined at a hinge. The hinge is assumed to be perfectly aligned and to be frictionless. In reality, however, joints are rarely hinged at all.

A typical *panel point* is shown in Figure 8-8(b). In that detail, all members at the panel point are attached to a gusset plate; their ends are much closer to being fixed than to being hinged. Timber trusses are usually fabricated similarly to the steel truss of Figure 8-8, with steel gusset plates being used to join the members at the panel points.

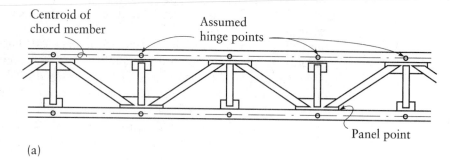

(a)

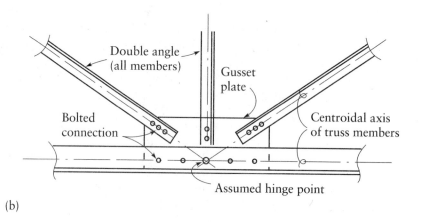

(b)

FIGURE 8-8 Typical truss panel point.

The difference between the joint conditions that are assumed for the analysis and the joint conditions that actually exist in the truss may seem to present a serious discrepancy. In most cases, it is not. The very slenderness of the truss members does not permit much moment to be developed when the panel point undergoes its very small rotations or deflections. The moments in the truss members are therefore quite low; and for long slender truss members, this small moment can be ignored with little loss of accuracy. In all the simple trusses discussed in this book, the primary stresses in all truss members can be assumed to consist exclusively of axial tension or compression.

It must immediately be acknowledged, however, that the moments occurring at the joints cannot always be ignored. Where members are heavy and lengths are short, these *secondary stresses* occurring at the joints may become significant. As a guide, when the L/d of a member (ratio of length to depth) is less than about 10, the effects of moments at the joints are probably becoming significant. The computation of such secondary stresses is a statically indeterminate problem, far beyond the scope of an introductory text such as this.

8.4 COMMON CONFIGURATIONS FOR TRUSSES

Some configurations for trusses have proved to be exceptionally workable in particular applications. As a result, these configurations have been used repeatedly and eventually were given names as particular types of trusses. Several such configurations, with their identifying names, are shown in Figure 8-9.

Trusses respond to flexure in the same way beams do, with members along the top of a simple span going into compression and members along the bottom going into tension. These upper and lower chords, also called the *compression chord* and the *tension chord*, are the members that primarily resist flexure. The vertical and diagonal members between these two chords are often called the *web members*; the load coming to these members is primarily due to the shearing forces in the truss.

Unlike solid beams, trusses may be varied in depth quite readily to suit increases or decreases in moment. It is no accident that the bowstring truss and the Parker truss of Figure 8-9 are shaped like a moment diagram. Similarly, even though the Fink truss and the Baltimore truss are rather crude approximations of a moment diagram, they represent distinct improvements over a solid beam of a fixed depth.

In some of the configurations of Figure 8-9, it becomes necessary to add members just to provide bracing points along the lengths of the longer members. Such is the case with the Baltimore truss and the K truss. Intermediate members in these trusses serve primarily to reduce member lengths and thereby maintain higher compression loads.

Where a deep truss such as the K truss is used to support a single-span bridge over a waterway, the clearance to the high-water mark may be so shallow that the entire truss must be placed above the level of the roadway. The bridge deck is then placed along the lower chord (or tension chord), and the compression chord is then set some 16 to 20 feet above the deck; this type of truss was shown in Figure 8-1. In such bridges, called *through truss bridges*, an additional system of bracing must be added across the top to provide stability for the compression chord.

In cases where there is enough clearance above the high-water mark, the entire truss can be placed below the level of the roadway and the deck can be placed along the top chord of the truss. In such a design, the deck also functions as a bracing system for the compression chords of the trusses. Such bridges, called *deck truss bridges*, require only nominal additional bracing along the tension chord at the bottom of the truss.

The truss configurations shown in Figure 8-9 are only a few of the ones in common use. Clearly, one of the more attractive features of a truss is its adaptability: truss configurations are readily altered to suit a particular problem posed by a particular site due to a particular load or a particular foundation condition. While the familiar configurations of Figure 8-9 provide a useful starting point, a competent designer need not feel constrained to stay within these more common configurations.

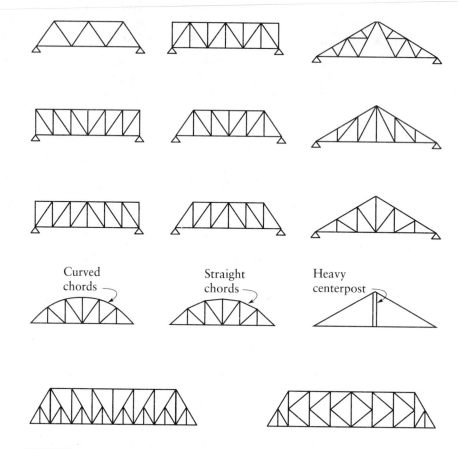

FIGURE 8-9 Common configurations for trusses.

8.5 REACTIONS ON TRUSSES

Reactions at truss supports are found exactly as they are found for solid beams. Rigid-body mechanics does not distinguish between a body that is solid and a body that is trussed. The reactions are identical for either case.

In general, however, trusses may employ unfamiliar shapes. A few examples using such shapes will illustrate the procedures for finding their reactions. In these examples, it must be remembered that a roller may develop either a positive or a negative reaction.

Example 8-1 Determine the reactions for the given truss under the indicated system of loads.

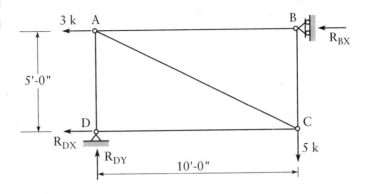

Solution A direction has been assumed for each of the reactions R_{DX}, R_{DY}, and R_{BX}. These are the only reactions that can be developed by the given supports, although their actual direction may turn out to run opposite to the assumed direction, and although one or more of them may actually turn out to be zero. The reactions are entered on the sketch in their assumed direction.

Summing moments about D yields the reaction R_{BX}:

$$\Sigma M_D = 0; \qquad 0 = -3(5) - R_{BX}(5) + 5(10)$$

$$R_{BX} = 7 \text{ kips in the direction shown.}$$

Summing forces vertically yields the reaction R_{DY}:

$$\Sigma F_V = 0; \qquad 0 = R_{DY} - 5$$

$$R_{DY} = 5 \text{ kips in the direction shown.}$$

Summing forces horizontally yields the reaction R_{DX}:

$$\Sigma F_X = 0; \qquad 0 = -3 - R_{DX} - R_{BX}$$

$$= -3 - R_{DX} - 7$$

$$R_{DX} = -10 \text{ kips}$$

$$= 10 \text{ kips opposite to the direction shown.}$$

As a check, moments may be taken about A or C:

$$\Sigma M_C = 0; \qquad 0 = -3\,(5) - R_{BX}\,(5) + R_{DY}\,(10)$$

$$= -3\,(5) - 7\,(5) + 5\,(10)$$

$$= 0 \qquad \text{(ok)}$$

Example 8-2   Determine the reactions for the given truss under the indicated system of loads.

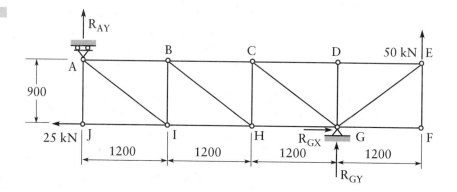

Solution   All the reactions that the supports can develop—but only the reactions that the supports can develop—have been entered on the sketch.
Summing moments about G yields the reaction R_{AY}:

$$\Sigma M_G = 0; \qquad 0 = R_{AY}\,(3.6) - 50\,(1.2)$$

$$R_{AY} = 16.7 \text{ kN in the direction shown.}$$

Summing forces vertically yields the reaction R_{GY}:

$$\Sigma F_V = 0; \qquad 0 = R_{AY} + R_{GY} + 50$$

$$= 16.7 + R_{GY} + 50$$

$$R_{GY} = -66.7 \text{ kN}$$

$$= 66.7 \text{ kN opposite to the direction shown.}$$

Summing forces horizontally yields the reaction R_{GX}:

$$\Sigma F_H = 0; \qquad 0 = -25 + R_{GX}$$

$$R_{GX} = 25 \text{ kN} \text{ in the direction shown.}$$

As a check, moments should be taken about some hinge point that does not include a reaction. Hinge point C is chosen for this case:

$$\Sigma M_C = 0; \qquad 0 = R_{AY}(2.4) + 25\,(0.9) - R_{GX}(0.9)$$

$$- R_{GY}(1.2) - 50\,(2.4)$$

$$= 16.7\,(2.4) + 25\,(0.9) - 25\,(0.9)$$

$$+ 66.7\,(1.2) - 50\,(2.4)$$

$$= 0 \qquad \text{(ok)}$$

Example 8-3   Determine the reactions for the given truss under the indicated system of loads.

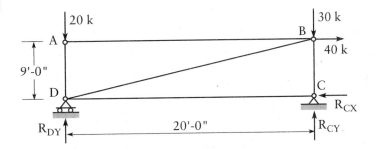

Solution   All the reactions that the supports can develop—but only the reactions that the supports can develop—have been entered on the sketch.
Summing moments about C yields the reaction R_{DY}:

$$\Sigma M_C = 0; \qquad 0 = -20(20) + R_{DY}(20) + 40(9)$$

$$R_{DY} = 2 \text{ kips in the direction shown.}$$

Summing forces vertically yields the reaction R_{CY}:

$$\Sigma F_V = 0; \qquad 0 = -20 + R_{DY} + R_{CY} - 30$$

$$= -20 + 2 + R_{CY} - 30$$

$$R_{CY} = 48 \text{ kips in the direction shown.}$$

Summing forces horizontally yields the reaction R_{CX}:

$$\Sigma F_H = 0; \qquad 0 = 40 - R_{CX}$$

$$R_{CX} = 40 \text{ kips in the direction shown.}$$

For a check, moments are summed about A:

$$\Sigma M_A = 0; \qquad 0 = 30(20) + R_{CX}(9) - 48(20)$$

$$= 30(20) + 40(9) - 48(20)$$

$$= 0 \qquad \text{(ok)}$$

Example 8-4   Determine the reactions for the given water tower under the indicated system of loads.

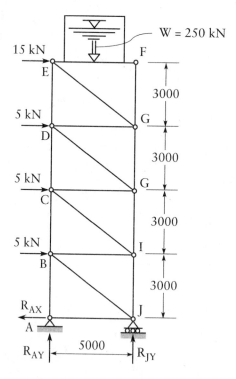

Solution   All the reactions that the supports can develop—but only the reactions that the supports can develop—have been entered on the sketch.

Summing moments about A yields the reaction R_{JY}:

$$\Sigma M_A = 0; \quad 0 = 5(3) + 5(6) + 5(9) + 15(12)$$

$$+ 250(2.5) - R_{JY}(5)$$

$$R_{JY} = 179 \text{ kN in the direction shown.}$$

Summing forces vertically yields the reaction R_{AY}:

$$\Sigma F_V = 0; \quad 0 = -250 + R_{AY} + R_{JY}$$

$$= -250 + R_{AY} + 179$$

$$R_{AY} = 71 \text{ kN in the direction shown.}$$

Summing forces horizontally yields the reaction R_{AX}:

$$\Sigma F_X = 0; \quad 0 = 15 + 5 + 5 + 5 - R_{AX} = 0$$

$$R_{AX} = 30 \text{ kN in the direction shown.}$$

For a check, sum moments about point F,

$$\Sigma M_F = 0; \quad 0 = -250(2.5) - 5(3) - 5(6) - 5(9)$$

$$+ R_{AX}(12) + R_{AY}(5)$$

$$= -625 - 15 - 30 - 45 + 360 + 355$$

$$= 0 \quad (\text{ok})$$

Trusses may also contain internal hinge points, similar to those discussed earlier for solid beams. Such internal hinges can be quite useful, serving to eliminate temperature stresses between unyielding supports or to eliminate secondary forces that might occur due to shifting foundations. Some examples will illustrate the solutions in instances where internal hinges occur.

Example 8-5   Determine the reactions for the given truss under the indicated system of loads.

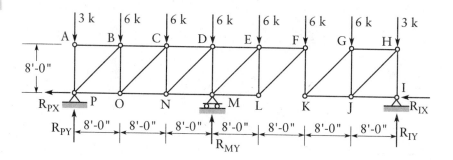

Solution   The free body *GHIJK* is removed first, and its reactions are computed. (Only those forces that can physically occur are shown on the free body.)

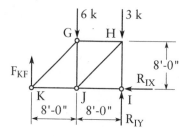

Summing moments about *K* yields reaction R_{IY}:

$$\Sigma M_X = 0; \qquad 0 = 6(8) + 3(16) - R_{IY}(16) = 0$$

$$R_{IY} = 6 \text{ kips in the direction shown.}$$

Summing forces vertically yields the member force F_{KF}:

$$\Sigma F_V = 0; \qquad 0 = F_{KF} - 6 - 3 + R_{IY}$$

$$= F_{KF} - 6 - 3 + 6$$

$$F_{KF} = 3 \text{ kips in the direction shown.}$$

Summing forces horizontally yields the reaction R_{IX}:

$$\Sigma F_H = 0; \qquad 0 = R_{IX}$$

since there are no horizontal loads anywhere on the system. Summing moments of the entire truss about M yields the reaction R_{PY}:

$$\Sigma M_M = 0; \quad 0 = R_{PY}(24) - 3(24) - 6(16) - 6(8) + 6(8)$$

$$+ 6(16) + 6(24) + 3(32) - 6(32)$$

$$R_{PY} = 1 \text{ kip in the direction shown.}$$

Summing moments of the entire truss about P yields the reaction R_{MY}:

$$\Sigma M_P = 0; \quad 0 = 6(8) + 6(16) + 6(24)(6)(32) + 6(40)$$

$$+ 6(48) + 3(56) - R_{MY}(24) - 6(56)$$

$$R_{MY} = 35 \text{ kips in the direction shown.}$$

Summing forces horizontally for the entire truss yields the reaction R_{PX}:

$$\Sigma F_H = 0; \quad 0 = R_{PX} + R_{IX}$$

$$= R_{PX}$$

Summing forces vertically over the entire truss provides a check on the calculations:

$$\Sigma F_V = 0; \quad 0 = R_{PY} - 3 - 6 - 6 - 6 - 6 - 6 - 3 + R_{MY} + R_{IY}$$

$$= 1 - 42 + 35 + 6$$

$$= 0 \quad \text{(ok)}$$

Example 8-6   Determine the reactions for the given truss under the indicated system of loads.

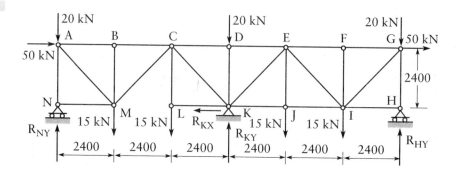

Solution   The portion *ACMN* is removed as a free body. All the loads that can occur on this portion of the truss are shown on the free body.

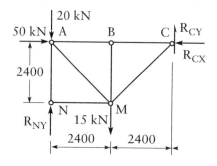

The sum of moments about point *C* yields the reaction R_{NY}:

$$\Sigma M_C = 0; \qquad 0 = -20(4.8) + R_{NY}(4.8) - 15(2.4)$$

$$R_{NY} = 27.5 \text{ kN in the direction shown.}$$

Summing moments of the entire truss about point *K* yields the reaction R_{HY}:

$$\Sigma M_K = 0; \qquad 0 = 27.5(7.2) - 20(7.2) - 15(4.8) - 15(2.4)$$

$$+ 20(7.2) + 15(4.8) + 15(2.4) + 50(2.4)$$

$$+ 50(2.4) - R_{HY}(7.2)$$

$$R_{HY} = 60.83 \text{ kN in the direction shown.}$$

Summing forces vertically yields the reaction R_{KY}:

$$\Sigma F_V = 0; \qquad 0 = 27.5 + 60.83 + R_{KY} - 120$$

$$R_{KY} = 31.67 \text{ kN in the direction shown.}$$

Summing forces horizontally yields the reaction R_{KX}:

$$\Sigma F_H = 0; \qquad 0 = 50 + 50 - R_{KX}$$

$$R_{KX} = 100 \text{ kN in the direction shown.}$$

Example 8-7   Determine the reactions for the given truss under the indicated system of loads.

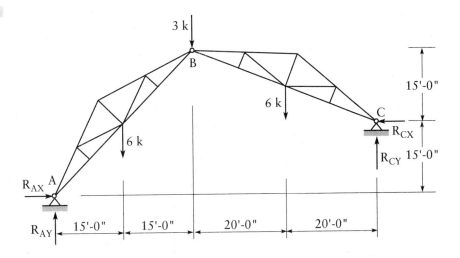

Solution   The structure is a three-hinged trussed arch, with four reactions at two levels. The side BC is taken first as a free body; moments are taken about B, yielding one equation in terms of the two reactions R_{CY} and R_{CX}:

$$\Sigma M_B = 0 \qquad \text{(for the truss } BC\text{)}$$

$$0 = 6(20) - R_{CY}(40) + R_{CX}(15)$$

Summing moments for the entire truss about point A yields a second equation in terms of the two reactions R_{CX} and R_{CY}:

$\Sigma M_A = 0$ (for the entire truss)

$0 = 6(15) + 3(30) + 6(50) - R_{CX}(15) + R_{CY}(70)$

The two equations are solved simultaneously:

$0 = 120 - 40\,R_{CY} + 15\,R_{CX}$

$0 = 480 - 70\,R_{CY} - 15\,R_{CX}$

$R_{CY} = 5.455$ kips; $R_{CX} = 6.545$ kips

Summing forces vertically yields reaction R_{AY}:

$\Sigma F_V = 0;$ $0 = R_{AY} - 6 - 3 - 6 + R_{CY}$

$R_{AY} = 9.545$ kips

Summing forces horizontally yields reaction R_{AX}:

$\Sigma F_H = 0;$ $0 = R_{AX} - R_{CX}$

$R_{AX} = 6.545$ kips

Summing moments of member AB about point B provides a check on the reactions,

$\Sigma M_A = 0$ (for the truss AB)

$0 = 9.545(30) - 6.545(30) - 6(15)$

$0 = 0$ (ok)

Example 8-8 Determine the reactions for the given truss under the indicated lateral loads.

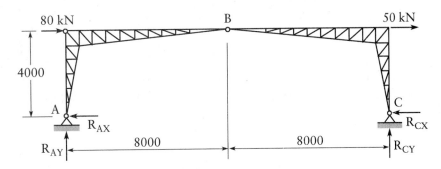

Solution The structure is a three-hinged arch, with four reactions at a single level. Summing moments about A yields the reaction R_{CY} at C:

$$\Sigma M_A = 0; \qquad 0 = 80(4) + 50(4) - R_{CY}(16)$$

$$R_{CY} = 32.5 \text{ kN in the direction shown.}$$

The portion BC is taken as a free body, and moments are summed about B to obtain reaction R_{CX}:

$$\Sigma M_B = 0; \qquad \text{(for free body } BC)$$

$$0 = -32.5(8) + R_{CX}(4)$$

$$R_{CX} = 65 \text{ kN in the direction shown.}$$

The reaction R_{AY} is found by summing vertical forces:

$$\Sigma F_V = 0; \qquad 0 = R_{AY} + R_{CY}$$

$$R_{AY} = -R_{CY}$$

$$= -32.5 \text{ kN}$$

$$= 32.5 \text{ kN opposite to the direction shown.}$$

The reaction R_{AX} is found by summing horizontal forces:

$$\Sigma F_H = 0; \qquad 0 = 80 + 50 - R_{AX} - R_{CX}$$

$$R_{AX} = 65 \text{ kN in the direction shown.}$$

It is noteworthy that the two applied lateral loads are unequal whereas the two horizontal reactions are equal.

In the four preceding examples of truss reactions, the geometrical config-uration of the truss members never entered the calculations. In fact, if the trusses had been solid beams, the reactions would have been the same. In rigid body mechanics, only the forces and the distances to their lines of action enter the calculations; the actual makeup of the member is of no consequence.

8.6 STATICALLY INDETERMINATE REACTIONS

Insofar as external reactions are concerned, there is no difference between the solid beams discussed in Chapter 2 and the trussed beams discussed here. All the rules and logic developed in Chapter 2 remain valid with respect to finding the external reactions for trussed systems. Size is of no consequence; the theory is the same whether the application is in subminiature biomedics or in a large river crossing.

Outside Problems Determine the reactions for the given trusses.

Problem 8-1*

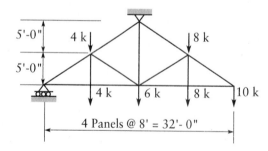

Problem 8-2

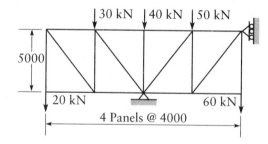

Problem 8-3*

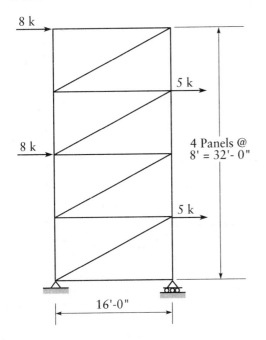

8 k

5 k

8 k

4 Panels @
8' = 32'- 0"

5 k

16'-0"

Problem 8-4

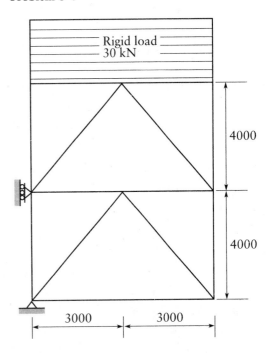

Rigid load
30 kN

4000

4000

3000   3000

Problem 8-5*

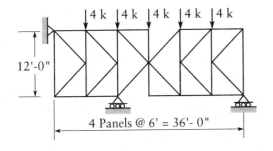

4 k 4 k 4 k 4 k 4 k

12'-0"

4 Panels @ 6' = 36'- 0"

Problem 8-6

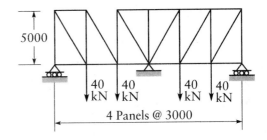

5000

40
kN 40
kN   40
kN 40
kN

4 Panels @ 3000

Problem 8-7*

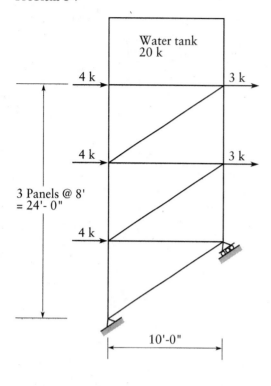

Problem 8-8

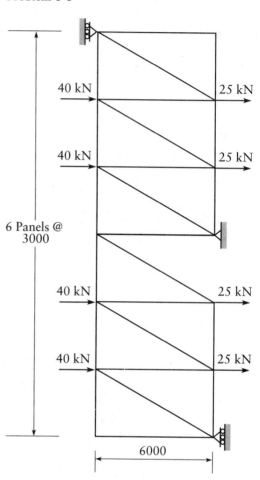

Problem 8-9*

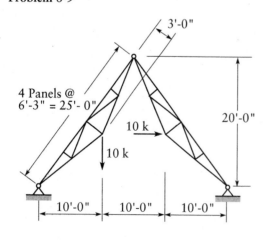

Problem 8-10

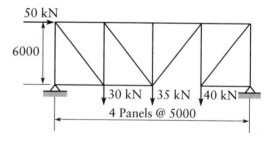

Problem 8-11*   Problem 8-12

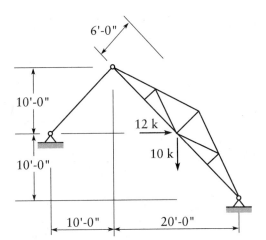

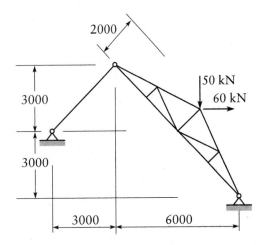

REVIEW QUESTIONS

1. Name three advantages that trusses have in comparison to solid, fixed-depth beams.

2. Name three disadvantages that trusses have in comparison to solid, fixed-depth beams.

3. Why is it usually necessary to brace the compression chord of trusses?

4. What is a "properly formed" truss?

5. Why is it necessary to avoid loading individual truss members in flexure?

6. Why is it desirable to have long truss members loaded in tension and short truss members loaded in compression?

7. Why must load reversals in a truss member be rigorously investigated?

8. In a truss analysis, the ends of the members are assumed to be hinged, but in reality this is rarely true. How is such an assumption justified?

9. At what point do secondary stresses become a problem in truss design?

10. What is the difference between a Parker truss and a bowstring truss?

11. What is the difference between a Pratt truss and a Howe truss?

12. What makes a truss a "simple" truss?

Graceful pedestrian bridge over Skyline Drive, Tacoma,
Washington. (Photograph courtesy Portland Cement
Association, reprinted by permission.)

Forces in Truss Members

Finding the forces in truss members is one type of problem that is used extensively in elementary statics; it is a very real and practical application of mechanics to engineering problems. The scope of such applications in elementary coursework, however, is usually quite shallow. A much deeper look at the analysis of trusses is presented in this chapter.

Certain aspects of the statics solutions are not always included in elementary statics. One such aspect is the way in which the fabrication methods affect the basic assumptions used in the analysis. A second aspect is the applicability of the solution to computerized methods. A third aspect is the consequences of load reversals in trusses; and a fourth is the use of "tension-only" members, called *counterdiagonals*. These and other special considerations can and do arise in routine truss design; these topics are among those included in this chapter.

9.1 LOADS IN MEMBERS BY THE METHOD OF JOINTS

The method of joints, or the method of force equilibrium, is the method of truss analysis commonly introduced in elementary statics for finding the forces in truss members. In the method of joints, each joint (hinge pin) is removed as a free body, and any unknown forces at the joint are found by summing forces in the horizontal and vertical directions. The solution progresses from joint to joint until the force in every member is known.

Since no resultant moment can exist at a joint, the requirement for moment equilibrium drops out, leaving only two equations of statics available to effect a solution. Consequently, for any free body of a joint, there can be no more than two unknown forces. When using the method of joints it is often necessary to plan carefully the sequence in which the joints will be solved, to ensure that no more than two unknowns appear in any one solution; such a planned approach to the solution is demonstrated in the examples presented later in this section.

In the method of joints, the values found at one joint are necessarily used in calculating the succeeding solutions at other joints. The member forces found in these solutions are then used in subsequent joints, and so on. The results from the earlier solutions thus propagate into all succeeding solutions until all forces are found.

Unfortunately, there is no way to check for numerical errors until the progression reaches the last joint, where the forces must balance. Thus, if an error occurs in the solution at one of the earlier joints, that error will then be carried through all the remaining calculations, being discovered only when forces at the last joint do not balance. Extreme care must therefore be exercised to avoid making numerical errors (in order to avoid the time-consuming task of tracking down such errors).

Where solutions are obtained by digital computer working with prepared software, the method of joints is widely used. Since machine computations are free of numerical errors, the possibility of making such errors cannot occur and the primary disadvantage of the method of joints disappears. The method of joints then becomes a fast, efficient and readily programmable solution.

Example 9-1

Using the method of joints, determine the force in each member of the given truss.

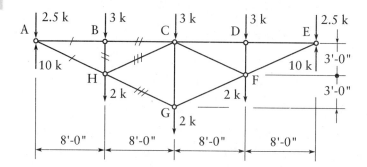

Solution

A sequence of joints is selected such that no more than two unknowns occur in any joint.

Begin at joint A, which has only two members; a single tally mark is placed on members AB and AH, indicating that the force in these members can be found.

Proceed now to joint H. Three unknown forces still exist at H; so this joint cannot be solved yet.

Look next at joint B. Only two unknown forces remain at joint B; a double tally mark is placed on the members BC and BH, indicating that the forces in these members can be found next.

Return now to joint H. Now there are only two unknowns; hence, joint H can be solved next. A triple tally mark is placed on members HC and HG to indicate that the forces in these members can be found next.

Proceed to the next joints. Joint C has three unknowns, but joint G has only two. Joint G is therefore chosen for solution next.

The procedure is repeated throughout the truss until all members bear a tally mark. In practice, a small number would be entered at each joint to indicate its place in the sequence of solutions; such numbering is omitted here to avoid cluttering the sketch even further.

The sequence of solutions is thus joints A, B, H, G, and C. In this particular truss, the remaining forces are found by symmetry.

Joint A is solved first. The hinge pin is removed as a free body with all forces shown. All unknown forces are assumed to be in tension. All known forces are entered in their correct directions. Slopes of member forces are shown on the accompanying sketch; vertical and horizontal components of force are then proportional, respectively, to the vertical and horizontal legs of the triangle.

Hence,

$$\Sigma F_V = 0 ; \qquad 0 = +10 - 2.5 - F_{AH}\left(\frac{3}{8.544}\right)$$

$$F_{AH} = +21.36 \text{ k} \quad (\text{tension})$$

$$\Sigma F_H = 0 ; \qquad 0 = F_{AH}\left(\frac{8}{8.544}\right) + F_{AB}$$

$$F_{AB} = -20.0 \text{ k} \quad (\text{compression})$$

Joint B is solved next. Force F_{AB} is now shown in the following sketch in its known condition of compression.

Hence,

$$\Sigma F_V = 0; \qquad 0 = 3 + F_{BH}$$

$$F_{BH} = -3 \text{ k} \quad \text{(compression)}$$

$$\Sigma F_H = 0; \qquad 0 = 20.0 + F_{BC}$$

$$F_{BC} = -20.0 \text{ k} \quad \text{(compression)}$$

Joint H is solved next, with forces F_{AH} and F_{BH} shown in the following sketch in their known conditions of tension and compression.

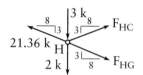

Hence,

$$\Sigma F_V = 0; \qquad 0 = -3 - 2 + 21.36\left(\frac{3}{8.544}\right)$$

$$- F_{HG}\left(\frac{3}{8.544}\right) + F_{HC}\left(\frac{3}{8.544}\right)$$

$$= 7.12 - F_{HG} + F_{HC}$$

$$\Sigma F_H = 0; \qquad 0 = -21.36\left(\frac{8}{8.544}\right) + F_{HG}\left(\frac{8}{8.544}\right) + F_{HC}\left(\frac{8}{8.544}\right)$$

$$= -21.36 + F_{HG} + F_{HC}$$

Solve simultaneously

$$F_{HC} = 7.12 \text{ k} \quad \text{(tension)}$$

$$F_{HG} = +14.24 \text{ k} \quad \text{(tension)}$$

Joint G is solved next. All known forces are shown in the following sketch in their known condition of tension or compression.

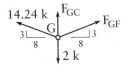

Hence,

$$\Sigma F_V = 0; \quad 0 = +14.24\left(\frac{3}{8.544}\right) + F_{GC} + F_{GF}\left(\frac{3}{8.544}\right) - 2$$

$$= +3.00 + F_{GC} + 0.351 F_{GF}$$

$$\Sigma F_H = 0; \quad 0 = -14.24\left(\frac{8}{8.544}\right) + F_{GF}\left(\frac{8}{8.544}\right)$$

$$F_{GF} = +14.24 \text{ kips} \quad \text{(tension)}$$

$$F_{GC} = -3 - 0.351(14.24) = -8 \text{ k} \quad \text{(compression)}$$

Joint C is solved next. The symmetry of the forces is known; this joint (shown in the following sketch) is therefore used to check the correctness of the calculations.

Hence,

$$\Sigma F_V = 0; \quad 0 = -7.12\left(\frac{3}{8.544}\right) - 3 + 8 - 7.12\left(\frac{3}{8.544}\right)$$

$$0 = 0 \quad \text{(ok)}$$

The final solution is summarized in the following sketch.

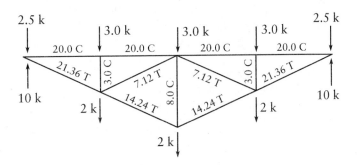

The conditions at joint B in the preceding example merit comment. Joint B has members in only two directions, joined at a right angle. There is no dispersion of load at the joint; all loads coming into joint B, either horizontally or vertically, are simply transmitted onward unchanged. Member BH under these conditions is called a "dead" member or a "transfer" member; its only real purpose is to transfer the 3 k load to joint H.

Example 9-2   Using the method of joints, determine the force in each member of the given truss.

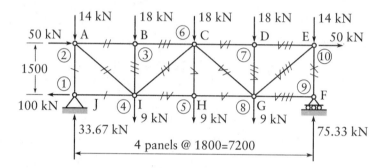

Solution   Reactions are computed first and entered on the sketch as loads, as shown.

This truss is unsymmetrically loaded; therefore, all member forces will be different, and every member force will have to be calculated. In addition, there are several transfer joints (joints J, B, H, D, and F). When the load on one side of any one of these joints is known, the load on the opposite side can be found simply by inspection; the free body of the joint need not be drawn.

Joint J is chosen for solution first, since it has only two members. One tally mark each is placed on member JI and on member JA; a circled 1 is entered at joint J to indicate its sequence for solution.

Joint A is chosen for solution next. Two tally marks are placed on the members whose forces are to be found, and a circled 2 is entered at this joint.

Joint B is next, then joints I, H, C, and so on. Tally marks are entered as Roman numerals corresponding to the circled joint numbers; that is, forces in members bearing tally marker VIII will be found when the joint bearing a circled 8 is solved.

As before, a free body of each hinge pin is drawn, with all unknown forces shown in tension and all known forces shown in their actual directions. The slopes of all angled members are shown on the sketch so that their vertical and horizontal components can be computed directly.

Joint J is solved by inspection:

$$F_{JA} = 33.67 \text{ kN}   \text{(C)}$$

$$F_{JI} = 100 \text{ kN}   \text{(T)}$$

Joint A (shown in the following sketch) is solved next.

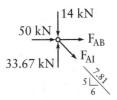

Here,

$$\Sigma F_V = 0; \qquad 0 = -14 + 33.67 - F_A\left(\frac{5}{7.81}\right)$$

$$F_{AI} = 30.72 \text{ kN} \quad (T)$$

$$\Sigma F_H = 0; \qquad 0 = 50 + F_{AB} + 30.72\left(\frac{6}{7.81}\right)$$

$$F_{AB} = -73.60 \quad (C)$$

Joint B is solved by inspection:

$$F_{BC} = -73.60 \text{ kN} \quad (C)$$

$$F_{BI} = 18 \text{ kN} \quad (C)$$

Joint I (shown in the following sketch) is solved next.

30.72 kN $\;$ 18 kN $\quad F_{IC}$

5 $\quad$ 5

6 $\quad$ 6 $\;\; F_{IH}$

100 kN $\;I$

9 kN

Here,

$$\Sigma F_V = 0; \qquad 0 = 30.72\left(\frac{5}{7.81}\right) - 18 - 9 + F_{IC}\left(\frac{5}{7.81}\right)$$

$$F_{IC} = 11.45 \text{ kN} \quad (T)$$

$$\Sigma F_H = 0; \qquad 0 = -30.72\left(\frac{6}{7.81}\right) - 100 + 11.45\left(\frac{6}{7.81}\right) + F_{IH}$$

$$F_{IH} = +114.80 \text{ kN} \quad (T)$$

Joint *H* is solved by inspection:

$$F_{HC} = +9 \text{ kN} \quad (T)$$

$$F_{HG} = +114.80 \text{ kN} \quad (T)$$

The solutions progress through the remaining joints in the sequence already established. Joint *E* provides a check on the results, since all forces coming to joint *E* have been computed elsewhere.

The results of the computations are entered on the following final load sketch, to be used for the final design of the truss members.

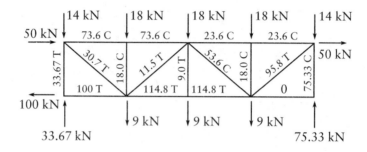

Example 9-3   Using the method of joints, determine the required sequence of solutions for solving the given *K* truss.

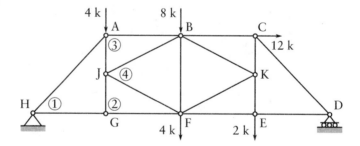

Solution   The solution progresses as usual up to joint 4, as shown. Thereafter, neither joint *B* nor joint *F* can be solved by force equilibrium, since both have three unknown forces.

The next joint (joint 5), therefore, must be joint *D*, and the solution then works backward through joints *E*, *C*, *K*, *F*, and *B*.

The last joint (joint *B*) is used to check for numerical errors, since all forces coming into joint *B* have been calculated elsewhere; if these forces do not balance, an error exists in one or more of the earlier joint solutions.

Outside Problems Using the method of joints, determine the forces in all members of the given trusses.

Problem 9-1*

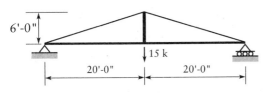

Problem 9-2

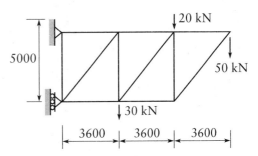

Problem 9-3*

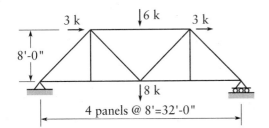

Problem 9-4

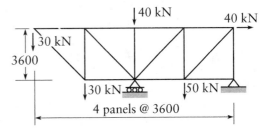

Problem 9-5*

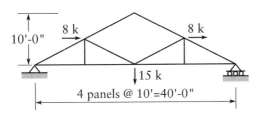

Problem 9-6

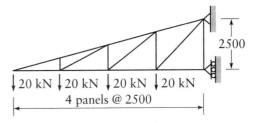

Problem 9-7*

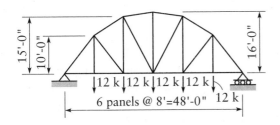

Problem 9-8

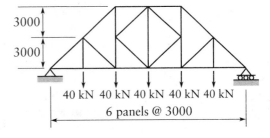

Problem 9-9*

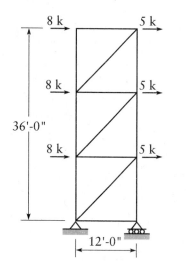

Problem 9-10

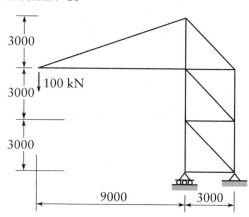

Problem 9-11*

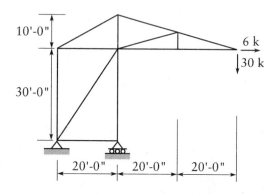

Problem 9-12

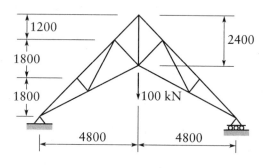

9.2 LOADS IN MEMBERS BY THE METHOD OF SECTIONS

An alternative method to the method of joints is also introduced in elementary statics. Called the method of sections, it consists of selectively choosing free bodies of the truss such that only one unknown force appears when moments are summed or when forces are summed. While the method of sections eliminates the propagation of error that can occur in the method of joints, it has the disadvantage of requiring a certain level of skill in the selection of the free bodies.

In the solutions of the following examples, separate free bodies are drawn to illustrate the method. In practice, only a line is usually drawn on the sketch of the truss, indicating the place where a section is to be taken; as the designer's skill develops, nothing more than a piece of scratch paper is needed, to cover the unwanted portion of the sketch while the moments or forces are being summed on the visible portion of the sketch.

It may not always be possible to eliminate all unwanted unknowns and leave only one unknown in the solution. In such cases, two equations in two unknowns may occur, requiring a simultaneous solution. Alternatively, it is perfectly permissible in the method of sections to solve a troublesome joint by the method of joints. The method of sections is not a rigid form of solution; any trick that will work can be employed.

Some examples will illustrate the method of sections.

Example 9-4   Using the method of sections, determine the forces in each member of the given truss.

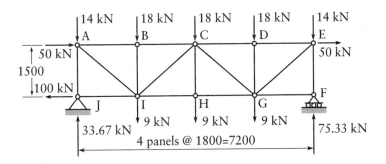

Solution   The first section is taken about midway into the first panel. The free body is drawn for that part of the truss to the left of this section line, as shown in the following sketch.

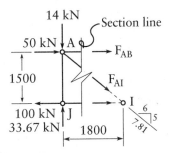

The unknown forces are shown in tension. Taking moments about joint A eliminates forces F_{AI} and F_{AB}, leaving only the force F_{JI}:

$$\Sigma M_A = 0; \qquad 0 = 100(1.5) - F_{JI}(1.5)$$

$$F_{JI} = +100 \text{ kN} \quad \text{(tension)}$$

Summing moments about joint I, outside the free body, eliminates forces F_{AI} and F_{JI}, leaving only the force F_{AB}:

$$\Sigma M_I = 0; \qquad 0 = 50(1.5) - 14(1.8) + 33.67(1.8) + F_{AB}(1.5)$$

$$\dot{F}_{AB} = -73.60 \text{ kN} \quad \text{(compression)}$$

Summing forces vertically eliminates both F_{JI} and F_{AB}, leaving only the force F_{AI}:

$$\Sigma F_V = 0; \qquad 0 = 33.67 - 14 - F_{AI}\left(\frac{5}{7.81}\right)$$

$$F_{AI} = +30.72 \quad \text{(tension)}$$

The force in member JA was not found in this first section. It is a transfer member, however, and its force can be found by inspection:

$$F_{JA} = -33.67 \text{ kN} \quad \text{(compression)}$$

Alternatively, if it had not been noted that member JA was a transfer member, a section might have been cut just below member AI, cutting both member JA and JI as shown in the following free body.

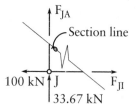

Summing forces vertically eliminates force F_{JI}:

$$\Sigma F_V = 0; \qquad 0 = 33.67 + F_{JA}$$

$$F_{JA} = -33.67 \text{ kN} \quad \text{(compression)}$$

Summing forces horizontally eliminates force F_{JA}:

$$\Sigma F_H = 0; \qquad 0 = -100 + F_{JI}$$

$$F_{JI} = +100 \text{ kN} \quad \text{(tension)}$$

The next section is taken about midway into the second panel. Again, the following free body is drawn for the portion of the truss to the left of the section.

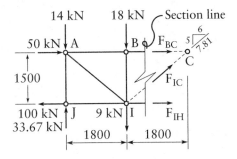

Summing moments about joint I eliminates forces F_{IH} and F_{IC}, leaving only force F_{BC}:

$$\Sigma M_I = 0; \quad 0 = 33.67\,(1.8) - 14(1.8) + 50\,(1.5) + F_{BC}\,(1.5)$$

$$F_{BC} = -73.60 \text{ kN} \quad \text{(compression)}$$

Summing moments about joint C eliminates forces F_{BC} and F_{IC}, leaving only the force F_{IH}:

$$\Sigma M_C = 0; \quad 0 = 33.67(3.6) + 100(1.5) - 14(3.6) - 18(1.8)$$

$$- 9(1.8) - F_{IH}(1.5)$$

$$F_{IH} = +114.80 \text{ kN} \quad \text{(tension)}$$

Summing forces vertically eliminates forces F_{BC} and F_{IH}, leaving only the force F_{IC}:

$$\Sigma F_V = 0; \quad 0 = 33.67 - 14 - 18 - 9 + F_{IC}\left(\frac{5}{7.81}\right)$$

$$F_{IC} = +11.45 \text{ kN} \quad \text{(tension)}$$

The force in member BI was not found in this section. It is a transfer member, however, and is solved by inspection:

$$F_{BI} = -18 \text{ kN} \quad \text{(compression)}$$

The next section is taken about midway into the third panel. The free body could be taken either to the right of the section or to the left of the section. The following sketch shows the free body to the left of the section.

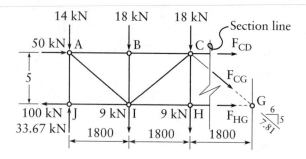

Summing moments about joint C eliminates forces F_{CD} and F_{CG}, leaving only the force F_{HG}:

$$\Sigma M_C = 0; \quad 0 = -14(3.6) - 18(1.8) + 100(1.5) + 33.67(3.6)$$

$$- 9(1.8) - F_{HG}(1.5)$$

$$F_{HG} = +114.80 \text{ kN} \quad \text{(tension)}$$

Summing moments about joint G eliminates forces F_{HG} and F_{CG}, leaving only the force F_{CD}:

$$\Sigma M_G = 0; \quad 0 = 50(1.5) - 14(5.4) - 18(3.6) - 18(1.8)$$

$$+ 33.67(5.4) - 9(3.6) - 9(1.8) - F_{CD}(1.5)$$

$$F_{CD} = -23.60 \text{ kN} \quad \text{(compression)}$$

Summing forces vertically eliminates forces F_{CD} and F_{HG}, leaving only F_{CG}:

$$\Sigma F_V = 0; \quad 0 = 33.67 - 14 - 18 - 9 - 18 - 9 - F_{CG}\left(\frac{5}{7.81}\right)$$

$$F_{CG} = -53.60 \text{ kN} \quad \text{(compression)}$$

The force in member HC is found by inspection:

$$F_{HC} = +9 \text{ kN} \quad \text{(tension)}$$

The last section is taken about midway into the fourth panel and the following free body is drawn to the right of the section line.

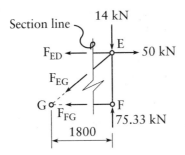

Summing moments about joint E eliminates forces F_{ED} and F_{EG}, leaving only the force F_{FG}:

$$\Sigma M_E = 0; \qquad 0 = F_{FG}(1.5)$$

$$F_{FG} = 0$$

Summing moments about joint G eliminates forces F_{EG} and F_{FG}, leaving only the force F_{ED}:

$$\Sigma M_G = 0; \qquad 0 = -F_{ED}(1.5) + 14(1.8) + 50(1.5) - 75.33(1.8)$$

$$F_{ED} = -23.60 \text{ kN} \quad \text{(compression)}$$

Summing forces vertically eliminates forces F_{ED} and F_{FG}, leaving only the force F_{EG};

$$\Sigma F_V = 0; \qquad 0 = -F_{EG}\left(\frac{5}{7.81}\right) + 75.33 - 14$$

$$F_{EG} = +95.80 \text{ kN} \quad \text{(tension)}$$

The force in member EF is found by inspection:

$$F_{EF} = -75.33 \text{ kN} \quad \text{(compression)}$$

The final results are shown in the following sketch; they are, of course, identical to those found in Example 9-2 by using the method of joints.

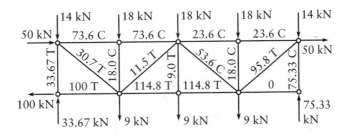

The solution of Example 9-4 is clean and straightforward. The results of one computation were never needed to enter into the next computation. If an error in a computation occurs, it affects only one member. (When all member forces have been found, the sum of forces horizontally and vertically at each joint can then be used to provide a fast and positive check on the correctness of the calculations.)

The method of sections works best when the top and bottom chords are parallel, as in Example 9-4. When the chords are not parallel, such as in a triangular Pratt or Howe truss, the method is not so clean. In such trusses, it is often necessary to take a separate section for each individual member; it may not be possible to solve for two or three members from a single section.

In the method of sections, it is always necessary to take a section that cuts a member if one is to find the force in that member. Either the member force itself may be used in the succeeding computations or its vertical and horizontal components may be used. Either way, the action lines of the force (or its components) must pass through the hinge points at its ends. The following example illustrates this point.

Example 9-5   Using the method of sections, determine the forces in each member of the given truss.

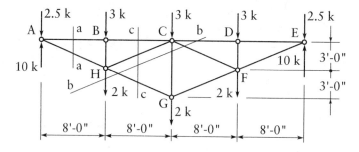

Solution   Section *a–a* is chosen first, as shown in the following sketch. Members *AB* and *AH* are cut by the section so that the forces in these members can be found.

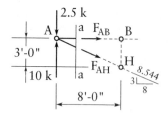

Hence,

$$\Sigma F_V = 0; \qquad 0 = 10 - 2.5 - F_{AH}\left(\frac{3}{8.544}\right)$$

$$F_{AH} = +21.36 \text{ k} \quad \text{(tension)}$$

$$\Sigma M_H = 0; \qquad 0 = (10)(8) - 2.5(8) + F_{AB}(3)$$

$$F_{AB} = -20.0 \text{ k} \quad \text{(compression)}$$

Section b–b is chosen next. Member HG is cut by this section in order that the force in this member can be found. Components of F_{HG} are shown on the following free body; their action lines must pass through joint H. Moments are summed about joint C to find F_{HG}.

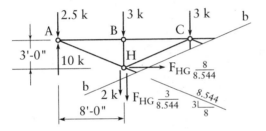

Hence,

$$\Sigma M_C = 0 = 10(16) - 2.5(16) - 3(8) - 2(8)$$

$$- F_{HG}\left(\frac{8}{8.544}\right)(3) - F_{HG}\left(\frac{3}{8.544}\right)(8)$$

$$F_{HG} = +14.24 \text{ k} \quad \text{(tension)}$$

Force in member BH is found by inspection

$$F_{BH} = -3 \text{ k} \quad \text{(compression)}$$

Section c–c is chosen next. Members BC and HC are cut by this section; their forces are to be found in this calculation. Moments are summed about joint A to find F_{HC} and about joint H to find F_{BC}.

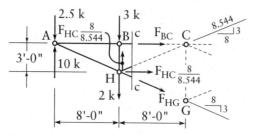

Hence,

$$\Sigma M_A = 0 = 3(8) + 2(8) - F_{HC}\left(\frac{3}{8.544}\right)8 - F_{HC}\left(\frac{8}{8.544}\right)3$$

$$F_{HC} = +7.12 \text{ k} \quad \text{(tension)}$$

$$\Sigma M_H = 0 = -2.5(8) + 10(8) + F_{BC}(3) = 0$$

$$F_{BC} = -20.0 \text{ k} \quad \text{(compression)}$$

The force in member CG is not readily found by the method of sections. It is therefore found by the method of joints, using joint G, as shown in the following sketch.

14.24 k $\uparrow F_{CG}$ 14.24 k

G $\downarrow$ 2 k

Hence,

$$\Sigma F_V = 0 = F_{CG} - 2 + 14.24\left(\frac{3}{8.544}\right) + 14.24\left(\frac{3}{8.544}\right)$$

$$F_{CG} = -8.0 \text{ k} \quad \text{(compression)}$$

The final results of the computations are shown in the following sketch; they are, of course, identical to those found in Example 9-1 by using the method of joints.

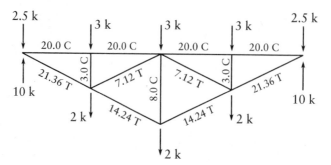

One useful application of the method of sections is in preliminary design, where the load in a particular member of a rather complex truss can be found in a single calculation. Such information is very useful when a designer is trying to decide how deep the overall truss should be or how wide the individual panels should be. The Parker roof truss of the next example illustrates such a calculation.

Example 9-6   Determine the force in the compression chord member *EF* for the given conditions of load on the Parker roof truss shown.

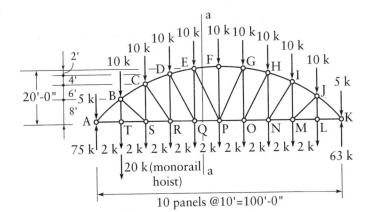

Solution   A section *a–a* is cut through panel *EFPQ*, as shown on the sketch. A piece of scratch paper is used to cover the portion of the truss to the right of this section. Moments to the left of the section are then summed about point *P*:

$$\Sigma M_P = 0 = 75(50) - 5(50) - 10(40) - 10(30) - 10(20) - 10(10)$$

$$- 20(30) - 2(40) - 2(30) - 2(20) - 2(10) + F_{EF}(20)$$

$$F_{EF} = -85 \text{ k} \quad \text{(compression)}$$

In this case, the force in member *EF* has been found directly by the method of sections, without the necessity to expend a great deal of labor in finding the forces in any of the other members.

Outside Problems   Problems 9-13 through 9-24.
Using the method of sections, determine the force in each member of the trusses given earlier in Problems 9-1 through 9-12. Check your results against the earlier solutions.

9.3 COMPOUND AND COMPLEX TRUSSES

A simple truss is formed by beginning with a base triangle, and then adding two members and their included hinge until the desired configuration is reached. Only trusses that can be formed entirely in this way are properly formed; they are both stable and statically determinate. Some typical simple trusses are shown in Figure 9-1(a).

A compound truss is formed by joining two or more simple trusses with an odd number of nonparallel joining members. In such a structure, a hinge may be shared by adjoining simple trusses, but no hinges may be added. Members, however, may not be shared by the simple trusses. Several compound trusses may in turn be jointed to form larger compound trusses. Typical compound trusses are shown in the sketches of Figure 9-1(b). Other compound trusses are the truss of Example 9-3 and the trusses of Problems 9-8 and 9-26.

Solving for forces in a compound truss is relatively straightforward. First, one must identify which members are the joining members. The force in each joining member is then found, usually by the method of sections. From that point onward, the remaining solutions focus on the simple trusses that make up the compound truss.

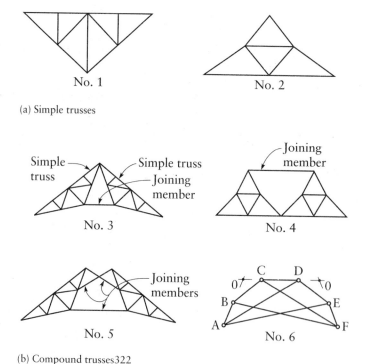

FIGURE 9-1 Simple and compound trusses.

Compound trusses such as truss No. 6 of Figure 9-1 are sometimes very difficult to recognize. Truss No. 6 is made up of two simple trusses ADE and FCB, with three joining members AB, CD, and EF. The solution in this case involves removing truss ADE as a free body and taking moments about O, thus obtaining the force in member EF. The force in member CD is then found by taking moments about point A. The force in member AB is found by taking moments about O'. With the forces in the joining members AB, CD, and EF now known, the remaining solution consists of solving the simple trusses ADE and FCB.

A great deal has been written about solving compound trusses, although such trusses are not often found in practice. A notable exception to this rule is the Fink truss (shown earlier in Figure 8-9), which is very commonly used for the roof structures of industrial steel buildings. Studying these more complicated truss systems offers an excellent means to develop depth of understanding in statics.

Another group of trusses, called *complex trusses*, do not fall into any precise classification; they are neither simple trusses nor compound trusses. A typical example of a complex truss is shown in Figure 9-2. Like compound trusses, complex trusses often seem to have more academic appeal than practical value.

The literature contains many in-depth references dedicated to solving compound and complex trusses. While a detailed study of such specialized truss systems is beyond the scope of an introductory text such as this, extended study of these systems is highly recommended to anyone interested in aircraft, naval architecture, or structures in space.

Some examples will illustrate the logic involved in obtaining a solution for a few compound trusses.

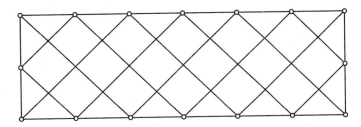

FIGURE 9-2 Complex truss.

Example 9-7   Determine a means to solve for the member forces in the given truss.

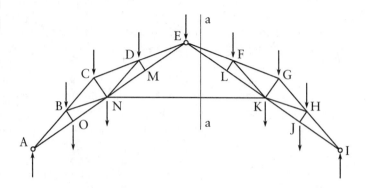

Solution   An attempt to perform a solution by the method of joints indicates that joints *A*, *B*, *O*, and *C* can be solved, as can joints *I*, *H*, *J*, and *G*. From that point, there are too many members at the remaining joints to permit a solution by force equilibrium.

A moment's reflection reveals that the truss is a compound truss, made up of simple trusses *ACENA* and *IGEKI*, connected by one joining member, member *NK*. A section *a–a* is cut to expose member *NK*; moments are taken to the left of the section about hinge point *E*, yielding a solution for the force in member *NK*.

With the force in member *NK* known, the remaining joints *N*, *M*, and *D* can be solved. Similarly, the forces at joints *K*, *L*, *F*, and *E* can be solved, with joint *E* being used to provide a check on the calculations.

Example 9-8   Determine a means to solve for the member forces in the given truss.

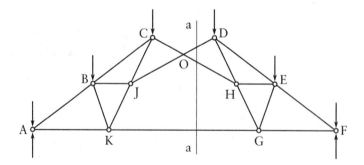

Solution   An attempt to plan a solution by the method of joints indicates that only joints *A* and *F* can be solved. From that point onward, there are too many members at the remaining joints to permit a solution by force equilibrium.

When examined more closely, the truss proves to be a compound truss, composed of two simple trusses *ACKA* and *FDGF*, connected by three non-parallel joining members *CH*, *DJ*, and *KG*. A section *a–a* is cut, exposing all three of these members. Moments are taken to the left of section *a–a* about point *O* (not a hinge) yielding a solution for the force in member *KG*. Moments about hinge point *J* then affords a solution for the force in member *CH*; and moments about hinge point *C* provides a solution for the force in member *JD*.

With the forces in the three joining members now known, the forces throughout the two simple trusses can be solved. Verification is left to the reader.

Example 9-9   Determine a means to solve for the member forces in the given truss.

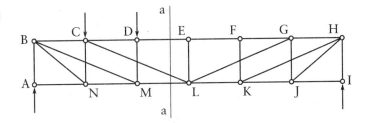

Solution   Only the forces in transfer members *AB*, *AN*, *DM*, *EL*, *FK*, *HI*, and *IJ* can be solved in this truss. All remaining joints have at least three unknown member forces to be solved, with only two equations of equilibrium available; they cannot be solved by force equilibrium.

Closer examination reveals that the truss *IHGFELKJI* can be properly formed as a simple truss. Similarly, the truss *ABCDLMNA* can be properly formed as a simple truss. The one remaining member—member *DE*—is therefore a joining member, and the overall truss can be recognized as a properly formed compound truss.

A section *a–a* is taken, exposing member *DE*. Moments taken to the left of section *a–a* about hinge *L* provide a solution for the force in member *DE*; since joints *D*, *E*, and *F* are transfer joints, the forces in members *CD*, *DE*, *EF*, and *FG* are all equal and are now known. The sum of vertical forces on this same section yields a solution for the force in member *CL*; and the sum of moments about hinge point *C* provides a solution for the force in member *ML*.

The solution can now proceed through the remaining members by the method of joints or by the method of sections. The solution of this particular truss thus progresses from the center of the truss toward the ends, whereas earlier solutions usually went from the end supports toward the center. Verification of the remaining solutions is left to the reader.

The following example presents two possible solutions for a truss that involves three unknowns at every joint. Conventional approaches, such as the method of joints and the method of sections, are applicable, but in a somewhat modified form.

Example 9-10   Determine a means to solve for the member forces in the given truss.

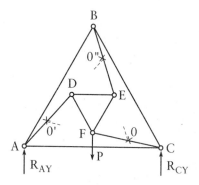

Solution   All joints in the given truss have three unknown forces; no joints can be solved directly by the method of joints, using only force equilibrium.

Upon examination, the truss proves to be a properly formed compound truss made up of two simple trusses, ABC and DEF, connected by three non-parallel joining members AD, BE, and CF. The simple truss DEF is removed as a free body that has three unknown reactions F_{DA}, F_{EB}, and F_{FC}. For the overall free body of DEF, there are three equations of equilibrium to be satisfied: $\Sigma F_V = 0$, $\Sigma F_H = 0$, and $\Sigma M_O = 0$. Applying the three equations of equilibrium yields three equations in the three unknown reactions; the three equations can then be solved simultaneously.

Once the forces in the three joining members are known, the remaining member forces can be found by force equilibrium at the joints.

Alternatively, the forces in the three joining members AD, BE, and CF can be found by the method of sections, without the necessity of solving simultaneous equations. The simple truss DEF is removed as a free body, as before; then moments are summed about point O, O', and O'' to find F_{DA}, F_{EB}, and F_{FC}, respectively. As a complication, however, some rather intricate calculations for moment arms must be made in this approach.

Trusses such as the one described in Example 9-10 have little practical value outside of their academic interest. They do, however, have an annoying habit of showing up on professional engineering examinations.

9.4 STATICAL INDETERMINACY AND INSTABILITY

A truss may contain an excess number of members, in which case too many forces may exist at a joint, rendering that joint unsolvable by statics alone. In such cases, the rigidity and size of the truss members (and their deformations) must be included in the solution. The solutions for such systems are termed, as before, *statically indeterminate solutions*.

Consider, for example, the truss of Figure 9-3. The two members in the center panel are assumed to be capable of sustaining either tensile or compressive loads.

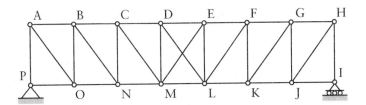

FIGURE 9-3 Internally indeterminate truss.

Upon examination, panel *DELM* proves to be improperly formed. The truss would be properly formed and solvable if one of these six panel members were eliminated. One of these six members is therefore extra, or *redundant*. The truss as configured is classified as statically indeterminate internally, because of having one redundant member. Neither the method of joints nor the method of sections can produce a correct solution that is in equilibrium at all four panel points *D*, *E*, *L*, and *M*. A solution is possible only if the deformations of the panel are included in the calculations.

Just as a truss may contain an excess number of members, making it statically indeterminate internally, it may lack a necessary member somewhere in its configuration, making it statically unstable. The truss then becomes a *mechanism*, or *link mechanism*, which will collapse under load. A truss is unstable when any joint in it is not capable of developing force equilibrium.

Consider, for example, the truss of Figure 9-4. Like the truss of Figure 9-3, this truss is improperly formed. By inspection, it is seen that member *EF* must carry the same force as the reaction at *F*; the joint *F* can therefore be in force equilibrium. With that force in member *EF*, however, the joint at *E* cannot develop the required force equilibrium; the truss is therefore unstable and will collapse when the loads are applied. (Adding a member *EG* would allow force equilibrium to develop at joint *E*, and the truss would then be stable—but panel *ABIJ* would still be improperly formed.)

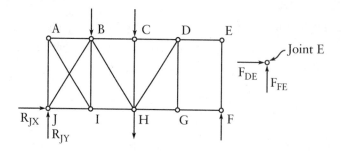

FIGURE 9-4 Unstable truss.

A relationship between the number of members required to connect a given number of joints in a properly formed truss can readily be derived. As was noted earlier, a simple stable truss is formed by starting with a base triangle, and then adding sets of two members and their included joint until the desired configuration is obtained. If m is the number of members, j is the number of joints, and s is the number of members in the base triangle, then

$$m - s = 2(j - 3) \tag{9.1}$$

where the base triangle is assumed to have three joints.

It was noted earlier (in Figure 8-2) that, if the base triangle has only two sides, it must have two hinged supports; if it has three sides it must have one hinged support and one roller. (A *hinged support* is defined here as a support that can develop both a horizontal and a vertical reaction.) On the base triangle, therefore,

$$s + h = 4 \tag{9.2}$$

where h is the number of hinged supports (either 1 or 2) and s is again the number of sides in the base triangle. The total number of supports (hinge or roller) may not exceed 2. When Equation 9.2 is substituted into Equation 9.1, the result states the relationship in a properly formed truss among the number of members, the number of joints, and the number of hinged supports:

$$m = 2(j - 1) - h \tag{9.3}$$

Equation 9.3 provides a means to determine tentatively whether a truss is statically indeterminate, determinate, or unstable. Given a truss with m members, j joints, and h hinged supports whose external reactions are known,

if $m > 2(j - 1) - h$, the truss contains an excess number of members and is internally indeterminate;

if $m = 2(j - 1) - h$, the truss is properly formed, statically determinate internally, and stable under loads;

if $m < 2(j - 1) - h$, the truss has a shortage of members and is an unstable mechanism.

Equation 9.3 has been applied to the trusses shown in Figure 9-5, with the results indicated in that figure. The equation does not reveal which member is the excess one, nor where the truss is lacking a member. It indicates only whether the truss is indeterminate, determinate, or unstable.

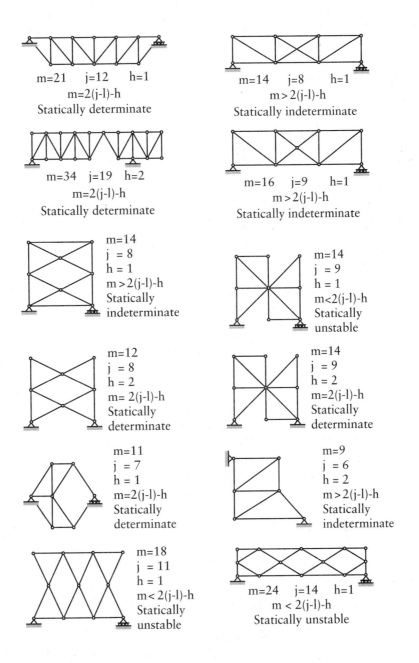

FIGURE 9-5 Tests for proper formation.

Like most such simplistic tests, Equation 9.3 fails under certain circumstances. The truss shown in Figure 9-4 is a good example. That truss contains 17 members, 10 joints, and 1 hinge, for which Equation 9.3 indicates a statically determinate, stable truss. In reality, however, the truss contains one statically indeterminate member at one end (member BJ), and it forms a link mechanism at the other end (panel $DEFG$); for the overall truss, the test fails completely.

The derivation of Equation 9.3 remains valid, however, when it is applied only to a portion of a truss. Again taking the truss of Figure 9-4 as an example, the test may be applied to the portion $ABIJ$, for which case $m = 6$, $j = 4$, and $h = 1$. The test now correctly shows that this portion of the truss is indeterminate, because of having one redundant member.

Similarly, the test may be applied to the portion $ACHJ$ of the truss of Figure 9-4, for which case $m = 10$, $j = 6$, and $h = 1$. The test shows this portion of the truss to be indeterminate, as well, again because it has one redundant member.

The test may be applied to the other end of the truss of Figure 9-4, too. For the portion of the truss $CEFH$, the values are $m = 8$, $j = 6$, and $h = 0$. The test correctly shows that this portion of the truss is unstable by two degrees: it lacks one member, and it lacks one hinged support. (In the derivation, it was assumed that the number of hinged supports in a properly formed truss should be at least 1.)

Thus, one may conclude that the test afforded by Equation 9.3 may fail at times. If one is the least suspicious of a particular result, the test should be applied to several portions of the truss to check the correctness of any questionable results. It must be remembered, however, that h was assumed in the derivation to be either 1 or 2; if the number of hinged supports in the free body is zero, the test will also include the shortage of one hinge in its result.

Since the test given by Equation 9.3 can sometimes fail (and therefore should always be viewed as to some extent unreliable), a more positive test should be applied when a result is questionable. In such cases the truss need only be checked to determine whether it is properly formed. If it is properly formed, it is both statically determinate and stable. If it is not properly formed, such a check will reveal very quickly whether it has excess members and is therefore statically indeterminate or whether it is lacking members and is therefore an unstable mechanism.

Outside Problems Determine whether the given truss is statically determinate externally, statically determinate internally, and stable under load. For clarity, hinges are shown as open circles. If no hinge is indicated where two members cross, the members pass freely across each other.

Problem 9-25*

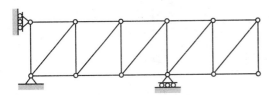

Problem 9-26

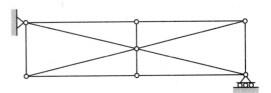

Problem 9-27*

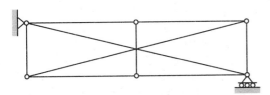

Problem 9-28

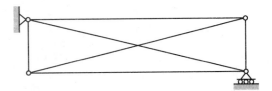

Problem 9-29*

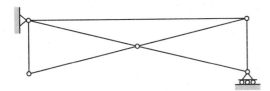

Problem 9-30

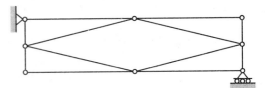

Problem 9-31*

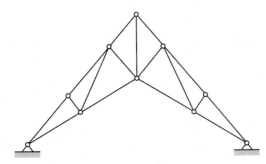

Problem 9-32

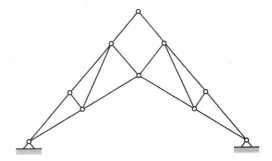

9.5 CROSS BRACING AND LOAD REVERSALS

When designing a truss for a fixed configuration of loads, one can arrange the diagonal members of the truss such that all of these members are in tension. Such a case is shown in Figure 9-6(a), where the load is positioned at panel point *N*. Some of the short vertical members are in compression, but all of the longer diagonal members are in tension. So long as the load remains in its present position, there is no danger that these longer diagonal members will be subject to compressive load and resultant buckling; the design can therefore be made at maximum efficiency of materials.

If the load in Figure 9-6(a) moves to panel point *L*, however, the diagonal members *FN* and *GM* will undergo a load reversal and go into compression. Such a case is shown in Figure 9-6(b). The efficiency of materials made possible by the configuration of Figure 9-6(a) is severely diminished by the load reversal that occurs in these two members.

Consider now the configuration of Figure 9-7, where all of the interior single diagonals have been replaced by two flexible steel cables. Since a cable cannot carry any compressive load at all, it will simply "sag" under compressive loading, and all the shear is then carried by the other diagonal. (In a rectangular truss panel, if the diagonal load in one direction is in compression, the diagonal load in the other direction is in tension.)

The truss of Figure 9-7 thus automatically reconfigures itself with each configuration of load, such that all diagonals remain in tension. Notice that, at the extreme end panels of this particular truss, the diagonal can never go into compression; hence, only a single diagonal need be provided. The vertical web members remain in compression; but since they are much shorter than the diagonals, these members are simply accepted as compression members.

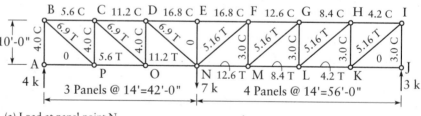

(a) Load at panel point N

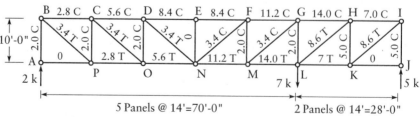

(b) Load at panel point L

FIGURE 9-6 Truss with diagonals in tension.

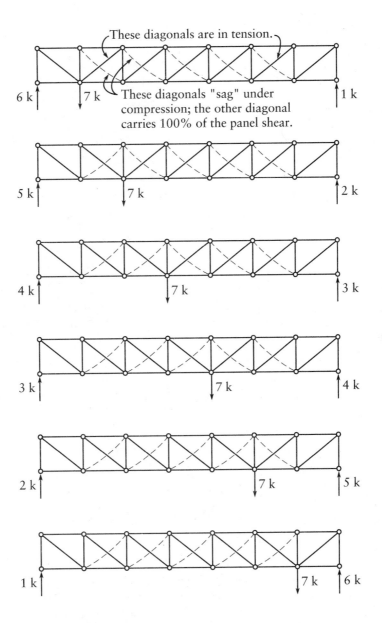

FIGURE 9-7 Truss with counterdiagonals.

The use of a second diagonal (called a *counterdiagonal* or, more simply, a *counter*) is quite common in the design of construction falsework. While the use of counters does produce additional clutter and sometimes reduces accessibility to the labor force, the efficiency of materials usually outweighs these concerns in such designs. In addition, they automatically take care of any unexpected load reversals—a reassuring safety feature.

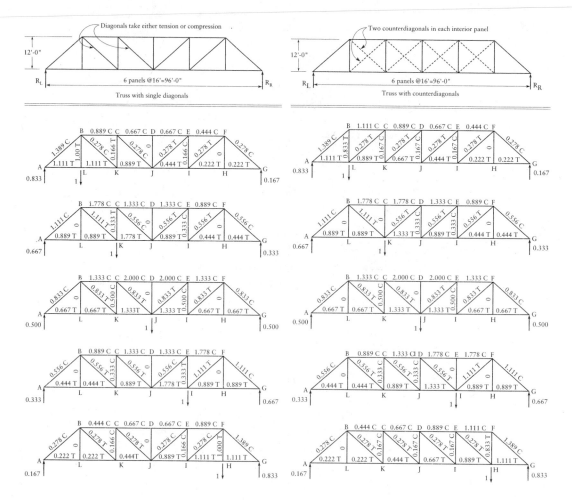

FIGURE 9-8 Comparison of truss designs.

In actual fact, the two diagonals need not be two flexible steel cables. In practice, they are more likely to be two slender threaded rods (with turn-buckles); or they could simply be long slender angles welded to the panel points at their ends. Regardless what the long slender member is actually composed of, its ability to carry compressive load is considered to be negligible; all shear across the panel is assumed to be carried by whichever diagonal goes into tension.

The reconfiguration of the truss corresponding to each new position of the load is very evident in the foregoing sketches. Again, the reconfiguration is automatic; it requires no design features other than the counterdiagonals.

It is interesting to compare two similar truss designs—one in which the diagonals are rigid fixed members, and one in which the diagonals are composed of flexible counterdiagonals. Such a comparison is shown in Figure 9-8. A unit load is placed at each of the lower panel points of the trusses shown.

Even a quick visual comparison between the two designs reveals significant differences in loads in all members, including diagonals, verticals, and chords. It must be concluded that the use of counterdiagonals significantly affects the loads in every member of the truss—not just those in the diagonals. A detailed analysis is therefore required for each possible load condition, since the configuration of the truss can change unpredictably in view of the multiplicity of loads that may come and go.

Since the configuration of the truss can change with each load condition, the use of superposition of loads is not permissible in any truss analysis involving counterdiagonals. In such trusses, the configuration of the truss corresponding to each load condition must be determined (largely by trial and error), and the analysis must be performed independently for that configuration and that load condition. If another load is added (as in superposition), the configuration of the truss may change significantly; a completely new analysis is then required for the altered configuration.

Outside Problems

Under the given load cases on the given trusses, determine which of the counterdiagonal members will be loaded and which will sag out of the way. Show a sketch of your results.

The following sketch applies to Problems 9-33 through 9-36.

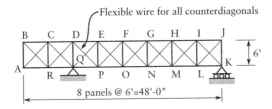

Problem 9-33 Downward 10 kip load at A, plus a downward 10 kip load at N.*

Problem 9-34 Downward 20 kip load at A, plus a downward 20 kip load at L.

Problem 9-35 Upward 40 kip load at A.*

Problem 9-36 Upward 10 kip load at A, plus a downward 10 kip load at O.

The following sketch applies to Problems 9-37 through 9-40.

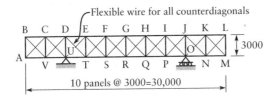

Problem 9-37 Downward 50 kN load at A, plus a downward 50 kN load at M.*

Problem 9-38 Downward 50 kN load at A, plus a downward 50 kN load at M, plus a downward 200 kN load at R.

Problem 9-39 Upward 50 kN load at A, plus a downward 50 kN load at M.*

Problem 9-40 Upward 50 kN load at A, plus an upward 50 kN load at M, plus a downward 100 kN load at R.

REVIEW QUESTIONS

1. In the method of joints, only the two equations of force equilibrium are used ($\Sigma F_X = 0$, $\Sigma F_Y = 0$). What happens to moment equilibrium ($\Sigma M_O = 0$)?

2. What is the primary hazard in performing manual solutions using the method of joints?

3. In applying the method of joints, why is it always advisable to plan the sequence in which the joints will be solved?

4. What is the major advantage of the method of sections over the method of joints?

5. How is a simple truss formed?

6. How is a compound truss formed?

7. What is the most reliable means to determine if a truss is statically determinate internally?

8. What is meant by the term *properly formed* as it is applied to trusses?

9. Why is a load reversal in a truss member potentially so dangerous?

10. Can load reversals occur in counterdiagonals? Explain.

11. How does cross bracing (counterdiagonals) relieve some of the problem of load reversals?

12. Why is it not permissible to use superposition in trusses that have counterdiagonals?

Mixture of forms and structure in the Epson America
Building, Torrance, California. (Photograph courtesy
Portland Cement Association, reprinted by permission.)

CHAPTER

10

Deformations in Simple Trusses

Trusses do not have a continuous elastic curve in the same sense that solid beams do. If the deformation curve of either the top chord or the bottom chord were plotted, the result would be a segmented series of straight lines joining the deflected hinge points. But the earlier methods of analysis using the elastic curve are based on the existence of a smooth and continuous elastic curve; these methods are therefore inappropriate for trusses.

In contrast to the methods of the elastic curve, the energy methods are readily applicable to trusses. If anything, the energy methods are simpler in their applications to trusses than in their applications to beams. Despite being simple, the calculations can become somewhat long and tedious, and both the length and the tedium of the solution increase with the number of members in the truss. Tabulating the calculations does much to increase speed and reduce errors; such tabulations are used repeatedly in this chapter for computing deformations in trusses.

10.1 APPLICATION OF THE CASTIGLIANO THEOREM TO TRUSSES

As developed in Chapter 6, the Castigliano theorem in its general form gives the deflection Δ_Z along the line of action of a load Z:

$$\Delta_z = \frac{\partial U}{\partial Z} \tag{10.1}$$

where U is the internal energy stored in the entire body of the structure. In a truss, where the only load on a truss member is tension or compression, the internal energy is given by

$$U = \int_0^L \frac{T^2 ds}{2EA} \tag{10.2}$$

where T is the total force in each member due to all loads acting on the truss.

In Equation 10.2, the limits on the integral indicate the entire truss, not an individual member. If the truss is composed of a finite number of m members, however, Equation 10.2 may be rewritten as

$$U = \sum_{i=1}^{m} \int_0^L \frac{T_i^2 ds_i}{2E_i A_i} \tag{10.3}$$

where the limits on the integral refer to the length of the individual member i. The integral term therefore becomes the energy stored in each member of the truss, and the sum of these individual values is the total energy stored in the entire truss.

Where E and A are constant throughout the length of the truss member, the energy U_i in a single truss member of length L_i becomes

$$U_i = \int_0^L \frac{T_i^2 ds}{2E_i A_i} = \frac{T_i^2 L_i}{2E_i A_i} \tag{10.4}$$

When Equation 10.4 is substituted into Equation 10.3, the result is the total energy in the truss:

$$U = \sum_{i=1}^{m} \int_0^L \frac{T_i^2 L_i}{2E_i A_i} \tag{10.5}$$

When this expression is differentiated with respect to a concentrated load Z, the end result is the Castigliano equation in its classical form as it applies to trusses:

$$\Delta = \sum_{i=1}^{m} \frac{T_i \left(\dfrac{\partial T_i}{\partial Z} \right) L_i}{E_i A_i} \tag{10.6}$$

For simplicity, the partial derivative is denoted z_i, and the final form of the Castigliano equation for trusses is

$$\Delta_z = \sum_{i=1}^{m} \frac{T_i z_i L_i}{E_i A_i} \tag{10.7}$$

where

Δ_z is the deflection along the action line of load Z;

m is the total number of members in the truss;

T_i is the total force in the member i due to all loads on the truss, including Z;

z_i is the partial derivative of T_i with respect to the load Z such that $z_i = \partial T_i / \partial Z$; L_i, E_i, and A_i are the length, elastic modulus, and cross-sectional area, respectively, of the member i.

Equation 10.7 can also be derived from the Maxwell Theorem of Reciprocal Displacements. Consider the general truss system of m members shown in Figure 10-1, loaded by some general system of loads. By the Maxwell theorem, the deflection Δ_{zi} along the action line of Z per unit of force T_i is equal to the deflection Δ_{iz} along the action line of T_i per unit of force Z.

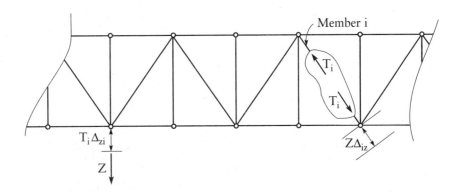

FIGURE 10-1 Maxwell theorem in trusses.

Stated mathematically, per unit of force both in member i and at the load Z,

$$\Delta_{zi} = \Delta_{iz} \qquad (10.8)$$

It is evident that $\Delta_{iz} = z_i L / A_i E_i$, where z_i is the force that occurs in member i per unit of load Z. Consequently, as shown in Figure 10-1,

$$\Delta_z = \sum_{i=1}^{m} T_i \Delta_{zi} \qquad (10.9)$$

Hence,

$$\Delta_z = \sum_{i=1}^{m} T_i \Delta_{iz} \qquad (10.10)$$

where

Δ_z is the total deflection along the action line of a force Z;

m is the total number of members in the truss;

T_i is the total force in the member i;

$\Delta_{iz} = z_i L_i / A_i E_i$, where z_i is the force in member i due to the load Z.

Physically, Δ_{iz} in Equation 10.10 represents the axial elongation or short-ening of member i per unit of load Z; therefore, by the Maxwell theorem, it represents the increase or decrease in Δ_z per unit of axial force T_i.

Equations 10.7 and 10.10 are of course functionally identical, which indi-cates only that the same conclusion can be reached by different logic. As a third alternative, the form of these equations in standard references is some-times shown by a virtual work derivation as

$$\Delta = \sum_{i=1}^{m} \frac{S_i s_i L_i}{E_i A_i} \tag{10.11}$$

where

S_i is the total force in the member i due to all real loads on the truss;

s_i is the load on the member i due to a unit load at the point where Δ is to be found;

L_i, E_i, and A_i are the length, elastic modulus, and cross-sectional area of member i.

However derived or developed, the applications of Equations 10.6, 10.7, 10.10, and 10.11 are identical. An example will illustrate how to apply the classical form of the solution, given by Equation 10.6.

Example 10-1   Determine the deflection of the given steel truss at joint E. All members are double angles, with total cross-sectional areas as indicated in the accompa-nying drawing.

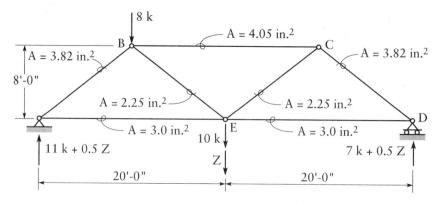

Solution The solution will be made by using the classical form of the Castigliano theorem (Equation 10.6):

$$\Delta = \sum_{i=1}^{m} \frac{T_i\left(\dfrac{\partial T_i}{\partial Z}\right)L_i}{E_i A_i}$$

First, a null load Z is added at the joint where the deflection is sought, as indicated on the preceding sketch. The reactions are then computed, to include the effects of the null load N; these reactions have been computed and entered on the sketch. The forces in each member can then be computed—either by the method of joints or by the method of sections—and the results tabulated. Such a tabulation follows.

MEMBER	L (in.)	A (in.²)	FORCE T (kips)	$\dfrac{\partial T}{\partial Z}$	$\dfrac{TL}{AE}$	$\dfrac{TL}{AE}\dfrac{\partial T}{\partial Z}$
AE	240.0	3.00	$+13.75 + 0.625\,Z$	$+0.625$	$+0.0379$	$+0.0237$
AB	153.7	3.82	$-17.61 - 0.800\,Z$	-0.800	-0.0244	$+0.0195$
BE	153.7	2.25	$+04.80 + 0.800\,Z$	$+0.800$	$+0.0113$	$+0.0091$
BC	240.0	4.05	$-17.50 - 1.250\,Z$	-1.250	-0.0358	$+0.0448$
CE	153.7	2.25	$+11.21 + 0.800\,Z$	$+0.800$	$+0.0264$	$+0.0211$
CD	153.7	3.82	$-11.21 - 0.800\,Z$	-0.800	-0.0156	$+0.0125$
DE	240.0	3.00	$+08.75 + 0.625\,Z$	$+0.625$	$+0.0241$	$+0.0151$
					$\Sigma =$	$+0.146$

As indicated in the tabulation, the first partial derivative of the force T is found; then the value of TL/AE is computed, with Z being assigned a value of zero. This result is multiplied by $\partial T/\partial Z$, and the results are summed. The final deflection is then

$$\Delta_E = \sum_{i=1}^{m} \frac{T_i\left(\dfrac{\partial T_i}{\partial Z}\right)L_i}{E_i A_i} = 0.146 \text{ in.}$$

Among those familiar with the applications of the Castigliano theorem to truss deflections, the "unit load" form of the equation given by Equation 10.10 is usually preferred over the classical form as given by Equations 10.6

and 10.7. When the unit load solution is used, a separate solution is prepared for T_i (the load in each member due to all actual loads) and for z_i (the load in each member per unit of load Z). An example will illustrate the procedure.

Example 10-2

Using the unit load method, determine the deflection of the given steel truss at joint G. All members are double angles, with total cross-sectional areas as indicated in the drawings.

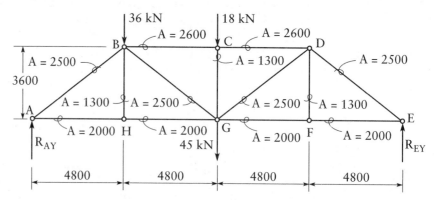

Solution

The solution will be made by using the unit load method, as defined by Equation 10.10:

$$\Delta_G = \sum_1^m T_i \Delta_{iz}$$

First, reactions are computed for the given load system; and then the force in each member is computed. Results are the force T_i, shown in the following sketch.

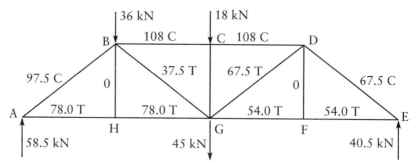

Next, the force in each member is computed for a unit load at G, the point where deflection is sought. Results are the forces n_i, shown in the following sketch.

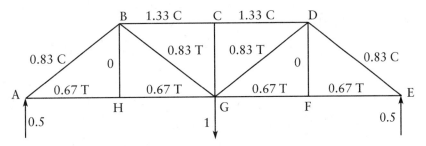

The following tabulation is made to evaluate Equation 10.10.

MEMBER	L (mm)	A (mm²)	z_i	$\Delta_{iz}\left(\dfrac{z_i L_i}{A_i E_i}\right)$	T_i (newtons)	$T_i \Delta_{iz}$
AH	4800	2000	+0.67	+ 8.00 × 10⁻⁶	+ 78000	+0.624
AB	6000	2500	−0.83	−10.00	− 97500	+0.975
BH	3600	1300	0	0	0	0
BG	6000	2500	+0.83	+10.00	+ 37500	+0.375
BC	4800	2600	−1.33	−12.31	−108000	+1.329
DC	4800	2600	−1.33	−12.31	−108000	+1.329
DG	6000	2500	+0.83	+10.00	+ 67500	+0.675
DF	3600	1300	0	0	0	0
ED	6000	2500	−0.83	−10.00	− 67500	+0.675
EF	4800	2000	+0.67	+ 8.00	+ 54000	+0.432
GF	4800	2000	+0.67	+ 8.00	+ 54000	+0.432
GC	3600	1300	0	0	− 18000	0
GH	4800	2000	+0.67	+ 8.00	+ 78000	+0.624

$$\Sigma = \overline{+7.470 \text{ mm}}$$

The final summation is the deflection at G:

$$\Delta_G = \sum_{i=1}^{m} T_i \Delta_{iz} = +7.470 \text{ mm}$$

The positive sign indicates that the deflection is in the same direction as the unit load.

10.2 MULTIPLE LOAD CASES

In general, several possible load cases can occur on a truss during its life, and each member of the truss must be designed to sustain the worst conditions resulting from any one of these possible load cases. Consequently, several investigations of the truss for its worst-case stresses and deformations are almost always required.

The procedure of solving a truss several times to account for a variety of possible load conditions can become quite tedious. Over the years, it has been found that such solutions may be simplified somewhat by solving first for a unit load at every hinge point where a load might occur or where a deflection may be sought. The results thus obtained may then be used to solve for stress or deformation anywhere in the truss under any possible load condition. An example will illustrate this "blanket" approach to the analysis.

Example 10-3

For the given steel truss, determine the deflection at joint I due to load case I and at joint J for load case II. Cross-sectional areas of the steel members are indicated on the sketch.

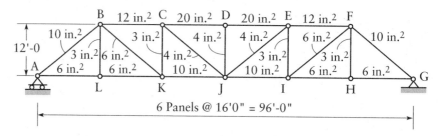

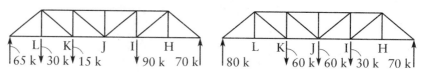

Solution

To begin, it is assumed that a load may occur at any of the lower panel points, L, K, J, I, or H. An analysis for forces is therefore performed for a unit load at any one of these five joints. The results of these analyses are shown in columns 4, 5, 6, 7, and 8 of the accompanying tabulation, where

$$\Delta = \sum_{1}^{m} T_i \Delta_{iz}$$

For load case I, the value of T_i in each member is found by multiplying the forces due to unit load at L by 30 kips, those due to unit load at K by 15 kips, and those due to unit load at I by 15 kips, and then summing the results. These results are shown in the table.

Member Forces Due to Unit
Load Located at Point

Member	l (in.)	A (in.²)	L	K	J	I	H	Load Case I $P_L = 30$ k $+P_K = 15$ k $+P_I = 90$ k T_i (kips)	z_i	Δ_{iz} zL/A	$T_i\Delta_{iz}$	Load Case II $P_K = 60$ k $+P_J = 60$ k $+P_I = 30$ k T_i (kips)	z_j	Δ_{iz} zL/A	$T_i\Delta_{iz}$
AL	192	06	+1.111	+0.889	+0.667	+0.444	+0.222	+086.63	+0.444	+14.21	+1231	+106.68	+0.667	+21.33	+2275
AB	240	10	−1.389	−1.111	−0.833	−0.556	−0.278	−108.38	−0.556	−13.33	+1445	−133.33	−0.833	−20.00	+2667
BL	144	03	+1.000	0	0	0	0	+030.00	0	0	0	0	0	0	0
BK	240	06	−0.278	+1.111	+0.833	+0.556	+0.278	+058.37	+0.556	+22.22	+1297	+133.33	+0.833	+33.33	+4444
BC	192	12	−0.889	−1.778	−1.333	−0.889	−0.444	−135.35	−0.889	−14.22	+1896	−213.33	−1.333	−21.33	+4550
CK	144	03	+0.167	+0.333	−0.500	−0.333	−0.167	−020.00	−0.333	−15.98	+0320	−020.00	−0.500	−24.00	+0480
CJ	240	04	−0.278	−0.556	+0.833	+0.556	+0.278	+033.37	+0.556	+33.33	+1112	+033.33	+0.833	+50.00	+1667
CD	192	20	−0.667	−1.333	−2.000	−1.333	−0.667	−160.00	−1.333	−12.80	+2048	−240.00	−2.000	−19.20	+4608
DJ	144	04	0	0	0	0	0	0	0	0	0	0	0	0	0
DE	192	20	−0.667	−2.000	−2.000	−1.333	−0.667	−160.00	−1.333	−12.80	+2048	−240.00	−2.000	−19.20	+4608
EJ	240	04	+0.278	+0.556	+0.833	−0.556	−0.278	−033.37	−0.556	−33.33	+1112	+066.67	+0.833	+50.00	+3333
EI	144	03	−0.166	−0.333	−0.500	+0.333	+0.166	+020.00	+0.333	+16.00	+0320	−040.00	−0.500	−24.00	+0960
EF	192	12	−0.444	−0.889	−1.333	−1.778	−0.889	−186.67	−1.778	−28.44	+5309	−133.33	−1.333	−21.33	+2844
FI	240	06	+0.278	+0.556	+0.833	+1.111	−0.278	+116.67	+1.111	+44.44	+5185	+116.67	+0.833	+33.33	+3889
FH	144	03	0	0	0	0	+1.000	0	0	0	0	0	0	0	0
GF	240	10	−0.278	−0.556	−0.833	−1.111	−1.389	−116.67	−1.111	−26.67	+3111	−116.67	−0.833	−20.00	+2333
GH	192	06	+0.222	+0.444	+0.667	+0.889	+1.111	+093.33	+0.889	+28.44	+2654	+093.33	+0.667	+21.33	+1991
IH	192	06	+0.222	+0.444	+0.667	+0.889	+1.111	+093.33	+0.889	+28.44	+2654	+093.33	+0.667	+21.33	+1991
IJ	192	10	+0.444	+0.889	+1.333	+1.778	+0.889	+186.67	+1.778	+34.13	+6371	+186.67	+1.333	+25.59	+4777
KJ	192	10	+0.889	+1.778	+1.333	+0.889	+0.444	+133.33	+0.889	+17.07	+2276	+213.33	+1.333	+25.59	+5459
KL	192	06	+1.111	+0.889	+0.667	+0.444	+0.222	+086.67	+0.444	+14.22	+1232	+106.67	+0.667	+21.33	+2275
											$\Sigma = 41{,}621$				$\Sigma = 55{,}151$

Similarly for load case II, the value of T_i in each member is found by multiplying the forces due to unit load at K by 60 k, those due to unit load at J by 60 kips, and those due to unit load at I by 30 kips, and then summing the results. These results are also indicated in the table.

For the tabulation, the values of z_i for load case I are simply the forces due to unit load at panel point I. Similarly, the values of z_i for load case II are simply the forces due to unit load at panel point J. For the sake of clarity, these values have been reentered in the appropriate columns in the tabulation.

The values of Δ_{iz} and $T_i\Delta_{iz}$ are then computed for the two load cases, and the results are summed. In this case, the value of E (in ksi) has been factored out, to be applied after the final summation is made. The final deflections are therefore the values from the table divided by 29,000 ksi. For load case I,

$$\Delta_I = \frac{41,621}{29,000} = 1.44 \text{ in.}$$

For load case II,

$$\Delta_J = \frac{55,151}{29,000} = 1.90 \text{ in.}$$

As before, the positive results indicate that the deflections occur in the same direction as the unit load.

Outside Problems Determine the deflection of the indicated joint. In all cases, the trusses are steel. Cross-sectional areas of the members are shown along the members.

Problem 10-1*
Vertical deflection at D.

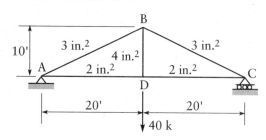

Problem 10-2
Vertical deflection at E.

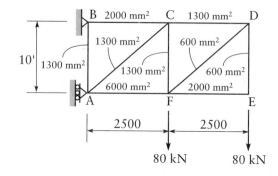

Problem 10-3*
Vertical deflection at G.

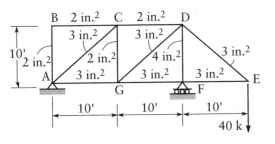

Problem 10-4
Vertical deflection at I.

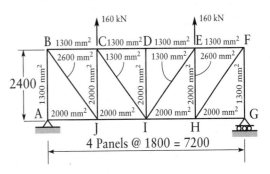

Problem 10-5*
Horizontal deflection at D.
Problem 10-6
Horizontal deflection at B.

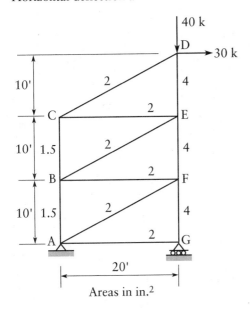

Problem 10-7
Vertical deflection at D.
Problem 10-8
Horizontal deflection at D.

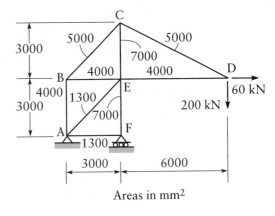

Areas in mm²

Problem 10-9*
Vertical deflection at *I*.
Problem 10-10
Horizontal deflection at *G*.

Problem 10-11
Vertical deflection at *G*.
Problem 10-12
Horizontal deflection at *E*.

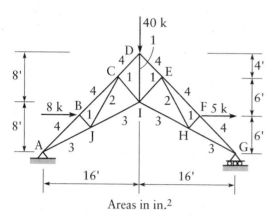

Areas in in.²

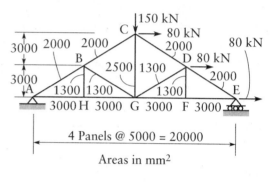

Areas in mm²

10.3 DEFLECTIONS UNDER MOVING LOADS

As noted earlier, trusses are often subject to heavy loads that move across the full length of the truss. Such loads occur not only on bridges but also in buildings where monorails or moving cranes are installed. Construction falsework is also subject to heavy moving loads, where forklifts or other motorized equipment are used to transport heavy materials at the upper levels.

The general approach that was introduced in the preceding section can readily be applied when the load case is a single moving load. An example will illustrate the method.

Example 10-4   For the given truss, determine the vertical deflection of joint *K* due to a 40 kip load moving across the length of the truss.

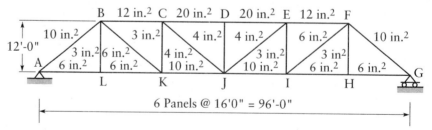

6 Panels @ 16'0" = 96'-0"

Solution   The load of 40 kips is assumed to act at any one of the lower panel points *L*, *K*, *J*, *I*, or *H*. An analysis for forces in each member is therefore performed for a unit load at each of these joints. The results are shown in the following sketches.

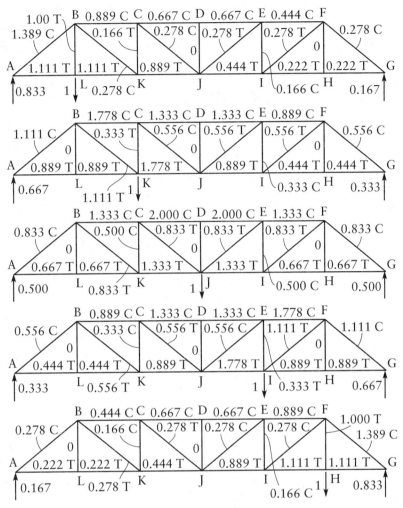

The loads from the sketches are entered in the tabulation accompanying this example, along with the lengths and areas of each member. As usual, a positive sign indicates tension, and a negative sign indicates compression.

The deflection calculations in the tabulation utilize a variation of Equation 10.10, according to which T_i is computed as 40 kips times the force due to unit load, with

$$\Delta_K = \sum_1^m T_i \Delta_{iz}$$

where

$$T_i \Delta_{iz} E = \frac{40 z_L z_K L}{A_i}$$

and where z_L is the force in member i due to a unit load at the joint where the 40-k load occurs.

Member	$\dfrac{L}{(\text{in.})}$	$\dfrac{A}{(\text{in.}^2)}$	Member Forces Due to Unit Load Located at Point					Δ_{ni} Due to Load at Joint				
			L	K	J	I	H	$\dfrac{40 n_L n_K L}{A}$ $T_i\Delta_{iz}E$	$\dfrac{40 n_K n_K L}{A}$ $T_i\Delta_{iz}E$	$\dfrac{40 n_J n_K L}{A}$ $T_i\Delta_{iz}E$	$\dfrac{40 n_I n_K L}{A}$ $T_i\Delta_{iz}E$	$\dfrac{40 n_H n_K L}{A}$ $T_i\Delta_{iz}E$
								L	K	J	I	H
AL	192	06	+1.111	+0.889	+0.667	+0.444	+0.222	+1264	+1012	+0759	+0506	+253
AB	240	10	−1.389	−1.111	−0.833	−0.556	−0.278	+1481	+1185	+0889	+0593	+297
BL	144	03	+1.000	0	0	0	0	0	0	0	0	0
BK	240	06	−0.278	+1.111	+0.833	+0.556	+0.278	−0494	+1975	+1481	+0988	+494
BC	192	12	−0.889	−1.778	−1.333	−0.889	−0.444	+1011	+2023	+1517	+1011	+506
CK	144	03	+0.167	+0.333	−0.500	−0.333	−0.167	+0107	+0213	−0320	−0213	−107
CJ	240	04	−0.278	−0.556	+0.833	+0.556	+0.278	+0371	+0741	−1111	−0741	−370
CD	192	20	−0.667	−1.333	−2.000	−1.333	−0.667	+0341	+0683	+1024	+0683	+341
DJ	144	04	0	0	0	0	0	0	0	0	0	0
DE	192	20	−0.667	−1.333	−2.000	−1.333	−0.667	+0341	+0683	+1024	+0683	+341
EJ	240	04	+0.278	+0.556	+0.833	−0.556	−0.278	+0371	+0741	+1111	−0741	−370
EI	144	03	−0.166	−0.333	−0.500	+0.333	+0.166	+0107	+0213	+0320	−0213	−107
EF	192	12	−0.444	−0.889	−1.333	−1.778	−0.889	+0253	+0506	+0759	+1011	+506
FI	240	06	+0.278	+0.556	+0.833	+1.111	−0.278	+0247	+0494	+0741	+0988	−247
FH	144	03	0	0	0	0	+1.000	0	0	0	0	0
GF	240	10	−0.278	−0.556	−0.833	−1.111	−1.389	+0148	+0296	+0444	+0592	+741
GH	192	06	+0.222	+0.444	+0.667	+0.889	+1.111	+0126	+0253	+0379	+0506	+632
IH	192	06	+0.222	+0.444	+0.667	+0.889	+1.111	+0126	+0253	+0379	+0506	+632
IJ	192	10	+0.444	+0.889	+1.333	+1.778	+0.889	+0303	+0607	+0910	+1214	+607
KJ	192	10	+0.889	+1.778	+1.333	+0.889	+0.444	+1214	+2427	+1820	+1214	+607
KL	192	06	+1.111	+0.889	+0.667	+0.444	+0.222	+1264	+1011	+0759	+0506	+253
							$\Sigma =$	8581	15,316	12,885	9093	5009
							$\dfrac{\sum T_i \Delta_{iz} E}{E} =$	0.296	0.528	0.443	0.314	0.173 inches

The tabulation is carried out for a load at each of the lower panel points L, K, J, I, and H. The sum of these columns, when divided by E, yields the deflection at the joint K as the load moves across the span:

$$\Delta_K = \sum_{i=1}^{m} \frac{T_i \Delta_{iz} E}{E} = \Sigma T_{iz} \Delta_{iz}$$

The values of the deflection Δ_K for each position of load are included in the table.

10.4 DEFORMATIONS OF CROSS-BRACED SHEAR PANELS

It was noted in Chapter 9 that trusses having counterdiagonals are used frequently in the practice, particularly in construction falsework and formwork. They are also used in routine buildings, such as the prefabricated steel buildings currently being manufactured by dozens of large and small fabricators in the United States. A commonly used structural system for one of these prefabricated buildings is shown in Figure 10-2.

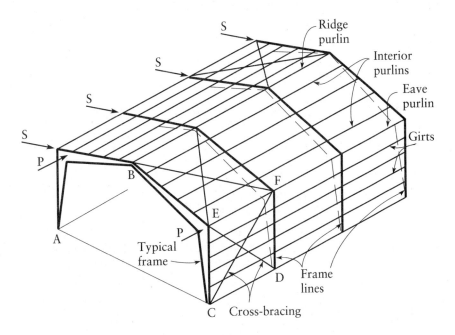

FIGURE 10-2 Typical prefab steel building.

Lateral loads delivered to the frames of the building may come from the sides (loads S) or from the ends (loads P); loads are fully reversible, of course. The side load S at each frame is resisted by the three-hinged arches spaced at regular intervals, such as frame ABC. Loads from the ends, such as load P, are resisted by cross-braced frames (often placed at only one end of the building), such as panel $CDFE$.

The eave purlin is a continuous compression member that can transmit loads from the far end of the building to the braced panel $CDFE$. The panel $CDFE$, a single-panel truss, therefore resists the lateral load P in either direction. The use of counterdiagonals, or cross-bracing, has been found to be an economical and simple design for such loading.

The two counterdiagonals, shown in Figure 10-2 as members CF and DE, are usually long rods, diameter 0.75 inch or larger, with ends upset and threaded. A turnbuckle is used to set the initial length. Such a long slender rod will buckle under the slightest compressive load; all the transverse shear on the panel will thus be carried by the rod that is in tension.

The deformation of the building along its length is thus limited entirely by this single counterdiagonal. Where brittle finishes are used, or where windows might be cracked due to excessive deformations, a check on the lateral deflection is warranted. The following example demonstrates such a check on a simple single-panel truss.

Example 10-5 Determine the longitudinal deflection of the steel building of Figure 10-2 under the indicated lateral loading. Average cross-sectional areas of the diagonals, frames, and purlins are given in mm² on the following sketch.

$E_S = 200,000$ N/mm²

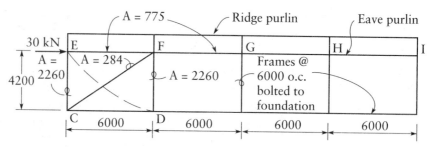

Solution The deflection is found by the Castigliano theorem. Member CD is the foundation and floor slab, whose area is infinitely large in comparison to the steel members. Equation 10.10 is used, where m is the number of members under load:

$$\Delta_E = \sum_{i=1}^{m} T_i \Delta_{iz}$$

An analysis is made first for unit load at E, yielding the values of z_i. T_i is found by multiplying that result by 30 kN; then $\Delta_i = z_i L_i/A_i$. The sum of $ET_i\Delta_i$ can then be found. Calculations are shown in the following tabulation.

MEMBER	L (in.)	A (in.^{2})	z_i	T_i (kips)	$\dfrac{z_i L_i}{A_i}$	$ET_i\Delta_{iz}$
EF	6000	775	−1.00	−30,000	−7.742	+232,000
FC	7324	284	+1.22	+36,620	+31.49	+1,153,000
FD	4200	2260	−0.70	−21,000	−1.309	+27,000
DC	6000	∞	0	0	0	0
CE	4200	2260	+0.70	+21,000	+1.309	+27,000

$$\Sigma = +1,439,000$$

The final deflection is found by dividing $ET_i\Delta_{iz}$ by the modulus of elasticity:

$$\Delta_E = \frac{ET_i\Delta_{iz}}{E} = \frac{1,439,000}{200,000}$$

$$= 7.20 \text{ mm} \qquad \text{(to the right)}$$

Under a load reversal, the other counterdiagonal (member ED) becomes the stressed member. Calculations for deflections in the trussed panel due to load at point I are thus identical to those for load at point E, and the deflection of the truss in either direction is the same.

However, for a load at point I, the axial shortening of the continuous eave purlin $FGHI$ will contribute to the total deflection of point I:

$$\Delta_I = 7.20 + \frac{PL}{AE} = 7.20 + \frac{30,000 \times 18,000}{775 \times 200,000}$$

$$= 10.68 \text{ mm} \qquad \text{(to the left)}$$

Towers used in construction falsework (to support the structure while it is being built) are commonly built with cross bracing, or counterdiagonals. An example of such a tower is shown in Figure 10-3.

Deflections in construction falsework are often critical, since construction tolerances must be maintained closely throughout the construction period. The tolerance at the top of the tower of Figure 10-3, for example, would probably be limited by building code requirements to less than 0.125 inches for each 5 feet of height. A fast check on such deflections is often necessary while the tower is being designed. A typical check on such deflections is given in the following example.

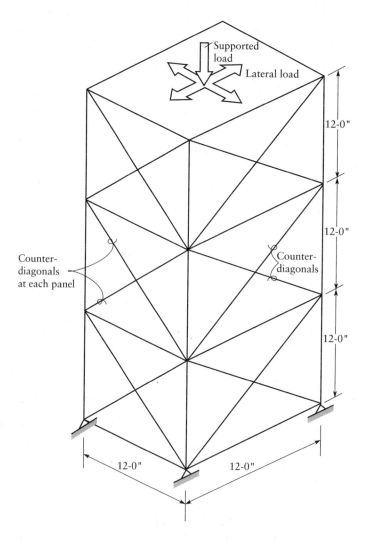

FIGURE 10-3 Typical falsework tower.

Example 10-6   Determine the deflection at the top of the falsework tower shown in Figure 10-3 for a total lateral load of 8600 lb. The tower is built of timber having a modulus of 1,700,000 psi and having the cross-sectional areas shown in the following sketch.

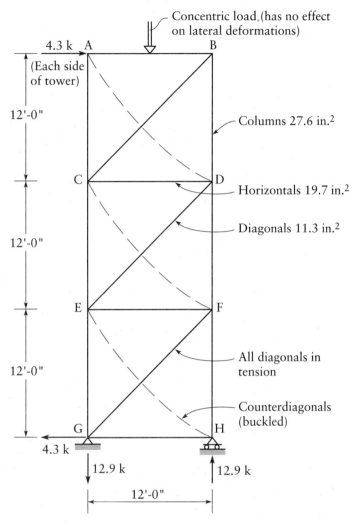

Solution   The deflection is again found by the unit load method:

$$\Delta = \sum_{1}^{m} T_i \Delta_{iz}$$

An analysis is first made for unit load at A, yielding the values of z_i. T_i is found by multiplying these values by 4.3 kips. Complete calculations are given in the following table.

MEMBER	L (in.)	A (in.^{2})	z_i	T_i (kips)	$\dfrac{z_i L_i}{A_i}$	$ET_i \Delta_{iz}$
AB	144	19.7	−1.000	−04.30	−07.31	+031
BC	204	11.3	+1.414	+06.08	+25.53	+155
BD	144	27.6	−1.000	−04.30	−05.22	+022
CA	144	27.6	0.000	00.00	00.00	000
CD	144	19.7	−1.000	−04.30	−07.31	+031
DE	204	11.3	+1.414	+06.08	+25.53	+155
DF	144	27.6	−2.000	−08.60	−10.43	+090
EC	144	27.6	+1.000	+04.30	+05.22	+022
EF	144	19.7	−1.000	−04.30	−07.31	+031
FG	204	11.3	+1.414	+06.08	+25.53	+155
FH	144	27.6	−3.000	−12.90	−15.65	+202
GE	144	27.6	+2.000	+08.60	+10.43	+090
GH	144	19.7	0.000	00.00	00.00	000

$$\Sigma = 984$$

The final deflection is found by dividing $\Sigma ET_i \Delta_{iz}$ by the elastic modulus (in ksi):

$$\Delta = \Sigma \frac{ET_i \Delta_{iz}}{E} = \frac{984}{1700}$$

$$= 0.58 \text{ in.}$$

The allowable deflection in such a tower would usually be limited to about 1/8 in. in 5 ft, or, for a 36-ft. tower, to about 0.9 in. The deflection of this tower falls within such commonly applied limits.

When the load is reversed, the diagonals also reverse, and the lateral deflection under a load reversal is the same for either direction of load.

10.5 ROTATIONS WITHIN A TRUSS

Occasionally, it may be desirable to know the rotation (rather than the deflections) of a certain member in a truss. Consider, for example, the truss of Figure 10-4, in which the angular rotation of member BG is to be found.

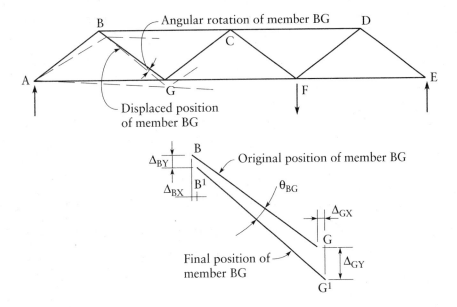

FIGURE 10-4 Rotations in a truss member.

Often, the simplest solution in such cases is to compute the vertical and horizontal displacements at points B and G from the Castigliano theorem, and then to compute the rotation of the member from these displacements. As indicated in Figure 10-4, for example, the displacement of point G relative to point B is simply the difference in their displacements:

$$\Delta_Y = \Delta_{GY} - \Delta_{BY}$$

$$\Delta_X = \Delta_{GX} - \Delta_{BX}$$

These relative displacements are shown in Figure 10-5.

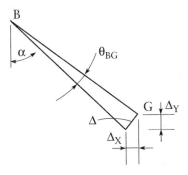

FIGURE 10-5 Relative displacements.

For computing the angle of rotation θ, the axial elongation of the member is ignored. Hence, for small angles of rotation, the angle is

$$\theta = \tan \theta = \frac{\Delta}{L}$$

where

$$\Delta = \sqrt{\Delta_y^2 + \Delta_x^2}$$

A problem similar to this one arises when a moment is to be applied to a truss. Since every panel point is a hinge, a moment can only be applied to a truss by taking the moment as a couple and applying the couple to two adjacent panel points. Such a case is shown in Figure 10-6, where a moment is to be applied across member CF.

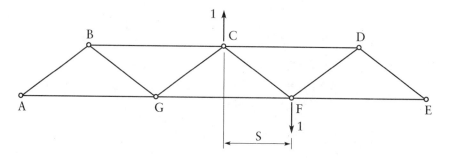

FIGURE 10-6 Moment on a truss.

A solution for the truss deformations—first for a load at point C, and then for a load at point F—will define the deformations throughout the truss. This combination provides a solution for a moment (couple) applied across member CF.

Outside Problems   Determine the indicated deformations in the steel trusses.

Problem 10-13*
Find the deflection at the free end
for a 30-kip load moving from A to
I to H to G to F.

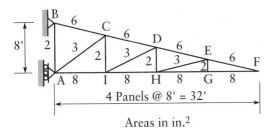

4 Panels @ 8' = 32'

Areas in in.²

Problem 10-14
Find the deflection at J due to a
80-kN load moving from A to L to
K to J to I to H to G.

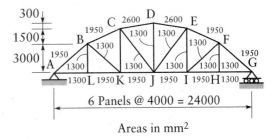

6 Panels @ 4000 = 24000

Areas in mm²

Problem 10-15*
Find the deflection at J due to a
40-kip load moving from A to L
to K to J to I to H to G.

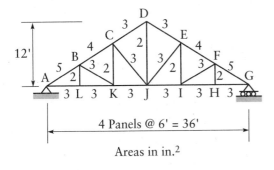

4 Panels @ 6' = 36'

Areas in in.²

Problem 10-16
Find the lateral deflection of joint A.
E= 200,000N/mm²
Areas: columns 400 mm²
           horizontals 200 mm²
           counters 500 mm²

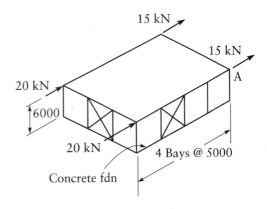

Concrete fdn

Problem 10-17*
Find the lateral deflection of joint A.
$E = 30 \times 10^6$ psi
Areas: columns 2.00 in.^{2}
        horizontals 1.00 in.^{2}
        counters 1.50 in.^{2}

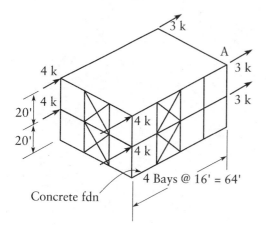

Problem 10-18
Find the lateral deflection of joint A.
$E = 200$ kN/mm^2
Areas: columns 2000 mm^2
        horizontals 800 mm^2
        counters 1000 mm^2

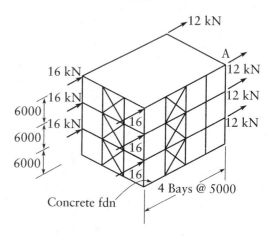

Problem 10-19*
Find the lateral deflection at the
top level of the steel truss.
    All verticals: A = 3.11 in.^{2}
All horizontals: A = 2.36 in.^{2}
    All counters: A = 0.40 in.^{2}

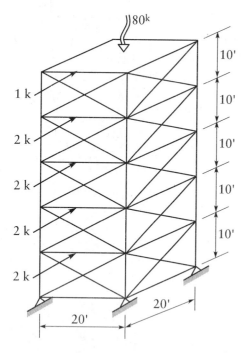

Problem 10-20
Find the lateral deflection at E.
for a 30-kN load moving from A to E.
    All verticals: A = 2620 mm^2
All horizontals: A = 1640 mm^2
    All counters: A = 387 mm^2

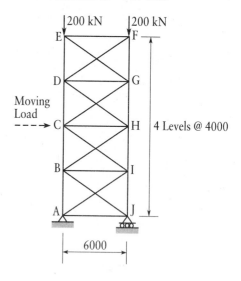

REVIEW QUESTIONS

1. Why wouldn't the method of double integration be used to find the deflection of a truss?

2. Using the Castigliano method, how would one find the deflection at the midpoint of a truss member rather than at the panel point?

3. What does using the unit load method accomplish in truss analysis?

4. If the unit load method of truss analysis is not used, how does one find the influence coefficient Z_i?

5. What is a counterdiagonal?

6. Since the addition of counterdiagonals adds members to a truss without adding joints, why does a truss fail to become statically indeterminate when counterdiagonals are added?

7. How is the angle of rotation of a truss member usually found?

8. How would one find the angle of rotation of a truss member by using a unit moment?

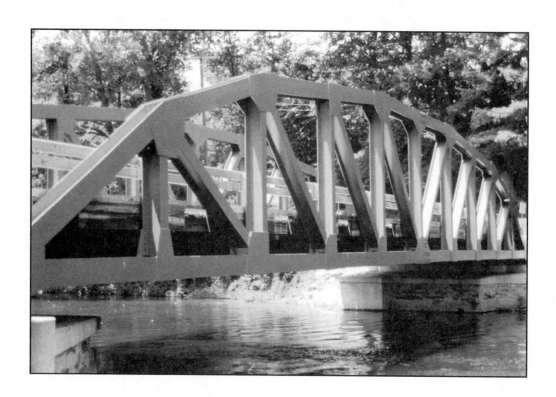

Classical steel truss over Paulins Kill Creek, Warren County,
New Jersey. (Photograph courtesy American Institute of
Steel Construction, reprinted by permission.)

11

Influence Lines

Influence lines are a type of graphic aid used in structural analysis when the structure is to be subjected to a set of moving loads. In the analysis of a bridge girder, for example, it may be necessary to find the maximum value of moment that can occur at some point A in the span as two or more 18-wheel trucks move across the bridge. The influence line is a graphic aid in such an analysis, permitting the moment at the particular point A to be recalculated readily as the sets of wheel loads shift to various locations along the span. After only a few trial locations for the loads, it is usually possible to find the location of the moving load that produces the maximum moment at point A.

The influence line can be applied for any function (reaction, shear, moment, or deflection), but a separate influence line must be drawn for each new function that is to be included; thus, a set of such influence lines would be required for the point A. A similar set of such influence lines must be drawn for each of the other points in the span that are to be investigated (shears are investigated near a support; moments are investigated near mid-span). The end result is that a set of influence lines must be drawn accurately to scale for each of the several points being investigated, and each such set must contain a separate influence line for each function (reaction, shear, moment, and deflection).

Obviously, influence lines represent a great deal of work when they become necessary in an analysis. Fortunately, influence lines for determinate structures can be prepared rather readily, but influence lines for indeterminate structures can sometimes be prohibitively difficult just due to the labor involved. While the concepts presented in this chapter are limited to determinate structures, these same concepts are equally applicable in later studies of indeterminate structures.

The use of influence lines has diminished sharply since the advent of the digital computer. A computerized solution allows a set of moving loads to be shifted to some new position anywhere along a span, with all effects of the load (shear, moment, and deflection) being recomputed for any point in the span in an instant. In effect, that is exactly the purpose of the influence line, although the influence line relies on manually adjusted positions of the load and manual readings of the graph.

Influence lines may be drawn for any type of structure (beam, truss, frame, plate, or shell), and they can be used to show the effect of any structural function (reaction, shear, moment, torque, axial force, slope, or deflection). They may be used to analyze either determinate or indeterminate structures, including cantilevers, simple beams, hinged beams, and three-hinged arches; and they may be used to analyze moving loads as well as complex patterns of static loads. Influence lines are, in fact, a general approach to any structural analysis where superposition of loads is valid.

Aside from their general applicability, influence lines are also a very effective tool for teaching structures: they require the student to visualize what is happening in one part of the structure due to loads moving around in some other part of the structure. Unfortunately, they are tedious, time-consuming, and repetitive. Fortunately, they can readily be generated by computer.

11.1 INFLUENCE LINES FOR A CANTILEVER

Consider the cantilever beam of Figure 11-1. It is desired to find the maximum shear and maximum moment that occur on this cantilever due to the given pattern of moving loads. Further, it is desired to find the maximum deflection both at the free end of the beam and at the midpoint of the beam.

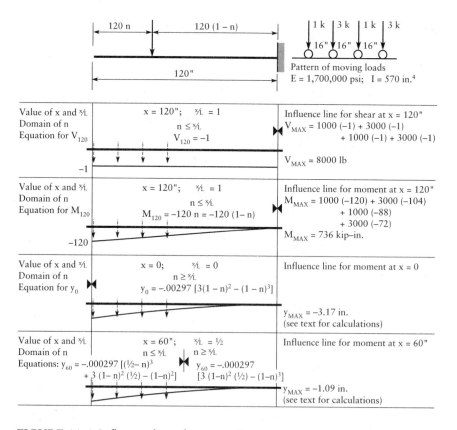

FIGURE 11-1 Influence lines for a cantilever.

Shear and moment are treated first. A unit load is placed at some point nL along the span, as shown in the figure. Since the point where shear and moment are to be computed (at $x = 120$ in.) is already known, the only remaining variable is the position factor n. There are only two possible domains for n: either the load is to the left of the point $x = 120$ in., for which case $n \leq x/L$; or the load is to the right of the point $x = 120$ in., for which case $n \geq x/L$. Since in this case the point being investigated is at the extreme right of the beam, $n \leq x/L$ for all positions of load.

The foregoing values of x, x/L, and the domain of n have been entered on the sketch in Figure 11-1. The shaded X ($\blacktriangleright\!\blacktriangleleft$) indicates the location of the point being investigated.

The shear and moment equations at $x = 120$ in. are now written for any position of the load:

$$V_{120} = -1$$

$$M_{120} = -1\,(120 - 120n) = -120\,(1 - n)$$

These equations have also been entered in Figure 11-1. The graphs of these two equations are now drawn; these graphs are the *influence lines* for the shear and moment at the fixed support.

The next step is to find the maximum value of moment produced at the fixed end by the set of moving loads. The loads are placed on the influence line at various locations until the maximum moment occurs. This is usually accomplished by sketching the pattern of loads to scale on a small piece of paper and moving it along the influence line, recalculating the moment at several trial locations, until the maximum value of moment is found. The moment is computed as the load times its influence value, as shown in Figure 11-2.

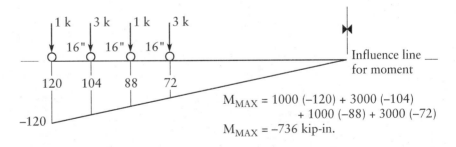

FIGURE 11-2 Computation of maximum moment.

In this very simple case, it is immediately obvious that the loads must be placed at the extreme left to produce the maximum value of moment. In more complex cases, several trial locations may be necessary. The result shown in Figure 11-2 may readily be verified by placing the loads on the beam in the indicated position and computing the moment at the support.

The influence lines for deflections are developed similarly. For deflections at the free end of the beam, $x/L = 0$; and in all cases, $n \geq x/L$. For deflections at the midpoint of the beam, $x/L = 1/2$; for this value of x/L, the two possible domains for n are $n \leq x/L$ and $n \geq x/L$. These values of x/L and n have been entered on the sketch of Figure 11-1.

The deflection y is computed by the methods of Chapter 4 (this particular case is given as case 2 of Table 4-1:

$$n \leq \frac{x}{L}; \qquad y = -\frac{PL^3}{6EI}\left[\left(\frac{x}{L} - n\right)^3 + 3\,(1-n)^2\left(1 - \frac{x}{L}\right) - (1-n)^3\right]$$

$$n \geq \frac{x}{L}; \qquad y = -\frac{PL^3}{6EI}\left[3\,(1-n)^2\left(1 - \frac{x}{L}\right) - (1-n)^3\right]$$

For deflection at the free end of the beam, where $x/L = 0$, $n \geq x/L$ and $P = 1$ lb,

$$y_0 = -0.000297\,[3\,(1-n)^2 - (1-n)^3]$$

This equation for y_0 has been entered in the sketch of Figure 11-1. The graph of this equation is the influence line for deflection at the free end of the beam for any position of load. The influence line is also shown in Figure 11-1.

For deflections at the midpoint of the beam, where $x/L = 1/2$, the two possible domains of n are $n \leq x/L$ and $n \geq x/L$. The values have been entered in the sketch of Figure 11-1. For $x/L = 1/2$ and $P = 1$ lb, the deflection equations become

$$n \leq \frac{x}{L}; \qquad y_{60} = -0.000297\left[\left(\frac{1}{2} - n\right)^3 + \frac{3}{2}\,(1-n)^2 - (1-n)^3\right]$$

$$n \geq \frac{x}{L}; \qquad y_{60} = -0.000297\left[\frac{3}{2}\,(1-n)^2 - (1-n)^3\right]$$

These equations for y_{60} have been entered in the sketch of Figure 11-1 in their corresponding domains. The graphs of these equations, each drawn within its proper domain of n, constitute the influence line for the deflection at mid-span. The influence line has been included in the sketch of Figure 11-1.

To permit computation of the maximum deflection y_0 at the free end of the beam, the pattern of loads is placed along the influence line in such a position as to produce the maximum value for y_0. In this particular case, the set of loads obviously should be placed as close to the free end of the beam as possible. The result is shown in Figure 11-3, along with the computation of maximum y_0. The computation of y_{60} is also included in Figure 11-3.

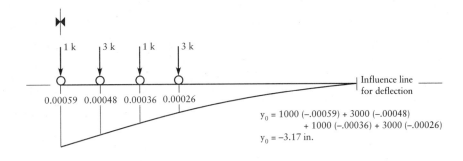

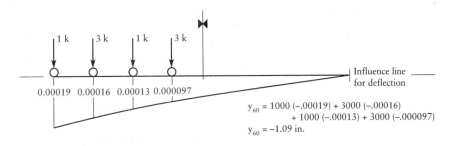

FIGURE 11-3 Computation of deflections.

The variable in the equations of influence lines is not the point x, since x is a fixed point for each influence line (designated by the symbol ▶◀ in the sketches). For influence lines, the variable is the position factor n, which determines the position of the unit load in the span. Keeping these two parameters in perspective is sometimes difficult for students just beginning their study of influence lines.

The application of influence lines to cantilevers is too simple to be of much value, except to illustrate the procedures. The procedures are quite similar in simple beams, however, and these are presented next.

11.2 INFLUENCE LINES FOR A SIMPLE BEAM

Consider the simple beam of Figure 11-4. It is desired to find the maximum value of shear just to the right of the left support due to the given pattern of loads. It is also desired to find the moment and deflection at midspan due to these same loads.

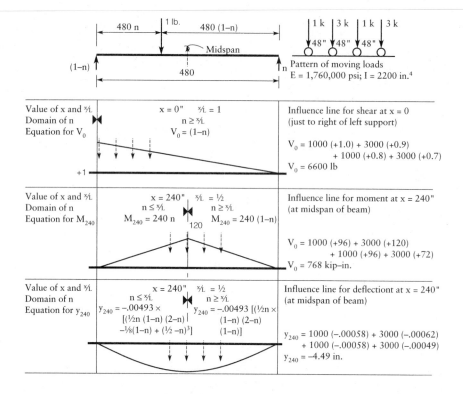

FIGURE 11-4 Influence lines for a simple beam.

As before, a unit load is placed at some point nL along the span, as shown. The reactions for the simple beam have been computed and entered on the sketch. Notice that the reactions vary with n; they are therefore given as equations in the variable n.

For the shear at the left support, $x = 0$, $x/L = 0$, and $n \geq x/L$ for all positions of load. The shear equation is written for the point just to the right of the support:

$$V_0 = +(1 - n)$$

The graph of this equation is the influence line for the shear at the left support; it is included in the sketch of Figure 11-4.

The maximum value of shear is found by placing the loads as close to the support as possible, as indicated in Figure 11-5. The influence values are scaled, and the maximum shear is computed, as shown in the figure.

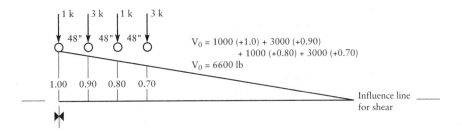

FIGURE 11-5 Computation of maximum shear.

Similarly, the moment equation is written for the midpoint of the beam:

$$n \leq \frac{x}{L}; \qquad M_{240} = +240n$$

$$n \geq \frac{x}{L}; \qquad M_{240} = 240(1-n)$$

The graphs of these two equations is the influence line for moment at midspan. The graphs are included in the sketch of Figure 11-4.

The maximum value of moment is found by placing the loads near midspan. After a few trials, the position of loads shown in Figure 11-6 is found to produce a probable maximum value. Some slight shifting of loads might produce a value of moment a small fraction higher than the one shown here, but such refinements need not be addressed in a situation where ordinate values are being scaled to one- or two-place accuracy.

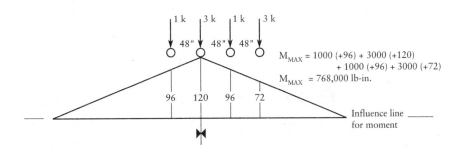

FIGURE 11-6 Computation of maximum moment.

The influence lines for deflections are developed by using the same methods that were used for cantilevers. The deflection at midspan is given as case 6 in Table 3-2. For $x/L = 1/2$, $P = 1$ lb, $E = 1,700,000$ psi, and $I = 2200$ in.[4],

$$n \le \frac{x}{L}; \quad y_{240} = -0.00493\left[\left(\frac{1}{2}\right)(n)(1-n)(2-n)\right.$$

$$\left. -\left(\frac{1}{8}\right)(1-n) + \left(\frac{1}{2}-n\right)^3\right]$$

$$n \ge \frac{x}{L}; \quad y_{240} = -0.00493\left[\left(\frac{1}{2}\right)(n)(1-n)(2-n) - \left(\frac{1}{8}\right)(1-n)\right]$$

The graphs of these two equations constitute the influence line for deflection at midspan. The equations and the graphs are included in Figure 11-4.

The maximum deflection is found by placing the loads near midspan. After a few trials, the position of loads shown in Figure 11-7 is found to produce a probable maximum value. The influence values are scaled, and the maximum deflection is computed as shown in the figure.

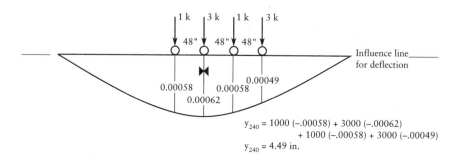

$$y_{240} = 1000\,(-.00058) + 3000\,(-.00062)$$
$$+ 1000\,(-.00058) + 3000\,(-.00049)$$
$$y_{240} = 4.49 \text{ in.}$$

FIGURE 11-7 Computation of maximum deflection.

The procedures illustrated here apply to all types of determinate structures. A beam with overhangs is considered next.

11.3 INFLUENCE LINES FOR A SIMPLE BEAM WITH OVERHANGS

Consider the simple beam with overhangs shown in Figure 11-8. It is desired to find the maximum value of shear just to the right of the left support due to the given pattern of loads. It is also desired to find the maximum values of both moment and shear that could occur at section a-a due to the same pattern of loads.

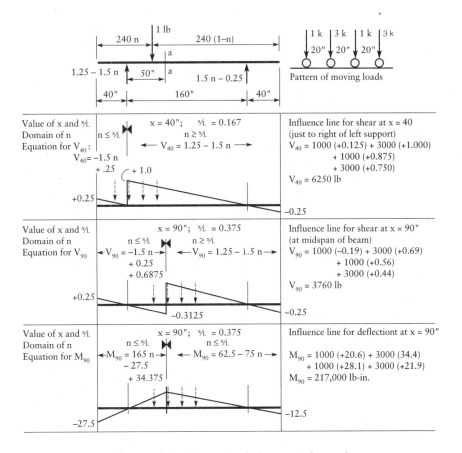

FIGURE 11-8 Influence lines for a simple beam with overhangs.

As before, a unit load is placed at some point nL along the span, as shown in Figure 11-8. The reaction equations have been expressed as functions of the variable n and entered on the sketch. For shear just inside the left support, $x = 40$ and $x/L = 0.1667$. The 1-lb. unit load in this case can be placed either to the left of the point or to the right of the point; hence,

$$n \leq \frac{x}{L}; \qquad V_{40} = -1.5n + 0.25$$

$$n \geq \frac{x}{L}; \qquad V_{40} = +1.25 - 1.5n$$

The graphs of these two equations constitute the influence line for shear just inside the left support. The graphs are included in the sketch of Figure 11-8.

The maximum value of shear V_{40} is found after making a few trial locations. The final location of the loads is shown in Figure 11-9. The influence values are scaled, and the maximum shear is computed as shown in the figure.

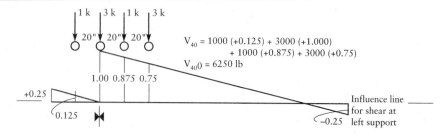

FIGURE 11-9 Computation of maximum shear at support.

The shear and moment equations at section a-a are found similarly. At section a-a, $x = 90$ and $x/L = 0.375$. The shear and moment equations are

$$n \leq \frac{x}{L}; \qquad V_{90} = -1.5n + 0.25$$

$$M_{90} = +165n - 27.5$$

$$n \geq \frac{x}{L}; \qquad V_{90} = +1.25 - 1.5n$$

$$M_{90} = +62.5 - 75n$$

The graphs of these equations are included in Figure 11-8; these graphs constitute the influence lines for shear and moment at section a-a.

The maximum values of V_{90} and M_{90} are found with the load positioned similarly to the locations shown in Figure 11-9, with the 1-kip load situated to the left of section a-a and the 3-kip load just to the right of section a-a. The maximum values of V_{90} and M_{90} are included in Figure 11-8.

One small trick is useful when writing shear and moment equations for influence lines. There are only two possible locations for the load: to the left or to the right of the point being examined. When the load is to the left, the shear and moment equations are found by summing shears and moments to the right of the point; when the load is to the right, the shear and moment equations are found by summing shears and moments to the left of the point. In this way, some of the algebraic manipulation (and some of the possibility of algebraic error) can be avoided.

11.4 INFLUENCE LINES FOR A HINGED BEAM

Influence lines are equally applicable to more complex beams, such as the hinged beam shown in Figure 11-10. For this beam, it is desired to know the maximum load that can occur on the hinge at B due to the given pattern of loads. In addition, it is desired to know the maximum moment that can occur over the support at C, as well as the maximum moment that can occur at midspan of the 360-in. span, shown as point E in Figure 11-10.

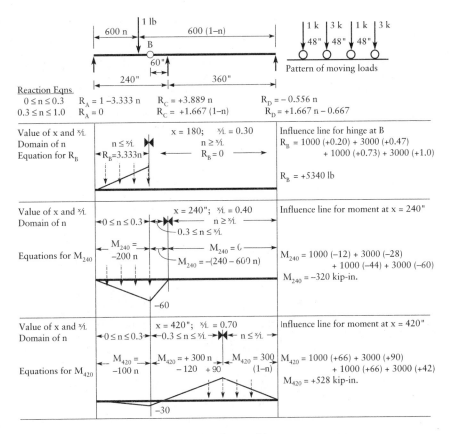

FIGURE 11-10 Influence lines for a hinged beam.

As always, a unit load is placed at some point *nL* along the span, as shown in Figure 11-10. During computation of the reactions for this unit load, however, it is found that a discontinuity in the reaction equations occurs when the load crosses the hinge at point *B*. The discontinuous equations for the reactions are shown in Figure 11-10. The discontinuity in the reaction equations of course creates a discontinuity in all succeeding equations based on the reactions.

The load acting on the hinge at *B* is simply the right reaction of the beam *AB*. The right reaction of the beam *AB* is entered on the sketch of Figure 11-10; the graph of that equation is the influence line for loads on the hinge.

The maximum value of R_B occurs when the set of moving loads is placed on the beam *AB* with the rightmost 3-kip load situated just to the left of point *B*. The loads for this case are shown in Figure 11-10.

The moment over the support at *C* is found by summing moments either to the right or to the left of point *C*, while observing the discontinuity in the reactions when *n* = 180. The result is shown in Figure 11-10, along with the corresponding influence line for the moment at *C*.

The maximum value for the moment at *C* occurs when the set of moving loads is placed to the left of point *B*, with the rightmost 3-kip load situated at point *B*. The resulting computation for moment at *C* is shown in Figure 11-10.

The moment at midspan of span *CD* is found similarly, by summing moments either to the right or to the left of point *E*, while observing the discontinuity in the reactions when $n = 180$ in. The graphs of the three equations form the influence line for moment at *E*; this influence line is shown in Figure 11-10.

The maximum value for the moment at *E* occurs when the interior 3-kip load is placed directly over point *E*, leaving one load to the left of *E* and the two remaining loads to the right of *E*. The computation for moment at *E* is shown in Figure 11-10.

11.5 INFLUENCE LINES FOR TRUSSES

Influence lines are as applicable to trusses as they are to beams. Since trusses are very commonly used to carry systems of moving loads, applications of influence lines to truss analysis become an essential study in structural analysis. Such applications include not only highway and railroad bridges, but also the trussed supports for the many industrial bridge cranes used in fabrication plants throughout the manufacturing industry.

Trusses are somewhat simpler than beams to analyze. There is no analysis for moment or shear in a truss; the only loads in a truss are the axial forces acting in each member. As a consequence, the only effect of a moving load on a truss is to alter the axial forces in the individual members.

A truss may be loaded only at its panel points. Consequently, a load moving the length of a truss must move from panel point to panel point in discrete jumps. There is no continuous position factor *n* as there was in beams, so there is no equation for the influence curve in a truss.

The same logic applies to deflections in trusses. The only deflections of interest are those at the panel points. The truss members form straight lines between the panel points and have no deflections other than those at their panel points. Deflection analysis in trusses is therefore limited to the deflections of selected panel points.

The truss analyses in the following sections include both of the foregoing applications of influence lines. The first analysis involves the forces in various members as a set of loads moves across the truss. The second analysis involves the deflection of a panel point for the same truss under the same set of moving loads. These two cases illustrate the most common uses of influence lines in truss analysis.

11.6 INFLUENCE LINES FOR FORCES IN TRUSS MEMBERS

Consider the truss of Figure 11-11. It is desired to find the maximum force that will occur in members *AB*, *CD*, and *IJ* as the given set of loads moves across the length of the truss. The loads are considered to act only on the lower panel points, as shown in the figure.

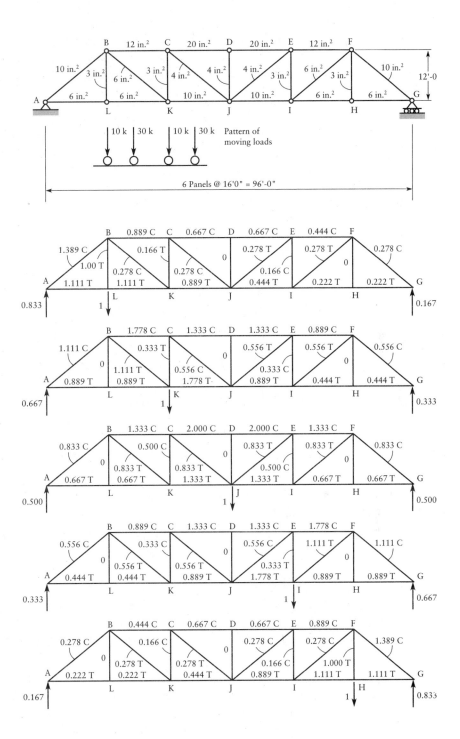

FIGURE 11-11 Unit loads at truss panel points.

The forces in each member of the truss are found for a unit load at each of the lower panel points. The forces are entered directly on the members, with C denoting compression and T denoting tension.

The influence lines for the forces in truss members AB, CD, and IJ are taken directly from the sketches of Figure 11-11. The force in member AB, for example, is zero when the load is located at joint A; 1.389 lb. compression when the load is at joint L; 1.111 lb compression when the load is at joint K; and so forth. The results are shown in the influence lines of Figure 11-12.

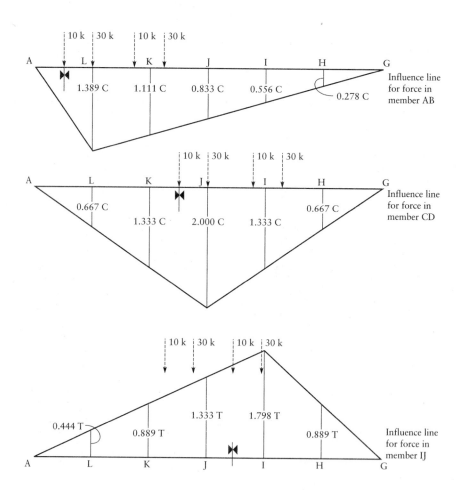

FIGURE 11-12 Influence lines for force in truss members.

The set of loads is moved along the span exactly as in beam analysis, until the maximum numerical value for force in each member is obtained. The final selected position for this example is shown in phantom lines in Figure 11-12. The final results are then computed by scaling the influence lines, as before;

$$F_{AB} = (10{,}000 \times 0.70) + (30{,}000 \times 1.39) + (10{,}000 \times 1.18)$$
$$+ (30{,}000 \times 1.04)$$

$$= 97{,}700 \text{ lb} \quad \text{(compression)}$$

$$F_{CD} = (10{,}000 \times 1.67) + (30{,}000 \times 2.00) + (10{,}000 \times 1.50)$$
$$+ (30{,}000 \times 1.17)$$

$$= 127{,}000 \text{ lb} \quad \text{(compression)}$$

$$F_{IJ} = (10{,}000 \times 1.00) + (30{,}000 \times 1.22) + (10{,}000 \times 1.56)$$
$$+ (30{,}000 \times 1.78)$$

$$= 116{,}000 \text{ lb} \quad \text{(compression)}$$

It should be noted from the sketches of Figure 11-11 that the force in members BK and CJ undergo a stress reversal as the load moves across the span. To design these members, one must find the largest compressive load that can possibly occur and the largest tensile load that can possibly occur; the loads will have to be positioned to produce these maximum values. The solution for these forces is included as one of the outside problems at the end of this chapter.

11.7 INFLUENCE LINES FOR DEFLECTIONS OF A TRUSS

For the truss of Figure 11-11, it is now desired to find the deflection of panel point K as the given set of loads moves across the span. As before, an influence line is needed—this time for the deflection of panel point K as a unit load is applied at each of the lower panel points.

The solution for the deflection of point K for a 40-kip load is given in the data of Example 10-4, although the concept of an influence line had not been developed at the time that Example 10-4 was presented. The deflections for a unit load are given in the following list.

Unit load at joint L: Deflection $= 0.0000074$ in.

Unit load at joint K: Deflection $= 0.0000132$ in.

Unit load at joint J: Deflection $= 0.0000111$ in.

Unit load at joint I: Deflection $= 0.0000079$ in.

Unit load at joint H: Deflection $= 0.0000043$ in.

When the unit load is located at one of the end points of the truss (point A or G), the deflection of joint K is, of course, zero.

The results of the analysis in Example 10-4 are plotted directly as the influence line for deflections at joint K; this influence line is shown in Figure 11-13. The positive direction of the influence line was taken as downward, and the coefficients are entered in inches.

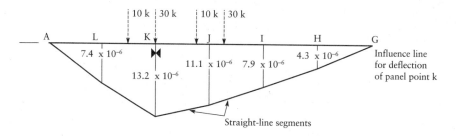

FIGURE 11-13 Influence line for panel point deflection.

The maximum deflection of panel point K is found with the loads positioned as shown in phantom in Figure 11-13. For that position of load,

$$\Delta_K = (10,000 \times 10.3 \times 10^{-6}) + (30,000 \times 13.2 \times 10^{-6})$$
$$+ (10,000 \times 11.6 \times 10^{-6}) + (30,000 \times 10.3 \times 10^{-6})$$
$$= 0.924 \text{ in.}$$

In summary, the influence line for deflections of panel point i in a truss is developed by plotting the deflection of panel point i for a unit load moving across the truss. The unit load is placed sequentially at each appropriate panel point in the span, and the deflection of panel point i is then computed by the methods of Chapter 10. The results, when plotted, constitute the influence line for deflection of panel point i.

Outside Problems The following system of loads applies to Problems 11-1 through 11-8 and 11-17 through 11-20. The load system can be reversed; that is, the system can be turned to travel in either direction.

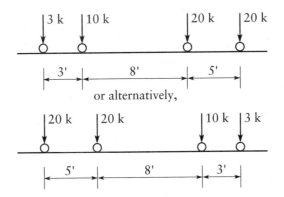

Problems 11-1 & 11-2*

Given: Cantilever beam, 20'-0" long.
To find: a. Maximum moment under the given load system.
　　　　　　b. Maximum shear under the given load system.

Problems 11-3 & 11-4

Given: Simple beam, 80'-0" span.
To find: a. Maximum moment under the given load system.
　　　　　　b. Maximum shear under the given load system.

Problems 11-5 & 11-6*

Given: Simple beam with two overhangs.
　　　　　Overhangs 30'-0" long; interior span 100'-0".
To find: a. Maximum positive moment under the given load system.
　　　　　　b. Maximum negative moment under the given load system.

Problems 11-7 & 11-8

Given: Two-span hinged beam, similar to the beam of Figure 11-10.
　　　　　Both spans 80'-0" long.
　　　　　Hinge located in right span, 12'-0" from the center support.
To find: a. Maximum positive moment under the given load system.
　　　　　　b. Maximum negative moment under the given load system.

Problem 11-9*

Plot the influence line for the reaction at point A of the truss of Problem 10-13.

Problem 11-10

Plot the influence line for the reaction at point G of the truss of Problem 10-14.

Problem 11-11*

Plot the influence line for the reaction at point A of the truss of Problem 10-15.

Problem 11-12

Plot the influence line for the reaction at point J of the truss of Problem 10-20.

Problem 11-13*

Plot the influence line for the force in member AC of the truss of Problem 10-13.

Problem 11-14

Plot the influence line for the force in member BK of the truss of Problem 10-14.

Problem 11-15*

Plot the influence line for the force in member CJ of the truss of Problem 10-15.

Problem 11-16

Plot the influence line for the force in member BH of the truss of Problem 10-20.

Problems 11-17 & 11-18*

Plot the influence line for the deflection at point F of Problem 10-13; then find the maximum deflection that will occur under the given load system.

Problems 11-19 & 11-20

Plot the influence line for the deflection at point J of Problem 10-15; then find the maximum deflection that will occur under the given load system.

REVIEW QUESTIONS

1. What is an *influence line*, as the term is used in structural analysis?
2. Can an influence line be used to find deflection?
3. Why has the use of influence lines declined so sharply in recent years?
4. Can influence lines be used to analyze indeterminate structures?
5. What is the major objection to the use of influence lines?

Reinforced concrete retaining wall with textured surface,
Colwyn Bay, England. (Photograph courtesy Portland
Cement Association, reprinted by permission.)

12

External Loads on Structures

The ways in which external loads may be imposed on a structural system are discussed in this chapter. Coverage is limited to structures that are less than about 65 feet in height, have a height-to-width ratio less than about 2, and incorporate a system of lateral bracing (rather than rigid joints) to resist lateral loads. For structures taller or more slender than this, both wind and earthquake loads increase significantly; and depending on the particular structure, the external loadings presented in this chapter may or may not be appropriate for analysis. Further, the internal response of taller, more slender structures to wind and earthquake loads can be quite different from that of lower structures; the methods presented here would have to be altered accordingly before being used on these taller structures.

The foregoing limitations on height, slenderness, and rigidity are not severe. Although they are highly visible, tall high-rise structures account for a very small portion of the total number of structures being built every day in every city and town in the world. The overwhelming majority of all structures now being built in the industry are low-rise, laterally braced, statically determinate structures; the discussions in this chapter concentrate on these low-rise structures.

Loads on the smaller structures just described are generally broken into two broad categories: gravity loads (dead and live), and lateral loads (wind and earthquake). In reality, live loads, wind loads, and earthquake loads may be highly dynamic; but in practice, such loads are transformed into equivalent static loads, and the structure is then designed for these equivalent static loads. Without exception, the individual members of routine structures are designed for static load conditions.

Environmental loads as a group are usually treated separately from the more traditional dead load, live load, wind load, and earthquake load. Environmental loads can vary widely due to such regional factors as climate, geography, and season. Such loads can include snow and ice in the northern latitudes, hurricane winds in the tropics, accumulation of windblown sand in the deserts, and rapid temperature changes in the path of chinook winds in Canada. The proper application of environmental loads depends on local practices; no attempt is made here to account for the multiplicity of special applications that exists at the local level.

In addition to the more conventional types of load, special types of loads may occur only while the structure is under construction. Typical of such construction loads are the loads due to plastic concrete: the concrete is initially a very heavy fluid, changing to a rigid solid after a short while. Such loads occurring on the construction falsework and formwork must be treated as special conditions of loading; they are not included in the discussions here.

This chapter presents methods for finding the loads that act *on* a structure. The distribution of these loads *within* the structure is treated in the next chapter. Of all the loads that can act *on* a routine structure, only the dead load (the actual weight of the structure) can be determined with any degree of accuracy; live loads, wind loads, and earthquake loads are represented by very rough estimates of things to come.

In the discussions of this chapter, the generic term *structure* is used instead of the architectural term *building*. The distinction is not great, but the term *structure*, as used here, includes industrial buildings and construction falsework as well as the usual applications to architectural buildings.

12.1 CATEGORIES OF LOAD

The first category of load is the gravity load, and the first gravity load to be considered is the dead load of the structure. As noted earlier, a *dead load* is a load arising from the actual weight of the structure and its components. Elements contributing to the dead load include windows, mullions, beams, floors, girders, columns, stairwells, plaster, rigid walls, electrical cable trays, and all other components that are rigidly fixed to the structural frame. They do not include carpets, file cabinets, shock-mounted mechanical equipment, furnishings, books, electrical cables, movable partitions, safes, or crane loads. With few exceptions, the dead load consists of the structural frame and all components rigidly attached to the structural frame; no loose items may be classified as dead loads.

The distinction whether a load is to be classified as a dead load or as some other type of load is important. Earthquake loads, for example, occur as a result of the rapid acceleration of the entire structure laterally when the earth moves sharply sideways underneath the structure. Only items that undergo lateral acceleration will create force ($F = ma$); hence, items in the structure that are fixed to the building must be distinguished from all others, because only the items of dead load will be used to calculate earthquake forces. The inclusion of nonfixed items in the dead load can produce wasteful overdesign for earthquake, while omission of fixed items can produce dangerous underdesign for earthquake. A careful determination of dead load is therefore an essential component of a realistic design for earthquake.

Another distinctive feature of dead load is that all of its components can be rather accurately defined. Their weights can be accurately determined, and structure can be provided within narrow limits to suit this well-defined part of the total load. The margin of error in the determination of dead load is *much* less than in the determination of live load, wind load, or earthquake load; hence, the factor of safety for dead load can be considerably less than it is for these other, less predictable loads. A reduced factor of safety for dead load is in fact used in the design of concrete structures, to produce a more efficient and more economical design with no sacrifice of overall quality. A careful determination of dead load is therefore an essential prerequisite for selecting the safety factors throughout the structure.

Further, the dead loads of a structure provide the primary contribution to foundation settlements, since foundation settlements are a function of the long-term loads on the foundations. Short-term loads such as wind loads and earthquake loads have little or no effect on settlements. The dead load plus some small portion of the live load are the only loads that are in place long enough to produce settlements; an accurate determination of dead load thus permits a more efficient foundation design to be made. A careful determination of dead load is therefore an essential component in making a realistic design for foundation settlements.

For the foregoing reasons, an accurate means to distinguish which loads on a structure are to be classified as dead load becomes quite important. One of the better means to judge whether a particular load is dead load is simply to determine whether the load will be accelerated laterally in an earthquake. If it undergoes lateral acceleration equal to the acceleration of the building frame, the load should be classified as a dead load; otherwise it should not.

According to the foregoing definition of dead load, the load must be accelerated at the same rate as the building frame. Even a slight sliding or rocking movement will disrupt the acceleration of an object to such an extent that its force becomes negligible. Items such as carpets, safes, books, and furnishings are unlikely to remain rigidly in position on the building frame; consequently, they will not develop a resisting force, and they should not be classified as dead loads.

For purposes of using this acceleration condition as a means to determine whether an item should be classified as dead load, it is irrelevant whether the structure is actually going to be subject to earthquake loading. The use of lateral earthquake accelerations simply provides a convenient way to make the determination. Once the items of dead load have been identified, the remaining gravity loads within the structure are classified by default as live loads.

The second gravity load that may act on a structure is the live load. A *live load* is any gravity load not classified as a dead load. Under this definition, for example, shock-mounted mechanical equipment in a building is classified as a live load. Since the mountings for such equipment will dampen the acceleration force, the equipment will not be accelerated with the building frame and therefore cannot be classified as a dead load. But since it is a gravity load, it must by default be classified as a live load. Thus, insofar as a dead load or live load classification is concerned, the load's short-term or long-term presence is not significant; the crucial question is whether the load is or is not accelerated with the structural frame.

The live load to which a structure may be subjected during its design life can vary widely, depending on the usage or occupancy of the structure. In addition, over the life of an architectural building, the usage itself can change sharply with each new tenant or each adaptation of the building to new functions. The live load for which a building is designed should, of course, include a reasonable allowance for possible changes.

The exact amount of live load to include in any structural design is largely a matter of individual judgment on the part of the designer to suit the particular client, the particular structural function, the particular site, and the particular city. Obviously, the design live load is not a consistent and well-defined quantity. Live load might better be regarded as an *allowable* load; under this interpretation, the structure can tolerate live loads arising from various functions of the structure up to some specified allowable amount. The concept of allowable live load is in fact widely used in the industry; and, in some cities, the building code requires that the allowable live load on a building floor be posted conspicuously on each floor of the building.

Arriving at a suitable and realistic live load for a structural design can sometimes be difficult. As a starting point, the building codes for a locality contain provisions for certain minimum live loads for various parts of a building, based on the occupancy (usage) of the buildings. Typical values for these minimum standards are presented later in this chapter.

The final category of load to be considered here is the lateral loads. Lateral loads are produced primarily by wind and earthquake; and since wind and earthquake forces vary with geographic location, a structure must be specifically designed to sustain prescribed wind and earthquake loads within the locale where it is to be built. Over the years, reliable and realistic data have been accumulated concerning wind and earthquake loading, so that a bracket of wind and earthquake loads can now be predicted for most localities with some degree of confidence.

Wind load on a structure arises from the pressure that a moving mass of air exerts on the structure. In some circumstances, the wind can also exert a suction force on the lee side of the structure. It may also exert a "lift" on the lee side of low gable roofs, similar to that exerted on an air foil. Or due to turbulence and eddy currents, the wind may produce unusually high magnifications of load at particular points of a structure—especially around gable points and eave corners. All such loads are included in building code requirements for the locality, or (more likely) the building code specifies an all-encompassing "blanket" load to be applied to the structure as a whole to allow for any such localized load concentrations.

Like wind, an earthquake produces a lateral load on a structure. Unlike wind, it also produces a vertical load as the earthquake "wave" passes under the structure. The vertical acceleration is so small, however, that no significant vertical forces are developed; since these vertical forces are not nearly as large as the dead and live loads, they are usually ignored. The lateral loads thus characterize earthquake loading, and these lateral loads must be provided for. Methods of analysis for lateral earthquake loads are presented in detail in Chapter 13.

Earthquake loads in the United States are not limited to Alaska and California, nor to the well-known San Andreas fault line. Earthquakes occur regularly over 95% of the area of the United States, some with intensities equal to those adjacent to the San Andreas fault. For example, probably the largest known earthquake on the North American continent in recorded history occurred near New Madrid, Missouri, in February 1812, reaching an estimated intensity of 8.6 on the Richter scale. The San Francisco earthquake of 1906 was, by comparison, a Richter 8.2 earthquake, and the Alaska earthquake of 1964 was a Richter 8.4 earthquake. Coping with earthquake loads constitutes a very real part of contemporary engineering design of structures in all geographic areas, and must be considered by any responsible designer of structures in today's practice.

12.2 LOAD COMBINATIONS

During its service life, a structure may be subject to dead loads, live loads, wind loads, and earthquake loads. In the normal service life of the structure, all of the dead load and some part of the live load can be expected to occur together. Moreover, while the structure is in service and therefore subject to this combination of dead and live loads, some additional level of loading due to wind or earthquake may occur. Consequently, the structure must be designed for some combination of all the vertical and lateral loads that might reasonably occur on it at the same time.

In arriving at some combination of loads for the design of the structure, it is unrealistic to assume that all of the maximum loads that might occur on a structure will occur simultaneously. It is unlikely, for example, that a structure will be subjected to a peak earthquake load at the same time that the wind is blowing at maximum velocity. Nor is it likely that the roof live load will be in place during peak wind velocities.

Further, it is not reasonable to require a structural material to sustain transient, rarely applied loads such as wind and earthquake loads at the same stress levels at which it must sustain long-term loads such as dead and live loads. A higher stress level (and possibly even limited damage) might be permitted to occur, for example, over the short duration of an earthquake, given that the maximum earthquake load (and limited damage) will likely occur only once in the life of the structure. Conversely, a reduced stress level might be advisable under a high sustained dead load (or prestressing load), that occurs at 100% of its design value 100% of the time.

In some circumstances, a lesser load (rather than a higher load) may cause worst-case stresses. For example, the capacity of a concrete column in moment can be seriously reduced when the sustained axial load is reduced. The worst-case load in such an instance may turn out to be the case in which axial loads are lightest.

In view of the wide variety of possibilities, a structure is almost without exception designed for several combinations of load rather than for just one combination. Over the years, several standard combinations of load have evolved, one of which usually produces worst-case loading on various structural members. In conjunction with these load combinations, the assumed overall stress levels are commonly allowed to increase by as much as 33%

whenever transient loads such as wind or earthquake are included. Further, the structure is usually checked for stress reversals under minimum vertical load (dead load only), applied in combination with the maximum lateral load (wind or earthquake).

The following list of load combinations identifies some of the more commonly used load cases:

$$\text{Dead load } + 100\% \text{ live load (or roof snow)} \qquad (12.1a)$$

$$(0.75) \, (\text{Dead load } + 100\% \text{ live load}$$
$$+ \text{ Wind or earthquake load }) \qquad (12.1b)$$

$$\text{Dead load } + \text{Wind or earthquake load} \qquad (12.1c)$$

Special load cases could, of course, be required for unusual circumstances. Notice that using 75% of a load at the usual allowable stress produces a 33% increase in stress at 100% of the load.

In addition to the foregoing load combinations for the structure itself, the foundations of the structure may have to be designed for other load conditions. One such extra condition is foundation settlements, which occur only under long-term sustained loads. To estimate settlements, one must first estimate the portion of the live load that will be in place long enough to produce settlements. The usual estimate is taken as 50% of the live load, although the estimate may range as low as 25% for a rarely used auditorium or as high as 75% for a fully stocked library. The following load combinations are commonly used for foundations:

$$\text{Dead load } + 100\% \text{ live load (for soil strength)} \qquad (12.2a)$$

$$\text{Dead load } + 50\% \text{ live load (for settlements)} \qquad (12.2b)$$

$$(0.75) \, (\text{Dead load } + 100\% \text{ live load}$$
$$+ \text{ Wind or earthquake load }) \qquad (12.2c)$$

$$\text{Dead load } + \text{Wind or earthquake load} \qquad (12.2d)$$

Equation 12.2(c) is applied to take soil strength into account, and Equation 12.2(d) is applied to take the possibility of overturning shearwall foundations into account.

The load combinations given in Equations 12.1 and 12.2 are among the most commonly used combinations in routine design. For special conditions, a designer may have to develop other combinations to anticipate a more severe worst-case condition. The final responsibility for correctly determining the design loads on a structural member rests with the designer.

12.3 BUILDING CODE REQUIREMENTS

Municipal building codes regulate numerous features in the design and construction of all buildings in the city. Provisions in the code concerning the structural design of buildings, however, constitute only a small portion of these codes. Far more extensive than the provisions for structural design are the provisions for electrical systems, for plumbing, for light and ventilation, and, most extensive of all, for fire safety.

A building code is a legal document that, when adopted by a city, attains the force of law. Enforcement of the building code is delegated to the building official for the city; this person, through a staff of plan reviewers and building inspectors, is responsible for seeing that all construction in the city conforms to the provisions of the building code. Even in small cities, the building official is a key figure in the city government.

The building code specifies only the minimum standards that must be met in design and construction. There is no assumption of liability by the city, however, if the code's minimum requirements prove to be inadequate for all conditions. Moreover, considerably higher standards may be required for such things as structural integrity, electrical safety, and adequate ventilation.

The existence of a building code does not relieve the designer of any responsibility for the integrity of the design. The person who signs the structural drawings remains professionally responsible and personally liable for the proper design of that structure. In the event of a structural failure, the designer cannot seek immunity from legal action on grounds that the design meets code requirements, because meeting minimum code requirements does not, in itself, guarantee structural adequacy.

Building codes apply only to a building that is to be built or to a remodeling project (if it is extensive enough). The authority of the building code does not extend to construction falsework or formwork, or to any other ancillary construction performed by the contractor engaged in the building construction. For the construction falsework and formwork, there are no design codes, no reviews, no inspectors and no controls; the contractor alone is responsible (and liable) for all aspects of the ancillary construction.

Insofar as structures are concerned, one important feature of the building code is its provisions for minimum design loads. In past years, those engaged in structural design came to rely heavily on code minimum standards as a reliable guide on which to base a design. In a push–pull reaction, those who write the codes have, over the same years, improved the standards for design loads to the point that the code minimum standards are now usually adequate for final design, particularly where wind and earthquake loads are involved. Frequently in today's industry, the code minimum standards for loads are accepted as a valid basis on which to base the final structural design. As always, however, the structural designer remains personally responsible to determine whether code minimum standards are in fact adequate for a particular project, or whether additional measures must be added.

Historically, a city might develop its own code or, in some cases, adopt another city's code and amend it to suit its own needs. Such circumstances surrounded the New York City building code which, in the early 1900s, was widely cited and quoted throughout the construction industry. Even today, the New York City building code remains one of the more impressive codes in the world and is still widely quoted and imitated by other cities.

In more recent times, the use of "model" codes has grown increasingly popular, particularly in smaller cities that recognize their need to have a detailed building code but simply cannot afford the expense of writing and maintaining one. Such cities now join an organization, at a nominal annual fee, and the organization thus funded produces and maintains a model building code for its members. Among the better known of these model codes is the Uniform Building Code, which is produced and maintained by the International Conference of Building Officials, based in Whittier, California. The Uniform Building Code is very popular in the western United States, and its provisions for earthquake loads have been widely adopted throughout much of the world. A model code that is very popular in the southern and southeastern United States is the Standard Building Code, which is produced and maintained by the Southern Building Code Congress International, Inc., based in Birmingham, Alabama. The Standard Building Code has in recent years focused attention on wind loading on low structures, significantly improving standards along the hurricane-prone Gulf Coast and southeast Atlantic Coast.

Typically, member cities cannot simply adopt the model code in its entirety and then pay no further attention to its municipal building code. Frequently, a city will have to enact legal amendments or revisions to the model code to suit the city's particular needs. As one may suppose, the building official is a key figure in identifying these needs and proposing suitable amendments for adoption by the city government.

Obviously, the structural design loads enumerated by one building code are very close to those given by similar codes; loads are not different because they happen to have been determined in Birmingham, Alabama, rather than in Whittier, California. But even though the end results must be quite similar, the approaches to the design may be quite different, and one code may require considerably more refined calculations than another code does. In this text, the more general approaches are usually presented, due largely to the author's lack of faith in the precision of highly refined calculations that begin with extremely arbitrary loads.

Building code requirements for earthquake-resistant structures are not intended to ensure that a structure will sustain earthquake loads without damage. An earthquake-resistant structure may, in fact, sustain serious damage in a major earthquake—possibly to such an extent that it may have to be torn down and rebuilt. An "earthquake-resistant" classification means only that the structure has been designed not to collapse and kill the occupants; however serious the damage, the structural frame is designed to stand until the human occupants can be evacuated. (In a similar context, a "fireproof" building will burn, but it, too, is designed to remain standing until the human occupants can be evacuated.)

REVIEW QUESTIONS

1. When structures reach a certain size, the way in which the structure responds to load undergoes significant change. What is that size, approximately?

2. What are the two broad categories of load to which a structure may be subjected, based on the direction of application of load?

3. Generally, what approach is used to design a structure for dynamic loading?

4. Generally, how are environmental loads integrated into structural analysis and design?

5. What are the two types of gravity loads?

6. How does one judge whether a gravity load should be classed as a dead load or as a live load?

7. For the four major loads (dead, live, wind, and earthquake), what is the relative accuracy with which each can be determined?

8. Identify three circumstances under which the accuracy of the dead load analysis can seriously affect later structural calculations.

9. How are foundation settlements generally incorporated into a structural analysis?

10. How do live loads on a steel building differ from those on a concrete building?

11. Generally, how are live loads determined?

12. What is the effect of building setbacks, notches, reveals, and so on, on a wind load?

13. Can one expect wind loads to be reasonably constant along the surface of a building? Explain.

14. How much of the United States is subject to earthquake loads?

15. How does one establish the combinations of load that will be used in the final design of a structure?

16. What is meant by the term *worst-case loading*?

17. By what reasoning is a stress increase permitted when wind and earthquake loads are included in a load combination?

18. What is the authority of the prevailing building code over the structural design of a project?

19. Other than structural adequacy, what aspects of building design are governed by the building code?

20. How are the provisions of the building code enforced?

21. To what extent does the building code govern the builder's construction of falsework, formwork, and other ancillary construction?

22. What is a model code?

23. How does a city adopt a model code?

24. Once a city adopts a model code, how does it handle special local circumstances and conditions such as those related to the city's geology, geography, or environment?

25. A "fireproof" building will in fact burn, and an "earthquake-resistant" building may in fact be destroyed by an earthquake. What is the real meaning of these two terms?

Bold functional use of reinforced concrete, Greensboro,
North Carolina. (Photograph courtesy Portland Cement
Association, reprinted by permission.)

CHAPTER

13

Load Calculations

This chapter presents standard methods to determine the magnitude and distribution of the loads that will be acting on a structure. As noted in Chapter 12, however, only the dead load can be determined with any degree of accuracy. The three remaining loads—live load, wind load, and earthquake load—can be predicted only within a broad range of probability.

These four loads are the only ones treated in this text. Other loads, including snow accumulation, blown sand accumulation, ponding of water on roofs, and other such environmental loads, are certainly real and legitimate loads to be considered in structural design, but these loads do not occur universally. The four loads treated in this text occur in almost all structural calculations. The less universal loads have been omitted in an effort to reduce clutter.

All loads, forces, and dimensions—both in this chapter and in Chapter 14—are expressed in imperial units. The reason is quite simple: the major building codes that prescribe these values give them in imperial units. An attempt is now underway to add metric units to the major codes, but so far it has only succeeded in cluttering the codes by listing metric conversions in parentheses following the imperial units. Currently, there is no SI edition for either of the two major codes (Standard Building Code or Uniform Building Code).

13.1 DEAD LOADS

Dead loads were defined earlier as those loads that will be accelerated laterally with the structural frame under earthquake motions. Dead loads include fenestration, exterior walls, fixed interior walls, floor slabs and beams, columns and girders, ceiling and roofing materials, plaster, tile, and any other materials rigidly attached to the structural frame. Dead loads are almost always permanent loads; they cannot usually be changed during the life of the structure except by additional construction or by rather drastic remodeling of the building itself.

A wide variety of materials may be used in the construction of the structure and then become part of the dead load. The weights of such items must be computed in any attempt to find the total dead load of the structure. A typical list of these materials, as well as of many other common construction materials is given in Table 13-1, along with their nominal weights.

Table 13-1 Dead Loads: Weights of Common Building Materials

Material	psf	Material	psf
Ceilings		Partitions	
Furred channel system	1	Clay tile	
Acoustic fiber tile	1	3 in.	17
Floors		4 in.	18
Concrete, per inch		6 in.	28
Stone	12 1/2	8 in.	34
Slag	11 1/2	10 in.	40
Lightweight	6 to 10	Gypsum block	
Fills, per inch		2 in.	9 1/2
Gypsum	6	3 in.	10 1/2
Sand	8	4 in.	12 1/2
Cinders	4	5 in.	14
Mortar bedding	9	6 in.	
Finishes, per inch		Plaster, per inch	
Terrazzo	13	Cement	10
Quarried tile	12 1/2	Gypsum	5
Mastic	11 1/2	Lathing	
Hardwood	5	Expanded metal	1/2
Softwood	4	Gypsum board 1/2 in.	2
Roofs		Walls	
Copper	1	Brick	
3-ply felt and gravel	5 1/2	4 in.	40
5-ply felt and gravel	6	8 in.	80
Shingles		12 in.	120
Wood	2	Hollow concrete block	
Asphalt	3	Heavy aggregate	
Clay tile	9 to 15	4 in.	30
Slate, 1/4 in.	10	6 in.	44
Sheathing, per inch		8 in.	56
Wood	4	12 in.	80
Gypsum	4	Light aggregate	
Insulation, per inch		4 in.	21
Loose	1/2	6 in.	30
Poured in place	2	8 in.	38
Rigid	1 1/2	12 in.	56
Corrugated asbestos, 1/2 in. thickness	3		
Corrugated steel deck		Clay tile	
16 ga.	2.7	4 in.	25
18 ga.	2.2	6 in.	30
20 ga.	1.6	8 in.	33
24 ga.	1.1	12 in.	45
28 ga.	0.7	Structural glass, 1 in.	15
		Timber, nominal weight	42 pcf
		Concrete, nominal weight	145 pcf

Adapted from the "Manual of Steel Construction," American Institute of Steel Construction, 9th Ed.

The computation of the dead load acting on a structure is usually performed with considerable care. Some examples will illustrate such computations for various common types of construction.

Example 13-1   Determine the dead load per square foot produced by the given floor system.

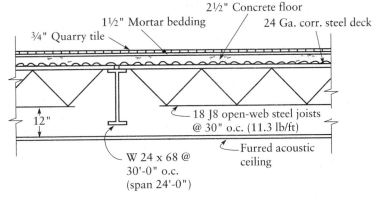

2½" Concrete floor
1½" Mortar bedding
24 Ga. corr. steel deck
¾" Quarry tile
12"
18 J8 open-web steel joists @ 30" o.c. (11.3 lb/ft)
W 24 x 68 @ 30'-0" o.c. (span 24'-0")
Furred acoustic ceiling

Solution   The dead loads for the floor system are found in Table 13-1. The relevant values are

3/4 in. quarry tile:	0.75×12.5	= 9.4 psf
1 1/2 in. mortar bedding:	1.50×9.0	= 13.5 psf
2 3/4 in. (avg.) concrete:	2.75×12.5	= 34.4 psf
Corrugated steel form:		= 1.1 psf
Steel joist:	$11.3 \text{ plf}/(30/12)$	= 4.5 psf
Furred ceiling:		= 1.0 psf
		Σ = 64.0 psf

Notice that, in the calculations, the weight of the steel joist is given in pounds per linear foot. To convert this value into an equivalent load in pounds per square foot, one must divide by the joist spacing in feet:

$$\frac{30}{12} = 2.5 \text{ ft}$$

Example 13-2   For the floor system of Example 13-1, determine the equivalent dead load per square foot that is to be carried by the steel girder W24 × 68.

Solution   Refer to the sketch of Example 13-1. In joist systems where joists are relatively closely spaced, the practice is to take the load as a uniformly distributed load on the girder rather than to use the joist reactions as discrete loads.
From Example 13-1,

$$w_{DL} = 64 \text{ psf}$$

To this load, the dead load of the girder must be added, expressed as a load per square foot. For the girder,

$$w_{DL} = \frac{68}{30} = 2.3 \text{ psf}$$

The total dead load is therefore

$$w_{DL} = 64 + 2.3 = 66.3 \text{ psf}$$

Example 13-3   For the accompanying configurations (page 401), determine the weight of the perimeter wall that must be carried by the floor girder. Give the result in pounds per linear foot of wall.

Solution   For standard masonry walls, tables are available that give nominal unit weights for various configurations. The configuration of this example is not a standard one, however, so the load must be computed independently.
The wall consists of window units 24 in. wide interspersed with masonry panels, also 24 in. wide. The load will be computed for a 48-in. (4-ft) length. The load on the girder will then be taken as the average load per foot of length of the wall.

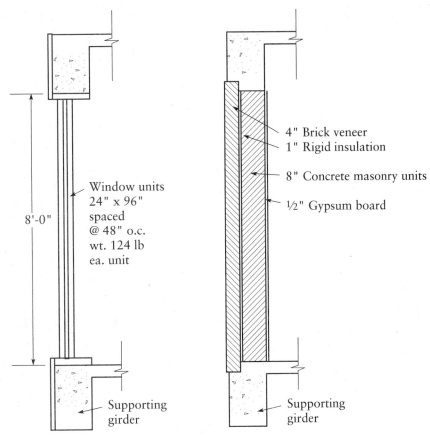

4" Brick veneer
1" Rigid insulation

8" Concrete masonry units

½" Gypsum board

Window units
24" x 96"
spaced
@ 48" o.c.
wt. 124 lb
ea. unit

8'-0"

Supporting girder

Supporting girder

In one 4'-0" segment, the following loads occur

Window unit		= 124 lb
4-in. brick veneer	40 psf × 8 ft × 2 ft	= 640 lb
8-in. CMU	38 psf × 8 ft × 2 ft	= 608 lb
1-in. rigid insulation	1.5 psf × 8 ft × 2 ft	= 24 lb
1/2-in. gypsum board	2 psf × 8 ft × 2 ft	= 32 lb
		$\Sigma = 1428$ lb

Weight per foot $= \dfrac{1428}{4}$

$w_{DL} = 357$ plf   (average load of wall)

Example 13-4 For the accompanying design, determine the dead load of the roof system. Give the result in psf on the horizontal projection of the roof.

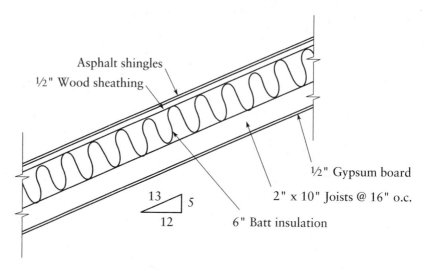

Solution The load is first computed per linear foot of roof along the slope:

$$\text{Weight per ft of a } 2 \times 10 \left[\text{actual dimensions: } 1\frac{1}{2} \times 9\frac{1}{2} \right]$$

$$= (1.5 \times 9.5 \times 12)\left(\frac{42}{1728}\right)$$

$$= 4.2 \text{ plf}$$

The roof load can now be computed:

Asphalt shingles		= 3 psf
1/2-in. wood sheathing	4 psf × 1/2 in.	= 2 psf
Batt insulation	1/2 psf × 6	= 3 psf
2 × 10 joists	4.2 plf × 12/16	= 3 psf
Gypsum board		= 2 psf
		Σ = 13 psf

On a 5:12 slope, the horizontal projection of the load is

$$w_{DL} = 13 \text{ psf} \times \left(\frac{13}{12}\right)$$

$$= 14 \text{ psf}$$

Notice that the 2×10 joists weigh 4.2 plf, but they are spaced at 16 in. o.c. Their weight per square foot is therefore

$$4.2 \text{ plf} \times \left(\frac{12}{16} \right) = 3.15 \text{ psf}$$

Outside Problems

Problem 13-1*

A flat roof is composed of three-ply felt and gravel over 3 inches of rigid insulation. The roof structure is a concrete deck 3" thick supported on concrete joists 6" wide, spaced at 36" on center; the overall depth of slab and joists is 17". A furred ceiling of acoustic tile is suspended horizontally from the joists. Sketch the system, and determine the dead load of the roof in pounds per square foot.

Problem 13-2

A roof slopes 9:12. The roofing consists of wood shingles attached to 5/8-in. oriented strand board sheathing. The sheathing is supported on $2" \times 10"$ wood joists spaced at 16" on center. The roof is insulated with loose insulation placed full depth between joists. The ceiling below is cement plaster, 3/4" thick, placed directly on the lower face of the joists. Sketch the system, and determine the dead load in pounds per square foot on the horizontal projected area.

Problem 13-3*

A roof slopes 5:12. The roofing consists of clay tile bedded in mortar averaging 1 1/2" thick on a cast-in-place deck of concrete, 2 1/2" thick. The roof is supported by a 20-gauge corrugated steel deck placed over open-web steel joists spaced at 48" on center. Joist weight is 6.8 plf. The insulation is blown loose between joists, averaging 9" in thickness. The acoustic fiber tile ceiling is suspended horizontally from the lower chord of the joists on a furred channel system. Sketch the system, and determine the dead load in pounds per square foot on the horizontal projected area.

Problem 13-4

A typical floor in a multistory building consists of a concrete tee beam system. The floor slab in the system is 4" thick, supported by tee beams having stems 10" wide. Tee beams are spaced at 8'-0" on center. The overall depth of slab and tee is 21". The floor surface is 3/4" hardwood parquet. The ceiling at the lower level is an acoustic fiber ceiling on a furred channel system, suspended from the concrete floor above. A load of 3 psf is to be allowed for mechanical ductwork and equipment, and a load of 2 psf is to be allowed for electrical cable trays and fixtures. Sketch the system, and determine the average dead load per square foot.

Problem 13-5*

A rooftop patio deck for an apartment building is to be built on poured-in-place insulation, with 3 1/2" average thickness, cast directly on a 20-gauge corrugated steel deck. The deck is to be supported by open-web steel joists spaced at 2'-8" on center; joist weight is 7.1 lb/ft. The wearing surface of the patio deck is to be quarried tile bedded in 1 1/2" mortar. The joist system must also support a mechanical equipment load of 4 psf and an electrical equipment load of 2 psf. The ceiling below the roof is to be metal lath and gypsum plaster, 3/4" thick, attached directly to the lower chord of the joists. Sketch the system, and determine the dead load in psf.

Problem 13-6

A timber floor for an industrial warehouse is composed of 2" × 6" decking supported by 4" × 10" timber joists spaced at 2'-8" on center. The joists are supported 6" × 16" girders, spaced at 12'-0" on center. Actual size of a 2 × 6 is 1 1/2" × 5 1/4", actual size of a 4 × 10 is 3 1/2" × 9 1/4" and actual size of a 6 × 16 is 5 1/4" × 15 1/4". Sketch the system, and determine the dead load of the floor system in psf.

Problem 13-7*

A masonry bearing wall 10'-0" high is to be built of lightweight concrete block, 12" thick, faced both sides with 4" brick. Sketch the wall section, and determine the dead weight of the wall per linear foot of length.

Problem 13-8

Lightweight concrete masonry units are considered to be 50% open cells. If 25% of the open cells are to be filled with concrete as a part of the earthquake reinforcement, what is the average weight of the resulting wall in pounds per square foot?

13.2 LIVE LOADS

Live loads are gravity loads that are not identified as dead loads. Obviously, this is a negative definition, in which live loads are identified by default when they fail to qualify as dead loads; if a gravity load is not a dead load, it is by default a live load. Alternatively, live loads might be defined more positively as those gravity loads on the structure that do not accelerate laterally at the same rate as the structural frame when the structure undergoes earthquake motion. A brief list of common live loads is given in Table 13-2. Live loads include all living beings, mobile loads, loose furnishings, unattached objects, and all other components in the building that will slip, slide, tilt, or wobble when the structural frame jerks sharply sideways in an earthquake. Most live loads are quite easy to identify. Others may take some thought. For example, a safe, that is rigidly bolted to the floor is a dead load, not a live load; but if that same safe were not bolted down, it would be a live load.

Table 13-2 Minimum Design Live Loads

a. Uniformly Distributed Live Loads Based on Occupancy

OCCUPANCY	psf	OCCUPANCY	psf
Armories and drill rooms	150	Residential	
Assembly halls and theaters		Multifamily units	
Fixed seats	60	Private apartments	40
Movable seats	100	Public rooms	100
Balconies, exterior	100	Corridors	60
Bowling alleys	75	Single-family units	
Dance halls	100	First floor	40
Dining areas	100	Habitable attics	30
Gymnasium floors	100	Storage areas	30
Hospitals		Hotels	
Operating rooms	60	Guest rooms	40
Private rooms	40	Public rooms	100
Wards	40	Primary corridors	100
Libraries		Public corridors	60
Reading rooms	60	Private corridors	40
Stack rooms	150	Schools	
Manufacturing	125	Classrooms	40
Marquees	75	Corridors	100
Office buildings		Stairs and fire escapes	100
Offices	80	Stands and bleachers	100
Lobbies	100	Stores, retail	
Penal institutions		First-floor rooms	100
Cell blocks	40	Upper floors	75
Corridors	100	Stores, wholesale	125

(continued)

Table 13-2 *(continued)*

b. Uniformly Distributed Live Loads Based on Use

USE	psf	USE	psf
Air-conditioning equipment	200	Garages, ramps, and drives	
Amusement-park structures	100	Trucks, 3 to 10 tons	150
Bakeries	150	Trucks above 10 tons	200
Boathouse floors	100	Greenhouses	150
Boiler rooms, framed	300	Hangars	150
Broadcasting studios	100	Incinerator floors	100
Catwalks	25	Kitchens, commercial	150
Dormitories		Laboratories, science	100
Partitioned	40	Laundries	150
Nonpartitioned	80	Libraries, corridors	100
Elevator machine rooms	150	Morgues	100
Fan rooms	150	Public rooms	100
File rooms		Rest rooms	60
Letter	80	Rinks, ice skating	250
Card	125	Storage, hay or grain	300
Addressograph	150	Telephone exchanges	150
Foundries	600	Toilet rooms	60
Fuel rooms, framed	400	Transformer rooms	200

Mechanical equipment that contains rotating machinery (motors, compressors, and so on) is almost always provided with shock-mounted supports to reduce vibration. Such supports also sharply reduce any lateral accelerations produced by an earthquake; hence, the equipment and housing are classified as live load. It does not matter that the equipment will be permanently in place for the life of the building. It is important only that the equipment will not be accelerated sideways at the same rate as the structural frame; it is therefore classified as live load.

The allowance for live load on a floor or a wall is almost always specified in pounds per square foot of surface area. The live load is considerably higher in corridors, where heavy foot traffic occurs, than in individual rooms, where loads are more uniformly dispersed. Implicitly, there is also the effect of dynamic loading in corridors, where the foot traffic by its dynamic characteristics can produce an increase in the vertical load. Consequently, building codes always specify a distinctly higher value of minimum loading for corridors than for other areas.

Another type of dynamic loading that can occur on a structure is that of a moving crane, a monorail, or any mobile equipment (forklifts, mobile dollies, cherry pickers, and so on) that is used to move, lift, or stack goods inside the structure. Lifting (or dropping) such cargo can produce dynamic loads considerably higher than the actual weight of the cargo. For such loads, a minimum increase of 33% in the static design load is usually specified by code.

Dynamic effects should not be underestimated. In a football stadium, for example, the design should allow for a capacity crowd as its maximum load. But in the last few seconds of an exciting game, that entire capacity crowd will often respond to a long pass or to a last-ditch reception by suddenly standing *en masse*, thereby producing an almost instantaneous acceleration of the entire live load; the resulting increase in the downward and lateral force on the stands can be as much as 30% to 50% of the static load. Such dynamic loads produced by a moving audience have been known to trigger catastrophic failures in bleachers and grandstands.

The effects of this type of dynamic loading are generically called "impact loading" on a structure. In most cases, the impact loading imparted by a particular live load is specified as a percentage of the live load. In a stadium, for example, the impact loading might be specified as 1/3 of the total live load. The minimum requirements for impact loading are usually included in the building code for the particular locale, but building codes are intended to be very general. The final value of impact loading to be used on a particular structure is governed by the judgment of the designer, with due regard for the minimums set forth in the building code.

Several special provisions concerning live loads are sometimes included in the building code. One such special provision is a requirement that the structure be able to sustain a 1-ton concentrated load at any point in the floor span; this 1-ton load supposedly represents a safe or other heavy mobile load that might be moved around in any room in the building. The 1-ton load is not to be applied on top of the regular live load, but is to be applied as an alternate load case. Such a concentrated load is rarely critical for flexural members or columns, but it often creates a critical condition for shear in beams when placed near a support; timber joists are particularly sensitive to such loading and should always be checked for this load concentration.

Another special provision that may be included in the building code is a reduction in roof live load when tributary areas are large. Roof live load usually corresponds to the weight of workmen who are building or reroofing the roof, along with the weight of their stacked materials or roofing equipment. If supports are only 6 feet apart, the entire 6 feet may well be subjected to the full live load. If the supports are 48 feet apart, however, it is unlikely that every square foot will be subject to the full live load; the building code may therefore allow a reduction in live load when tributary areas are large. The local building code should always be examined for this possible reduction.

Another special provision in some building codes is a permissible reduction in column live loads for multistory buildings. This provision recognizes that every floor in a multistory building is unlikely to be loaded to its maximum capacity at the same time. Accordingly, the building code may allow a reduction in column and foundation loads to more reasonable levels with no sacrifice of quality or structural integrity. Notice that the reduction does *not* apply to floor loads; each floor must still be designed for the full specified live load. But when the total vertical load is computed for the columns and their foundations, a reduction in column live load may be permitted because of the improbability that maximum load will exist simultaneously at every story. Again, the local building code should be examined for this possible reduction.

One last point concerning live loads merits attention. In earlier discussions, it was noted that a piece of shock-mounted mechanical equipment mounted on the roof of a building would be classified as live load. Such equipment is indeed heavy, but in many cases its weight per square foot is less than the uniform live load. An air-conditioning heat exchanger, for example, might measure 6 ft by 15 ft and weigh 1400 pounds; the unit weight of such a heat exchanger however, is only 16 psf—less than the usual roof live load of 20 psf. Obviously, the entire live load of 20 psf is unlikely to occur over this area if the heat exchanger is in place; it is left to the individual designer to choose which load is most appropriate—the actual live load of 16 psf, the uniform generic load of 20 psf, or some combination of both.

Some examples will demonstrate how to calculate the live loads acting on various parts of a structure.

Example 13-5

For the joist system of Example 13-1, determine the live load to be carried by the joist if the joist lies directly under a corridor in an elementary school.

Solution

For schools, the corridor live load is taken from Table 13-2 as 100 psf. Hence,

Live load per joist = 100 psf

Example 13-6

For the joist system of Examples 13-1 and 13-2, determine the live load on the W24 × 68 girder for the part of a flooring system that supports a classroom in an elementary school.

Solution

For a school classroom, the floor live load is taken from Table 13-2 as 40 psf. Hence,

Live load per girder = 40 psf

From the foregoing examples, it appears that the type of construction has no influence on the selection of the live load. The building may be built in steel, timber, or concrete, but the live load remains the same. Only the function of the building is considered when the live load is selected.

Example 13-7 A floor system in a library reading room is supported by 2×10 joists at 16 in. o.c.; the joists span 18'-0". The dead weight of the entire floor system is 21 psf. Code requires that the floor system be able to sustain a 2000-lb load placed anywhere in the room. Determine the design shear force at the end of a joist.

Solution For a dead load of 21 psf, the dead load per foot is

$$w_{DL} = 21 \times \left(\frac{16}{12} \right) = 28 \text{ plf}$$

on one joist. For a library reading room, live load is taken from Table 13-2 as 60 psf. Hence,

$$w_{LL} = 60 \times \left(\frac{16}{12} \right) = 80 \text{ plf}$$

on one joist. Total load per joist is then

$$w_{TOTAL} = 28 + 80 = 108 \text{ plf}$$

Reaction (shear) on a span of 18 ft = $wL/2$;

$$V = \frac{wL}{2} = 108 \times \left(\frac{18}{2} \right) = 972 \text{ lb}$$

As an alternate load case, a 2000-lb load is placed at the end of the joist, as shown in the following sketch.

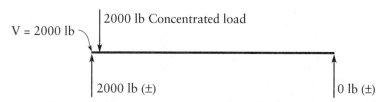

V = 2000 lb   2000 lb Concentrated load

2000 lb (±)   0 lb (±)

The design load for shear for the concentrated load is thus 2000 lb. Use $V = 2000$ lb shear per joist.

Example 13-8 Determine the design live load for the bleachers in a football stadium, using an impact factor of 33%.

Solution From Table 13-2, the design live load is 100 psf, with an impact factor of 33%. Hence,

$$w_{LL} = 100 \times 1.33 = 133 \text{ psf} \quad \text{(live load)}$$

From the foregoing examples, it should be apparent that selecting live load is rarely difficult or complicated when the architectural uses of the building are well defined. When parts of a single building have different uses, however, such as the various parts of a hotel, just keeping track of the various floor live loads can be tedious.

Outside Problems Determine the live load per square foot to be used in the following applications.

Problem 13-9* Private residential apartments.

Problem 13-10 Gymnasium floors, with 33% localized impact.

Problem 13-11* Interior machinery and equipment rooms.

Problem 13-12 Roof mounted air-conditioning equipment.

Problem 13-13* School corridors.

Problem 13-14 Library stacks.

Problem 13-15* Automobile parking garage ramps.

Problem 13-16 Commercial iron foundry floors.

13.3 WIND LOADS

Wind loads are by far the most common of the major lateral loads that occur on structures. In the Mississippi Valley, where winds rarely exceed 90 mph, the wind loads on buildings can be quite nominal. Along the Atlantic Coast, however, hurricane winds of more than 120 mph can occur with some regularity; and since wind pressure increases with the square of wind velocity, the wind loading along the Atlantic Coast is often the dominant load case. In either case, however, the design of a structure to sustain a wind load, at whatever the wind velocity, follows the same general procedures.

The wind force on a structure is obviously proportional to wind velocity. Wind velocity, in turn, depends to a great extent on latitude, geography, climate, terrain, and local site obstructions. The maximum wind velocity that might occur at a particular site is therefore very difficult to predict accurately; it is always very sensitive to local conditions.

On a broad geographical basis, wind velocity charts have been created to show generally the maximum wind velocities that may be expected within various regions. Figure 13-1 shows one such chart for the United States; the indicated wind velocities are those at a standard height of 30 feet above the surface. In view of the highly approximate nature of any such forecast, the chart is probably as accurate as anything that can reasonably be developed.

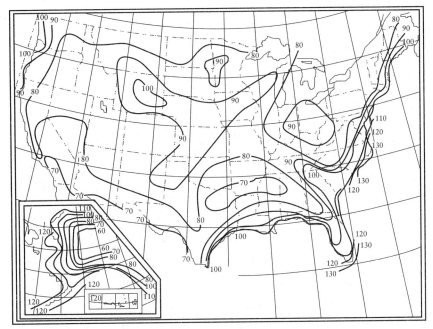

Source: Standard Building Code, 1982 edition

FIGURE 13-1 Basic wind speeds in miles per hour.

The wind pressure on a structure increases with the height of the structure, being somewhat less near the ground than at higher elevations. For calculations, a reference "stagnation" pressure is chosen at some standard height above ground level, usually 30 feet. The stagnation pressure is the pressure produced by the wind when all of its kinetic energy ($1/2\ mv^2$) is transformed into static pressure. At the 30-ft level, the reference stagnation pressure p_{REF} in pounds per square foot is given by the equation

$$p_{REF} = 0.00256\ V^2 \tag{13.1}$$

where V is the wind velocity in miles per hour.

At heights other than 30 feet, the variation in wind pressure is computed by applying a factor to this reference stagnation pressure. A typical variation is given by

$$p_s = 0.00256 \ V^2\left(\frac{H}{30}\right)^{\frac{2}{7}} \qquad\qquad (13.2)$$

where H is the height above ground, and where H has a minimum value of 15 feet. The value of this stagnation pressure p_s in Equation 13.2 has been computed for various heights and wind velocities and has been tabulated in Table 13-3 for ready reference.

Table 13-3 Basic Wind Pressures in psf

HEIGHT ABOVE GROUND (FEET)	WIND VELOCITY (IN mph)						
	70	80	90	100	110	120	130
0	10	13	17	21	25	30	36
15	10	13	17	21	25	30	36
20	11	15	18	23	28	33	39
25	12	16	20	24	29	35	41
30	13	16	21	26	31	37	43
35	13	17	22	27	32	39	45
40	14	18	23	28	34	40	47
45	14	18	23	29	35	41	49
50	15	19	24	30	36	43	50
55	15	19	25	30	37	44	51
60	15	20	25	31	38	45	53
65	15	20	26	32	39	46	54
70	16	21	26	33	39	47	55

The wind pressures given by Equation 13.1 and tabulated in Table 13-3 are simply reference (or stagnation) wind pressures for various wind velocities at various heights above ground level. The pressure exerted on an actual structure may vary considerably from these values, depending on the configuration or shape of the structure. To account for such variations in shape, the actual pressure is found by applying a "shape factor" to the reference pressures. These shape factors are significantly affected by the general angle the structure makes to the ground, and by whether it is vertical, inclined, or horizontal; consideration of these angles is included in Table 13-4, where typical shape factors are listed.

TABLE 13-4 Shape Factors for Primary Frames and Systems

Vertical Surfaces

SHAPE OF VERTICAL SURFACE	SHAPE FACTOR NORMAL TO PROJECTED SURFACE AREA
Rectangular prismatic structures[1]	1.3
Cylinders (chimneys, tanks, etc.)	0.7
Flat planes (signs, fences, billboards)	1.4
Partially open surfaces[2]	
10% solid	0.35
20% solid	0.55
40% solid	0.80
60% solid	0.80
80% solid	1.20
100% solid	1.30

Inclined Surfaces

INCLINATION OF SURFACE FROM HORIZONTAL[3]	SHAPE FACTOR NORMAL TO AN INCLINED WINDWARD SURFACE	SHAPE FACTOR NORMAL TO AN INCLINED LEEWARD SURFACE
80°–90°	treat as a vertical surface	
70°–80°	0.80 pressure	0.70 suction
60°–70°	0.65 pressure	0.70 suction
50°–60°	0.55 pressure	0.70 suction
40°–50°	0.25 pressure	0.70 suction
30°–40°	0.25 suction	0.70 suction
20°–30°	0.75 suction	0.70 suction
10°–20°	0.93 suction	0.70 suction
0°–10°	treat as a horizontal surface	
overhangs and eaves[4]	1.50 suction	1.50 suction

Horizontal Surfaces

TYPE OF SURFACE	SHAPE FACTOR NORMAL TO WINDWARD THIRD OF SURFACE AREA	SHAPE FACTOR NORMAL TO LEEWARD TWO–THIRDS OF SURFACE AREA
Enclosed buildings	1.0 suction	0.75 suction
Buildings having one or more sides open	1.5 suction	1.25 suction
Overhangs and eaves[4]	1.5 suction	1.50 suction

[1]Distributed 0.8 pressure at windward side plus 0.5 suction at leeward side.
[2]Shape factor to be applied to gross area of surface.
[3]For buildings with one or more sides open, add 1.0 suction to all suction factors.
[4]This factor is not additive; it is treated as a separate load in all cases.

The shape factors of Table 13-4 are extracted generally from the Standard Building Code, 1982 edition. They are typical of the factors contained in any common building code. While there may be some variation in approach, all of the well-known codes necessarily produce similar values for the wind pressure acting on a structure.

In addition to the overall average wind load to be borne by the primary structural system, there may be localized concentrations of pressure. Such localized concentrations can occur around building components that directly receive the wind pressure and then transfer the resulting force to the primary structural system. A tabulation of typical factors to be applied to such components is given in Table 13-5.

Table 13-5 Shape Factors for Transfer Members

Components Transferring Wind Load to the Primary Structure

COMPONENTS HAVING VERTICAL SURFACES[1]	SHAPE FACTORS IF COMPONENT IS ON WINDWARD SIDE	SHAPE FACTORS IF COMPONENT IS ON LEEWARD SIDE
Exterior walls of closed buildings, including fixed glass, glazing, windows, doors, fixed panels, veneer facings, and supporting members	1.1 (pressure)	1.1 (suction)
Exterior walls of buildings with one or more sides open, including fixed glass, glazing, windows, doors, fixed panels, veneer facings, and supporting members	1.1 (pressure)	1.5 (suction)

[1]For inclined surfaces and horizontal surfaces, the shape factors given in Table 13-4 remain valid.

A few moments of reflection concerning Table 13-5 are in order. For example, consider a long line of vertical plate glass windows located on the windward side of a building when the building is subjected to a basic wind pressure of 30 psf. The overall average pressure (given by Table 13-4) to be sustained by the primary structural system on that side of the building is 0.80×30 or 24 psf. But locally, at the plate glass windows themselves, the attachments, seals, glass, and fittings may be subject to concentrations that can produce much higher peak pressures (given by Table 13-5)—up to 1.1×30 or 33 psf. The localized peak pressure is thus some 38% above the average pressure. This peak pressure is used when the window frames and attachments are being designed, although the overall average pressure is used for design of the supporting structural frame.

The 38% increase in local pressure indicated by the foregoing example is not unreasonable or unusual. Such localized pressure concentrations are often quite high and can produce unexpected and sometimes dangerous structural damage. Localized pressure concentrations due to wind load may be among the most underrated hazards in all of structural design.

A few examples will demonstrate how to calculate wind pressures acting against a structure, including the variation of the pressure with height.

Example 13-9   The rectangular building shown in the accompanying sketch is of diaphragm/shear panel construction with masonry filler walls; it has a total dead weight of 2520 tons. The building is located in the vicinity of Nashville, Tennessee. Determine the following pressures, taken at midheight of each story.

1. Design wind pressure on the structural frame.

2. Design wind pressure on the windward walls.

3. Design wind pressure on the leeward walls.

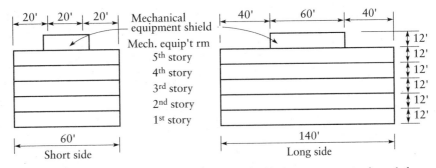

Solution   The wind velocity in the vicinity of Nashville, Tennessee, is found from Figure 13-1 to be nearly 90 mph. Therefore, a velocity of 90 mph will be used in this example. For this wind velocity, the reference stagnation pressure is

$$p_{REF} = 0.00256 \ V^2 = 21 \text{ psf}$$

The design wind pressure to the middle of each 12-ft story may be calculated from Equation 13.2 or interpolated from Table 13-3:

at 6 ft above ground, $p_S = 17$ psf

at 18 ft above ground, $p_S = 18$ psf

at 30 ft above ground, $p_S = 21$ psf

at 42 ft above ground, $p_S = 23$ psf

at 54 ft above ground, $p_S = 25$ psf

at 66 ft above ground, $p_S = 26$ psf

These wind pressures are the stagnation pressures. The design wind pressures for a rectangular shape are found by using these stagnation pressures with the shape factor of 1.3 given in Table 13-4. The final design wind pressures on the structural frame are shown in the following sketch.

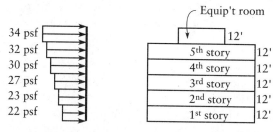

The design pressures against the windward and leeward walls are also prescribed in Table 13-4 (in note 1); the pressure on the two sides of a rectangle is distributed as 80% pressure on the windward side and 50% suction on the leeward side. The results are shown in the following sketch.

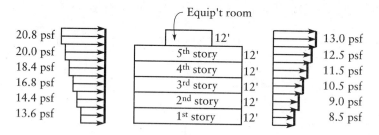

Except in relation to story height, the actual dimensions of the building of Example 13-9 never entered into the solution for pressures. The silhouette dimensions do enter the design later, however, when forces are computed.

Example 13-10   A cylindrical silo 16 ft in diameter and 50 ft high is to be built in the vicinity of Wichita, Kansas. The silo is to be of steel construction, with a total dead weight of 8400 lb. The silo will be bolted to a concrete foundation slab, and will contain silage weighing 26 lb/ft³. Determine the design wind pressure at 10-ft increments along the height of the silo.

Solution   According to Figure 13-1, the wind velocity in the vicinity of Wichita is taken as 90 mph. The design wind pressure at 10-ft intervals along the silo may be computed from Equation 13.2 or read from Table 13-3. The increment of 10 feet is arbitrarily chosen; it produces even increments over the 50-ft. height of the structure. Hence, the design wind pressures are.

at 5 ft. above ground, $p_s = 17$ psf

at 15 ft. above ground, $p_s = 17$ psf

at 25 ft. above ground, $p_s = 20$ psf

at 35 ft. above ground, $p_s = 22$ psf

at 45 ft. above ground, $p_s = 23$ psf

The shape factor for a cylinder is found in Table 13-4 to be 0.70. The final wind pressures against the silo are therefore 0.7 times the stagnation pressures. The final results are shown in the following sketch.

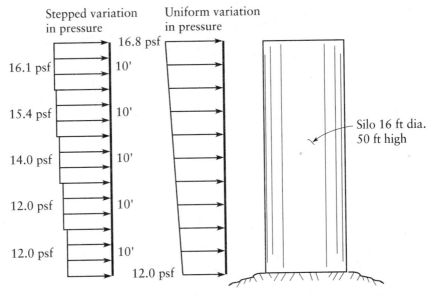

For comparison, the wind pressure is also computed as if the variation were a straight line from bottom to top. The pressure at the bottom would be $0.70 \times 17 = 12.0$ psf, and the pressure at the top would be $0.7 \times 24 = 16.8$ psf. These results are also shown in the sketch.

Example 13-11   A water tower is to be constructed near Portland, Oregon, from rough-sawn timber; the configuration is shown in the accompanying sketch. The total dead weight of tower and tank is to be 6700 lb; the steel tank alone will weigh 1400 lb. Determine the wind pressures acting on the structure.

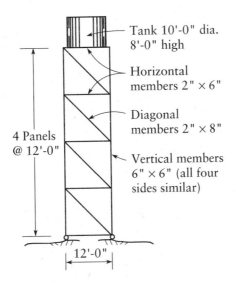

Solution   A typical panel is shown in the following sketch.

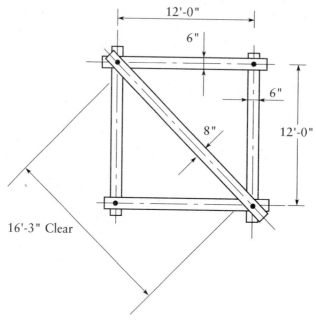

It is assumed that the wind "sees" both sides of the tower as it passes through the truss. The solid portion of the projected area is therefore taken as the solid area on two sides, divided by the overall projected area:

$$\text{Open area} = (11.5 \text{ ft} \times 11.5 \text{ ft} - 0.67 \text{ ft} \times 16.25 \text{ ft})$$
$$= 485 \text{ ft}^2$$

$$\text{Total area} = 12.5 \times 48.25$$
$$= 603 \text{ ft}^2$$

$$\text{Solid portion} = 2\frac{(603 - 485)}{603}$$
$$= 39.1 \approx 40\%$$

According to Table 13-4, the shape factors are 0.8 on the truss and 0.7 on the cylindrical tank. The wind velocity near Portland, Oregon, is found from Figure 13-1 to be 100 mph. Wind pressures may be computed from Equation 13.2 or interpolated from Table 13-3:

at 6 ft above ground, $p_s = 21$ psf

at 18 ft above ground, $p_s = 22$ psf

at 30 ft above ground, $p_s = 26$ psf

at 42 ft above ground, $p_s = 28$ psf

at 53 ft above ground, $p_s = 30$ psf

The pressure distribution is found by using these stagnation pressures in conjunction with the shape factors found previously. Final results are shown on the following sketch.

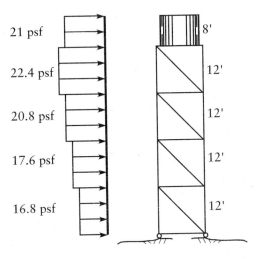

The calculations in Example 13-10 for projected area are somewhat rough. Elaborate refinements in such calculations are unwarranted, however, in view of the approximate nature of the design wind velocity, the wind distribution, and the shape factors. In such circumstances, rough calculations, conscientiously applied, are entirely adequate.

The foregoing examples demonstrate only the calculation of overall average wind pressures acting against the surface of a structure. It remains now to calculate the forces—rather than the pressures—that act on the structure itself. One useful concept in calculating such forces is the base shear, or total resisting force acting at the base of the structure to oppose the total wind force.

Winds act to move the building across the earth's surface, as indicated in Figure 13-2. The foundations of the building oppose the wind force, as shown. The total resisting force is called the *base shear*, which can of course occur in either direction.

The wind force acting at any level on the structure shown in Figure 13-2 is equal to the wind pressure at that level times the appropriate surface area at that level. The pressure changes with height, however, and in many instances the structure's configuration changes considerably with the height of the structure. The total wind force on the structure is therefore the sum of the pressure p_i at any level i times the area A_i at that level:

$$\text{Wind force} = \text{Base shear} = V_B = \Sigma p_i A_i \qquad (13.3)$$

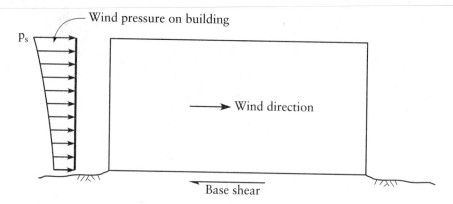

FIGURE 13-2 Base shear due to wind.

The base shear V_B can act in either direction along the major axes of the building as wind direction changes. Wind directions that occur at some angle to the major axes of the building are not used; such refinements are not justified in view of the approximate nature of the wind load itself.

In addition, a "base shear" can be computed at any convenient baseline, not just at the foundation. The wind base shear above the fourth floor of a building, for example, is computed as the shear force developed by all wind forces above that base—that is, above the fourth floor. The base need not be at the ground level.

The wind "sees" the structure as if it were a flat silhouette, projected horizontally onto a flat screen. Setbacks, reveals, recesses, and other surface features of the structure may produce localized pressure concentrations, but they do not affect the overall average pressure against the primary structure. The force at any level is simply the overall average pressure at that level times the projected area at that level, as indicated by Equation 13.3.

To simplify calculations, the wind pressure is taken in stepped increments, as shown in Figure 13-3. The pressure at any level is computed at midheight of that level. The sum of the forces above each story then represents the wind shear at that story.

In some municipalities, the building code may require that certain important buildings be designed for higher wind loads than other buildings of comparable size and shape in the vicinity. Typical buildings included in this category are hospitals, fire stations, civil emergency centers, and police stations. The increased wind load is obtained by multiplying the wind pressures of Table 13-1 by an *importance factor I*, which may range as high as 1.25 for some buildings. For the sake of simplicity, the importance factor is taken here at its base value of 1.

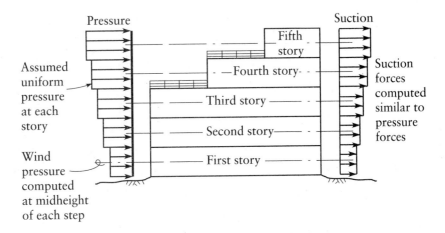

FIGURE 13-3 Typical application of wind pressures.

Example 13-12   Determine the base shears due to wind for the building of Example 13-9. The building and its wind pressures are represented in the accompanying sketch.

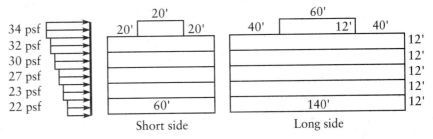

Short side   Long side

Solution   The total force at various levels is computed simply as pressure times area. There will therefore be two base shears—one when the wind is normal to the short side of the building, and a second when the wind is normal to the long side of the building.

For wind normal to the short side, the forces are

at equipment room,	$p_6 = 34 \times 20 \times 12$	$= 8160$ lb
at fifth floor,	$p_5 = 32 \times 60 \times 12$	$= 23{,}040$ lb
at fourth floor,	$p_4 = 30 \times 60 \times 12$	$= 21{,}600$ lb
at third floor,	$p_3 = 27 \times 60 \times 12$	$= 19{,}440$ lb
at second floor,	$p_2 = 23 \times 60 \times 12$	$= 16{,}560$ lb
at first floor,	$p_1 = 22 \times 60 \times 12$	$= 15{,}840$ lb

$$\text{Base shear} = \Sigma = 104{,}640 \text{ lb}$$

For wind normal to the long side, the forces are

at equipment room, $p_6 = 34 \times 60 \times 12 = 24{,}480$ lb

at fifth floor, $p_5 = 32 \times 140 \times 12 = 53{,}760$ lb

at fourth floor, $p_4 = 30 \times 140 \times 12 = 50{,}400$ lb

at third floor, $p_3 = 27 \times 140 \times 12 = 45{,}360$ lb

at second floor, $p_2 = 23 \times 140 \times 12 = 38{,}640$ lb

at first floor, $p_1 = 22 \times 140 \times 12 = 36{,}960$ lb

$$\text{Base shear} = \Sigma = 249{,}600 \text{ lb}$$

The final base shears are shown in the following sketch.

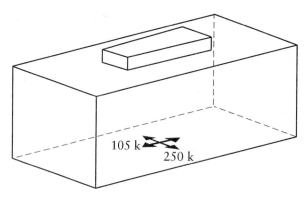

The forces are shown in two directions, since wind can come from either direction.

Example 13-13   Determine the base shear due to wind for the silo of Example 13-10. Determine also the overturning moment at the foundation due to the wind load. The silo and its wind pressures are shown in the following sketch.

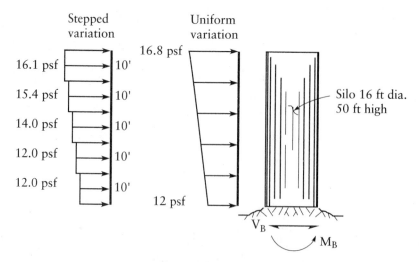

Solution   The total force is simply the sum of the pressures at any level times the area at that level. For convenience, the pressures have been computed at 10-ft increments. The 10-ft increment is entirely arbitrary; the increment might just as easily have been chosen as 8 ft or 6 ft or 5 ft. The 10-ft increment does produce an even number of increments in the 50-ft height, however, and is therefore a convenient increment to use.

The base shear is simply the sum of forces:

$$\text{at fifth level,} \quad p_{45} = 16.1 \times 16 \times 10 = 2576 \text{ lb}$$

$$\text{at fourth level,} \quad p_{35} = 15.4 \times 16 \times 10 = 2464 \text{ lb}$$

$$\text{at third level,} \quad p_{25} = 14.0 \times 16 \times 10 = 2240 \text{ lb}$$

$$\text{at second level,} \quad p_{15} = 12 \times 16 \times 10 = 1920 \text{ lb}$$

$$\text{at first level,} \quad p_{5} = 12 \times 16 \times 10 = 1920 \text{ lb}$$

$$\text{Base shear} = \Sigma = 11{,}120 \text{ lb}$$

The overturning moment is the sum of moments:

$$\text{Overturning } M = (P_{45} \times 45) + (P_{35} \times 35) + (P_{25} \times 25)$$
$$+ (P_{15} \times 15) + (P_{5} \times 5)$$
$$= 297 \text{ kip-ft}$$

For comparison, the same calculations are carried out for the uniform variation in pressure, shown in the defining sketch. The results are

$$V_B = 11{,}520 \text{ lb}$$

$$M = 304 \text{ kip-ft}$$

In view of the approximate nature of wind analysis, the difference between the two results is insignificant. Thus, for low structures, the variation in wind pressure may alternatively be taken as a straight-line variation, if desired.

Example 13-14   Determine the base shear for the water tower of Example 13-11. Determine also the overturning moment produced by the wind loads. The tower and its wind pressures are shown in the following sketch.

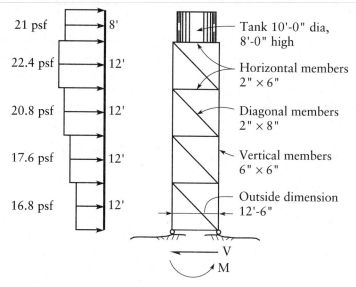

Solution   The shape factor for this tower has already been applied to the solution for the pressures; it is not applied again for the areas.

The total force is thus the corrected pressure times the gross area, as indicated in note 2 of Table 13-4. The base shear is the sum of these forces, and the overturning moment is the sum of the moments caused by these forces:

at water tank, $P_5 = 21.0 \times 8 \times 10$ $= 1{,}680$ lb;
    $M = 1680 \times 52$ $= 87.4$ kip-ft

at level 4, $P_4 = 22.4 \times 12.5 \times 12$ $= 3{,}360$ lb;
    $M = 3360 \times 42$ $= 141.1$ kip-ft

at level 3, $P_3 = 20.8 \times 12.5 \times 12$ $= 3{,}120$ lb;
    $M = 3120 \times 30$ $= 93.6$ kip-ft

at level 2, $P_2 = 17.6 \times 12.5 \times 12$ $= 2{,}640$ lb;
    $M = 2640 \times 18$ $= 47.5$ kip-ft

at level 1, $P_1 = 16.8 \times 12.5 \times 12$ $= 2{,}520$ lb;
    $M = 2520 \times 6$ $= 15.1$ kip-ft

Base shear $= \Sigma = 33{,}320$ lb
$\Sigma M = 384.7$ kip-ft

Since the tower has the same horizontal projection in all four directions, the base shear is also the same in all four directions.

The foregoing examples demonstrate how to calculate the wind shear acting on a structure, including the total shear, or base shear, on its foundations. These are the wind loads acting *on* the structure. Earthquake loads can be calculated very similarly; calculations for earthquake loads acting *on* a structure are presented in the next section.

Outside Problems

Problem 13-17* Determine the maximum wind stagnation pressure likely to occur at 30 ft above the ground in the vicinity of Oklahoma City.

Problem 13-18 Plot a pressure–velocity curve showing the wind pressures generated from ground level to a height of 100 ft by wind having a velocity of 105 mph.

Problem 13-19* Plot the pressure–velocity curve against a vertical rectangular prismatic structure 84 ft high produced by a wind of 95 mph.

Problem 13-20 Plot the pressure–velocity curve against a vertical cylindrical smokestack 60 ft high produced by a wind of 115 mph.

Problem 13-21* A double-sided billboard is to be built such that bills may be displayed on both sides. The designer proposes that, for stability, the two billboards be built in a triangular shape, as shown in the accompanying sketch. Determine whether the wind loads would be higher or lower on this configuration than they would be on a single vertical billboard.

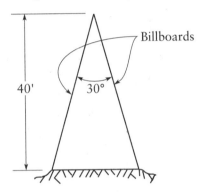

Problem 13-22 Access to a rooftop patio in a flat-roofed apartment building in Columbus, Ohio, is provided by a stairwell located near the center of the building plan. Roof level is 80 ft above adjacent ground level. At the roof, the top of the stairwell is enclosed by a rectangular shelter 12 ft square projecting 8 ft above the roof level, with doors on two opposite sides of the projection. Determine the design wind pressures on the two doors.

Problem 13-23* An automobile parking building 100 ft square, located in Albuquerque, New Mexico, is roughly 50% open on all sides. The building consists of four parking floors, each with a 10-ft story height, with parking on the roof as well. Determine the wind pressure distribution on the building from ground level to roof level.

Problem 13-24 Determine the wind load per foot of length to be used in building an 8" lightweight concrete block fence 6'-0" high in Phoenix, Arizona. The top of the strip footing is to be essentially at grade. Determine also the width of the strip footing such that tension will not be produced on the underlying soil.

Problem 13-25* Determine the base shear and the overturning moment due to wind for the conical smoke stack shown in the accompanying sketch. The tower is located in central Ohio.

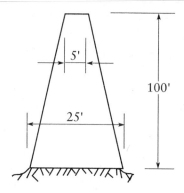

Problem 13-26 Silhouette dimensions of a church in Chicago are shown in the accompanying sketch. Determine the base shears due to wind in both the x and the y directions, and locate the lines of action of these forces on the ground-floor plan.

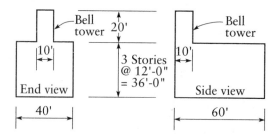

Problem 13-27* A building in Pittsburgh, Pennsylvania, has the silhouette shapes on two sides, as shown in the accompanying sketch. Determine the base shears due to wind in both the x and the y directions, and locate the lines of action of these forces on the ground-floor plan.

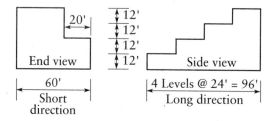

Problem 13-28 A square-timber trussed tower is built of 6" × 6" vertical posts, 2" × 8" horizontal members, and 1" × 6" counterdiagonals; all dimensions are actual sizes. All panels of the truss are 10' wide and 10' high. Determine the shape factor for this tower.

13.4 EARTHQUAKE LOADS

Earthquake forces in a structure are created when the earth takes a sharp lateral displacement underneath the structure. The magnitude of such motions can be quite high; displacements of 8 inches or more can be expected, depending on the type of soil. This high-velocity displacement at the base of a building can have devastating effects unless the structural system has been properly designed to accommodate it.

A typical system of earthquake forces is shown in Figure 13-4. The inertial forces in the structure are directly proportional to the mass (or weight) being accelerated, $F = ma$. Much higher forces are therefore generated in a massive, heavy structure built of concrete than in a lighter structure built of timber or steel. Furthermore, much higher forces are generated in an extremely rigid box structure than in a flexible structure, since the accelerations of the building components are significantly higher in a rigid structure.

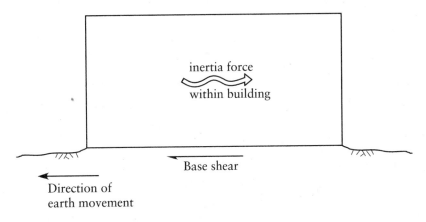

FIGURE 13-4 Base shear due to earthquake.

Earthquakes are produced by sudden slips along fracture lines in the earth's crust. Some of these fracture lines (such as the San Andreas fault in California) are visible at the surface and others (such as the New Madrid fault in Missouri) are buried deep underground. Either way, their effects are the same: a shock wave is generated that produces a series of sharp but random lateral movements in the surrounding terrain. The intensity of the shock wave diminishes quickly as it spreads outward from the actual slip line, or epicenter.

The level of intensity of an earthquake therefore depends on one's proximity to the epicenter, as well as on the strength of the temblor at its epicenter. Near the epicenter, the intensity is high, while only a short distance away the intensity rapidly dissipates. A map showing the expected intensity of earthquakes in the United States is given in Figure 13-5; in the map, the expected intensity in an area is termed the "seismic risk" of the area. The second-tier term *seismic* is used in the literature to refer to the effects of earthquakes; it comes from the Greek word for earthquake, *seismos*.

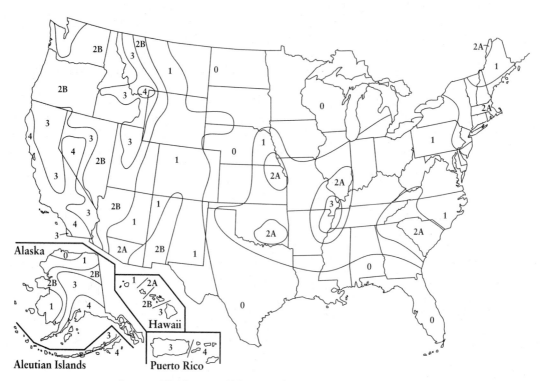

Source: Uniform Building Code, 1991 edition

FIGURE 13-5 Earthquake risk zones in the United States.

The base shear created by earthquake motions under a building is expressed as a factor times the dead weight of the entire building. Some structural designers also include 25% of the live load as being a part of the accelerated mass; but under the definition of dead loads used in this text, such an additional load is not appropriate.

In recent years, research into the effects of earthquakes on structures has sharply increased. As the level of knowledge has grown, the complexity of the design codes and building codes has grown correspondingly. The complexity, however, is concentrated largely on the response of structures to earthquake motions; the method of determining the earthquake forces themselves has changed little over the years.

The research shows a definite soil–structure interaction during an earthquake. Because of this interaction, the actual magnitude of the earthquake forces acting on a structure can vary sharply with the dynamic period of oscillation of the structure; but for low structures (less than about 65 feet in height), the period of oscillation is so short that its effects become negligible. Consequently, for these low structures, the base shear V_B produced by earthquake motions becomes quite simple to calculate:

$$V_B = 2.75\left(\frac{Z}{R_W}\right)W \qquad\qquad (13.4)$$

where

V_B is the total lateral force (base shear) acting in any direction due to the acceleration of masses above this level, or base;

Z is a risk zone factor corresponding to the risk zones given in the map of Figure 13-5;

R_W is an interactive response factor accounting for the dynamic response of the structure to lateral motions at its foundations;.

W is the dead weight of the structure and its fixed components above the level where V_B is being computed.

The value of Z to be used in Equation 13.4 is prescribed by code:

Zone 1:   Z = 0.075

Zone 2a: Z = 0.15

Zone 2b: Z = 0.20

Zone 3:   Z = 0.30

Zone 4:   Z = 0.40

The values of R_W are also prescribed by code. Representative values of R_W are listed in Table 13-6.

In Table 13-6, the value of R_W for water tanks applies only to the tank and its contents—not to the supporting structure. The municipal building code of a particular community may permit other values of R_W for special cases. Detailed familiarity with the local building code is, of course, essential.

As in the case of wind loading, the building code may impose an "importance factor" on earthquake loading. The end effect is to produce a slightly larger factor of safety for buildings that will be critically needed following a disastrous earthquake. For such buildings, the base shear is multiplied by the importance factor that may be as high as 1.25. For the sake of simplicity, the importance factor in succeeding examples is taken at its base value of 1.0.

Table 13-6 Interactive Response Factor (R_W) Values

Values of R_W for Buildings

TYPE OF STRUCTURE	R_W
Structures where walls carry both vertical loads and lateral loads	
Plywood walls	8
Concrete or masonry walls	6
Steel tension-only braced walls	4
Heavy timber walls	4
Structures where walls carry only shear; and columns carry all vertical loads	R_W
Plywood shear panels	9
Concrete or masonry shear panels	8
Concentric braced frames	8
All other shear panels	7
Moment-resisting frames	R_W
Steel frames	6
Concrete frames[1]	5

Values of R_W for Nonbuilding Structures

TYPE OF STRUCTURE	R_W
Tanks, vessels, and spheres	3
Stacks, chimneys, and silos	4
Trussed towers	4
Signs and billboards	5
Cooling towers	5
Lumped masses	4

[1]Concrete frames are prohibited in Zones 3 and 4.

Examination of Equation 13.4 reveals that, in most of the areas of high earthquake intensity (Zone 3), the maximum earthquake force on statically determinate diaphragm-and-shear panel structures is some 10% to 12% of the gravitational dead weight. In areas of light intensity (Zone 1), this factor drops to about 3% of the gravitational dead weight. These percentages of the gravitational dead weight of the structure are commonly termed the earthquake "g-load" or "g-forces" acting on the structure.

The approach to earthquake analysis taken in the foregoing discussions is extracted from the Uniform Building Code, which, in the United States, is probably the most widely used of all earthquake design codes. The simplified approach presented here is possible only because the dynamic period of oscillation (the harmonic frequency) of low, laterally braced structures is so short that it cannot reasonably be matched by the earthquake motions to produce resonance. For taller or for more flexible structures, such a matching of frequencies can occur, in which case the dynamic properties of the structure can no longer be ignored. The study of the dynamic response of tall flexible structures to random earthquake motion is far beyond the scope of an elementary text such as this.

The following examples will demonstrate how to calculate base shear on a typical small structure.

Example 13-15

For the building of Example 13-9, determine the base shear due to earthquake. The total dead weight of the building is given as 2520 tons. The building, located in Nashville, Tennessee, is shown in the accompanying sketch.

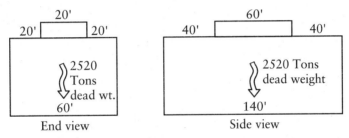

End view   Side view

Solution

The risk zone for Nashville is found from Figure 13-5 to be Zone 2a; therefore, the zone factor Z prescribed by code is 0.15. The building is of diaphragm/shear panel construction with masonry walls, for which the interactive response factor is 8. The base shear is therefore

$$V_B = 2.75 \left(\frac{Z}{R_W} \right) W$$

$$= 2.75 \times \left(\frac{0.15}{8} \right) \times 2520 \times 2000$$

$$= 260{,}000 \text{ lb}$$

The building, with its base shears due to earthquake, is shown in the following sketch.

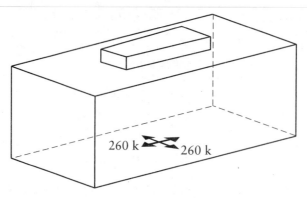

Notice that, unlike wind, earthquake loads are not influenced by long and short dimensions. In this case, the earthquake loads are larger than the wind loads and therefore would govern the design.

Example 13-16   Determine the base shear and overturning moment due to earthquake for the silo of Example 13-10. Assume that the silo will be 80% filled at the time the earthquake load occurs. The steel silo, located near Wichita, Kansas, is 16 ft in diameter, weighs 8400 lbs and is bolted to a concrete foundation. The silo is shown in the accompanying sketch.

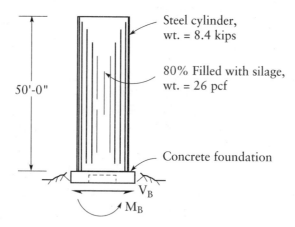

Solution   From the map of Figure 13-5, the risk zone for Wichita is taken as Zone 1. The value of Z for Zone 1 is prescribed by code as 0.075. The value of R_W for silos is found from Table 13-1 to be 4.

The dead weight of the cylinder and silage, when the silo is filled to 80% capacity, is

$$W_{DL} = 0.80\pi r^2 h\, W_{\text{SILAGE}} + W_{\text{CYL}}$$
$$= 0.80\pi \times 8^2 \times 50 \times 26 + 8400$$
$$= 209.1 \text{ k} \quad (\text{for the silage}) + 8.4 \text{ k} \quad (\text{for the cylinder})$$
$$= 217.5 \text{ kips}$$

The lateral earthquake force is then found from Equation 13.4:

$$V_B = 2.75\left(\frac{Z}{R_W}\right)W$$
$$= 2.75 \times \left(\frac{0.075}{4}\right) \times (209.1 + 8.4)$$
$$= 10{,}780 \text{ lb} \quad (\text{for the silage}) + 433 \text{ lb} \quad (\text{for the cylinder})$$
$$= 11.2 \text{ kips}$$

From the accompanying sketch, the overturning moment is

$$M = 10{,}780 \times 20 + 433 \times 25$$
$$= 226 \text{ kip-ft}$$

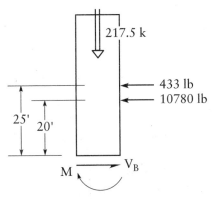

For this structure, the wind load and the earthquake load are of comparable magnitude.

Example 13-17   Determine the base shear due to earthquake for the elevated water tank of Example 13-11. The tower is located in Portland, Oregon. The tank is assumed to be full. The structure is shown in the accompanying sketch.

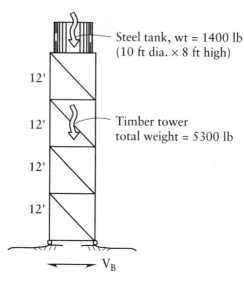

Steel tank, wt = 1400 lb
(10 ft dia. × 8 ft high)

12'

12'   Timber tower
total weight = 5300 lb

12'

12'

V_B

Solution   The earthquake risk zone for Portland is found from Figure 13-5 to be Zone 2. The factor Z for Zone 2b is prescribed by code to be 0.20.

The interactive response factor R_W in this case has two values. For the tank and contents, R_W is 3. For the tower, R_W is 4. The total base shear is therefore the sum of these two elements.

The dead load of the tank and its contents is taken as

$$W_{DL} = W_{WATER} + W_{TANK}$$
$$= 62.4 \times \pi \times 5^2 \times 8 + 1400$$
$$= 41{,}000 \text{ lb}$$

The dead load of the tower is given as 5300 lb. The base shear is then

$$V_B = 2.75\left(\frac{Z}{R_W}\right)W_{TANK} + 2.75\left(\frac{Z}{R_W}\right)W_{TOWER}$$
$$= \left[2.75 \times \left(\frac{0.20}{3}\right) \times 41{,}000\right] + \left[2.75 \times \left(\frac{0.20}{4}\right) \times 5300\right]$$
$$= 7516 \text{ lb} \quad \text{(for the tank)} + 729 \text{ lb} \quad \text{(for the tower)}$$
$$= 8245 \text{ lb}$$

From the accompanying sketch, the overturning moment is

$$M = (7516 \times 52) + (729 \times 24)$$
$$= 408 \text{ kip-ft}$$

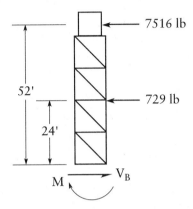

For this structure, the earthquake loads are much smaller than the wind loads; considerations of wind load will therefore govern the design of the structure.

The foregoing examples demonstrate how to calculate the earthquake forces acting on a structure, including the total shear, or base shear, acting at the foundations. These are the earthquake loads that act *on* the structure. Their effects *within* the structure itself are presented in the next chapter.

Outside Problems

Problem 13-29* What is the earthquake g-load for a steel safe weighing 3600 lb in earthquake risk Zone 2?

Problem 13-30 The mass of all dead load above the surface of the fifth floor of a steel rigid-frame building is 912 slugs. In risk Zone 3, how much shearing force will this mass deliver to the fifth floor in an earthquake?

Problem 13-31* A water tank is 10 ft in diameter and 10 ft high, and is mounted on a concrete slab on grade in earthquake risk Zone 3. The earthquake g-load is reported to be 8260 lb. How full was the tank assumed to be when this g-load was computed? (Assume that the weight of the tank is negligible in comparison to the weight of the water.)

Problem 13-32 A circular stack 20 ft in diameter and 100 ft high is centered on a concrete pad 30 ft square. The total dead weight of the stack and its foundation is 120 tons. The stack is located in risk Zone 2. Is there any chance that the foundation will slip along its interface with the soil if the coefficient of friction is 0.18? Is there any chance that the foundation will lift off the soil at one side? (Assume that the center of gravity of all the masses is roughly at midheight of the stack.)

REVIEW QUESTIONS

1. How does one distinguish between dead loads and live loads?

2. Why are gravity loads on a sloping surface always converted into a load on the horizontal projection?

3. Why is shock-mounted permanent equipment not classed as dead load, even though it is permanently mounted to the structural frame?

4. How is impact loading, or dynamic loading, treated in an analysis of live loads?

5. When the building code requires that a concentrated load be placed randomly at any point in a floor, what members and what stresses are most likely to be affected by the load?

6. What is the justification for permitting the design live load to a supporting member to be reduced when the tributary area to the member is large?

7. What is meant by the term *wind stagnation pressure*?

8. What type and shape of structure is assumed to exist when stagnation pressure is being calculated?

9. Does wind pressure increase or decrease with height?

10. How does wind pressure distribute itself around a rectangular prismatic structure?

11. Does suction pressure occur on a vertical cylindrical structure?

12. For an open carport consisting of four columns and a flat roof, what is the design wind pressure on the roof?

13. At what angle of inclination from horizontal does the wind pressure on a surface reach its minimum?

14. What is the shape factor for a windward surface inclined exactly 30° from horizontal? Exactly 40° from horizontal?

15. How can things attached to the building frame experience more wind load than the building frame itself?

16. Two areas in the United States are in an earthquake risk zone identified as Zone 4. Where are they?

17. What is the justification for an "importance factor" in wind and earthquake loadings?

18. What is meant by the term *g-load*?

19. Why is the possibility that resonance will occur during earthquake excitation considered to be so slight on low, broad structures?

20. At roughly what height of structure does the likelihood of resonance start to be a serious concern?

Highway-highway bridges of flat slab reinforced concrete construction. (Photograph courtesy of Portland Cement Association, reprinted by permission.)

14

Distribution of Loads Within a Structure

The discussions of Chapter 13 were limited to the determination of loads that act *on* a structure. In those discussions, no effort was made to find the distribution of these loads within the structure itself, nor was any effort made to define the particular structural elements that would actually resist the load. This chapter proceeds into these logical next steps, that is—to determine the way in which the structure as a whole will resist the applied loads and to determine the associated design load that must be borne by every one of the resisting members.

The discussions of this chapter are concentrated primarily on simple structural systems: structural systems that are statically determinate both internally and externally. Statically determinate structural systems behave quite similarly with regard to how they sustain their applied loads; they behave so similarly, in fact, that general observations can be developed that will apply to all such systems, regardless of their exact configurations. Another feature of these statically determinate structural systems is that the necessary calculations for loads depend only on simple statics, with no reliance on assumed deformations; the results, therefore, are accurate and believable.

All external loads acting on a structure must eventually be resisted by the foundation. Consequently, when a structure is being analyzed for a particular load, the analysis must include the total "load path" from the point where the structural system first receives the load to the point where the load is finally transmitted to the supporting soil. This total load path is one of the primary focal points of this chapter; the load paths for both vertical and horizontal loads are traced here in detail.

14.1 TYPES OF STATICALLY DETERMINATE SYSTEMS

All statically determinate structural systems carry their loads in much the same way. A typical reinforced concrete diaphragm/shearwall system is shown in Figure 14-1; there, the lateral load is transmitted to the foundation by the rigid concrete shearwalls or shear panels. The rigid horizontal diaphragm (the concrete floor) maintains the shape of the building at each level as it transmits horizontal loads to the shearwalls. Notice that columns carry only vertical loads; the entire lateral load is resisted by the shearwalls. (In Figure14-1, interior columns have been omitted for the sake of clarity.)

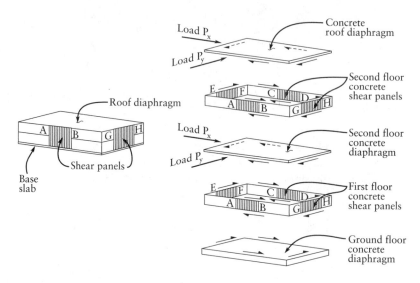

FIGURE 14-1 Two story concrete diaphragm and shearwall system.

The shearwalls indicated in Figure 14-1 can resist only lateral loads that are parallel to the wall. The set of walls AB and CD, for example, will resist the load P_x, which acts parallel to them. Under a load that acts transversely to them, such as the load P_y, walls AB and CD will bend (or tilt) slightly, but they are too flexible to offer any real resistance to P_y.

Similarly, walls EF and GH will resist any loads that act parallel to them, such as the load P_y. But under a load that acts transversely to them, such as the load P_x, these walls will simply bend (or tilt) slightly; they will offer no real resistance to P_x. Two sets of walls, one set in each direction, are thus required to sustain lateral loads coming from any direction.

The braced steel panel system of Figure 14-2 resists loads in much the same way that the concrete diaphragm/shearwall system of Figure 14-1 does. Vertical loads are carried by the steel columns, which have simple hinged supports at top and bottom. Horizontal loads are received by the rigidly braced horizontal floor system and are then transmitted to the vertically braced steel panels. It is usually unnecessary to brace every panel of the horizontal diaphragm; in most cases, bracing the perimeter panels is usually enough to maintain the horizontal shape and integrity of the floor and its horizontal framing system.

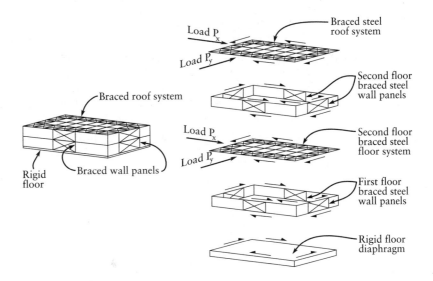

FIGURE 14-2 Two story braced steel frame.

Similarly, the braced timber post-and-beam system of Figure 14-3 functions in the same general way as the concrete system and the steel system just described. In a typical timber system, both the floor system and the shear panels are sheathed with structural plywood, although in recent years oriented strand board has gained widespread use. The system shown in Figure 14-3 is classed as post-and-beam construction, but the same system also works very well in light frame construction, where ordinary stud walls are used to carry the vertical loads.

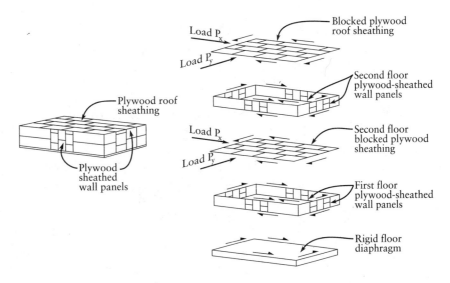

FIGURE 14-3 Two story braced timber post-and-beam system.

It should not be inferred from the details of Figures 14-1, 14-2, and 14-3 that there can be no mixing of materials and systems. In place of the trussed steel floor system shown in Figure 14-2, for example, floor systems could also be made of lightweight concrete, 2 1/2 to 4 in. thick, cast onto a corrugated steel form that in turn has been welded to the joists. Such a floor system, shown in Figure 14-4, is commonly used; it forms an effective and very rigid concrete diaphragm for the steel-framed building, eliminating the need for the horizontal cross bracing around the perimeter of the floor.

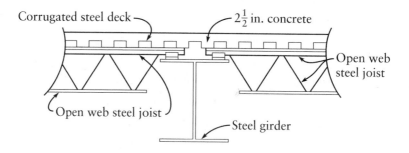

FIGURE 14-4 Mixed concrete and steel system.

So, too, the reinforced concrete system of Figure 14-1 can be modified to incorporate reinforced masonry shearwalls rather than the concrete shearwalls shown. The use of reinforced masonry shearwalls in conjunction with reinforced concrete flooring and roofing systems is popular in tropical areas, where hurricane winds are a dominant design load. Such a mixed system is economical, simple to build, impervious to insects, and is not susceptible to rust or decay.

Similarly, the plywood diaphragm of Figure 14-3 can be used with the steel framing system of Figure 14-2, using nailers attached to the steel beams to achieve continuity of the plywood diaphragm, as shown in Figure 14-5. This mixture of systems (shown in Figure 14-5) is efficient, lightweight, and economical. Earthquake loads are considerably reduced through the use of lightweight systems of this type, making such mixtures of timber and steel an attractive alternative in areas where earthquakes are a major hazard.

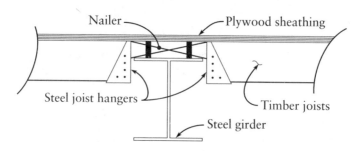

FIGURE 14-5 Mixed steel and timber system.

It is appropriate here to restate the assumption that all connections every-
where in these systems are regarded as hinged. Columns and walls are
assumed to be hinged to the diaphragms at each floor level, and all beams
are assumed to be simply supported at every support. A horizontal diaphragm is regarded as constituting a large continuous plate fitted with a long
piano hinge that connects it to each vertical shear panel. These long hinges
can transmit shear forces along the length of the shear panel, but they cannot
develop moment transverse to the panel.

All of the systems shown in Figures 14-1, 14-2, and 14-3 are considered
to be statically determinate. So, too, are all of the variations and mixtures of
these systems just described. No deformations need be considered in order
to find the forces in these systems. The systems are indeed subject to excessive deformations, however, and controlling or limiting their deformations
can often become very troublesome. Means to identify and limit these deformations are included in subsequent sections.

A generic description of simple statically determinate structural systems
can now be made. As indicated in the sketch of a generic system in Figure
14-6, a typical diaphragm/shearwall structural system has a rigid horizontal
diaphragm at each floor level and at the roof. All beams and girders supporting these floor and roof diaphragms are simply supported and statically
determinate. Further, the system has either columns or bearing walls, hinged
at top and bottom, that carry the vertical loads. Finally, the system has vertical shear panels that resist all the lateral loads.

As used in the foregoing description, a horizontal "diaphragm" may be a
braced steel or timber floor system, rather than a continuous concrete or plywood diaphragm, provided that the bracing is adequate to maintain the horizontal shape and integrity of the floor under the racking produced by lateral
loads. Similarly, a "shear panel" may be a braced or trussed steel or timber
panel; or it may be a solidly sheathed timber panel, a solid concrete panel,
or a masonry wall.

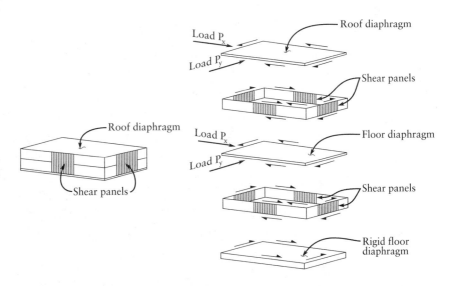

FIGURE 14-6 Generic two story diaphragm and shear panel system.

All statically determinate structural systems fall into the configuration just described, and all can readily be analyzed in accordance with methods that produce accurate and believable results. For small buildings, the diaphragm-and-shearwall structural system is adaptable to a wide variety of architectural designs; it can be executed in a single material or in a mixture of materials, and it can be built with only nominal control over construction tolerances. It is best applied only to relatively low structures, however, and even then it can present rather difficult foundation conditions; such problems are discussed in more detail in subsequent sections.

Often, one difficult adjustment a student must make in performing an analysis on an entire building involves being able to visualize large parts of the structural system, such as those indicated in Figures 14-1, 14-2, and 14-3. Up to this point in this text, for example, the analysis of structures has concentrated on individual pieces and parts of a structural system—not on large parts of the system or on the overall system as a whole. The same principles of statics that apply to small systems apply equally well to the structure as a whole; the difference is only a matter of scale, not of concept. For the sake of illustration, the discussions in this chapter will repeatedly demonstrate the applications of simple statics to these overall structural systems.

14.2 UNSYMMETRICAL SYSTEMS

A basic assumption made throughout this chapter is that the shearwalls in the resisting structure are essentially concentric; that is, they are symmetrical around the lateral loads. To achieve such a concentric or symmetric shearwall system, the structure must be designed such that two walls of comparable size are properly positioned to either side of the lateral load, as indicated in Figure 14-7; the reaction at each wall is then roughly half the lateral load, as shown. (A variation of up to 20% in the symmetry is usually acceptable without seriously affecting the distribution of load.) In such systems, the horizontal diaphragm has little or no tendency to rotate in its horizontal plane, and the system may be treated as statically determinate insofar as loads and reactions are concerned.

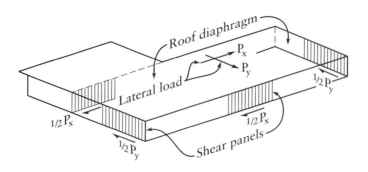

FIGURE 14-7 Symmetry of loads and reactions.

Notice that the conditions of symmetry apply only to the lines of action of the loads and reactions, not to the structure itself. As shown in Figure 14-7, the structure need not be symmetrical so long as the resultant of applied loads at any level is located approximately midway between the resultants of the two reactions. In any event, however, the shear load due to wind is unlikely to fall along exactly the same line of action as the shear load due to earthquake; it has already been observed that some variation in the symmetry is permissible, to account for such discrepancies.

Symmetrical systems are not the only ones that can sustain lateral loads. Unsymmetrical systems such as the one shown in Figure 14-8 can also sustain lateral loads, but the reliability of such systems is open to considerable uncertainty. The system shown in Figure 14-8 is an extreme case; it is called a *three-wall system*. Due to their questionable performance under service conditions, three-wall systems are severely limited by code in regions of high earthquake risk.

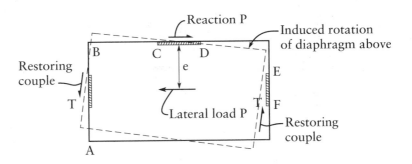

FIGURE 14-8 Three-wall system.

In the three-wall system of Figure 14-8, the earthquake load P is assumed to act through the center of gravity of the floor mass. It is therefore eccentric to the only shearwall that can resist it, wall CD. The load P and its reaction along the axis of the shearwall CD form a couple, Pe, which induces the rotation shown. The applied couple Pe must then be opposed by a like couple induced into the other two shear panels. Such a system is thus statically determinate and—theoretically, at least—structurally sound.

But however sound the theory may be, the performance of three-wall systems under actual loading has proved to be erratic. Use of such systems is therefore not recommended. While they are permitted by code in low-intensity earthquake zones, their reliability remains dubious. As a lateral load-carrying system, a three-wall system should be used only where loads are known absolutely to be low and where foundation conditions are known absolutely to be unyielding.

Further development of three-wall systems is not included in this text. The study of three-wall systems and their foundation problems is deferred to future studies of earthquake-resistant structures, where the subject can be treated in rigorous detail.

Four-wall systems that are significantly unsymmetrical produce torsional rotations such as those that occur in three-wall systems. A four-wall system of this type is shown in Figure 14-9. In unsymmetrical shearwall structures, the torsional rotations occur about a center of rotation, or *center of rigidity*. The torque that creates the rotations is, as before, the applied load P times the eccentricity e. The torsion thus created must then be resisted by an opposing couple that is induced into the other set of shearwalls.

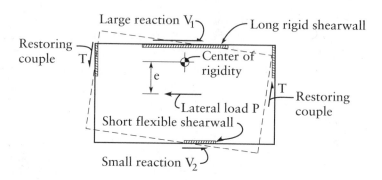

FIGURE 14-9 Loads on an unsymmetrical shearwall system.

As is the case with three-wall systems, the reliability of highly unsymmetrical shearwall systems like the one shown in Figure 14-9 is subject to question. Even a small variation in foundation resistance can completely alter the assumed indeterminate deformations. Calculations based on such unreliable factors should not be the basis for something as critical as structural integrity.

Unsymmetrical systems such as the one shown in Figure 14-9 do not receive further analysis in this text. They, too, are deferred to advanced studies of earthquake-resistant structures.

14.3 DISTRIBUTION OF DEAD LOAD

The first structural system to receive and support the dead loads of a building is typically some kind of flooring system. In turn, the flooring system is typically supported by modular columns or bearing walls. This generalization includes perimeter walls and fenestration, which must first be carried by some type of floor girders. Similarly, all dead loads located at the interior of each floor level are first received by the floor joists and beams, then transmitted to the supporting girders, and thereafter transmitted to the vertical columns or bearing walls.

For structures that have no recognizable floor system (such as falsework towers used to support higher-level construction work), the dead load is simply the dead load of the object being supported. The dead load that is tributary to each leg of a falsework tower, for example, must be calculated independently; and the members of the tower must be designed accordingly. More often, however, the tower supports a floor system; the floor system, in turn, is designed to receive a concrete casting or some other specific construction load. By far the most common means to carry dead load in a structure is through some kind of flooring system or roofing system framed into vertical supports.

Floor and roof systems are composed generally of the flooring or roofing material, together with the supporting joists, beams and girders. The joists are supported by beams; the beams are supported by girders; and the girders are supported by vertical columns, pilasters, or other bearing members. As a means to distinguish among joists, beams, and girders, members are classified herein as girders if they are supported by vertical supports, and as beams if they are supported by horizontal supports; joists are simply a special case of repetitive beams that are so slender as to require bridging. For consistency with this definition, a long bearing wall supporting a series of repetitive framing members is treated as a horizontal support.

The dead load tributary to a joist is taken to include all dead load on the joist halfway to the next adjacent member; the dead load tributary to a beam is taken to include all dead load on the beam halfway to the next adjacent beam or other similar member; and the dead load tributary to a girder is taken to include all dead load on the girder halfway to the next girder or other similar support. Alternatively, the dead load to a beam or a girder may be taken to comprise the dead load reactions of all members that are framed into it.

The foregoing generalizations may seem somewhat crude, particularly since the dead load can be rather accurately determined. The portion of the dead load to be carried by a particular beam may, in fact, be slightly more or slightly less than half of the dead load between this beam and the next beam, depending on the configuration of the load and its location in the span. Over the years, however, it has been found that, for routine structures, such variations are generally negligible and that the simpler approximation can be applied with reasonably accurate results. In cases where a distinctly unsymmetrical load will obviously load one particular member more than another, the actual reactions may be calculated and used throughout the remainder of the analysis.

Some examples will illustrate how to calculate the dead load tributary to a typical beam and girder.

Example 14-1

For the accompanying design, determine the dead load of the roof per foot of length along the frame.

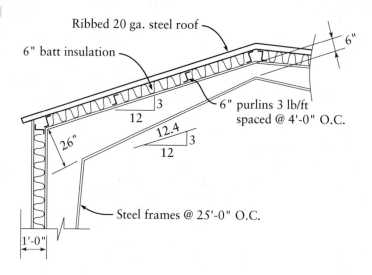

Ribbed 20 ga. steel roof

6" batt insulation

6" purlins 3 lb/ft spaced @ 4'-0" O.C.

26"

1'-0"

Steel frames @ 25'-0" O.C.

Solution   Dead loads are found in Table 13-1:

Ribbed steel roof	1.6 lb/ft^2
Insulation	3.0 lb/ft^2
Add purlin 3 lb/ft/4 ft	0.75 lb/ft^2
	$\Sigma = 5.35$ lb/ft^2

On a frame spacing of 25 feet,

$$w_{DL} = 5.35 \times 25 = 134 \text{ lb/linear ft}$$

On the horizontal projected area,

$$w_{DL} = 134 \times \frac{12.4}{12} = 138 \text{ lb/linear ft}$$

Therefore, use $w_{DL} = 138$ lb/lf on the horizontal projection.

Example 14-2

For the accompanying design, determine the dead load per foot of length on the open-web steel joists and on the steel girders supporting the joists. Include a movable partition load of 11 psf with the dead loads. Joist spacing is 3'-0" for all joists.

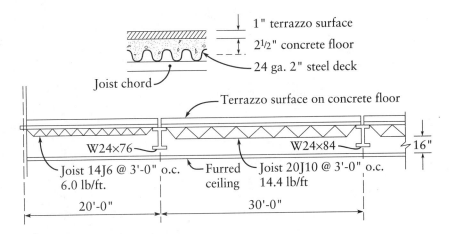

Solution

The dead loads are found in Table 13-1:

Partition load	11 psf
1" terrazzo surface	13 psf
3 1/2" concrete deck	44 psf
24-gauge steel deck	1.1 psf
Furred ceiling	1 psf
	$\Sigma = 70$ psf

At end span, add equivalent joist weight:

$$\text{Joist wt.} = \frac{6.0}{3} = 2.0 \text{ psf}$$

$$\text{Total dead load per ft} = (70 + 2) \times 3 = 216 \text{ plf}$$

At interior spans, add equivalent joist weight:

$$\text{Joist wt.} = \frac{14.4}{3} = 4.8 \text{ psf}$$

$$\text{Total dead load per ft} = (70 + 4.8) \times 3 = 224 \text{ plf}$$

At end bays, add the steel girder:

$$\text{Girder wt.} = \frac{76}{(10 + 15)} = 3 \text{ psf}$$

$$\text{Total dead load per ft} = (70 + 2 + 3)(10 + 15) = 1875 \text{ plf}$$

At interior bays, add the steel girder:

$$\text{Girder wt.} = \frac{84}{30} = 3 \text{ psf}$$

$$\text{Total dead load per ft} = (70 + 4.8 + 3)(30) = 2330 \text{ plf}$$

Use the following dead loads:

20 ft. span,	Joist 14J6,	DL = 216 plf
30 ft. span,	Joist 20J10,	DL = 224 plf
End bay,	Girder W24 × 76,	DL = 1875 plf
Interior bay,	Girder W24 × 84,	DL = 2330 plf

The foregoing examples dealt only with the flooring and roofing systems. The dead loads delivered to the columns and bearing walls that ultimately must support these floor and roof systems are treated in generally the same way. With little error, the dead load tributary to a column or bearing wall may be taken as the sum of all dead loads halfway to the next vertical support in any direction. As before, a load placed unsymmetrically between two or more supports will be distributed to the supports proportionally to its distance from the support.

Some examples will illustrate how to compute dead loads tributary to a support.

Example 14-3   For the accompanying design, determine the dead load of the roof per foot of length on the two 8-in. masonry bearing walls.

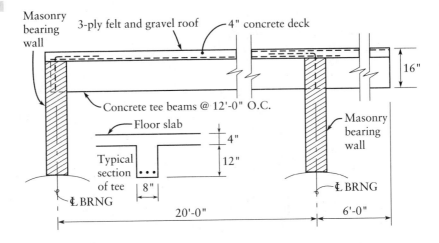

Solution   The dead loads are found from Table 13-1:

3-ply felt roofing	5.5 psf
4-in. concrete deck	50.0 psf
Σ =	55.5 psf

Add equivalent beam weight:

$$\text{Beam wt.} = \frac{\left(8 \times \dfrac{12}{144}\right)(145)}{12} = 8.1 \text{ psf}$$

Total weight of roof and beams:

Total dead load = 55.5 + 8.1 = 64 psf

Load at wall at left side:

$$w_{DL} = 64 \times (10' + 0.67') = 683 \text{ plf}$$

Load at wall at right side:

$$w_{DL} = 64 \times (10' + 6') = 1024 \text{ plf}$$

Example 14-4   For the accompanying design, determine the design dead load on columns
C1 and C2.

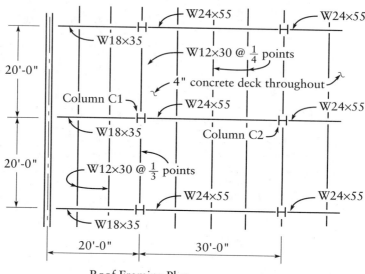

Roof Framing Plan

Solution   Dead loads are found from Table 13-1:

Concrete deck 12.5×4,   dead load = 50 psf

Girder linear loads are converted into loads per square foot:

Girder W18 × 35, $w_{DL} = \dfrac{35}{20} = 1.75$ psf

Girder W24 × 55, $w_{DL} = \dfrac{55}{20} = 1.83$ psf

Beam linear loads are converted into loads per square foot:

On 20 ft span, $w_{DL} = 30\left(\dfrac{20}{3}\right) = 4.5$ psf

On 30 ft span, $w_{DL} = 30\left(\dfrac{30}{4}\right) = 4.0$ psf

Load on column C1:

Tributary area at W18 × 35,   Area = $10 \times 20 = 200$ ft^2
Tributary area at W24 × 55,   Area = $15 \times 20 = 300$ ft^2

Total load = $200\,(50 + 1.75 + 4.5) + 300\,(50 + 1.83 + 4.0)$
= 28 kips

Load on column C2:

Tributary area at $W24 \times 55$, Area $= 20 \times 30 = 600 \ \text{ft}^2$

$$\text{Total load} = 600 \, (50 + 1.83 + 4.0)$$
$$= 34 \ \text{kips}$$

Final loads:

Column C1, use $P_{DL} = 28$ kips

Column C2, use $P_{DL} = 34$ kips

Outside Problems

Odd-numbered problems are answered in the Answer Section.

Refer to Building Configuration No. 1, given at the end of the chapter.

Problems 14-1 through 14-4

Determine the dead load delivered to the first four column footings along line A.

Problems 14-5 through 14-8

Determine the dead load delivered to the first four column footings along line D.

Refer to Building Configuration No. 2, given at the end of the chapter.

Problems 14-9 through 14-12

Determine the dead load delivered to the four column footings along line 1.

Problems 14-13 through 14-16

Determine the dead load delivered to the four column footings along line 5.

14.4 DISTRIBUTION OF LIVE LOAD

The distribution of live load to its supporting members follows much the same pattern as the distribution of dead load. Live load is generally much simpler to deal with, however, since it does not depend on the type of construction. A live load of 100 psf for corridors, for example, is the same for steel buildings, for timber buildings, and for concrete buildings.

For purposes of computing live load on a floor framing member, the live tributary to a joist is taken to include the live load on the joist halfway to the next adjacent member; the live load tributary to a beam is taken to include the live load on the beam halfway to the next adjacent beam or other similar member; and the live load tributary to a girder is taken to include the live load on the girder halfway to the next adjacent girder or other corresponding support. Alternatively, the live load to a beam or a girder may be taken as the live load reactions of all members that are framed into it.

The calculations for the live load tributary to a flooring member are thus quite similar to the corresponding calculations for dead load. The calculations are simplified somewhat by the fact that live loads consist of rather arbitrarily assumed uniform loads, unlike the more exactly determined dead loads.

Some examples will illustrate how to calculate live loads tributary to joists, beams, and girders. For ease of comparison, these examples refer to the same examples used earlier to calculate dead loads.

Example 14-5

For the roof system of Example 14-1, determine the roof live load tributary to the building frame. Use an average live load of 30 lb/ft^2.

Solution

Refer to the sketch of Example 14-1. On the horizontal projection,

$$\text{Load per foot of length} = 30 \times 25 = 750 \text{ plf}$$

Use $w_{LL} = 750$ plf on the horizontal projection of the frame.

Example 14-6

For the floor system of Example 14-2, determine the floor live load tributary to the joists and girders. Use a live load of 40 lb/ft^2.

Solution

Refer to the sketch of Example 14-2. Here,

$$\text{Load per foot on all joists} = 40 \text{ psf} \times 3 = 120 \text{ plf}$$

$$\text{Load per foot on end girder} = 40 \times 25 = 1000 \text{ plf}$$

$$\text{Load per foot on interior girder} = 40 \times 30 = 1200 \text{ plf}$$

The foregoing examples dealt with live loads on the flexural members in a flooring or roofing system. Calculations of live loads tributary to columns or to bearing walls are treated similarly. The live load tributary to a vertical support is taken to include the live load halfway to the next vertical support in any direction. Concentrated live loads are distributed to the nearest supports in proportion to their distance from the supports.

Outside Problems

Refer to Building Configuration No. 1, given at the end of the chapter.

Problems 14-17 through 14-19

Determine the live load on the column footings at A-1, A-2, and B-4.

Problems 14-20 through 14-22

Determine the live load on the column footings at B-1, B-2, and B-3.

Refer to Building Configuration No. 2, given at the end of the chapter.

Problems 14-23 through 14-25

Determine the live load on the column footings at A-1, A-2, and B-3.

Problems 14-26 through 14-28

Determine the live load on the column footings at B-1, B-2, and C-3.

14.5 DISTRIBUTION OF WIND LOAD

Wind load is delivered to a structure at the exterior walls, with inward pressure occurring at the windward side and outward suction occurring at the leeward side. A typical case of wind loading is shown in Figure 14-10.

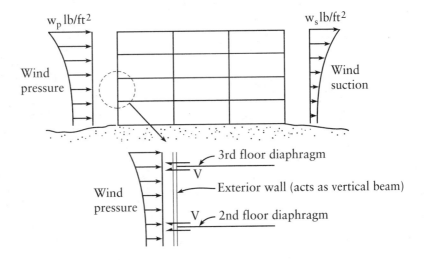

FIGURE 14-10 Wind loads at exterior walls.

At each level of a building, the exterior walls act as vertical beams extending between two diaphragms; their upper and lower reactions are the shearing forces shown in Figure 14-10. Mullions and walls are similarly designed as vertical beams between the two resisting diaphragms (floor or roof). Wind does not produce any loading on interior walls.

The loads thus delivered to each diaphragm are then transmitted to a set of vertical shear panels (or shearwalls). Where shear panels or shearwalls are used to resist lateral load, any columns used in the design are considered to be effective only in carrying vertical load; columns do not carry lateral load in this type of structure.

The loads delivered to the shear panels are then transmitted through the full height of the building down to the foundations, as indicated in Figure 14-11. The loads shown in Figure 14-11 are assumed to include both pressure forces and suction forces. Two sets of two shear panels each are located at each floor level; one set is effective when wind occurs along one axis of the building; the other set is effective when wind occurs along the other axis. For the symmetrical system of Figure 14-11, the wind loads are assumed to be distributed equally between the two panels in each set.

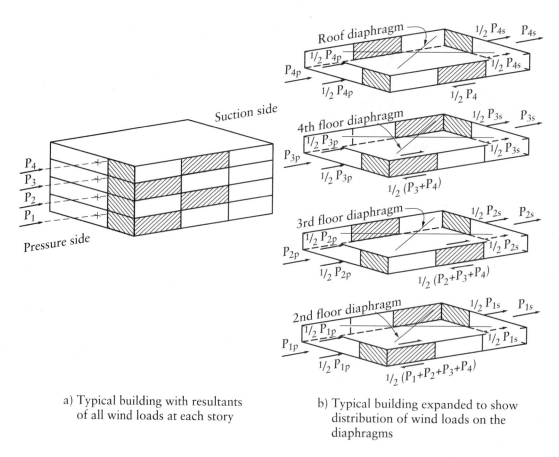

a) Typical building with resultants
of all wind loads at each story

b) Typical building expanded to show
distribution of wind loads on the
diaphragms

FIGURE 14-11 Distribution of wind load.

As noted earlier, all lateral loads are carried entirely by shearing forces that act along the full length of the vertical wall panels—hence the name *shear panel* for these structural elements. The shears, however, form an overturning couple on these panels that induces additional loads into the columns at each end of the panel; these vertical column forces and their resulting foundation loads are discussed further in subsequent sections. It is simply observed at this point that a typical shear panel has load-distributing edge members at top and bottom to deliver the lateral load to the panel and that it has columns at both vertical sides to resist the overturning effects induced by the lateral load.

A shear panel can be shifted longitudinally anywhere along the line of action of its intended load without affecting the magnitude of the load or the symmetry of the load system. The only change produced by making such a shift involves a change of the point where the shear panel is attached to the diaphragm. The attachment between the shear panel and the diaphragm must act as a hinge in one direction, but it must develop shear in the other direction, so that it functions somewhat like a long piano hinge.

The shear panels in Figure 14-11 are shown at the exterior wall lines, but they could just as easily be placed at some interior wall line. The concrete walls used as firewalls around an elevator shaft or a stairwell, for example, are sometimes designed to function also as shearwalls and as bearing walls. In all cases, however, to enhance stability and to control deflections, the two panels in any set of shear panels should be positioned as far apart as is reasonably possible; it is therefore common practice to place them at exterior wall lines.

In the load distribution shown in Figure 14-11, the shear panels at the top floor carry all of the wind load that occurs above the level of the floor diaphragm. These loads, along with the loads delivered to the floor diaphragm, are transmitted in turn to the shear panels at the next lower floor. Similarly, the shear panels at the next lower floor must carry the entire lateral load down to the next lower floor diaphragm, as indicated in the figure. The total shear at any level can therefore be computed simply as the sum of all shears above that level.

The shear panels need not all be aligned vertically. Some of the shear panels of Figure 14-11 are shown in staggered locations to illustrate this point. As a practical matter, however, these panels usually are stacked in a straight line vertically.

Only the set of shear panels that is oriented parallel to the wind is assumed to be effective in resisting the wind loads. The second set of shear panels (those oriented perpendicular to the wind) are assumed to have piano hinges at top and bottom and therefore to be ineffective. When the wind shifts to the other direction, however, this second set of shear panels becomes effective and the first set becomes ineffective.

An example will illustrate how to compute wind forces throughout a typical diaphragm-and-shearwall structure. This structural system is a straightforward symmetrical system with two sets of shear panels.

Example 14-7   Determine the wind forces acting at the top and at the bottom of each shear panel in the given concrete structure. Determine also the column loads induced by wind. The wind velocity is 100 mph. Pressures corresponding to the given wind velocity are shown in the profile and include a shape factor of 1.3 for the prismatic shape.

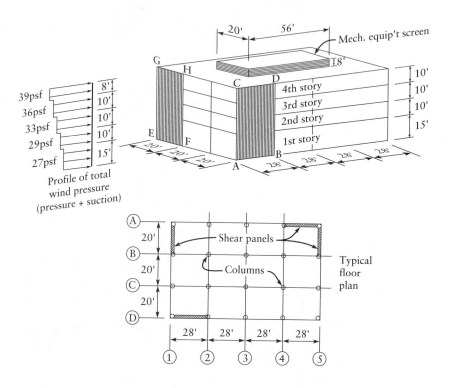

Solution   Wind load against the short side of the building is considered first.

Shear panel *ABCD* is shown in the following sketch. The wind shear forces delivered to each diaphragm have been computed and entered on the sketch. The height of the shear panel at any level is considered to extend from the bottom face of the diaphragm above to the top face of the diaphragm below. Supporting calculations for the indicated loads are shown after the sketch.

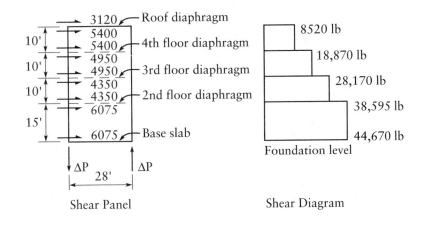

Shear Panel   Shear Diagram

Shear above roof level	$= 39 \text{ psf} \times 8 \times \dfrac{20}{2}$
	$= 3120 \text{ lb}$
Shear on the 4th-floor shear panel	$= 3120 + 5400$
	$= 8520 \text{ lb}$
Shear on the 3rd-floor shear panel	$= 8520 + 5400 + 4950$
	$= 18{,}870 \text{ lb}$
Shear on the 2nd-floor shear panel	$= 18{,}870 + 4950 + 4350$
	$= 28{,}170 \text{ lb}$
Shear on the 1st-floor shear panel	$= 28{,}170 + 4350 + 6075$
	$= 38{,}595 \text{ lb}$
Base shear on the foundations	$= 38{,}595 + 6075$
	$= 44{,}670 \text{ lb}$

The resultant horizontal shears and the induced vertical shears along the columns are shown (in pounds) in the following sketches.

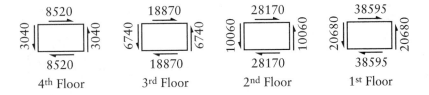

Since the wind can come from either direction, the column loads may increase or decrease by the amounts shown. Change in column loads at each end of panel *ABCD* is then

4th-floor columns, $\Delta P = \pm 3040$ lb

3rd-floor columns, $\Delta P = \pm 6740$ lb

2nd-floor columns, $\Delta P = \pm 10{,}060$ lb

1st-floor columns, $\Delta P = \pm 20{,}680$ lb

At the foundations, $\Delta P = \pm 20{,}680$ lb

Base shear per line, $V_B = \pm 44{,}670$ lb

Wind load is now taken against the long side of the building.

Shear panel *EFGH* is shown in the following sketch. The wind shear forces delivered to each diaphragm have been computed and entered on the sketch. The height of the shear panel at any level is considered to extend from the bottom face of the diaphragm above to the top face of the diaphragm below. Supporting calculations for the indicated loads are shown after the sketch.

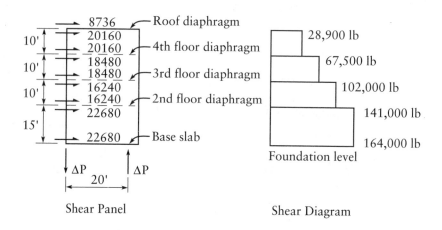

Shear Panel   Shear Diagram

Shear above roof level $= 39 \text{ psf} \times 8 \times \dfrac{56}{2}$

$= 8740$ lb

Shear on the 4th-floor shear panel $= 8740 + 20{,}160$
$= 28{,}900$ lb

Shear on the 3rd-floor shear panel $= 28{,}900 + 20{,}160 + 18{,}480$
$= 67{,}500$ lb

Shear on the 2nd-floor shear panel $= 67{,}500 + 18{,}480 + 16{,}240$
$= 102{,}000$ lb

Shear on the 1st-floor shear panel $= 102{,}000 + 16{,}420 + 22{,}680$
$= 141{,}000$ lb

Base shear on the foundations $= 141{,}000 + 22{,}680$
$= 164{,}000$ lb

The resultant horizontal shears and the induced vertical shears along the columns are shown (in pounds) in the following sketches.

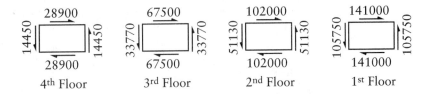

| 4th Floor | 3rd Floor | 2nd Floor | 1st Floor |

Since the wind can come from either direction, the column loads may increase or decrease by the amounts shown. Change in column loads at each end of panel *EFGH* is then

4th-floor columns, $\Delta P = \pm 14{,}450$ lb

3rd-floor columns, $\Delta P = \pm 33{,}770$ lb

2nd-floor columns, $\Delta P = \pm 51{,}130$ lb

1st-floor columns, $\Delta P = \pm 105{,}750$ lb

At the foundations, $\Delta P = \pm 107{,}500$ lb

Base shear per line, $V_B = \pm 164{,}000$ lb

Notice that the lateral load distribution in the structure of Example 14-7 is statically determinate. The horizontal diaphragms in such symmetrical structures do not undergo any horizontal rotations. Therefore, the only movement of the horizontal diaphragm is a simple translation in the direction of loading. Under these conditions, only the set of shear panels parallel to the wind receives load; the other set of panels receives no load and the system is thus rendered statically determinate.

The foregoing discussions have presented analyses for load in shear panels and diaphragms when a symmetrical structure is subjected to wind loads. The analysis for earthquake loads is quite similar—except, of course, with regard to the manner in which the load is generated and applied. The next section presents the analysis for such earthquake loads.

Outside Problems

Refer to Building Configuration No. 1, given at the end of the chapter.

Problem 14-29*

Determine the forces acting at the top and at the bottom of the shear panels at each story on line A and line E due to wind load against the short side of the building. Determine also the change in column loads at the ends of these shear panels due to this wind load. Wind velocity is 120 mph.

Problem 14-30

Determine the forces acting at the top and at the bottom of the shear panels at each story on line 1 and line 5 due to wind load against the long side of the building. Determine also the change in column loads at the ends of these shear panels due to this wind load. Wind velocity is 120 mph.

Refer to Building Configuration No. 2, given at the end of the chapter.

Problem 14-31*

Determine the forces acting at the top and at the bottom of the shear panels at each story on line A and line D due to wind load against the short side of the building. Determine also the change in column loads at the ends of these shear panels due to this wind load. Wind velocity is 90 mph.

Problem 14-32

Determine the forces acting at the top and at the bottom of the shear panels at each story on line 1 and line 5 due to wind load against the long side of the building. Determine also the change in column loads at the ends of these shear panels due to this wind load. Wind velocity is 90 mph.

14.6 DISTRIBUTION OF EARTHQUAKE LOAD

Earthquake forces are generated by the acceleration of masses. Under earthquake accelerations, every molecule of every structural member contributes to the earthquake force. Unlike wind forces, from which pressure occurs only at exterior surfaces, earthquake forces are generated within every molecule of every mass that makes up the dead load of the structure; typical results of such loading are shown in Figure 14-12.

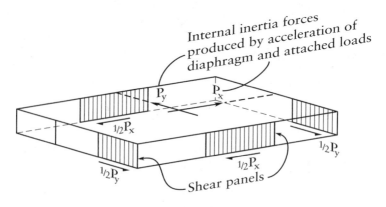

FIGURE 14-12 Earthquake loads on vertical panels.

As in the calculation of wind load, the total lateral shear force to be borne by the shear panels at any level is calculated simply as the sum of all forces above that level. In contrast to wind loads, however, lateral earthquake forces are generated both at interior walls and at exterior walls. Nonetheless, in practice, the wind load normal to exterior walls almost always proves to be much larger than the corresponding earthquake loads normal to those walls; consequently, wind load, rather than earthquake load, almost always governs the design of exterior walls in bending. Even so, the design must be checked, however cursorily, to see which load governs.

As indicated in Figure 14-12, the earthquake load generated between any two floor levels is first transmitted to the floor (or roof) diaphragm; this, in turn, transmits the load to the vertical shear panels. From that point onward, the analysis is identical to the one used for wind loading.

A typical distribution of earthquake loads throughout a symmetrical structure is shown in Figure 14-13. The similarities between this figure and Figure 14-11 (for wind load) are obvious. The similarities extend to the calculations, as well.

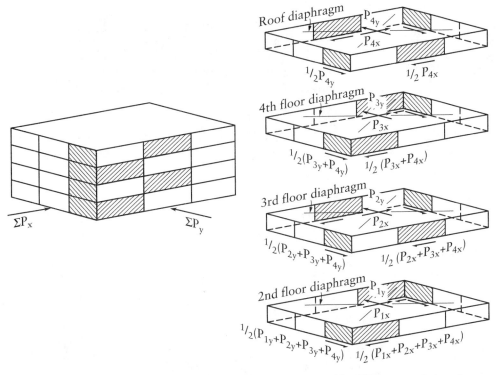

a) Typical building subject to
base shear due to earthquake

b) Typical building expanded to show
distribution of earthquake loads

FIGURE 14-13 Distribution of earthquake load.

An example will illustrate the distribution of lateral shearing forces due to earthquake in a symmetrical system.

Example 14-8   Determine the earthquake forces acting on the shear panels at each story of the concrete structure of Example 14-7. Determine also the column loads induced by the earthquake forces. The earthquake risk zone in this case is Zone 3; the importance factor is 1.0. Dead loads are given in the listing after the sketch.

Dead load of roof-mounted equipment = 26,300 lb
Dead load of roof screen wall = 6100 lb

Dead load of roof diaphragm = 670,000 lb
Dead load of items attached to roof = 81,600 lb

Dead load of 4th-floor diaphragm = 810,000 lb
Dead load of items attached to diaphragm = 170,000 lb

Dead load of 3rd-floor diaphragm = 820,000 lb
Dead load of items attached to diaphragm = 176,000 lb

Dead load of 2nd-floor diaphragm = 830,000 lb
Dead load of items attached to diaphragm = 185,000 lb

Dead load of base slab = 403,000 lb
Dead load of items attached to base slab = 91,000 lb

Solution   The base shear is given by Equation 13.4:

$$V_B = 2.75\left(\frac{Z}{R_W}\right)W$$

For Zone 3, $Z = 0.30$. For concrete structures, $R_W = 6$. At any level i,

$$V_i = 2.75\left(\frac{0.30}{6}\right)W = 0.1375\,W$$

where W is the dead load above the level i where V is being calculated.

A diagram of the dead load is given next, along with the values of shear calculated for each level.

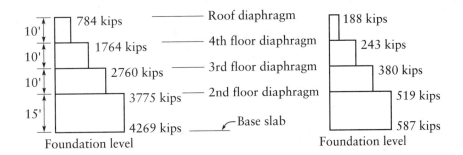

For panel *ABCD*, given a panel width of 28 ft, with half the load going to this panel and the other half going to the panel on the other side of the structure, the shears are shown in the following sketches.

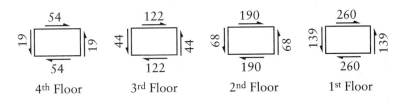

Similarly, for panel *EFGH*, given a panel width of 20 ft, the shears are shown in the following sketch.

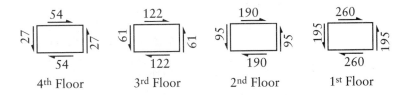

The changes in column loads at each side of panel *ABCD* are

4th-floor columns,	$\Delta P = 19$ kips
3rd-floor columns,	$\Delta P = 44$ kips
2nd-floor columns,	$\Delta P = 68$ kips
1st-floor columns,	$\Delta P = 139$ kips
At the foundations,	$\Delta P = 139$ kips
Base shear,	$V_B = 294$ kips at each panel

The changes in column loads at each side of panel *EFGH* are

4th-floor columns,	$\Delta P = 27$ kips
3rd-floor columns,	$\Delta P = 61$ kips
2nd-floor columns,	$\Delta P = 95$ kips
1st-floor columns,	$\Delta P = 95$ kips
At the foundations,	$\Delta P = 195$ kips
Base shear,	$V_B = 294$ kips at each panel

Due to the required conditions of symmetry, the horizontal diaphragm of Examples 14-7 and 14-8 did not undergo any horizontal rotations. The only displacement of the horizontal diaphragm was its horizontal translation.

Outside Problems

Refer to Building Configuration No. 1, given at the end of the chapter.

Problem 14-33*

Determine the forces due to earthquake that act on the shear panels at each story on line A and on line E. Determine also the change in the column loads at the ends of these shear panels due to earthquake. The risk zone location is Zone 3; the importance factor is 1.

Problem 14-34

Determine the forces due to earthquake that act on the shear panels at each story on line 1 and on line 5. Determine also the change in the column loads at the ends of these shear panels due to earthquake. The risk zone location is Zone 3; the importance factor is 1.

Refer to Building Configuration No. 2, given at the end of the chapter.

Problem 14-35*

Determine the forces due to earthquake that act on the shear panels at each story on line A and on line D. Determine also the change in the column loads at the ends of these shear panels due to earthquake. The risk zone location is Zone 3; the importance factor is 1.

Problem 14-36

Determine the forces due to earthquake that act on the shear panels at each story on line 1 and on line 5. Determine also the change in the column loads at the ends of these shear panels due to earthquake. The risk zone location is Zone 3; the importance factor is 1.

14.7 LOADS WITHIN DIAPHRAGMS AND SHEAR PANELS

In the preceding sections, methods were presented for finding the loads delivered to a diaphragm or shear panel. No attempt in those calculations was made to define the distribution of loads within any of the diaphragms or shear panels; the members were simply assumed to be adequate to receive and redistribute the loads. In this section, the distribution of loads within a diaphragm or shear panel will be examined.

Diaphragms and shear panels are treated simply as extremely thin structural elements whose primary value resides in their ability to sustain shearing forces. Their thickness is so slight in comparison to their length and width that they may be likened to very thin membranes, much like sheet metal. A concrete building floor 100 ft × 100 ft × 4 inches thick, for example, has the same dimensional scale as a machine part made of 19-gauge sheet metal, 12 in. × 12 in. square. Either may be regarded as a very thin membrane, capable of developing high resistance in shear (if properly introduced) but incapable of developing any significant resistance in bending.

Further, the "scale" effect extends to other aspects of stress. A hole or reentrant corner in a machine part made of 19-gauge sheet metal, for example, will introduce a significant "stress raiser" into the part; indeed, a stress concentration factor as high as 2.5 or even 3.0 might be expected. A concrete diaphragm 100 ft square is no different. A stairwell opening in a concrete diaphragm can introduce significant stress concentrations at the reentrant corners, and some means to disseminate these stresses must be included in the design. As a general rule, the concepts of stress concentrations discussed in courses on elementary strength of materials in relation to sheet metal machine parts apply equally well to diaphragms and shear panels in building construction; the relative scales of both are quite comparable.

Consider, for example, the typical concrete floor diaphragm from a multistory building shown in Figure 14-14. Stairwell or elevator openings at each end of such buildings are invariably essential to the function of the building and must be provided. The reentrant corners at $E2$ and $B5$, however, introduce significant stress concentrations under shearing loads, particularly those developed during the violent random motion of an earthquake. Additional reinforcement or other strengtheners in such locations are usually necessary.

Locations where a load is abruptly introduced into a diaphragm typically require some additional strengthening. One such location in the slab of Figure 14-14 is at the end of the shear panels, $C2$ and $D5$, where the entire shear load from the floor abruptly begins to be transferred from the diaphragm to the shear panel. In most cases, the inclusion of a heavy beam or girder (such as those at lines 2 and 5) will be adequate to effect this kind of load. If no such member exists, additional reinforcement or other strengtheners may be required; these are shown, for the sake of illustration, at points $C2$ and $D5$ in Figure 14-14.

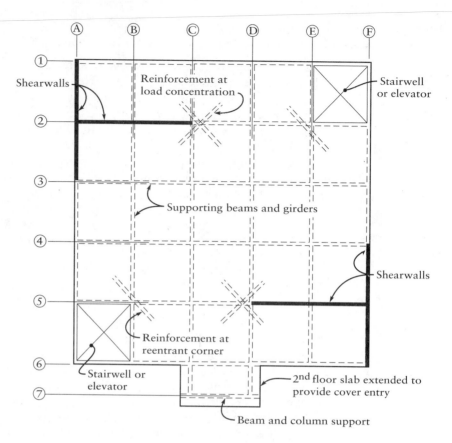

FIGURE 14-14 Stress concentrations in a diaphragm.

Earlier, it was noted that the diaphragms in a diaphragm/shear panel system must maintain the shape of the building at each floor level. If the floor slab were removed, for example, the framing members of Figure 14-14 would have little resistance to "racking" loads, and the rectangular shapes between beams would deform readily into parallelograms. The diaphragm must therefore sustain the shearing stresses that might occur from such racking loads; but in so doing, it becomes susceptible to high stress concentrations at all discontinuities, electrical chases, reentrant corners, plumbing penetrations, and load points (shear panels).

In most cases, the shearing stress levels in a diaphragm are not inordinately high; and even with a stress concentration factor of 3, the stresses at reentrant corners may seem to fall within permissible levels. There are many unknowns, however, and prudent designers should rely on intuition as well as on numbers when designing diaphragms and shear panels.

Consider the cantilevered portion of the diaphragm given in Figure 14-14 shown in greater detail in Figure 14-15. Notice that this portion of the diaphragm is assumed to be cantilevered from the basic building where all the shear panels are located. The resisting moment is developed by a couple located along the beam lines at C and D, while the entire shearing load is carried by the diaphragm. The diaphragm is thus assumed to be of no help in developing the resisting moment; the diaphragm carries only the shearing force V_x.

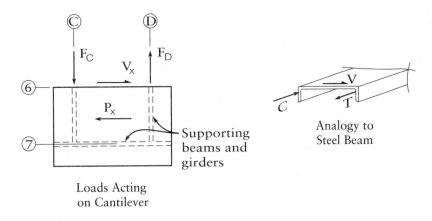

Loads Acting
on Cantilever

FIGURE 14-15 Cantilevered portion of diaphragm.

Such idealistic simplifications are commonly made in the analysis of diaphragms. The loads that are assumed to act on the cantilever in Figure 14-15 are directly analogous to those that are commonly assumed to act on a steel beam, in which the flanges (edge members) carry only tension or compression, and the web (diaphragm) carries only shear. A typical steel beam with this simplified stress pattern is included for comparison in Figure 14-15. Again, the differences in size between a small steel beam and the entire wing of a building should be viewed as differences in scale only; within their elastic range, both are considered to respond to flexure in essentially the same way.

The distribution of shears within an irregular diaphragm is shown in Figure 14-16. The diaphragm in this case is a second-floor diaphragm that has openings cut into it for the usual stairwell/elevator shaft. The overall diaphragm is quite irregular.

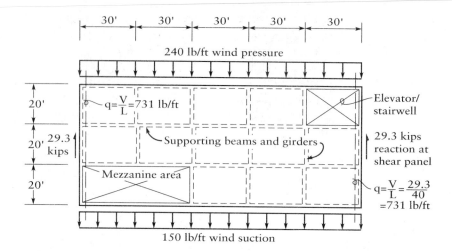

FIGURE 14-16 Irregular diaphragm under wind load.

The wind loads at each side of the building are delivered to the diaphragm, as usual, by beam action in the exterior walls. The reactions due to these loads are then developed by the vertical shear panels; these reactive forces are shown at the sides of the diaphragm.

The diaphragm of Figure 14-16 may be viewed as a very deep, simply supported beam with a very short span. The heavy edge members form the flanges of the deep beam, and the diaphragm forms the web. For such a beam, the shears are assumed to be distributed uniformly across the full width of the web (the diaphragm), as shown. The shear flow q at any section is then calculated as the total shear force at the section divided by the length of material subject to that force. Typical results of such calculations are shown in Figure 14-16. The result of primary interest is, as indicated, the highest level of stress.

A heavy edge member has been provided at all four sides of the diaphragm. For such a configuration, the analogy to the steel section shown earlier in Figure 14-15 remains valid, with the edge members being the flanges and the diaphragm being the web. With only small error, the distribution of shear flow q across the diaphragm can then be assumed to remain constant.

More importantly, however, all major shear loads transmitted into and out of the thin diaphragm must be delivered by these heavy edge members. The edge members serve to prevent concentrations of load from being introduced into the thin diaphragm. They also deliver the uniformly distributed loads from the diaphragm to the shear panels without producing an abrupt change in stress either in the thin diaphragm or in the thin shear panel. They thus constitute an essential part of the concept of diaphragm-and-shearwall construction.

The internal distribution of shear flow that is assumed for the diaphragm also applies to the vertical shear panels at either side of the diaphragm. In

their case, however, the analogy to steel beams must be to very deep cantilever beams, projecting upward out of their foundations. Such a shear panel
is shown in Figure 14-17.

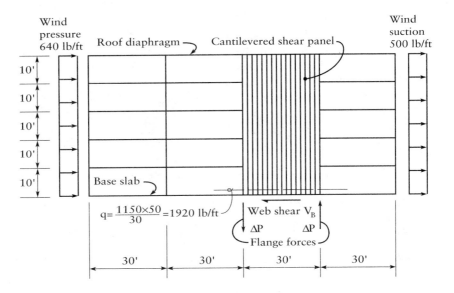

FIGURE 14-17 Shear panel as a cantilever beam.

The shear panel of Figure 14-17 may be viewed as a deep cantilever beam,
loaded by the lateral wind loads at the sides of the building. The analogy to
the steel beam of Figure 14-15 remains valid; that is, the columns at each
side of the shear panel form the flanges of the beam, and the shear panel
forms the web. (Notice that the columns also serve as edge members.) As
before, the shear flow across the panel may be assumed to be distributed uniformly across the width of the panel. As a related matter, the vertical loads
ΔP that are to be taken by the foundations to either side of the panel can also
be very important, particularly when they cause uplift of the foundations;
such cases are discussed further in the next section.

The maximum shear flow q in the panel of Figure 14-17 is calculated as
shown in the figure. The shear force causing this maximum shear flow is the
sum of all shear forces above the base:

$$V = (640 + 500)(50) = 57.5 \text{ kips}$$

and the length of panel that must sustain this load is the panel width of 30 ft.
The shear flow is then

$$\frac{57,500}{30} = 1920 \text{ lbs/ft}$$

As is usual in structures, only the maximum value is of interest; all other values of shear flow in the panel fall below this value.

Any openings in the shear panels (such as doors or windows) are likely to create stress raisers at the reentrant corners. A stress concentration factor of 2.5 is considered appropriate at such points. To offset this increase in stress, the thickness of the shear panel may be increased proportionately in those areas. Alternatively, continuous edge members may be added around the opening or, in concrete or masonry construction, additional reinforcement may be added in the plane of the shear panel.

To illustrate the effects of such openings, a shear panel that has two of these openings is shown in Figure 14-18. For simplicity, the shear across the panel is assumed to be constant. The relative deformations (the shear detrusions γ_1, γ_2, and γ_3) are shown in dashed lines.

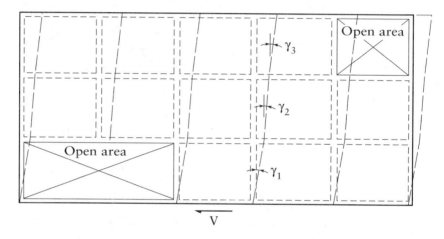

FIGURE 14-18 Detrusion in a shear panel.

In Figure 14-18, continuous distribution members have been provided around each opening. These members serve to smooth out and to distribute the abrupt change in shear stress that must occur when the effective area abruptly changes. The members shown in Figure 14-18 are somewhat extreme; ordinarily, they would not need to be extended to the full width and full depth of the panel.

14.8 FOUNDATION LOADS AT SHEAR PANELS

In diaphragm/shearwall structures, the overturning effect of the lateral loads is resisted entirely by the shear panels. Under the lateral loads, the shear panels undergo an overturning rotation, as shown in Figure 14-19, and the entire building "racks" or "drifts" through an angle, as indicated. The bottom surface of the shear panel must, of course, rotate through the same angle, producing sharply increased (or decreased) displacements at the foundations.

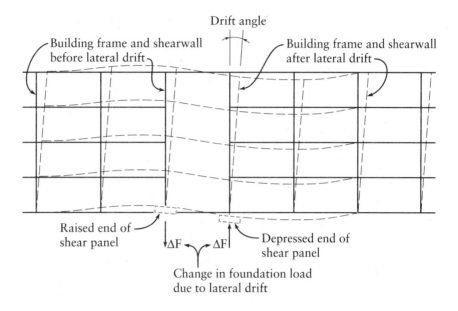

FIGURE 14-19 Drift angle in a building.

The drift angle shown in Figure 14-19 is limited by code to 0.005 radians. Excessive drift is highly damaging to glass and to finishes, as well as to the structure, and must be tightly controlled in the structural design. An angle of 0.005 radians is about 1 part in 200, or 5/8 inch per story, or 1 inch in 16 feet; an angle of this size, if it occurs, can produce serious problems. Although a drift angle of 0.005 radians is permitted by code, about half this much drift is usually the preferred maximum.

Control over the drift angle must be exercised by the structural engineer during the design of the structural system for the building. To obtain such control, the designer may have to perform some intricate juggling of the footing sizes, column loadings, and panel lengths. For the sake of the foundation design, however, such control within the structural design must be accomplished, and the drift angle must never be permitted to exceed 0.005 radians, even when lateral load is at its maximum.

In addition to the foregoing limit on drift, practical limitations on foundation settlements place a further limit on the amount of rotation the shear panel can be allowed to undergo. In the design shown in Figure 14-20, for example, the foundations should probably be designed with a maximum settlement S under gravity loading of about 1 inch. Assuming that the foundations are properly designed, the shear panel will settle uniformly under its gravity loads such that long-term settlements at both ends are roughly equal before the lateral loads occur.

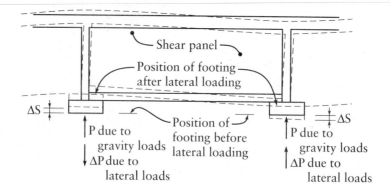

FIGURE 14-20 Shearwall footing pressures.

When the short-term lateral loads eventually occur, the panel of Figure 14-20 presumably will rotate through its drift angle of 0.005 radians, at which point the uplift ΔS at the raised end will just barely have relieved all of the soil pressure at that end, producing zero pressure there. At that angle of drift, the downward load at the other end must be equal to the sum of all the panel loads at both ends, which is taken here to be the limiting case. Since the panel is subject to load reversals, each of the footings at the ends of a shear panel must be designed to take the sum of all the loads that can occur at the panel (not just the load that can occur at one end).

The actual magnitude of the differential movement ΔS depends on the modulus of subgrade reaction for short-term loading—a highly uncertain property in soils. Depending on the source of data, the modulus for short-term loading may be estimated as anywhere from 3 to 30 times the modulus for long-term loading. With such a range of estimates, any attempt to calculate the actual rotation is hopeless. All estimates agree, however, that the soil is more rigid, not less rigid, under transient short-term loads. Consequently, it is reasonable to take as the limiting case the situation where the uplift due to the drift angle produces zero soil pressure at one end of the panel.

The limiting case is shown in Figure 14-20. By the time the drift angle reaches 0.005 radians, the pressure at one end of the shear panel is assumed to have only just decreased to zero; the load at the loaded end then becomes the sum of all tributary vertical loads—roughly double its initial load (assuming that the two foundation loads are about equal). The restoring moment produced by the foundations is then limited to the value of the couple $P_W s/2$, where s is the span between the footings, and P_W is the sum of all tributary vertical loads. The restoring moment can be increased in two ways: by using a longer shear panel, or by incorporating additional shear panels in the design.

If a higher resisting moment is needed, several alternative configurations are readily possible. One possibility is simply to extend a heavy grade beam outward from the base of the panel to the adjacent footings at either end, as shown in Figure 14-21. Analysis of the panel of Figure 14-21 reveals that the restoring moment produced by the extended foundation can be up to three times higher than that of the unextended foundation.

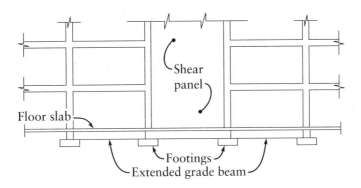

FIGURE 14-21 Extended grade beams.

In subsequent discussions in this text, the vertical design load on either of the two footings at the ends of a shear panel will be taken as the sum of all tributary vertical loads due to dead load plus live load, designated herein as P_W. The restoring moment offered by the shear panel is computed in accordance with this limiting value of P_W; it is assumed that the structure itself is properly designed to resist lateral loads with this maximum level of restoring moment.

14.9 REINFORCED CONCRETE STRUCTURAL SYSTEMS

The structural systems discussed in this chapter do not explicitly include conventional reinforced concrete frames, even though such reinforced concrete structures commonly utilize diaphragm-and-shear panel systems to resist lateral loads. The reason they have not been specifically mentioned heretofore is that the horizontal beams and girders in such concrete frames are invariably designed as continuous members and hence produce a statically indeterminate structural frame. The solution of these statically indeterminate frames has not yet been presented; it is presented in a later chapter.

Conventional texts on the design of reinforced concrete present a highly simplified analysis of the gravity loads on these continuous frames. The simplified analysis utilizes "blanket" coefficients for computing the statically indeterminate reactions at the ends of each reinforced concrete member; the blanket coefficients are published by the American Concrete Institute (ACI) in their publication ACI 318. The coefficients, called the ACI coefficients, are widely used throughout the industry for designing reinforced concrete members under gravity loads. The ACI coefficients (and the simplified analysis) do not include any provisions for lateral loads, however, so other provisions must be made for these loads.

Lateral loads on statically indeterminate concrete frames are commonly resisted through the addition of a separate diaphragm-and-shear-panel system such as the ones presented in this chapter. Consequently, even though the vertical load-carrying system is statically indeterminate, the lateral load-carrying system can be designed independently as a statically determinate system. The methods of this chapter are entirely valid for lateral load analysis and for design of this type of lateral load-carrying system in concrete frames.

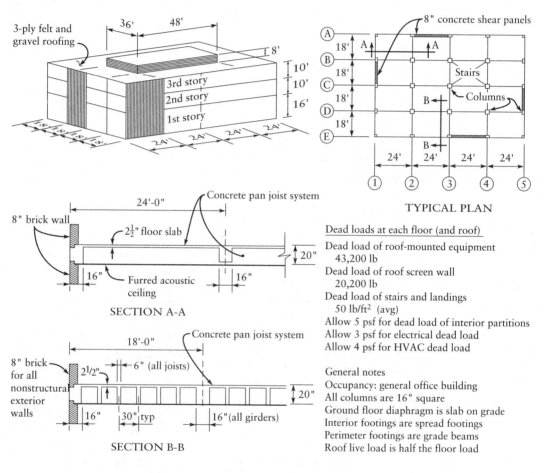

TYPICAL PLAN

Dead loads at each floor (and roof)

Dead load of roof-mounted equipment
  43,200 lb
Dead load of roof screen wall
  20,200 lb
Dead load of stairs and landings
  50 lb/ft² (avg)
Allow 5 psf for dead load of interior partitions
Allow 3 psf for electrical dead load
Allow 4 psf for HVAC dead load

General notes
Occupancy: general office building
All columns are 16" square
Ground floor diaphragm is slab on grade
Interior footings are spread footings
Perimeter footings are grade beams
Roof live load is half the floor load

SECTION A-A

SECTION B-B

Outside Problems Building Configuration No.1

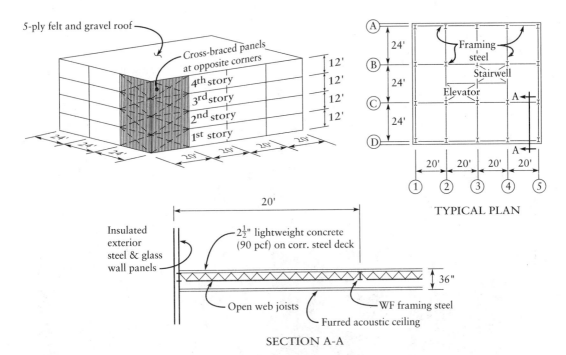

5-ply felt and gravel roof

Cross-braced panels at opposite corners

4th story
3rd story
2nd story
1st story

12'
12'
12'
12'

24' 24' 24'

20' 20' 20' 20'

TYPICAL PLAN

Framing steel

Stairwell

Elevator

24'
24'
24'

20' 20' 20' 20'

Insulated exterior steel & glass wall panels

20'

$2\frac{1}{2}$" lightweight concrete (90 pcf) on corr. steel deck

36"

Open web joists

WF framing steel

Furred acoustic ceiling

SECTION A-A

Dead loads at each floor (and roof)

Weight of framing steel	5.4 psf
Weight of joists and steel deck	3.9 psf
Weight of panels covering bracing	11.0 psf
Weight of other exterior panels	7.0 psf
Weight of miscellaneous steel	3.0 psf
Allow for interior partitions	5.0 psf
Allow for electrical deadload	2.0 psf
Allow for HVAC deadload	5.0 psf
Weight of stairs and landings	50.0 psf

General notes

Occupancy: luxury condominium apartments
Ground floor diaphragm is slab on grade
Interior footings are spread footings
Perimeter footings are grade beams
Elevator is hydraulic, supported from base
Roof live load is half the floor load

Outside Problems Building Configuration No.2

U.S. Courthouse and Federal Office Building, Orlando, Florida, built with precast beams and columns. (Photograph courtesy Portland Cement Association, reprinted by permission.)

CHAPTER

15

Indeterminate Single-Span Structures

The methods of analysis presented in the preceding chapters for determinate structures are used for indeterminate structures as well. The only difference between determinate structures and indeterminate structures is that additional conditions (other than the statics conditions) must be used to find the reactions on indeterminate structures. Once the reactions are known, there is then no difference in any of the remaining analysis or design procedures.

The basic methods for finding the reactions on indeterminate single-span structures are introduced in this chapter. Such structures typically include beams, portal frames, gable frames, tied frames, hinged arches, and tied arches. Sketches of some of the more common single-span structures are shown in Figure 15-1.

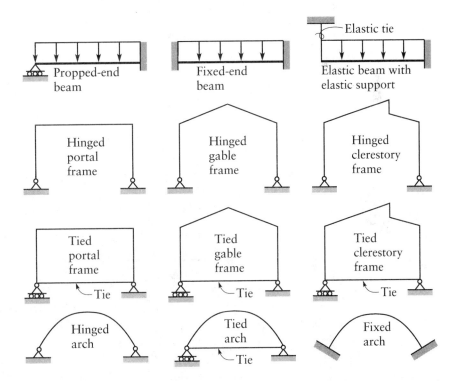

FIGURE 15-1 Common indeterminate single-span structures.

479

Once the reactions are known, the procedures for completing the shear and moment diagrams, for finding deflections, and for locating points of inflection are the same as those developed earlier. These remaining procedures will be included in the indeterminate solutions of this chapter only for a few select cases, primarily to remind the student what the next steps would be. As a rule, however, these final chapters on indeterminate structures concentrate on finding indeterminate reactions; the analysis generally stops when the reactions are found.

It has been noted repeatedly in earlier discussions that no more than three reactions can occur in a planar structure if the structure is to remain statically determinate. If more than three unknowns exist, the additional unknowns are termed *redundants*. For each redundant, one additional condition (usually a deformation condition) must be found.

The simplest type of indeterminate structure is a propped beam; the analysis of propped beams will be considered first.

15.1 PROPPED-END BEAMS

Consider the beam of Figure 15-2. The free body of the beam shows all the reactions that can occur at each support, but only the reactions that can occur at each support. A total of four reactions occur on the beam.

Notice the use of the double subscripts for all reactions. The first subscript denotes location; the second denotes direction. The moment M_{BA} is read as "moment at B toward A." (In continuous members, treated later, the distinction becomes necessary.)

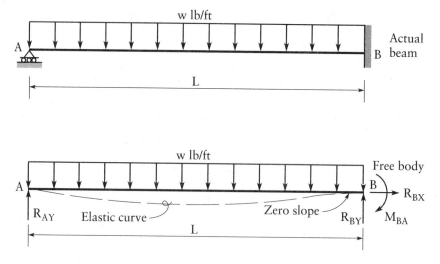

FIGURE 15-2 Propped-end beam.

The beam of Figure 15-2 is called a propped-end beam; it is commonly used as a starting point in one of the more specialized methods of analysis (presented in the next chapter). Because it has four reactions altogether, it has one redundant reaction; the propped-end beam is therefore said to be 1 degree indeterminate. One additional condition must be found if a solution is to be obtained.

For the beam of Figure 15-2, the reaction R_{AY} is selected as the redundant. From the three equilibrium conditions ($\Sigma F_X = 0$, $\Sigma F_Y = 0$, and $\Sigma M_O = 0$), the remaining reactions are expressed in terms of the chosen redundant. The sum of vertical forces yields such an expression for the reaction R_{BY}:

$$\Sigma F_Y = 0; \qquad R_{AY} - wL + R_{BY} = 0$$
$$R_{BY} = wL - R_{AY} \tag{15.1}$$

The sum of moments about B eliminates R_{BY} and R_{BX}, yielding an expression for M_{BA}:

$$\Sigma M_B = 0; \qquad R_{AY}L - \frac{1}{2}wL^2 + M_{BA} = 0$$
$$M_{BA} = \frac{1}{2}wL^2 - R_{AY}L \tag{15.2}$$

The sum of horizontal forces yields an expression for R_{BX}:

$$\Sigma F_X = 0; \qquad R_{BX} = 0 \tag{15.3}$$

The first solution for reactions uses the area moment theorems, or the method of the elastic curve. In an area moment solution, one finds a point on the elastic curve of the beam where the tangential deviation is known or where the angle between two tangents is known. Such a point provides the one additional condition that is required for a solution.

The free body, with its elastic curve, is shown in Figure 15-3. The tangent to the elastic curve is drawn at B; since this tangent passes through point A, the deviation at A with respect to the tangent at B is zero:

$$t_{AB} = 0 = \frac{A_M \bar{x}}{EI} \tag{15.4}$$

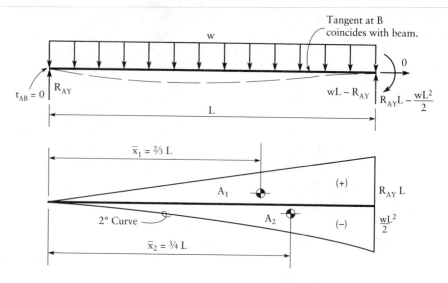

FIGURE 15-3 Area moment solution of propped-end beam.

Equation 15.4 provides the one additional condition required for solution, that is, that the moment of the bending moment diagram about A is known to be zero. Hence,

$$t_{AB} = 0 = \frac{A_M \bar{x}}{EI} = \frac{A_1 x_1 + A_2 x_2}{EI} \tag{15.5}$$

$$0 = A_1 x_1 + A_2 x_2$$

where

$$A_1 = \left(+\frac{1}{2} R_{AY} L \right) L = +\frac{1}{2} R_{AY} L^2$$

$$x_1 = \frac{2}{3} L$$

$$A_2 = \left(-\frac{1}{2} w L^2 \right)\left(\frac{1}{3} L \right) = -\frac{1}{6} w L^3$$

$$x_2 = \frac{3}{4} L$$

Hence,

$$0 = \left(\frac{1}{2} R_{AY} L^2 \right)\left(\frac{2}{3} L \right) - \left(\frac{1}{6} w L^3 \right)\left(\frac{3}{4} L \right)$$

$$R_{AY} = \frac{3}{8} w L \tag{15.6a}$$

The remaining reactions can now be found from the earlier statics relationships:

$$R_{BY} = wL - R_{AY} = \frac{5}{8}wL \qquad (15.6b)$$

$$M_{BA} = \frac{1}{2}wL^2 - R_{AY}L = \frac{1}{8}wL^2 \qquad (15.6c)$$

$$R_{BX} = 0 \qquad (15.6d)$$

Equations 15.6 offer the solution for the four reactions acting on the given propped-end beam.

The procedures for drawing the shear and moment diagrams and finding the inflection point remain exactly the same as those used earlier and will not be repeated here. For future reference, however, this very important beam configuration and its completed shear and moment diagrams are shown in Figure 15-4. Notice that the moment diagram of Figure 15-4 has been drawn with positive moments downward; the moment diagram then falls on the "tension" side of the beam.

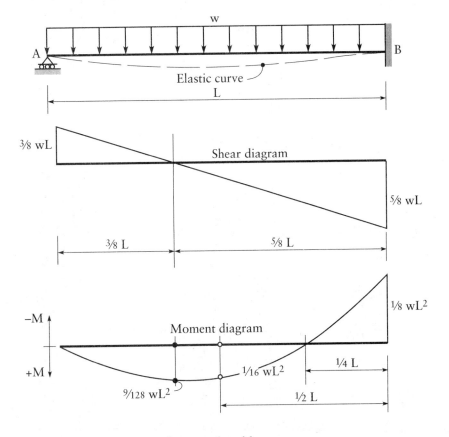

FIGURE 15-4 Summary of propped-end beam.

The reactions of the propped-end beam of Figure 15-4 could just as easily have been found from the Castigliano theorem. For such a solution, refer to the free body shown in Figure 15-5. The reaction R_{AY} is again chosen as the redundant, but in the Castigliano solution it is chosen because its deflection Δ_{AY} is known to be zero. As before, the remaining reactions are then expressed in terms of the chosen redundant.

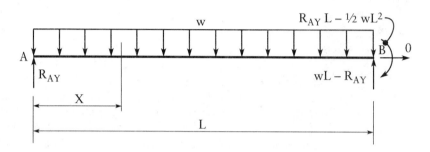

FIGURE 15-5 Free body of propped beam.

The deflection Δ_{AY} of the reaction R_{AY} is zero, as noted, which provides the required additional condition for solution. The Castigliano solution for the deflection of R_{AY} is

$$\Delta_{AY} = 0 = \int_0^L \frac{M_S\left(\dfrac{\partial M_S}{\partial R_{AY}}\right)ds}{EI} \tag{15.7}$$

The moment equation and the partial derivatives are:

$$0 \le x \le L; \qquad M_x = R_{AY}x - \frac{1}{2}wx^2; \qquad \frac{\partial M_x}{\partial R_{AY}} = x; \qquad ds = dx$$

These values are substituted, yielding the integral form

$$0 = \int_0^L \frac{\left(R_{AY}L - \dfrac{1}{2}wx^2\right)(x)\,dx}{EI}$$

$$= \frac{R_{AY}}{EI}\int_0^L x^2 dx - \frac{\dfrac{1}{2}w}{EI}\int_0^L x^3 dx$$

$$= \frac{R_{AY}}{EI}\left.\frac{x^3}{3}\right|_0^L - \frac{\dfrac{1}{2}w}{EI}\left.\frac{x^4}{4}\right|_0^L$$

For constant EI,

$$0 = \frac{R_{AY}L^3}{3} - \frac{wL^4}{8}$$

$$R_{AY} = \frac{3}{8}wL \tag{15.8}$$

The value of R_{AY} found by this means is of course the same as that found by the method of the elastic curve. The remainder of the solution is identical to that given earlier and will not be repeated here.

A deflection or a tangential deviation need not be zero in order to provide a known condition of deformation. If the deflection of an elastic support can be expressed in terms of the redundant, it can also serve as the additional deformation condition. A numerical example will illustrate such a solution.

Example 15-1   Determine all reactions for the given steel beam. The tie bar is steel, 1 in. diameter.

$I = 248$ in.^{4}

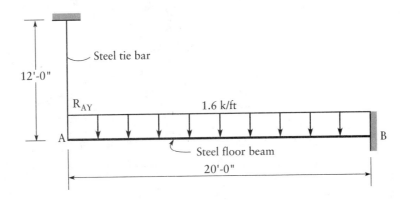

Solution   The free body of the beam is shown in the following sketch. There are four unknown reactions, as shown; the beam is one degree indeterminate. The reaction R_{AY} is selected as the redundant and the other three reactions are expressed in terms of R_{AY}, using the three equations of statics.

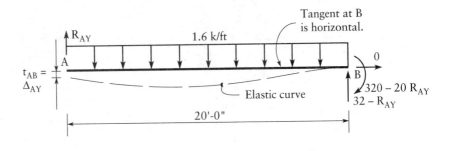

The deflection Δ_{AY} is the axial elongation of the tie bar due to the axial force R_{AY}. In units of kips and feet,

$$\Delta_{AY} = \frac{R_{AY}L}{AE}$$

where

$$L = 12 \text{ ft}$$
$$A = \frac{\pi(1^2)}{4} \times \frac{1}{12^2} = 0.00545 \text{ ft}^2$$
$$E = 29,000\,(12^2) = 4.176 \times 10^6 \text{ ksf}$$

and

$$\Delta_{AY} = (527 \times 10^{-6})\, R_{AY}$$

It is elected to perform the solution by using area moment methods. The deviation t_{AB} is equal to the deflection Δ_{AY}:

$$\Delta_{AY} = t_{AB} = \frac{A_M \bar{x}_A}{EI} \tag{15.9}$$

where moments are to be taken about the deviation line at A.

The moment diagram by parts is shown in the following sketch.

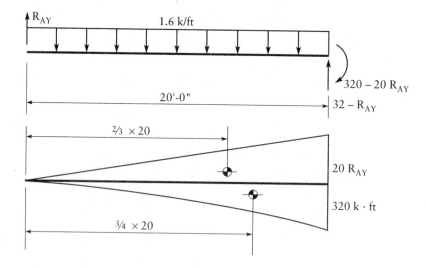

The displacement Δ_{AY} is now equated to the tangential deviation. Δ_{AY} is negative, since t_{AB} falls below the tangent.

$$(-527 \times 10^{-6}) R_{AY} = \frac{A_M \bar{x}}{EI} = \frac{A_1 x_1 + A_2 x_2}{EI}$$

where

$$A_1 = 20 R_{AY} (20) \left(\frac{1}{2} \right) = 200 R_{AY} \text{ kip-ft}$$

$$x_1 = \frac{2}{3} (20) = 13.33 \text{ ft}$$

$$A_2 = -320 (20) \left(\frac{1}{3} \right) = -2133 \text{ kip-ft}$$

$$x_2 = \frac{3}{4} (20) = 15.0 \text{ ft}$$

$$E = 4,176,000 \text{ kips/ft}^2$$
$$I = 248 \text{ in.}^4 = 0.01196 \text{ ft}^4$$

so that

$$(-527 \times 10^{-6}) R_{AY} = \frac{200 R_{AY} (13.33) - 2133 (15)}{(4,176,000)(0.01196)}$$
$$R_{AY} = 11.88 \text{ kips} \tag{15.10a}$$

The other reactions are found from the static relations shown on the free body.

$$R_{BY} = 20.12 \text{ kips} \tag{15.10b}$$

$$R_{BX} = 0 \tag{15.10c}$$

$$M_{BA} = 82.4 \text{ kip-ft} \tag{15.10d}$$

$$\Delta_{AY} = (-527 \times 10^6) R_{AY}$$
$$= 0.00626 \text{ ft} = 0.0751 \text{ in.} \tag{15.10e}$$

As a matter of interest, the end reaction found earlier for the beam of Figure 15-2 was found to be $R_{AY} = \frac{3}{8}wL$. That beam, however, had a rigid support rather than an elastic support. If the beam of Example 15-1 had had a rigid support instead of an elastic support, its reaction at A would have been

$$R_{AY} = \frac{3}{8}wL = 0.375\,(1.6)(20) = 12.0 \text{ kips}$$

This value of 12 kips for a rigid support compares to the value of 11.88 kips for an elastic support. Evidently, the steel tie bar provides a very rigid, essentially unyielding support for the floor beam. Such tie bars are often used in engineered structures.

Now that the reactions of the beam of Example 15-1 are known, all further calculations are the same as those presented in earlier chapters. The equation of the elastic curve, for example, can be found routinely now that the reactions are known.

Example 15-2 Determine the equation of the elastic curve for the beam of Example 15-1.

$EI = 49{,}945 \text{ kip-ft}^2$

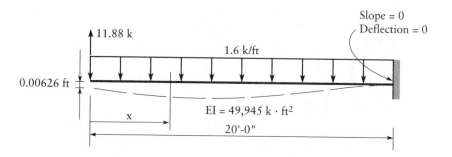

Solution The differential equation of the elastic curve is given by

$$\frac{d^2y}{dx^2} = \frac{M_x}{EI} \tag{15.11}$$

The moment equation is written in the usual way:

$$M_x = 11.88x - \frac{1}{2}(1.6x^2) = 11.88x^2 - 0.8x^2$$

The slope at any point is found by integrating once:

$$EI\frac{d^2y}{dx^2} = 11.88x - 0.80x^2$$

$$EI\frac{dy}{dx} = \frac{11.88x^2}{2} - \frac{0.80x^3}{3} + C_1$$

$$= 5.94x^2 - 0.2667x^3 + C_1$$

The constant of integration C_1 is evaluated at the point $x = 20$, where the slope is zero. At $x = 20$,

$$EI\frac{dy}{dx} = 0 = 5.94\,(20)^2 - 0.2667\,(20)^3 + C_1$$

$$C_1 = -2376 + 2133 = -243$$

The final equation for the slope of the beam is then

$$EI\frac{dy}{dx} = 5.94x^2 - 0.2667x^3 - 243$$

Integrating again yields the equation for deflections:

$$EIy = \frac{5.94x^3}{3} - \frac{0.2667x^4}{4} - 243x + C_2$$

The constant C_2 is evaluated at the point $x = 0$, where the deflection is -0.00626 ft:

$$49,945\,(-0.00626) = C_2$$

$$C_2 = -313$$

The final equation of the elastic curve is thus found to be

$$y = 10^{-6}\,(39.64x^3 - 1.335x^4 - 4860x - 6260) \tag{15.12}$$

At this point, the solution looks questionable. The constant of integration C_2 was evaluated for the boundary condition that $y = -0.00626$ at $x = 0$. The deflection must also be zero at $x = 20$ ft, but this boundary condition has not been imposed. It appears that one of the boundary conditions will not be satisfied. A numerical check will show whether the equation is correct. At $x = 20$,

$$y = 10^{-6}\,(317,100 - 213,600 - 97,200 - 6260)$$

$$= 0 \qquad \text{(ok—the solution satisfies all conditions)}$$

The procedures of the foregoing examples are applicable for any location of the support, or *prop*. A numerical example will illustrate the solution when the beam has an overhang.

Example 15-3   Determine all reactions on the given beam.

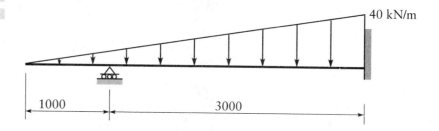

Solution   The free body of the beam is shown in the following sketch. There are four unknown reactions, so the beam is one degree indeterminate. The reaction R_{AY} is selected as the redundant; its deflection Δ_{AY} is zero. The other three reactions are expressed in terms of the redundant R_{AY}, using the three conditions of statics.

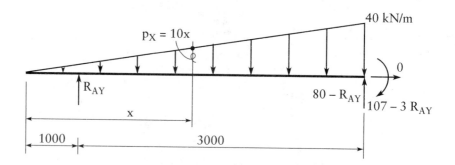

The solution will be obtained using the Castigliano theorem. The known condition is, as stated, that the deflection of the force R_{AY} is zero:

$$\Delta_{AY} = 0 = \int_0^L \frac{M_s\left(\dfrac{\partial M_s}{\partial R_{AY}}\right)ds}{EI} \tag{15.13}$$

The intensity of the load at x is found by ratios:

$$\frac{p_x}{x} = \frac{40}{4}$$

$$p_x = 10x$$

With $ds = dx$, the moment equation and its derivatives can be calculated. For $0 \leq x \leq 1$,

$$M_x = -p_x\left(\frac{1}{2}x\right)\left(\frac{1}{3}x\right) = -1.667x^3; \qquad \left(\frac{\partial M_x}{\partial R_{AY}}\right) = 0$$

For $1 \leq x \leq 4$,

$$M_x = -p_x\left(\frac{1}{2}x\right)\left(\frac{1}{3}x\right) + R_{AY}(x-1)$$

$$= -1.667x^3 + R_{AY}(x-1); \qquad \left(\frac{\partial M_x}{\partial R_{AY}}\right) = x-1$$

These values are substituted back into the Castigliano equation:

$$\Delta_{AY} = 0 = \int_0^1 \frac{(-1.667x^3)(0)\,dx}{EI}$$

$$+ \int_1^4 \frac{[-1.667x^3 + R_{AY}(x-1)]\,(x-1)dx}{EI}$$

The stiffness EI drops out, leaving

$$0 = -1.667\int_1^4 x^3(x-1)\,dx + R_{AY}\int_1^4 (x-1)^2 dx$$

$$= \frac{-1.667x^5}{5}\bigg|_1^4 + \frac{1.667x^4}{4}\bigg|_1^4 + \frac{R_{AY}(x-1)^3}{3}\bigg|_1^4$$

$$R_{AY} = 26.08 \text{ kN} \tag{15.14a}$$

The remaining reactions are calculated from the statics relations shown on the free body:

$$R_{BY} = 53.92 \text{ kN} \tag{15.14b}$$

$$R_{BX} = 0 \tag{15.14c}$$

$$M_{BA} = 28.76 \text{ kN-m} \tag{15.14d}$$

As stated earlier, propped beams are used as a starting point in some of the more specialized methods of structural analysis, one of which is presented in the next chapter. A summary of selected common load cases is therefore appropriate at this point (see Table 15-1). Verification of some of these cases is included in the outside problems.

Like simple beams, propped-end beams may be designed with a variable depth, in which case the moment of inertia becomes a variable. The section may be stepped, as shown in Figure 15-6(a), or it may be continuously variable (tapered), as shown in Figure 15-6(b). Stepped beams are likely to be fabricated in steel; tapered beams may be either steel or concrete.

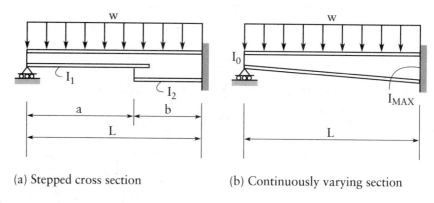

(a) Stepped cross section   (b) Continuously varying section

FIGURE 15-6 Propped-end beams with variable sections.

Table 15-1   Reactions for Propped-end Beams

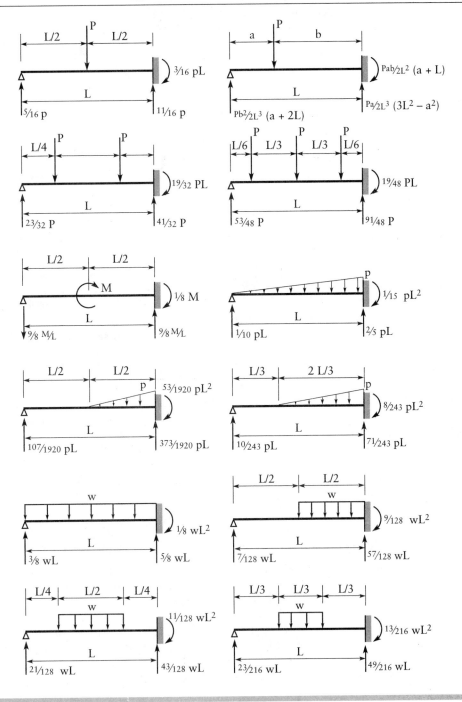

The analysis of propped-end beams of variable section follows the procedures just developed. Some numerical examples will illustrate the solution for the indeterminate reactions.

Example 15-4   Solve for the reactions on the given beam.

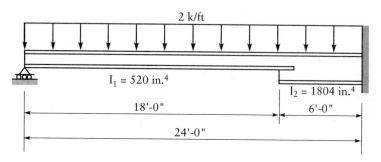

Solution   The free body of the beam, with all its reactions, is shown in the following sketch. Notice that the moment of inertia has been changed into a ratio, with the smallest moment of inertia being used as the reference value. The reason for this procedure will become apparent in the integrations that follow.

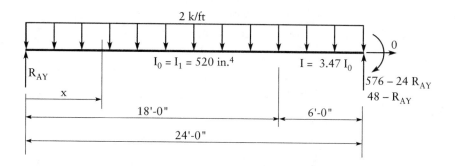

It is elected to solve this problem using the Castigliano theorem, and then check the solution using area moment. The reaction R_{AY} is chosen as the redundant; its deflection at A is zero. The discontinuity in the cross section must be recognized in the integrations:

$$
\Delta_{AY} = 0 = \int_0^{18} \frac{M_s \left(\dfrac{\partial M_s}{\partial R_{AY}} \right) ds}{EI} + \int_{18}^{24} \frac{M_s \left(\dfrac{\partial M_s}{\partial R_{AY}} \right) ds}{EI} \tag{15.15}
$$

The moment equation and its derivatives are found as usual.

For $0 \leq x \leq 18$,

$$M_x = R_{AY}x - \frac{1}{2}(2x^2); \qquad \left(\frac{\partial M_x}{\partial R_{AY}}\right) = x; \qquad I_x = I_0; \qquad ds = dx$$

For $18 \leq x \leq 24$,

$$M_x = R_{AY}x - \frac{1}{2}(2x)^2; \qquad \left(\frac{\partial M_x}{\partial R_{AY}}\right) = x; \qquad I_x = 3.47I_0;$$

$$ds = dx$$

These quantities are substituted into Equation 15.15. The term EI_0 drops out, and the result is

$$\Delta_{AY} = 0 = \int_0^{18} (R_{AY}x - x^2)(x)dx + \int_{18}^{24} \frac{1}{3.47}(R_{AY}x - x^2)(x)dx$$

$$= R_{AY}\frac{x^3}{3}\bigg|_0^{18} - \frac{x^4}{4}\bigg|_0^{18} + \frac{1}{3.47}R_{AY}\frac{x^3}{3}\bigg|_{18}^{24} - \frac{1}{3.47}\frac{x^4}{4}\bigg|_{18}^{24}$$

$$R_{AY} = 15.7 \text{ kips} \qquad\qquad\qquad\qquad\qquad\qquad\qquad (15.16a)$$

From the statics relationships shown on the free body,

$$R_{BY} = 32.3 \text{ kips} \qquad\qquad\qquad\qquad\qquad\qquad\qquad (15.16b)$$

$$R_{BX} = 0 \qquad\qquad\qquad\qquad\qquad\qquad\qquad\qquad (15.16c)$$

$$M_{BA} = 199 \text{ kip-ft} \qquad\qquad\qquad\qquad\qquad\qquad\qquad (15.16d)$$

The solution just obtained by the Castigliano theorem can be verified by area moment. For an area moment solution, the tangential deviation at A with respect to a tangent at B is zero; t_{AB} is therefore selected as the additional known condition. The integral form of area moment theorem II, as given by Equation 5.6, is used:

$$t_{AB} = 0 = \int_0^{18} \frac{M_x x \, dx}{EI} + \int_{18}^{24} \frac{M_x x \, dx}{EI} \qquad\qquad\qquad (15.17)$$

Equation 15.17 is identical to Equation 15.15, where the partial derivative is x. Consequently, the solution from this point forward is also identical.

When area moment is used on beams of variable section, using areas of the moment diagrams becomes so involved that it is rarely worth the effort. It is usually easier and more direct to evaluate the integral forms given by

Equations 5.3 and 5.6. Depending on the choice of redundant, their application will be identical to the Castigliano solution.

The reactions of a beam having a stepped cross section, such as the one in the foregoing example, can readily be compared to those of a like beam of constant cross section. For a beam of constant section, the reaction R_{AY} was found earlier (see Figure 15-4) to be $R_{AY} = \frac{3}{8}wL$. For the foregoing span and loads, if the section had been constant,

$$R_{AY} = 18 \text{ kips}; \quad R_{BY} = 30 \text{ kips}; \quad R_{BX} = 0;$$
$$M_{BA} = 144 \text{ kip-ft}$$

Comparing these reactions with the reactions for a stepped beam—

$$R_{AY} = 15.7 \text{ kips}; \quad R_{BY} = 32.3 \text{ kips}; \quad R_{BX} = 0;$$
$$M_{BA} = 199 \text{ kip-ft}$$

—one might suspect that the stiffer, less flexible section at B attracts a higher proportion of the load, both in the reaction R_{BY} and in the moment M_{BA}. Such a characteristic is indeed true, that stiffening an indeterminate beam locally does tend to produce larger reactions in the locally stiffened portion of the beam.

Beams of continuously varying section are also subject to solution by the methods just presented. As was observed in earlier chapters, however, when a variable appears in the denominator of an integral, a numerical integration is almost always easier to perform than a closed-form solution. Such a numerical integration is used in the next example.

Example 15-5   Determine the reactions on the given beam.

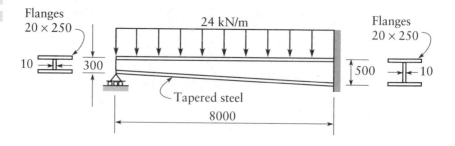

Flanges
20 × 250

24 kN/m

Flanges
20 × 250

10   300

500   10

Tapered steel

8000

Solution The free body of the beam is shown in the following sketch. It is elected to solve this beam by using the Castigliano theorem, with the reaction R_{AY} being the redundant and $\Delta_{AY} = 0$.

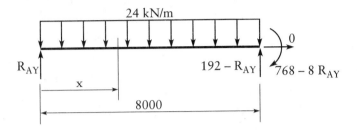

The Castigliano solution is given by

$$\Delta_{AY} = 0 = \int_0^L \frac{M_s \left(\dfrac{\partial M_s}{\partial R_{AY}} \right) ds}{EI_x} = \sum_{i=1}^m \frac{M_i \left(\dfrac{\partial M_i}{\partial R_{AY}} \right) ds}{EI_i} \qquad (15.18)$$

The moment equation and partial derivatives can now be determined.

For $0 \le x \le 8$:

$$M_s = R_{AY}x - 12x^2; \qquad \frac{\partial M_s}{\partial R_{AY}} = x; \qquad ds = dx$$

Moment of inertia I_x is continuously variable

Since I_x is variable, a numerical integration of Equation 15.18 will be performed, using eight strips of 1 meter each. The depth d will be calculated at the center of each strip, and the moment of inertia will be calculated for that depth.

The beam is divided into eight strips as shown in the following sketch. The relevant values for each strip are given in the accompanying tabulation.

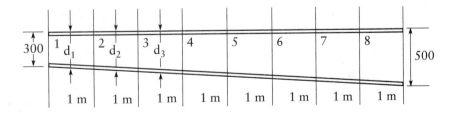

STRIP i	Δx (m)	x_i (m)	d_i (mm)	I_i (m⁴)	M_i (kN·m)	$\dfrac{\partial M_i}{\partial R_{AY}}$	$M_i \dfrac{\partial M_i}{\partial R_{AY}}\dfrac{\Delta x}{I_i}$
1	1	0.5	312.5	231×10^{-6}	$0.5R_{AY} - 3$	0.5	$1082R_{AY} - 6494$
2	1	1.5	337.5	274×10^{-6}	$1.5R_{AY} - 27$	1.5	$8212R_{AY} - 147{,}810$
3	1	2.5	362.5	322×10^{-6}	$2.5R_{AY} - 75$	2.5	$19{,}410R_{AY} - 582{,}298$
4	1	3.5	387.5	373×10^{-6}	$3.5R_{AY} - 147$	3.5	$32{,}842R_{AY} - 1{,}379{,}356$
5	1	4.5	412.5	429×10^{-6}	$4.5R_{AY} - 243$	4.5	$47{,}203R_{AY} - 2{,}548{,}951$
6	1	5.5	437.5	488×10^{-6}	$5.5R_{AY} - 363$	5.5	$61{,}988R_{AY} - 4{,}091{,}189$
7	1	6.5	462.5	553×10^{-6}	$6.5R_{AY} - 507$	6.5	$76{,}401R_{AY} - 5{,}959{,}313$
8	1	7.5	487.5	621×10^{-6}	$7.5R_{AY} - 675$	7.5	$90{,}580R_{AY} - 8{,}152{,}174$

$$\Sigma = 337{,}720R_{AY} - 22{,}867{,}600$$

The sum is then substituted into Equation 15.18 (the modulus of elasticity E has been factored out):

$$0 = 337{,}720R_{AY} - 22{,}867{,}600$$
$$R_{AY} = 67.71 \text{ kips} \tag{15.19a}$$

The other reactions are found from the statics relations shown on the free body:

$$R_{BY} = 124.3 \text{ kN} \tag{15.19b}$$

$$R_{BX} = 0 \tag{15.19c}$$

$$M_{BA} = 226.3 \text{ kN} \cdot \text{m} \tag{15.19d}$$

Alternatively, this example can be solved by directly evaluating the integral of Equation 15.18. For that case, it is necessary to express the moment of inertia in terms of x:

$$I_x = \left.\frac{bh_s^3}{12}\right|_{\text{SOLID}} - \left.\frac{bh_v^3}{12}\right|_{\text{VOID}}$$

where

$$h_s = 300 + 200\frac{x}{8000}$$

and

$$b_v = 260 + 200\frac{x}{8000}$$

Hence,

$$I_x = \frac{250}{12}\left(300 + 200\frac{x}{8000}\right)^3 - \frac{240}{12}\left(260 + 200\frac{x}{8000}\right)^3$$

The integral form then becomes

$$0 = \int_0^{8000} \frac{(R_{AY}x - 12x^2)(x)dx}{I_x}$$

An evaluation of this integral by standard software yields

$$R_{AY} = 67.9 \text{ kips}$$

This relatively exact result compares to the result of 67.7 kips obtained in the manual tabulation on the basis of only eight elements.

If the beam of Example 15-5 had been of constant cross section, the reaction could have been found from the formulas given in Equations 15.6a–d:

$$R_{AY} = \frac{3}{8}wL = 72 \text{ kN} \qquad\qquad R_{BY} = \frac{5}{8}wL = 120 \text{ kN}$$

$$R_{BX} = 0 \qquad\qquad\qquad\qquad M_{BA} = \frac{1}{8}wL^2 = 192 \text{ kN} \cdot \text{m}$$

These results may be compared to the results just obtained for the tapered beam. It is again noteworthy that the stiffer, less flexible portion of the beam attracts a higher proportion of the load, both in reactive forces and in reactive moments.

Outside Problems

Problem 15-1* Verify the solution shown in Table 15-1, first column, third row.

Problem 15-2 Verify the solution shown in Table 15-1, second column, fourth row.

Problem 15-3* Verify the solution shown in Table 15-1, second column, fifth row.

Problem 15-4 Verify the solution shown in Table 15-1, first column, sixth row.

Using either the method of least work or the method of area moment, determine the reactions on the given propped-end beams.

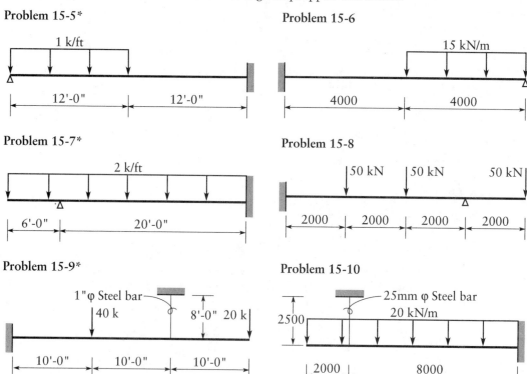

Problem 15-5*

1 k/ft

12'-0"   12'-0"

Problem 15-6

15 kN/m

4000   4000

Problem 15-7*

2 k/ft

6'-0"   20'-0"

Problem 15-8

50 kN   50 kN   50 kN

2000   2000   2000   2000

Problem 15-9*

1"φ Steel bar
40 k   8'-0" 20 k

10'-0"   10'-0"   10'-0"

$E = 29 \times 10^6$ psi; $I = 812$ in.^{4}

Problem 15-10

25mm φ Steel bar
2500   20 kN/m

2000   8000

$E = 200000$ N/mm^2; $I = 337 \times 10^6$ mm^4

Problem 15-11*

Solve Problem 15-9 for the case where the right support has a total displacement of 1.00 in. downward.

Problem 15-12

Solve Problem 15-10 for the case where the left support receives a total displacement of 20 mm upward.

Problem 15-13*

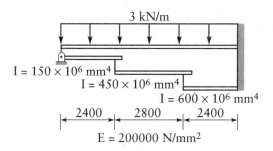

3 kN/m

$I = 150 \times 10^6$ mm^4
$I = 450 \times 10^6$ mm^4
$I = 600 \times 10^6$ mm^4

2400 | 2800 | 2400

$E = 200000$ N/mm^2

Problem 15-14

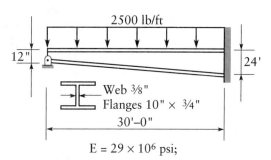

2500 lb/ft

12"

24'

Web ⅜"
Flanges 10" × ¾"

30'-0"

$E = 29 \times 10^6$ psi;

15.2 FIXED-END BEAMS

The propped-end beam considered in the preceding section is fixed at only one end. A second type of statically indeterminate beam is fixed at both ends. Such a beam is shown in Figure 15-7, along with its free body reactions. Like the propped-end beam, the fixed-end beam is used as a starting point in advanced methods of analysis.

Analysis of a fixed-end beam proceeds much as does analysis of a propped-end beam; the primary difference is that there is one more redundant in a fixed-end beam.

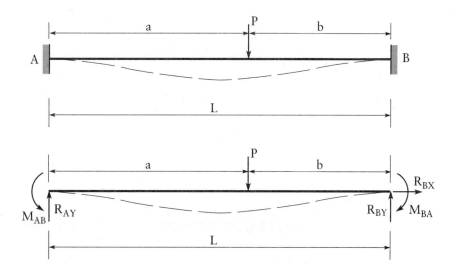

FIGURE 15-7 Fixed-end beam.

It has been assumed in the free body of Figure 15-7 that the "fixed" end at *A* does not develop a horizontal reaction. If it did, the thermal loads would probably destroy the beam. It is commonly assumed with respect to fixed-end beams that only one support can develop a horizontal reaction.

There are five unknown reactions in the beam of Figure 15-7, so it is two degrees indeterminate. Two deformation conditions must therefore be found in order to obtain a solution. For this case, the two reactions at A—R_{AY} and M_{AB}—are chosen as the redundants. The remaining three reactions at B are expressed in terms of R_{AY} and M_{AB} from the three equations of statics, as usual.

The free body of the fixed-end beam is shown in Figure 15-8. The tangents to the elastic curve are drawn both to point A and to point B; the two tangents are seen to coincide. Thus the tangential deviations t_{AB} and t_{BA} are both zero, providing the two additional known conditions required for a solution. The second area moment theorem may be applied twice to obtain a solution:

$$t_{AB} = 0 = \frac{A_M \bar{x}_A}{EI} \tag{15.20a}$$

$$t_{BA} = 0 = \frac{A_M \bar{x}_B}{EI} \tag{15.20b}$$

where $\bar{x}_A$ indicates that moments are to be taken about the deviation line at A, and $\bar{x}_B$ indicates that moments are to be taken about the deviation line at B.

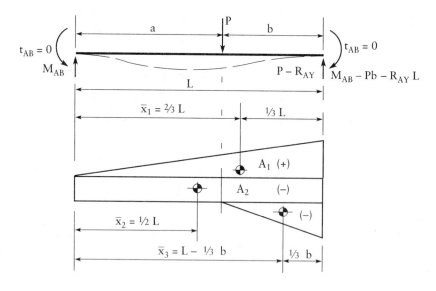

FIGURE 15-8 Area moment solution of a fixed-end beam.

Alternatively, both the first and the second area moment theorems might be used to reach the same result, since the angle between the tangent at A and the tangent at B is also zero.

$$\phi_{AB} = 0 = \frac{A_M}{EI} \tag{15.21a}$$

$$t_{AB} = 0 = \frac{A_M \bar{x}_A}{EI} \tag{15.21b}$$

For this solution, the alternative two conditions given by Equations 15.21a and b are arbitrarily chosen:

$$0 = A_M = A_1 + A_2 + A_3$$

where

$$A_1 = R_{AY}L\,(L)\left(\frac{1}{2}\right)$$
$$A_2 = -M_{AB}L$$
$$A_3 = -Pb\,(b)\left(\frac{1}{2}\right)$$

$$0 = R_{AY}L^2 - 2M_{AB}L - Pb^2 \tag{15.22a}$$

The solution has so far yielded one equation in two unknowns. Equation 15.21b is now evaluated:

$$0 = A_M \bar{x}_A = A_1 \bar{x}_1 + A_2 \bar{x}_2 + A_3 \bar{x}_3$$

where

$$A_1 = R_{AY}L\,(L)\left(\frac{1}{2}\right); \qquad \bar{x}_1 = \frac{2}{3}L$$
$$A_2 = -M_{AB}L; \qquad \bar{x}_2 = \frac{1}{2}L$$
$$A_3 = -Pb\,(b)\left(\frac{1}{2}\right); \qquad \bar{x}_3 = L - \frac{1}{3}b$$

$$0 = R_{AY}L - \frac{3M_{AB}}{2} - \frac{3Pb^2\left(L - \frac{1}{3}b\right)}{2L^2} \tag{15.22b}$$

Equations 15.22a and b are solved simultaneously to find

$$R_{AY} = \frac{Pb^2(3a+b)}{L^3} \tag{15.23a}$$

$$M_{AB} = \frac{Pab^2}{L^2} \tag{15.23b}$$

The remaining reactions are found from the statics conditions

$$R_{BY} = \frac{Pa^2(a+3b)}{L^3} \tag{15.24a}$$

$$M_{BA} = \frac{Pa^2b}{L^2} \tag{15.24b}$$

$$R_{AX} = 0 \tag{15.24c}$$

The same techniques developed in earlier chapters are used to draw the shear and moment diagrams. The results are summarized in Figure 15-9.

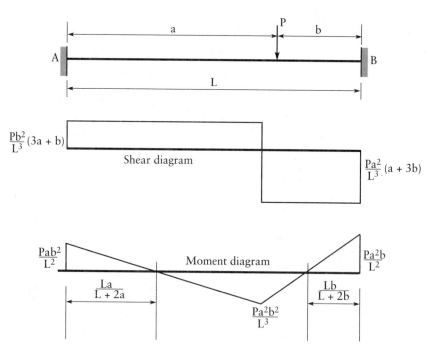

FIGURE 15-9 Summary of a fixed-end beam.

The reactions of the fixed-end beam of Figure 15-9 can be found alternatively by the use of the Castigliano theorem. For such a solution, refer to the free body of Figure 15-10. The reactions R_{AY} and M_{AB} are again chosen as the redundants, since both the deflection and rotation at A are zero.

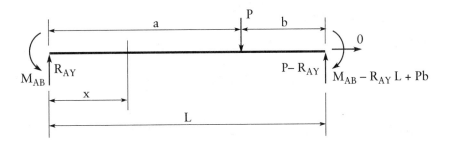

FIGURE 15-10 Free body of a fixed-end beam.

The slope and deflection at A are given by the Castigliano theorem:

$$\theta_A = 0 = \int_0^L \frac{M_s\left(\dfrac{\partial M_s}{M_{AB}}\right)ds}{EI} \tag{15.25a}$$

$$\Delta_A = 0 = \int_0^L \frac{M_s\left(\dfrac{\partial M_s}{\partial R_{AY}}\right)ds}{EI} \tag{15.25b}$$

With $ds = dx$, the moment equations and partial derivatives can be found as usual.

For $0 \le x \le a$,

$$M_x = -M_{AB} + R_{AY}x\,; \qquad \frac{\partial M_x}{\partial M_{AB}} = -1\,; \qquad \frac{\partial M_x}{\partial R_{AY}} = x$$

For $a \le x \le L$,

$$M_x = -M_{AB} + R_{AY}x - P(x-a)\,;$$

$$\frac{\partial M_x}{\partial M_{AB}} = -1\,; \qquad \frac{\partial M_x}{\partial R_{AY}} = x \tag{15.26}$$

These values are substituted into Equation 15.25a to produce

$$\theta_A = 0 = \int_0^a \frac{(-M_{AB} + R_{AY}x)(-1)dx}{EI}$$
$$+ \int_a^L \frac{(-M_{AB} + R_{AY}x) - P(x-a)(-1)dx}{EI}$$
$$= M_{AB}L - \frac{1}{2}R_{AY}L^2 + \frac{1}{2}Pb^2 \tag{15.27a}$$

Equation 15.14b is evaluated similarly:

$$0 = -M_{AB} + \frac{2R_{AY}L}{3} - \frac{2PL(L^3 - a^3)}{3L^3} + \frac{Pa(L^2 - a^2)}{L^2} \tag{15.27b}$$

Equations 15.27a and b are solved simultaneously, yielding (after a considerable amount of juggling)

$$R_{AY} = \frac{Pb^2(3a+b)}{L^3} \tag{15.28a}$$

$$M_{AB} = \frac{Pab^2}{L^2} \tag{15.28b}$$

These solutions are of course identical to those obtained by the area moment solution. The remainder of the solution is identical to that shown earlier, and it is not repeated here.

Any of the reactions may be selected as the redundants in an area moment solution. Once the redundants are chosen, however, all the other reactions are expressed in terms of these redundants by simple static relations, as shown in the foregoing procedures. From that point forward, the moment diagram by parts can only be expressed in terms of the chosen redundants.

In a solution that uses the Castigliano method, a reaction may be chosen as a redundant only if its deflection (or rotation) is known. As in the area moment solution, however, once the redundants have been chosen, all other reactions must be expressed in terms of the chosen redundants.

In all of the preceding solutions, the additional conditions required for the indeterminate solution have always involved the use of known deformations at some point. Symmetry (or antisymmetry) may also be used as one—but only one—additional condition. An example will illustrate the use of symmetry to provide one of the additional conditions.

Example 15-6   Determine the reactions on the given fixed-end beam.

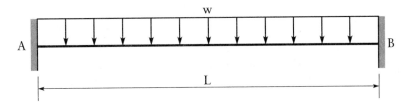

Solution   The free body of the beam is shown in the following sketch, with all reactions labeled. Due to symmetry, the two vertical reactions must be equal; the sum of vertical forces then produces their solution. In addition, due to symmetry, the two end moments M_{AB} and M_{BA} must be equal, but their magnitude cannot be found by statics.

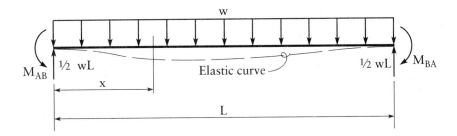

It is elected to solve for the remaining redundant by the Castigliano theorem. The moment M_{AB} is chosen as the redundant; its rotation about A is zero. Hence,

$$\theta_A = 0 = \int_0^L \frac{M_s\left(\dfrac{\partial M_s}{\partial M_{AB}}\right)ds}{EI_x} \tag{15.29}$$

With $ds = dx$, the moment equation and the partial derivatives can be found. For $0 \leq x \leq L$,

$$M_x = -M_{AB} + \frac{1}{2}wLx - \frac{1}{2}wx^2; \qquad \frac{\partial M_x}{\partial M_{AB}} = -1$$

The moment equation and its derivative are substituted into Equation 15.29. For constant moment of inertia, the term EI drops out. Hence,

$$0 = \int_0^L \left(-M_{AB} + \frac{1}{2}wLx - \frac{1}{2}wx^2 \right)(-1)\,dx$$

$$M_{AB} = \frac{1}{12}wL^2 \tag{15.30}$$

The shear and moment diagrams can now be drawn on the basis of the methods developed in earlier chapters. They are summarized in the following sketch.

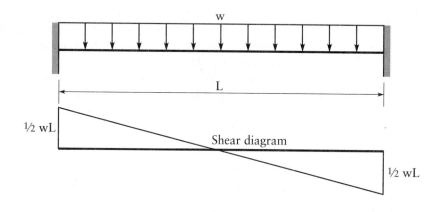

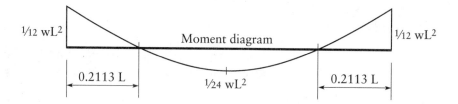

The uniformly loaded fixed-end beam of Example 15-6 is a very important case in structural analysis. It appears again and again in advanced methods of analysis; but more importantly, beams with fully restrained or partially restrained ends are among the most common load cases in all of indeterminate structures. Students should commit the shear and moment diagrams of Example 15-6 to memory; these will be used often enough in the career of a civil engineer to make the effort worthwhile.

A worthwhile comparison of three uniformly loaded beams can now be made. Consider the three beams shown in Figure 15-11—one simply supported beam, one propped-end beam and one fixed-end beam.

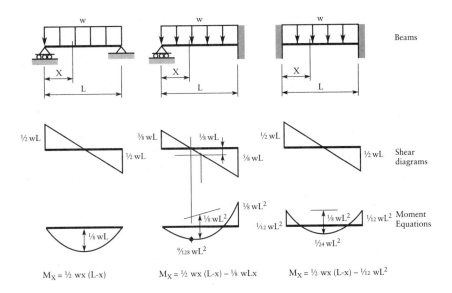

FIGURE 15-11 Comparison of uniformly loaded beams.

It is immediately evident that the shear diagrams of the simply supported beam and the fixed-end beam are identical. This feature is true for all symmetrically loaded beams (but only for symmetrically loaded beams): adding symmetrical end moments does not change the shears.

It is also evident that the shape of the shear diagram for the propped-end beam is the same as the shear diagrams for the other two beams, except that it has been translated downward by an amount M_{BA}/L. It has not been skewed; it has only been translated. This feature is true for all unsymmetrical end restraints: the shear diagram may be shifted up or down due to the occurrence of end moments, but the shear diagram will not be skewed by end moments.

Notice particularly the moment diagrams. The overall depth of all three diagrams is $\frac{1}{8}wL^2$. This constant depth is reflected in the first term of the moment equations that accompany the sketches. The remaining terms of the moment equations serve to lift or to skew the moment diagram.

One way to visualize the moment diagram is to imagine the moment diagram of a uniformly loaded beam as a draped chain. One end of the chain may be raised, as in the propped-end beam, but the depth of the drape at midspan is unchanged. Or both ends may be raised, as in the fixed-end beam, but the depth of the drape at midspan again remains unchanged. This aspect of moment diagrams—that the end moments may be increased, decreased, or skewed without affecting the vertical depth—is a very useful feature when one is designing reinforced concrete beams; the feature is treated fully in textbooks on reinforced concrete.

Applied loads are not the only things that can produce flexure in indeterminate beams. Displacement of a support due to foundation settlements is a common occurrence in structures; such displacements, even small ones, can produce significant flexure in a structure.

The fixed-end beam of Figure 15-12 is subject to settlement of a support, as shown. The differential settlement Δ occurs between the original as-built positions of the left and right supports. The ends remain fixed, but the left end has been translated downward by the amount Δ. It is assumed that the deflection Δ is known, or that it has been assigned a value as a result of the soils analysis.

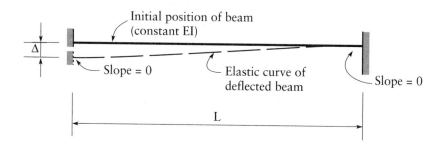

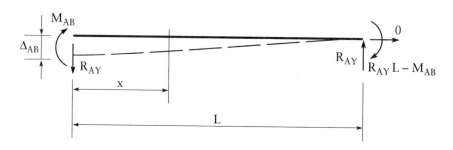

FIGURE 15-12 Displacement of supports.

The reactions of the beam of Figure 15-12 will be solved by using the Castigliano theorem. The reactions R_{AY} and M_{AB} are chosen as the redundants; the displacement and rotation of these reactions are known. The Castigliano solutions for the slope and displacement of the reactions are

$$\theta_A = 0 = \int_0^L \frac{M_s\left(\frac{\partial M_s}{\partial M_{AB}}\right)ds}{EI} \qquad (15.31a)$$

$$\Delta_{AY} = \Delta = \int_0^L \frac{M_s\left(\frac{\partial M_s}{\partial M_{AB}}\right)ds}{EI} \qquad (15.31b)$$

With $ds = dx$, the moment equation and the partial derivatives are found as usual.

For $0 \leq x \leq L$,

$$M_x = -R_{AY}x + M_{AB}; \qquad \frac{\partial M_x}{\partial M_{AB}} = +1; \qquad \frac{\partial M_x}{\partial R_{AY}} = -x$$

These values are substituted into Equations 15.31a and b to find

$$0 = \int_0^L (-R_{AY}x + M_{AB})(+1)dx$$

$$= -\frac{1}{2}R_{AY}L^2 + M_{AB}L$$

$$0 = \int_0^L (-R_{AY}x + M_{AB})(-x)dx$$

$$= +\frac{1}{3}R_{AY}L^3 - \frac{1}{2}M_{AB}L^2$$

The simultaneous solution of these equations yields

$$R_{AY} = \frac{12EI}{L^3}\Delta \qquad\qquad\qquad\qquad (15.32a)$$

$$M_{AB} = \frac{6EI}{L^2}\Delta \qquad\qquad\qquad\qquad (15.32b)$$

As stated earlier, the reactions produced by displacement of supports can be significant, even for relatively small values of displacement. This particular problem, however, occurs only in indeterminate structures; settlement of supports has no such effect on determinate structures. Consequently, when foundation conditions are uncertain, a prudent designer may well choose to use a determinate system rather than an indeterminate system, to avoid this kind of problem with settlements.

Once the reactions for an indeterminate structure are known, all succeeding calculations become the same as those presented earlier for determinate systems. For example, the deflection at midspan of the fixed-end beam of Example 15-6 can readily be found by using area moment methods.

Example 15-7 Determine the deflection at midspan of the beam of Example 15-6.

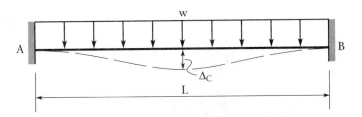

Solution   The free body, with its reactions, is shown in the following sketch. A tangent to the elastic curve at midspan is drawn on the sketch, indicating that the deflection at midspan is equal to the tangential deviation t_{AC} at point A. The moment diagram by parts between A and C is drawn for the area moment solution.

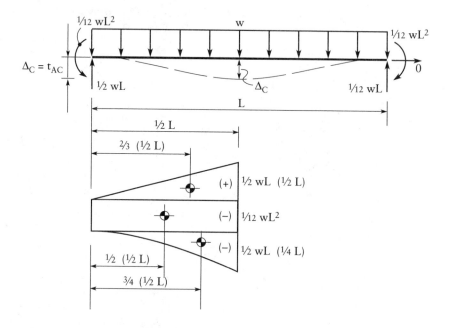

The deviation t_{AC} is found by taking the moment of the moment diagram about the deviation line at A:

$$\Delta_C = t_{AC} = \frac{A_M \bar{x}_A}{EI} = \frac{A_1 \bar{x}_1 + A_2 \bar{x}_2 + A_3 \bar{x}_3}{EI} \tag{15.33}$$

where

$$A_1 = \frac{1}{2} w L \left(\frac{1}{2}L\right)\left(\frac{1}{2}L\right)\left(\frac{1}{2}\right) = \frac{1}{16} w L^3$$

$$x_1 = \frac{2}{3}\left(\frac{1}{2}L\right) \qquad\qquad = \frac{1}{3}L$$

$$A_2 = \frac{1}{12} w L^2 \left(\frac{1}{2}L\right) \qquad = \frac{1}{24} w L^3$$

$$x_2 = \frac{1}{4}L \qquad\qquad\qquad = \frac{1}{4}L$$

$$A_3 = \frac{1}{2} w L \left(\frac{1}{4}L\right)\left(\frac{1}{2}L\right)\left(\frac{1}{3}\right) = \frac{1}{48} w L^3$$

$$x_3 = \frac{3}{4}\left(\frac{1}{2}L\right) \qquad = \frac{3}{8}L$$

$$\Delta_C = \frac{wL^4\left(\dfrac{1}{48} - \dfrac{1}{96} - \dfrac{3}{384}\right)}{EI} = \frac{(8 - 4 - 3)\,wL^4}{384EI}$$

$$= \frac{wL^4}{384EI} \tag{15.34}$$

The sign of t_{AC} is positive, indicating that the tangent lies below the elastic curve at point A.

It is informative to compare this result with the result obtained in Table 4-2, case 2, for a simply supported beam with no end moments. For a simple beam, at midspan,

$$\Delta = \frac{5wL^4}{384EI}$$

A comparison with Equation 15.34 indicates that the deflection at midspan for a fixed-end beam is only 20% of that for a simply supported beam. The comparison points out another feature of indeterminate structures that is well worth remembering: beam deflections where end moments exist are significantly lower than beam deflections for simple beams without such end moments. The reduction is rarely as much as 80% (as it is in this example), but it is nonetheless significant.

Some numerical examples will illustrate other features of the analysis of fixed-end beams.

Example 15-8   Determine the reactions on the given fixed-end beam.

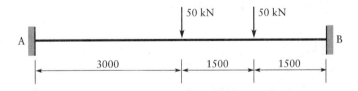

Solution   The free body sketch of the beam is shown in the following sketch, with all reactions shown. As with other fixed-end beams, the beam has five reactions and is therefore two degrees indeterminate. The reactions R_{AY} and M_{AB} are chosen as the redundants; in both cases their deflection (or rotation) is zero.

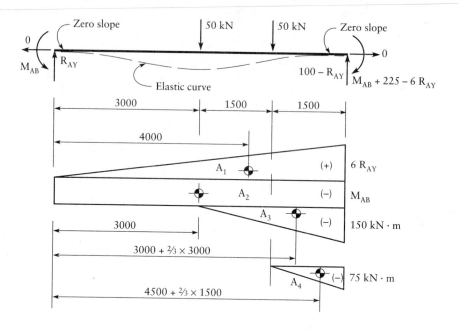

The tangents to the elastic curve at A and B coincide, yielding two conditions: the angle between the tangents at A and B is zero and the tangent at B passes through point A, making $t_{AB} = 0$. When stated mathematically, these two conditions become

$$\phi_{AB} = 0 = \frac{A_M}{EI} \tag{15.35a}$$

$$t_{AB} = 0 = \frac{A_M \bar{x}_A}{EI} \tag{15.35b}$$

Equation 15.35a is evaluated first. The denominator is constant and cancels out. Hence,

$$0 = A_M = A_1 + A_2 + A_3 + A_4$$

where

$$A_1 = 6R_{AY}(6)\left(\frac{1}{2}\right) = +18R_{AY}$$

$$A_2 = -M_{AB}(6) \qquad = -6M_{AB}$$

$$A_3 = -150(3)\left(\frac{1}{2}\right) = -225$$

$$A_4 = -75(1.5)(2) = -56.25$$

$$0 = 3R_{AY} - M_{AB} - 46.9 \tag{15.36a}$$

Equation 15.35b is evaluated next. The denominator again cancels out. Hence,

$$0 = A_1 x_1 + A_2 x_2 + A_3 x_3 + A_4 x_4$$

where

$$A_1 = +18R_{AY}; \qquad x_1 = 4$$
$$A_2 = -6M_{AB}; \qquad x_2 = 3$$
$$A_3 = -225; \qquad x_3 = 5$$
$$A_4 = -56.25; \qquad x_4 = 5.5$$

$$0 = 4R_{AY} - M_{AB} - 79.7 \qquad\qquad (15.36b)$$

Equations 15.36a and b are solved simultaneously to find R_{AY} and M_{AB}. The other two reactions are found from the statics conditions shown on the free body:

$$R_{AY} = 32.8 \text{ kN} \qquad\qquad (15.37a)$$

$$R_{BY} = 67.2 \text{ kN} \qquad\qquad (15.37b)$$

$$M_{AB} = 51.5 \text{ kN} \cdot \text{m} \qquad\qquad (15.37c)$$

$$M_{BA} = 79.7 \text{ kN} \cdot \text{m} \qquad\qquad (15.37d)$$

The reactions just found for the beam of Example 15-8 could also have been found by using the results obtained earlier for the beam shown in Figure 15-9. Such a solution by superposition of load cases is presented in the next example.

Example 15-9 Determine the reactions on the given fixed-end beam.

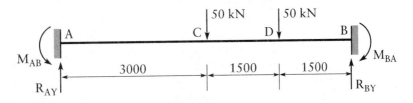

Solution   The reactions due to the 50-kN load at C are found first. For the formulas of Figure 15-9, with $a = b = 3$ m, $L = 6$ m, and $P = 50$ kN,

$$R_{AY} = \frac{Pb^2\,(3a+b)}{L^3} = \frac{50\,(3^2)(9+3)}{6^3} = 25 \text{ kN}$$

$$M_{AB} = \frac{Pab^2}{L^2} = \frac{50(3)(3^2)}{6^2} = 37.5 \text{ kN} \cdot \text{m}$$

$$R_{BY} = R_{AY} = 25 \text{ kN}$$

$$M_{BA} = M_{AB} = 37.5 \text{ kN} \cdot \text{m}$$

The initial findings $R_{BY} = R_{AY}$ and $M_{BA} = M_{AB}$ for the final two equations in the preceding set of four are due to symmetry.

The reactions for the 50-kN load at D are found next. For the formulas given with Figure 15-9, with $a = 4.5$ m, $b = 1.5$ m, $L = 6$ m, and $P = 50$ kN,

$$R_{AY} = \frac{Pb^2\,(3a+b)}{L^3} = \frac{50\,(1.5^2)(13.5+1.5)}{6^3} = 7.8 \text{ kN}$$

$$M_{AB} = \frac{Pab^2}{L^2} = \frac{50\,(4.5)(1.5^2)}{6^2} = 14.1 \text{ kN} \cdot \text{m}$$

$$R_{BY} = \frac{Pa^2\,(a+3b)}{L^3} = \frac{50\,(4.5^2)(4.5+4.5)}{6^3} = 42.2 \text{ kN}$$

$$M_{BA} = \frac{Pa^2 b}{L^3} = \frac{50\,(4.5^2)(1.5)}{6^3} = 42.2 \text{ kN} \cdot \text{m}$$

The final result is the sum of the two cases:

$$R_{AY} = 32.8 \text{ kN} \tag{15.38a}$$

$$R_{BY} = 67.2 \text{ kN} \tag{15.38b}$$

$$M_{AB} = 51.6 \text{ kN} \cdot \text{m} \tag{15.38c}$$

$$M_{BA} = 79.7 \text{ kN} \cdot \text{m} \tag{15.38d}$$

Within the normal limits of roundoff error, these results are of course identical to those obtained in Example 15-8.

Like propped-end beams, fixed-end beams are also used as a starting point in certain types of more specialized analysis, one of which is presented in the next chapter. A summary of selected common load cases is therefore given in Table 15-2 for future reference. Verification of some of the cases in Table 15-2 is included in the outside problems.

Table 15-2 Reactions on Fixed-end Beams

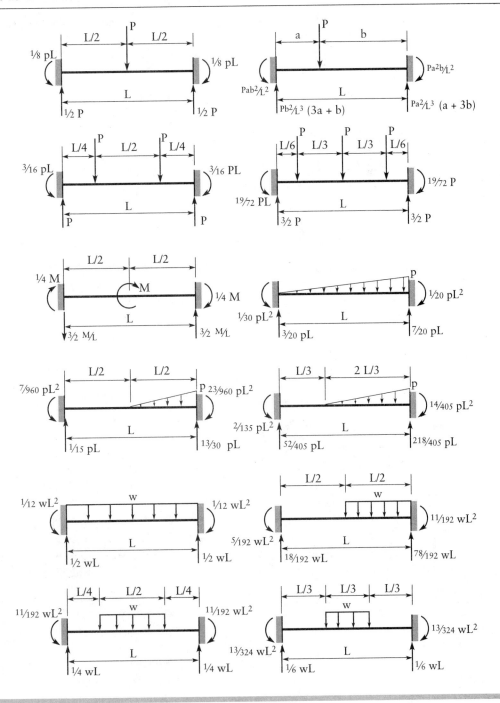

**Outside
Problems**

Problem 15-15* Verify the solution shown in Table 15-2, first column, third row.

Problem 15-16 Verify the solution shown in Table 15-2, second column, fourth row.

Problem 15-17* Verify the solution shown in Table 15-2, second column, fifth row.

Problem 15-18 Verify the solution shown in Table 15-2, first column, sixth row.

Using either the method of least work or the method of area moment, determine the reactions on the given fixed-end steel beams.

Problem 15-19*

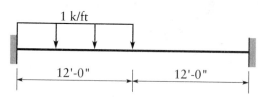

Problem 15-20

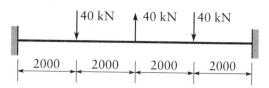

Problem 15-21*

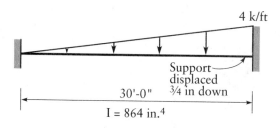

Problem 15-22

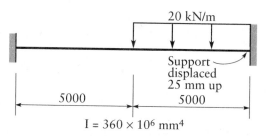

Problem 15-23*

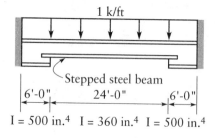

Problem 15-24

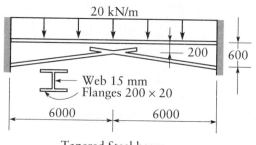

Tapered Steel beam

15.3 PORTAL FRAMES

Single-span frames such as those shown earlier in Figure 15-1 are popular in today's industry. One of the simpler types of such frames is the *portal frame*, shown in Figure 15-13.

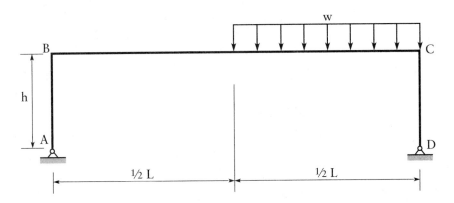

FIGURE 15-13 Typical portal frame.

The portal frame shown in Figure 15-13 is symmetrical, but it is loaded unsymmetrically. As a result, the frame will undergo some sidesway, or drift, under the indicated loads. *Under all deformations, the joints at B and C must maintain their 90° angles.* These rigid joints, or knees, are a critical feature of modern framed structures; it is the source of their ability to sustain lateral loads, and it is the reason they are called *rigid frames*.

Frames that have their supports at the same level (such as the frame of Figure 15-13) have a simplifying feature: the two vertical reactions at *A* and *B* are statically determinate. Future calculations will take advantage of this feature wherever possible.

The free body of the portal frame of Figure 15-13 is shown in Figure 15-14, along with its four reactions. In beams, only one support can be allowed to develop a horizontal reaction, due primarily to the effects of thermal expansion or contraction. In frames, however, such a restriction is not necessary; thermal deformations simply add to the bending moments.

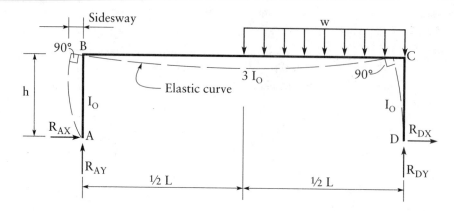

FIGURE 15-14 Free body of portal frame.

Taking moments about point A or about point D eliminates three of the four unknown reactions, allowing a statically determinate solution for R_{AY} and R_{DY}:

$$\Sigma M_A = 0; \quad \left(\frac{1}{2}wL\right)\left(\frac{3}{4}L\right) - R_{DY}L = 0; \quad R_{DY} = \frac{3}{8}wL$$

$$\Sigma M_D = 0; \quad \left(\frac{1}{2}wL\right)\left(\frac{1}{4}L\right) - R_{AY}L = 0; \quad R_{AY} = \frac{1}{8}wL$$

Only the two horizontal reactions R_{AX} and R_{DX} now remain unknown, and the sum of horizontal forces shows that these two reactions must be equal and opposite. These reactions cannot be found by statics; they must be found through other methods.

The free body of the frame is repeated in Figure 15-15, with the unknown reactions expressed in terms of the redundant R_{AX}.

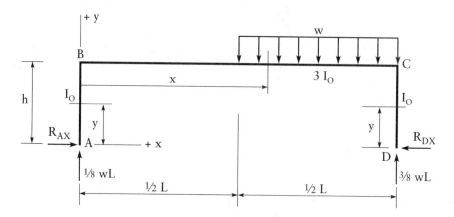

FIGURE 15-15 Portal frame and reactions.

The horizontal deflection at A is given by the Castigliano solution:

$$\Delta_{AX} = 0 = \int_0^L \frac{M_S \left(\dfrac{\partial M_S}{\partial R_{AX}} \right) ds}{EI} \tag{15.39}$$

For this case, where EI is constant, the term EI cancels out. The origin of x and y is chosen to be at A. The moment equations and the partial derivatives can now be determined.

From A to B, with $0 \le y \le h$,

$$M_s = -R_{AX}y; \qquad \frac{\partial M_S}{\partial R_{AX}} = -y; \qquad ds = dy$$

From B to E, with $0 \le x \le 1/2\ L$,

$$M_s = -R_{AX}h + \frac{1}{8}wlx; \qquad \frac{\partial M_S}{\partial R_{AX}} = -h; \qquad ds = dx$$

From E to C, with $0 \le x \le L$,

$$M_s = -R_{AX}h + \frac{1}{8}wlx - \frac{1}{2}w \left(x - \frac{1}{2}L \right)^2; \qquad \frac{\partial M_S}{\partial R_{AX}} = -h; \qquad ds = dx$$

From D to C, with $0 \le y \le h$,

$$M_s = +R_{AX}y; \qquad \frac{\partial M_S}{\partial R_{AX}} = +y; \qquad ds = dy$$

The integration is carried out,

$$\Delta_{AX} = 0 = \int_0^h (-R_{AX}y)(-y)\,dy + \int_0^{\frac{L}{2}} \left(-R_{AX}h + \frac{1}{8}wLx \right)(-h)\,dx$$

$$+ \int_{\frac{L}{2}}^{L} \left[-R_{AX}h + \frac{1}{8}wLx - \frac{1}{2}w \left(x - \frac{1}{2}L \right)^2 \right](-h)\,dx$$

$$+ \int_0^h (R_{AX}y)(y)\,dy$$

$$R_{AX} = \frac{wL^3}{8h\,(3L + 2h)} \tag{15.40a}$$

$$R_{DX} = -R_{AX} \tag{15.40b}$$

On this frame, one effect of the load is to cause the bases of the two columns to try to move outward; the horizontal reactions develop the necessary restraining force.

The solution for reactions on frames is very clumsy if one tries to use the methods of the elastic curve (area moment). More sophisticated techniques derived from area moment are readily applied to frames; one such technique is presented in the next chapter. For now, solutions of single-span frames will be accomplished by using energy methods.

Typically, the moment of inertia of all three members of a portal frame is rarely constant, as was assumed in the foregoing case. Usually, the horizontal member is significantly heavier than the columns. As the span L increases, the positive moment on the girder becomes significantly larger, and the girder becomes much larger than the columns; the moment of inertia of the girder is typically three to five times larger than that of the columns.

The preceding method of analysis was introduced conceptually in Chapter 6 as the method of least work. The key to using this method lies in recognizing that the displacement of a reaction at a rigid support is zero and that the Castigliano solution for that displacement is equal to zero. (The name *least work* comes from the property that a function is at its maximum or minimum point when its derivative is zero.) Engineering students have sometimes made rather pointed comments about the name.

In years past, the method of least work was not a very popular method, primarily because of the long and involved evaluations of the definite integrals that are necessary. As a consequence of the intricate calculations, the chance of error is high and the time spent in tracking down errors becomes correspondingly high. In general, other methods have been preferred.

In recent years, however, the development of computer evaluation of definite integrals has triggered renewed interest in the method of least work. The integral forms of the preceding solution, for example, can be entered in standard CAE software, and an evaluation of the definite integrals (with no numerical errors) will be provided in only a few seconds. With the primary objection to the method of least work thus removed, interest in the method seems likely to continue to increase.

A numerical example will further demonstrate the method of least work as it is applied to wind loads on a portal frame.

Example 15-10 Determine the reactions on the given portal frame.

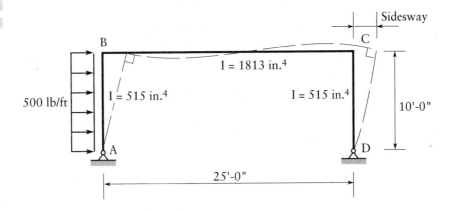

Solution The free body of the frame is shown in the following sketch, with all reactions shown. The vertical reactions are found by summing moments about A and B; they are statically determinate. The moments of inertia are expressed as ratios in the solution. The origin of the coordinate axes is taken at A.

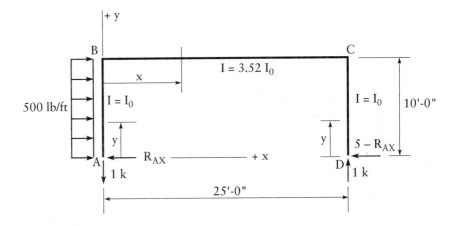

The solution will be performed by using the Castigliano theorem. The reaction R_{AX} is chosen as the redundant; its deflection is zero. The horizontal reaction at B is expressed in terms of the redundant R_{AX}.

The deflection of R_{AX} is given by the Castigliano theorem:

$$\Delta_{AX} = 0 = \int_0^L \frac{M_S\left(\frac{\partial M_S}{\partial R_{AX}}\right)ds}{EI} \tag{15.41}$$

The moment equation and the partial derivatives can now be determined. From A to B, with $0 \le y \le 10$,

$$M_Y = R_{AX}y - 0.25y^2; \qquad \frac{\partial M_Y}{\partial R_{AX}} = y; \qquad I = I_0; \qquad ds = dy$$

From B to C, with $0 \le x \le 25$,

$$M_X = 10R_{AX} - 25 - x; \qquad \frac{\partial M_X}{\partial R_{AX}} = 10; \qquad I = 3.52I_0;$$

$$ds = dx$$

From D to C, $0 \le y \le 10$,

$$M_Y = (5 - R_{AX})y; \qquad \frac{\partial M_Y}{\partial R_{AX}} = -y; \qquad I = I_0; \qquad ds = dy$$

These values are substituted into Equation 15.41. EI_0 is factored out. Hence,

$$\Delta_{AX} = 0 = \int_0^{10} (R_{AX}y - 0.25y^2)(y)\,dy$$

$$+ \frac{1}{3.52}\int_0^{25} (10R_{AX} - 25 - x)(10)\,dx$$

$$+ \int_0^{10} (5 - R_{AX})(y)(-y)\,dy \tag{15.42}$$

$$R_{AX} = 3.60 \text{ kips} \tag{15.43a}$$

$$R_{DX} = 5 - 3.60 = 1.40 \text{ kips} \tag{15.43b}$$

It is interesting to note that the reaction on the windward side is some $2\frac{1}{2}$ times larger than the reaction on the leeward side. Such a disproportionate distribution of load can be expected when lateral loads occur only on one side.

One may also wonder what the effect was of making the horizontal girder so much heavier than the columns. If all members had been made the same size, the factor 3.52 would have dropped out of the second integral of Equation 15.42. The solution for R_{AX} and R_{DX} would then have been, for constant EI,

$$R_{AX} = 3.68 \text{ kips} \tag{15.44a}$$

$$R_{DX} = 1.32 \text{ kips} \tag{15.44b}$$

When the results given by Equations 15.44a and b for constant EI are compared to Equations 15.43a and b for a heavy roof girder, the difference appears to be negligible. Handbook tables for wind load reactions are typically computed for constant EI, however, and one may doubt the accuracy of such tables. Nonetheless, for a typical case, such as that of Example 15-10, the generalized handbook values, although approximate, may be used with some degree of confidence in preliminary design.

It is not necessary here to place the column supports at the same level, as was done in the preceding examples. The supports may be stepped at widely varying heights, as shown in Figure 15-16. The biggest disadvantage of these solutions is that the vertical reactions are no longer statically determinate, which complicates the calculations somewhat.

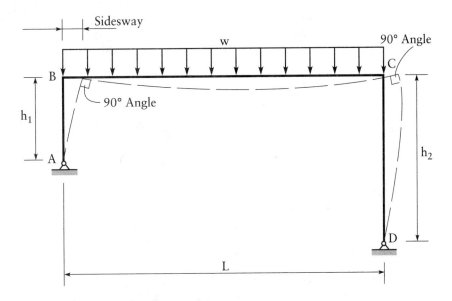

FIGURE 15-16 Portal frames with stepped supports.

A numerical example will illustrate the solution for reactions on a portal frame that has stepped supports.

Example 15-11   Determine the reactions on the given frame.

$E = 200,000 \text{ N/mm}^2$

$I = 400 \times 10^6 \text{ mm}^4$

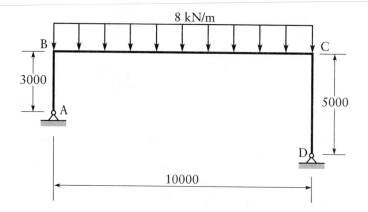

Solution   The free body of the given frame is shown in the following sketch. There are four reactions, and the frame is one degree indeterminate. The lateral deflection of the reaction R_{AX} is zero; this reaction will serve as the redundant. The remaining three reactions are expressed in terms of the chosen redundant. The origin of the coordinate axes is chosen to be at A, as shown on the sketch.

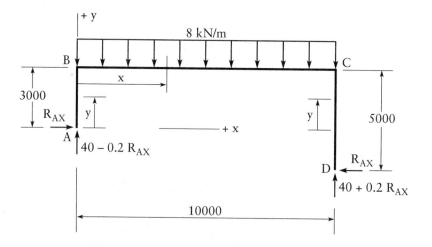

The lateral deflection of the reaction R_{AX} is given by the Castigliano theorem:

$$\Delta_{AX} = 0 = \int_0^L \frac{M_S \left(\dfrac{\partial M_S}{\partial R_{AX}} \right) ds}{EI} \qquad (15.45)$$

The moment equations and partial derivatives can now be determined.

From A to B, $0 \leq y \leq 3$,

$$M_Y = -R_{AX}y; \qquad \frac{\partial M_Y}{\partial R_{AX}} = -y; \qquad ds = dy$$

From B to C, $0 \leq x \leq 10$,

$$M_X = -R_{AX}(3) + (40 - 0.2R_{AX})x - 4x^2; \qquad \frac{\partial M_X}{\partial R_{AX}} = -3 - 0.2x;$$

$$ds = dx$$

From D to C, $-2 \leq y \leq 3$

$$M_Y = +R_{AX}(y+2); \qquad \frac{\partial M_Y}{\partial R_{AX}} = y+2; \qquad ds = dy$$

The equations and derivatives are substituted into Equation 15.45, yielding, for constant EI,

$$EI\Delta_{AX} = 0$$
$$= \int_0^3 (-R_{AX}y)(-y)dy$$
$$+ \int_0^{10} [-R_{AX}(3) + (40 - 0.2R_{AX})x - 4x^2](-3 - 0.2x)dx$$
$$+ \int_{-2}^3 [R_{AX}(y+2)](y+2)dy$$
$$R_{AX} = 12.46 \text{ kN} \tag{15.46a}$$

in the direction shown.

The remaining reactions are found from the statics conditions shown on the free body:

$$R_{AY} = 37.5 \text{ kN} \tag{15.46b}$$

in the direction shown;

$$R_{BX} = 12.46 \text{ kN} \tag{15.46c}$$

in the direction shown;

$$R_{BY} = 42.5 \text{ kN} \tag{15.46d}$$

in the direction shown.

The lateral sway of an indeterminate portal frame is determined by means of the same methods used earlier for determinate frames. There is an added complication, however: the solution for the partial derivative (the unit dummy load analysis) is also statically indeterminate.

An example of using the Castigliano solution to find the sidesway of an indeterminate frame—in this instance the sidesway of the preceding example—follows.

Example 15-12   Determine the amount of sidesway that will occur in the frame described in Example 15-11 and shown in the accompanying figure. The sidesway is considered to be the lateral deflection of the girder *BC*.

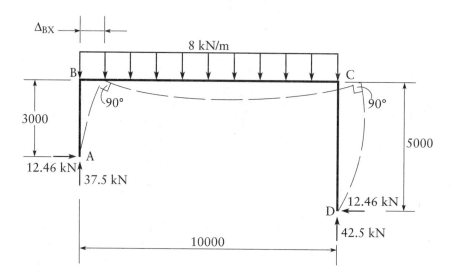

Solution   The lateral deflection of the girder *BC* is shown in the preceding sketch as Δ_{BX}. The deflection will be found by the Castigliano solution, using the unit load method. For constant *EI*,

$$EI\Delta_{BX} = \int_0^L Mm\,ds \tag{15.47}$$

where

M is the moment due to actual loads;

m is the moment due to unit load at B;

ds is the differential length dx or dy.

The moment due to actual loads can readily be found by using the indeterminate reactions already determined in Example 15-11. In the equations for these moments, the origin of the coordinate axes is again taken at A. The following sketch will be used in writing the moment equations.

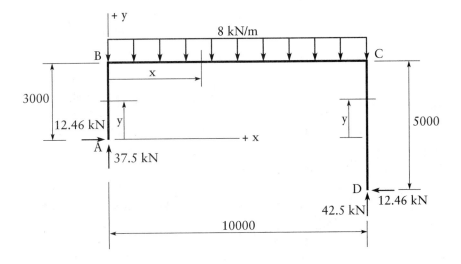

From A to B, $0 \le y \le 3$,

$$M_Y = -12.46y \tag{15.48a}$$

From B to C, $0 \le x \le 10$,

$$M_X = -12.46\,(3) + 37.5x - 4x^2 \tag{15.48b}$$

From D to C, $-2 \le y \le 3$,

$$M_Y = +12.46\,(y+2) \tag{15.48c}$$

The moment m due to unit load at B cannot yet be found. The indeterminate solution for the reactions due to the unit load must first be determined. That solution is obtained next.

The free body of the frame with unit load at B is shown in the following sketch. The horizontal reaction at A is chosen as the redundant; all other reactions are expressed in terms of this redundant.

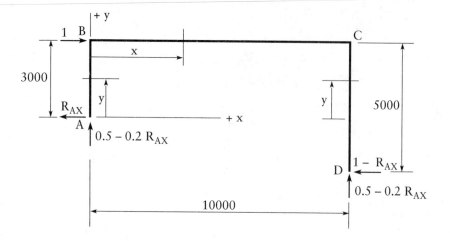

The lateral deflection is given by the Castigliano solution:

$$\Delta_{AX} = 0 = \int_0^L \frac{M_S \left(\dfrac{\partial M_S}{\partial R_{AX}} \right) ds}{EI} \tag{15.49}$$

The moment equations and derivatives can now be identified.
From A to B, $0 \leq y \leq 3$,

$$M_Y = +R_{AX} y; \qquad \frac{\partial M_Y}{\partial R_{AX}} = y; \qquad ds = dy$$

From B to C, $0 \leq x \leq 10$,

$$M_X = R_{AX}(3) - (0.5 - 0.2 R_{AX}) x; \qquad \frac{\partial M_X}{\partial R_{AX}} = 3 + 0.2x;$$

$$ds = dx$$

From D to C, $-2 \leq y \leq 3$,

$$M_Y = (1 - R_{AX})(y + 2); \qquad \frac{\partial M_Y}{\partial R_{AX}} = -y + 2; \qquad ds = dy$$

The moment equations and derivatives are substituted into Equation 15.49, yielding, for constant EI,

$$0 = \int_0^3 (R_{AX}y)(y)dy + \int_0^{10} [3R_{AX} - (0.5 - 0.2R_{AX})x](3 + 0.2x)dx$$

$$- \int_{-2}^3 (1 - R_{AX})(y + 2)^2 dy$$

$$R_{AX} = 0.701 \tag{15.50a}$$

in the direction shown.

The remaining reactions are found from the statics relationships shown on the free body:

$$R_{AY} = 0.360 \tag{15.50b}$$

in the direction shown;

$$R_{BX} = 0.299 \tag{15.50c}$$

in the direction shown;

$$R_{BY} = 0.360 \tag{15.50d}$$

in the direction shown.

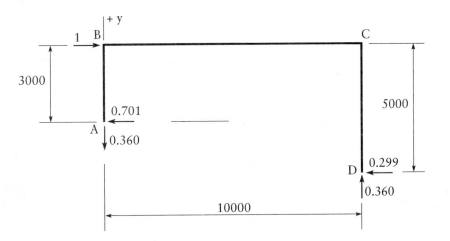

With the reactions due to unit load now known, the equations for the moment m due to the unit load at B can now be written.

From A to B, $0 \leq y \leq 3$,

$$m_Y = +0.701y \tag{15.51a}$$

From B to C, $0 \le x \le 10$,

$$m_X = 0.701\,(3) - 0.360x \tag{15.51b}$$

From D to C, $0 \le y \le 3$,

$$m_X = 0.299\,(y + 2) \tag{15.51c}$$

Equations 15.48 and 15.51 are now substituted into the Castigliano solution for deflection Δ_{BX}, given by Equation 15.47:

$$
\begin{aligned}
EI\Delta_{BX} &= \int_0^3 (-12.46y)(+0.701y)\,dy \\
&+ \int_0^{10} [-12.46\,(3) + (37.5x - 4x^2)]\,[0.701\,(3) - 0.360x]\,dx \\
&+ \int_{-2}^3 [12.46\,(y + 2)\,](0.299)(y + 2)\,dy \\
&= +202.5 \\
\Delta_{BX} &= +0.00253 \text{ m} = 2.53 \text{ mm} \tag{15.52}
\end{aligned}
$$

in the direction shown.

It should be apparent that the solution for deflections in an indeterminate frame is indeed tedious, although the procedure is in no way different than that developed for determinate structures. To recapitulate, the procedure consists of the following steps:

1. Find the moment M_s due to actual loads (an indeterminate solution).
2. Find the moment m_s due to unit load at the point where deflection is sought (another indeterminate solution).
3. Evaluate the Castigliano (unit load) solution for the deflection.

$$\Delta_s = \int_0^L \frac{M_s m_s\,ds}{EI}$$

The problem in such solutions, of course, is that the indeterminate solutions can become quite lengthy, and the chance of numerical error increases exponentially with the length. If one has access to the appropriate mathematics software, much of the tedium (and the numerical error) can be avoided. In practice, the solution would probably be taken one step farther and solved by one of the many structures programs available for such problems. For the student, however, learning the solution techniques is of primary importance; when the student can understand the software, the student can use the software.

The outward thrusts produced at the base of a rigid frame can sometimes be troublesome. One remedy for managing the thrust loads is a tie bar, like the one shown in Figure 15-17. Tie bars are commonly used to take thrust loads, in order to circumvent difficult foundation problems.

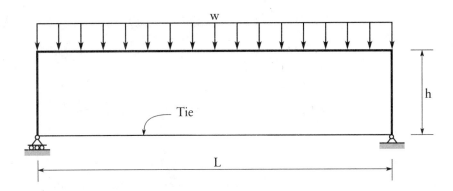

FIGURE 15-17 Tied portal frame.

The procedures used to find the reactions for a tied frame are similar to those already introduced. A numerical example will demonstrate the application to a tied portal frame.

Example 15-13 Determine the reactions on the given tied portal frame.

For the columns, $I = 415$ in.^{4} = 0.0104 ft^4
For the girder, $I = 1366$ in.^{4} = 0.0659 ft^4
For the tie bar, $A = 0.785$ in.^{2} = 0.00545 ft^2
For steel, $E = 29,000,000$ psi = 4,176,000 ksf

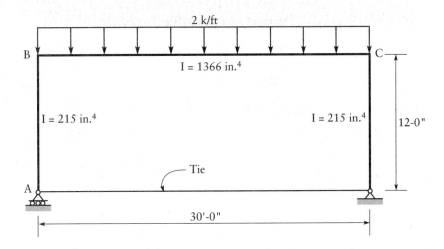

Solution   The free body of the frame is shown in the following sketch, along with all reactions. The lateral deflection of the frame at A is the elongation of the tie bar due to the axial load R_{AX} in the tie bar.

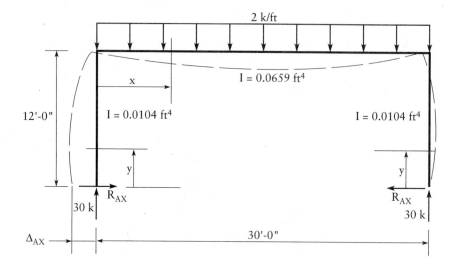

The reaction R_{AX} is chosen as the redundant. Its deflection is readily expressed in terms of R_{AX}.

$$\Delta_{AX} = \frac{R_{AX}L}{AE}$$

$$= \frac{(R_{AX})(30)}{(0.00545)\,(4,176,000)}$$

$$= (1318 \times 10^{-6})\,R_{AX} \qquad (15.53)$$

The deflection of the redundant at A is given by the Castigliano theorem:

$$\Delta_{AX} = \int_0^L \frac{M_S\left(\dfrac{\partial M_S}{\partial R_{AX}}\right)ds}{EI} \qquad (15.54)$$

This deflection is equated to the deflection of the tie bar. The deflection is negative since it is opposite to the direction of R_{AX}:

$$(-1318 \times 10^{-6})\,R_{AX} = \int_0^L \frac{M_S\left(\dfrac{\partial M_S}{\partial R_{AX}}\right)ds}{EI} \qquad (15.55)$$

The origin of the coordinate axes is placed at A. The moment and the partial derivatives can now be identified.

From A to B, $0 \leq y \leq 12$,

$$M_Y = -R_{AX}y; \qquad \frac{\partial M_Y}{\partial R_{AX}} = -y; \qquad I = 0.0104 \text{ ft}^4; \qquad ds = dy$$

From B to C, $0 \leq x \leq 30$,

$$M_X = 30x - x^2 - 12R_{AX}; \qquad \frac{\partial M_X}{\partial R_{AX}} = -12; \qquad I = 0.0659 \text{ ft}^4;$$

$$ds = dx$$

From D to C, $0 \leq y \leq 12$,

$$M_Y = +R_{AX}y; \qquad \frac{\partial M_Y}{\partial R_{AX}} = +y; \qquad I = 0.0104 \text{ ft}^4; \qquad ds = dy$$

These values are substituted into Equation 15.55:

$$(-1318 \times 10^{-6}) R_{AX} = \int_0^{12} \frac{(-R_{AX}y)(-y)dy}{(4,176,000)(0.0104)}$$

$$+ \int_0^{30} \frac{(30x - x^2 - 12R_{AX})(-12)dx}{(4,176,000)(0.0659)}$$

$$+ \int_0^{12} \frac{(R_{AX}y)(y)dy}{(4,176,000)(0.0104)}$$

$$R_{AX} = 4.51 \text{ kips} \tag{15.56}$$

The reaction R_{AX} can also be computed for this frame for a case where the supports are rigid, unyielding hinges (instead of the steel tie bar). The result, computed aside, is that R_{AX} is 4.65 kips when supports are unyielding hinges compared to the value of 4.51 kips with a tie bar. These results again verify that steel ties provide a very rigid, almost unyielding support in such applications.

In addition to being subject to the usual gravity loads and lateral loads, frames can be subject to thermal loads—that is, loads that occur as a result of changing temperatures. Thermal loading is a characteristic feature of indeterminate structures; it does not exist in determinate structures. Thermal loading occurs entirely as a result of restraint against expansion or contraction. If there are no restraints, there is no thermal load.

Thermal loading can sometimes be large enough to pose a problem in indeterminate frames, particularly in instances where the frame is exposed to high summer temperatures but where the foundation remains at a much lower temperature due to its direct contact with the much cooler earth. The difference in temperature between the frame and its foundation in such cases can be as much as 120 Fahrenheit degrees, or even more. When conditions are severe, a thermal analysis becomes necessary.

The standard procedure for making a thermal analysis of a frame can be summarized as follows:

1. Remove all points of restraint against thermal expansion or contraction (artificially make the frame statically determinate).

2. Arbitrarily select some point in the frame as a reference point from which thermal expansion or contraction can be measured.

3. Permit the frame to expand or contract freely in all directions from that reference point under the specified change in temperature.

4. Determine the amount of thermal expansion or contraction that occurs at each point of restraint, measured from the previously selected reference point.

5. Apply the indeterminate reactions necessary to overcome these thermal expansions or contractions and to restore the frame to its restrained position.

6. Determine the magnitudes of these indeterminate reactions.

As always, it is advantageous to look for symmetry of deformations in order to reduce the number of unknowns in the solution.

A numerical example will demonstrate the procedure for finding reactions due to temperature differences between a portal frame and its foundations.

Example 15-14   Determine the reactions on the given steel frame due to a temperature difference of 100 Fahrenheit degrees between the frame and its foundation. The thermal coefficient of expansion for steel is 6.5×10^{-6} in./in./°F.

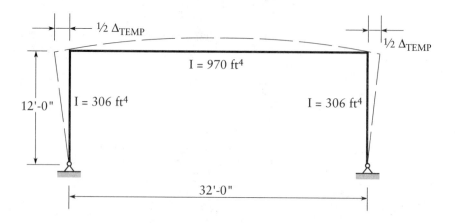

Solution   The free body of the frame is shown in the following sketch. It is elected in this case not to take advantage of the symmetry; all of the thermal growth is shown at one side. Point D is taken as the reference point; all thermal growth is measured from this point. The reaction R_{AX} is then applied to restore the deflection at A to zero. Vertical reactions are zero.

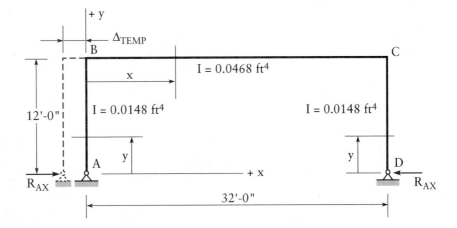

The thermal growth relative to point D at 100 Fahrenheit degrees difference in temperature is found from basic laws of physics:

$$\Delta_{TEMP} = (\alpha)(\Delta T)(L) = (0.0000065)(100)(32)(12)$$
$$= 0.2496 \text{ in.} = 0.0208 \text{ ft}$$

away from point D.

The displacement of the force R_{AX} in restoring the base of the frame at point A to its original restrained position is found from the Castigliano theorem:

$$\Delta_{AX} = \int_0^L \frac{M_S\left(\dfrac{\partial M_S}{\partial R_{AX}}\right)ds}{EI} \tag{15.57}$$

The origin of the coordinate axes is chosen at A. The moment equation and its partial derivatives can now be identified.

From A to B, $0 \le y \le 12$,

$$M_Y = -R_{AX}y; \qquad \frac{\partial M_Y}{\partial R_{AX}} = -y; \qquad ds = dy$$

From B to C, $0 \leq x \leq 32$,

$$M_X = -R_{AX}(12) ; \qquad \frac{\partial M_Y}{\partial R_{AX}} = -12 ; \qquad ds = dx$$

From D to C, $0 \leq y \leq 12$,

$$M_Y = +R_{AX}y ; \qquad \frac{\partial M_Y}{\partial R_{AX}} = +y ; \qquad ds = dy$$

These values are substituted into Equation 15.57 to find

$$\Delta_{TEMP} = 0.0208 = \int_0^{12} \frac{(-R_{AX}y)(-y)dy}{(4,176,000)(0.0148)}$$
$$+ \int_0^{32} \frac{(-R_{AX})(12)(-12)dx}{(4,176,000)(0.0468)}$$
$$+ \int_0^{12} \frac{(R_{AX}y)(y)dy}{(4,176,000)(0.0148)}$$

$$R_{AX} = 0.493 \text{ kips} \qquad\qquad\qquad (15.58)$$

to restore point A to zero deflection.

In the frame of Example 15-14, the solution for reactions due to the thermal load indicates that the thermal load is not large enough to pose a serious problem. For heavy, stiff frames, however, thermal loads can sometimes constitute an important design consideration.

All of the frames discussed so far have had hinged bases. When foundation conditions are suitable, it is possible to fix the column bases, as in Figure 15-18 for a portal frame under wind load. Where foundation conditions permit such designs, fixed bases can contribute significantly to the overall rigidity of a frame.

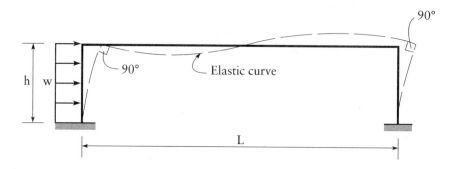

FIGURE 15-18 Portal frame with fixed bases.

A numerical example will illustrate the solution for wind load on a portal frame that has fixed bases. The solution is quite lengthy; to simplify the presentation, the solution is condensed into a blocked-out form. The lengthy integrations in the following example were performed by standard CAD mathematics software.

Example 15-15   Determine the reactions on the given fixed-base portal frame.

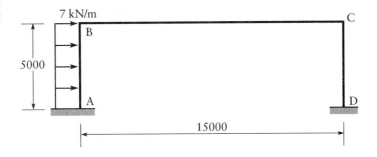

Solution   The free body of the frame is shown in the following sketch. The frame has six reactions; it is therefore three degrees indeterminate. The three deformations at the support at A (two displacements, one rotation) are all zero, corresponding to the reactions R_{AX}, R_{AY}, and M_{AB}. These three reactions are chosen as the three redundants for use in the Castigliano solution. The remaining reactions at D are expressed in terms of the three redundants.

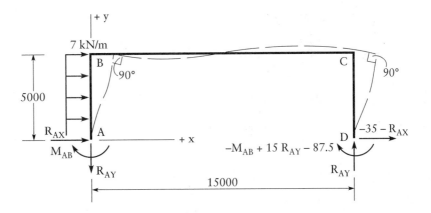

The Castigliano equations for these three redundants are

$$\Delta_{AX} = 0 = \int_0^L \frac{M\left(\dfrac{\partial M_S}{\partial R_{AX}}\right)ds}{EI} \qquad (15.59\text{a})$$

$$\Delta_{AY} = 0 = \int_0^L \frac{M_S\left(\frac{\partial M_S}{\partial R_{AY}}\right)ds}{EI} \tag{15.59b}$$

$$\theta_A = 0 = \int_0^L \frac{M_S\left(\frac{\partial M_S}{\partial M_{AB}}\right)ds}{EI} \tag{15.59c}$$

The coordinate axes are chosen with the origin at A, as shown in the sketch. The moment equations can now be determined.

From A to B,

$$M_Y = -R_{AX}y + M_{AB} - 3.5y^2$$

From B to C,

$$M_X = -R_{AX}(5) + M_{AB} - R_{AY}x - 87.5$$

From D to C,

$$M_Y = +R_{AX}y - M_{AB} + R_{AY}(15) - 17.5(5 - 2y)$$

The partial derivatives and the differentials are found as usual.

From A to B,

$$\frac{\partial M_Y}{\partial R_{AX}} = -y; \qquad \frac{\partial M_Y}{\partial R_{AY}} = 0; \qquad \frac{\partial M_Y}{\partial M_{AB}} = +1; \qquad ds = dy$$

From B to C,

$$\frac{\partial M_X}{\partial R_{AX}} = -5; \qquad \frac{\partial M_X}{\partial R_{AY}} = -x; \qquad \frac{\partial M_X}{\partial M_{AB}} = +1; \qquad ds = dy$$

From D to C,

$$\frac{\partial M_Y}{\partial R_{AX}} = +y; \qquad \frac{\partial M_Y}{\partial R_{AY}} = +15; \qquad \frac{\partial M_Y}{\partial M_{AB}} = -1; \qquad ds = dx$$

These values are substituted into Equations 15.21a, b, and c to find (with EI factored out)

$$EI\Delta_{AX} = 0 = \int_0^5 (-R_{AX}y + M_{AB} - 3.5y^2)(-y)dy$$

$$+ \int_0^{15} (-5R_{AX} + M_{AB} - R_{AY}x - 87.5)(-5)dx$$

$$+ \int_0^5 [R_{AX}y - M_{AB} + 15R_{AY} - 17.5(5 - 2y)](+y)dy$$

$$EI\Delta_{AX} = 0 = \int_0^5 (-R_{AX}y + M_{AB} - 3.5y^2)(0)dy$$

$$+ \int_0^{15} (-5R_{AX} + M_{AB} - R_{AY}x - 87.5)(-x)dx$$

$$+ \int_0^5 [R_{AX}y - M_{AB} + 15R_{AY} - 17.5(5 - 2y)](15)dy$$

$$EI\Delta_{AX} = 0 = \int_0^5 (-R_{AX}y + M_{AB} - 3.5y^2)(+1)dy$$

$$+ \int_0^{15} (-5R_{AX} + M_{AB} - R_{AY}x - 87.5)(+1)dx$$

$$+ \int_0^5 [R_{AX}y - M_{AB} + 15R_{AY} - 17.5(5 - 2y)](-1)dy$$

The results of these three rather lengthy integrations are three equations in the three redundants R_{AX}, R_{AY}, and M_{AB}.

$$-7473.96 = 458.33R_{AX} + 750.00R_{AY} - 100.00M_{AB}$$

$$-9843.75 = 750.00R_{AX} + 2250.00R_{AY} - 187.50M_{AB}$$

$$+1458.33 = 100.00R_{AX} - 187.50R_{AY} + 25.00M_{AB}$$

These three equations are solved simultaneously to find

$$R_{AX} = -28.13 \text{ kN} \tag{15.60a}$$

$$R_{AY} = +1.30 \text{ kN} \tag{15.60b}$$

$$M_{AB} = -44.44 \text{ kN} \cdot \text{m} \tag{15.60c}$$

The remaining reactions are computed from the statics relationships given on the free body:

$$R_{DX} = -6.87 \text{ kN} \tag{15.60d}$$

$$R_{DY} = +1.30 \text{ kN} \tag{15.60e}$$

$$M_{DC} = -23.56 \text{ kN} \cdot \text{m} \tag{15.60f}$$

Outside Problems   Determine the reactions on the given steel frames.

Problem 15-25*

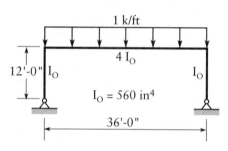

Problem 15-26

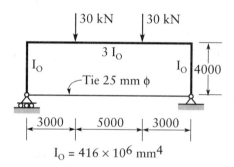

Problem 15-27*

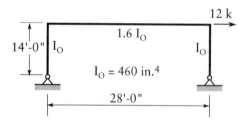

Problem 15-28

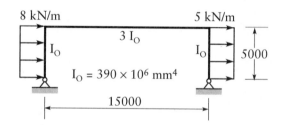

Problem 15-29* Determine the reactions on the frame of Problem 15-27 for the case where the frame is subject to a temperature increase of 120 Fahrenheit degrees. Do not include the 12 kip lateral load in this analysis. For steel, the thermal coefficient of expansion is 6.5×10^{-6} in./in./°F.

Problem 15-30 Determine the reactions on the frame of Problem 15-28 for the case where the frame is subject to a temperature change of 65 Celsius degrees. Do not include the wind load in this analysis. For steel, the thermal coefficient of expansion is 11×10^{-6} m/m/°C.

Problem 15-31*

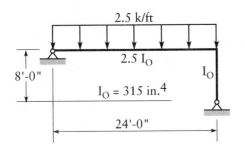

Problem 15-32

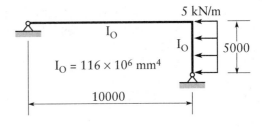

Problem 15-33*

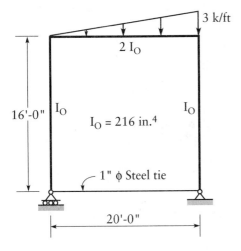

Problem 15-34

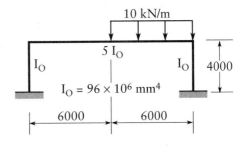

15.4 GABLE FRAMES

Another very popular configuration for a rigid frame in today's industry is the gable frame. Although usually symmetrical, the gable frame can readily be conformed to special applications such as solar panels or clerestory effects, as shown in Figure 15-19. As always in rigid frames, joints must remain absolutely rigid under load; there can be no angular change at any joint due to loads.

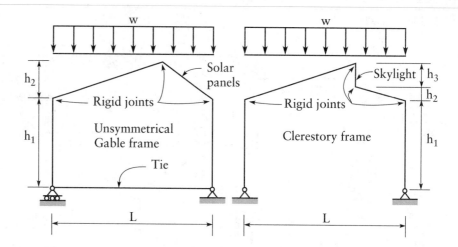

FIGURE 15-19 Gable frame with hinged column bases.

The solution for the reactions of a gable frame such as that of Figure 15-19 generally follows the same procedures as were demonstrated earlier. A numerical example will illustrate the procedures as they apply specifically to gable frames.

Example 15-16   Determine the reactions on the given gable frame. Moment of inertia I is constant for all members. The tie is a steel bar, 1.25 inches in diameter.

$$I = 248 \text{ in.}^4 = 0.01196 \text{ ft}^4$$

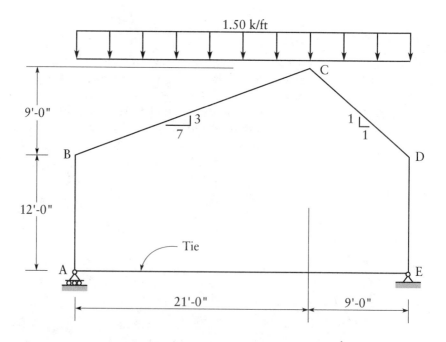

Solution   The free body of the frame is shown in the following sketch. There are four reactions, as shown; the frame is therefore one degree indeterminate. The lateral deflection of the reaction at A is the elongation of the tie bar; this reaction, R_{AX}, is chosen as the redundant. The two vertical reactions are statically determinate; their magnitudes are shown on the sketch. The other horizontal reaction (at E) is expressed in terms of the redundant R_{AX}.

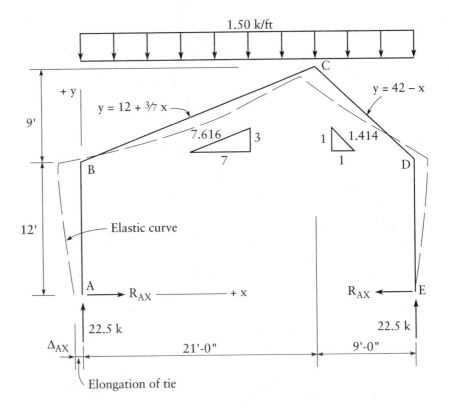

The lateral deflection of the redundant R_{AX} is the elongation of the tie bar:

$$\Delta_{AX} = \frac{R_{AX}L}{AE}$$
$$= (843 \times 10^{-6})\,R_{AX}$$

where

$L = 30$ ft
$A = 0.7854\,(1.25)^2 = 1.2272$ in.$^2 = 0.00852$ ft^2
$E = 4{,}176{,}000$ k/ft^2

The lateral deflection Δ_{AX} is also given by the Castigliano theorem. The two solutions for the deflection are equated to find the magnitude of the redundant R_{AX}:

$$\Delta_{AX} = (-843 \times 10^{-6})\, R_{AX} = \int_0^L \frac{M_S\left(\dfrac{\partial M_S}{\partial R_{AX}}\right) ds}{EI} \tag{15.61}$$

The x- and y-coordinate axes are chosen with their origin at A, as shown in the preceding sketch. The differential ds is usually taken on the same axis as the loads: if the loads lie along a y-axis, the differential ds is taken as dy; if the loads lie along the x-axis, the differential ds is taken as dx.

The moment equations and the partial derivatives can now be determined.

From A to B, with $0 \le y \le 12$,

$$M_Y = -R_{AX}y; \qquad \frac{\partial M_Y}{\partial R_{AX}} = -y; \qquad ds = dy$$

From B to C, with $0 \le x \le 21$,

$$y = 12 + \left(\frac{3}{7}x\right) = 12 + 0.4286x$$

$$M_X = -R_{AX}y + 22.5x - 0.75x^2$$

For the integration, the moment equation must be expressed entirely in terms of x, where $y = 12 + 0.4286x$:

$$M_X = -R_{AX}(12 + 0.4286x) + 22.5x - 0.75x^2;$$

$$\frac{\partial M_X}{\partial R_{AX}} = -(12 + 0.4286x); \qquad ds = \left(\frac{7.616}{7}\right)dx$$

From C to D, with $21 \le x \le 30$,

$$y = 42 - x$$
$$M_X = -R_{AX}y + 22.5x - 0.75x^2$$

For the integration, the moment equation must be expressed entirely in terms of x, where $y = 42 - x$:

$$M_X = -R_{AX}(42 - x) + 22.5x - 0.75x^2; \qquad \frac{\partial M_X}{\partial R_{AX}} = -(42 - x);$$

$$ds = \frac{1.414}{1}dx = 1.414dx$$

From D to C, $0 \le y \le 12$,

$$M_Y = +R_{AX}y; \qquad \frac{\partial M_Y}{\partial R_{AX}} = +y; \qquad ds = dy$$

The moments, partial derivatives, and differentials are substituted into Equation 15.61, where $EI = 4{,}176{,}000(0.01196) = 49{,}945$ kip-ft^2:

$$(-843 \times 10^{-6}) R_{AX} = \int_0^{12} \frac{(-R_{AX}y)(-y)dy}{49{,}945}$$

$$+ \int_0^{21} \frac{\left\{ \begin{array}{l} [-R_{AX}(12 + 0.4286x) + 22.5x - 0.75x^2] \\ \times(-12 - 0.4286x)(1.088)dx \end{array} \right\}}{49{,}945}$$

$$+ \int_{21}^{30} \frac{\left\{ \begin{array}{l} [-R_{AX}(42 - x) + 22.5x - 0.75x^2] \\ \times(-42 + x)(1.414)dx \end{array} \right\}}{49{,}945}$$

$$+ \int_0^{12} \frac{(R_{AX}y)(+y)dy}{49{,}945}$$

These integrals are evaluated to find

$$R_{AX} = 6.14 \text{ kips} \qquad\qquad (15.62)$$

The final reactions are shown on the following sketch.

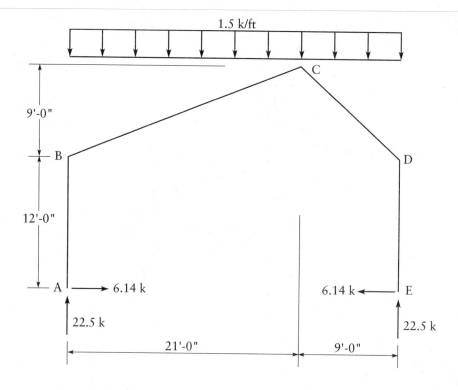

The analysis of clerestory frames differs from that of other gable frames only in the obvious fact that the line integral of the Castigliano solution has one more term. A numerical example will demonstrate the procedure for wind loads on a clerestory frame. The wind load in the example consists of pressure load on one side and suction load on the other in the ratio of 8:5; such a distribution of wind load is a code requirement.

Example 15-17   Determine the reactions on the given clerestory frame. The moment of inertia I is constant throughout the frame.

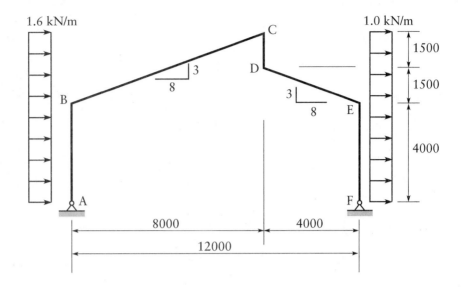

Solution   The free body of the frame is shown in the following sketch, along with its four reactions. The frame is one degree indeterminate. The vertical reactions are statically determinate; their values have been computed and entered on the sketch.

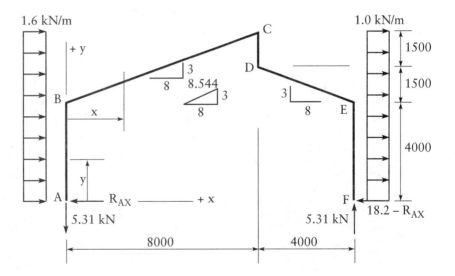

The solution will be performed by means of the Castigliano theorem. The deflection of R_{AX} is zero; and the reaction R_{AX} is chosen as the redundant. The denominator term EI cancels out. The origin of the coordinate axes is taken at A. Hence,

$$\Delta_{AX} = 0 = \int_0^L \frac{M_S\left(\dfrac{\partial M_S}{\partial R_{AX}}\right)ds}{EI} \tag{15.63}$$

Since the loads are on the y-axis, the differential ds is taken on the y-axis. The moment equations and the partial derivatives can now be determined.

From A to B, with $0 \le y \le 4$,

$$M_Y = R_{AX}y - 0.8y^2 \, ; \qquad \frac{\partial M_Y}{\partial R_{AX}} = +y \, ; \qquad ds = dy$$

From B to C, $4 \le y \le 7$,

$$x = (y-4)(2.6667) \, ; \qquad M_Y = R_{AX}y - 0.8y^2 - 5.31x \, ;$$

$$\frac{\partial M_Y}{\partial R_{AX}} = +y \, ; \qquad ds = \left(\frac{8.544}{3}\right)dy$$

From F to E, $0 \le y \le 4$,

$$M_Y = (18.2 - R_{AX})\,y - 0.5y^2 \, ; \qquad \frac{\partial M_Y}{\partial R_{AX}} = -y \, ; \qquad ds = dy$$

From E to D, $4 \le y \le 5.5$,

$$x = 12 - (y-4)(2.6667) \, ;$$

$$M_Y = (18.2 - R_{AX})\,y - 0.5y^2 - 5.31\,(12-x) \, ; \qquad \frac{\partial M_Y}{\partial R_{AX}} = -y \, ;$$

$$ds = \left(\frac{8.544}{3}\right)dy$$

From D to C, $5.5 \le y \le 7$,

$$M_X = (18.2 - R_{AX})\,y - 0.5y^2 - 5.31\,(4.0) \, ; \qquad \frac{\partial M_Y}{\partial R_{AX}} = -y \, ;$$

$$ds = dy$$

The equations and derivatives are substituted into the Castigliano equation (Equation 15.63):

$$0 = \int_0^4 (R_{AX}y - 0.8y^2)(y)dy$$

$$+ \int_4^7 [R_{AX}y - 0.8y^2 - 5.32\,(y-4)(2.6667)\,]\,(y)\left(\frac{8.544}{3}\right)dy$$

$$+ \int_0^4 [\,(18.2 - R_{AX})\,y - 0.5y^2\,](-y)\,dy$$

$$+ \int_4^{5.5} [\,(18.2 - R_{AX})\,y - 0.5y^2 - 5.31\,(y-4)$$

$$\times (2.6667)\,](-y)\left(\frac{8.544}{3}\right)dy$$

$$+ \int_{5.5}^7 [\,(18.2 - R_{AX})\,y - 0.5y^2 - 5.31\,(4.0)\,]\,(-y)\,dy$$

These integrals are evaluated to find

$$R_{AX} = 10.16 \text{ kN} \tag{16.64}$$

Specialty frames such as clerestory frames and solar array frames seem to be growing in popularity for use in greenhouses and in specialized industrial applications, among others. The analysis of such frames, although tedious, is quite straightforward; every concept in the least work analysis of gable frames was encountered in the analysis of portal frames.

Outside Problems   Determine the reactions on the given steel frames.

Problem 15-35*

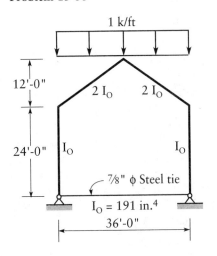

Problem 15-36

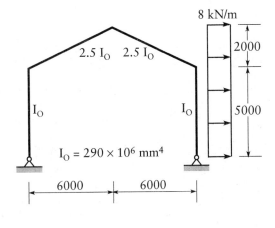

Problem 15-37*

$\Delta_{TEMP} = 120°$ F

6'-0"

I_O I_O

14'-0" $I_O = 406$ in.^{4} I_O

6'-0"   18'-0"

Problem 15-38

15 kN/m

3 I_O 4000

3 I_O 4000

3 I_O

12000   2 I_O I_O 10000

Steel tie 20 mm ϕ

$I_O = 191 \times 10^6$ mm^4

12000   12000

Problem 15-39*

800 lb/ft   500 lb/ft

6'-0"   3 I_O 3 I_O

6'-0"   3 I_O

12'-0" I_O I_O

$I_O = 312$ in.^{4}

12'-0"   24'-0"

Problem 15-40

20 kN

4 I_O 3000

4 I_O

3000

I_O 3 I_O

$I_O = 130 \times 10^6$ mm^4

3000

5000   5000

15.5 PARABOLIC ARCHES

In addition to single-span frames, the single-span arch is a very popular structure in today's industry. The single-span arch is almost always tied, but occasionally in bridge construction the bases may be fixed. A tied arch is statically indeterminate; its analysis is quite similar to the analyses just presented for tied frames.

Engineers commonly use a particular form of the equation of a parabola when they are dealing with a parabolic arch; the origin of x and y are taken at one side of the arch rather than at the midpoint. Such an arch, along with its defining equation, is shown in Figure 15-20.

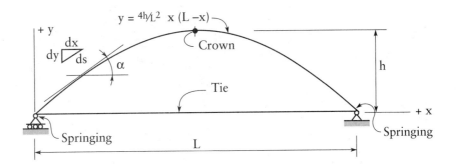

FIGURE 15-20 Equation of a parabolic arch.

The slope of the arch at any point along its centerline is the angle α:

$$\cos \alpha = \frac{dx}{ds}$$

$$dx = ds \cos \alpha \qquad (15.64)$$

The relationship between ds and dx given by Equation 15.64 will be used later in the Castigliano integral.

The cross section of an arch is rarely of constant depth. Rather, the depth of the cross section is usually somewhat thicker at the springing than at the crown. If the moment of inertia at the crown is taken as the reference value I_0, the moment of inertia I_x at a distance x from the origin may be expressed as

$$I_X = I_0 \sec \alpha \qquad (15.65)$$

Use of the approximate variation given by Equation 15.65, coupled with the relationship between ds and dx given by Equation 15.64, permits one to evaluate the Castigliano equation without its having a variable in the denominator. While the variation is indeed only an approximation, its use allows a closed-form solution to be made for the reactions on a parabolic arch. Further, it has already been demonstrated in the analysis of frames that the variation in I has a somewhat minor influence on the accuracy of the analysis; this same relatively minor influence on accuracy is also true with respect to arches.

A hinged arch under uniform load is shown in Figure 15-21. The free body is also shown; with its four reactions, the arch is one degree indeterminate. For a Castigliano solution, the reaction R_{AX} is chosen as the redundant; its deflection Δ_{AX} is zero. Where the supports are at the same level, the vertical reactions are statically determinate (as they were in frames); the values of the vertical reactions are shown on the free body.

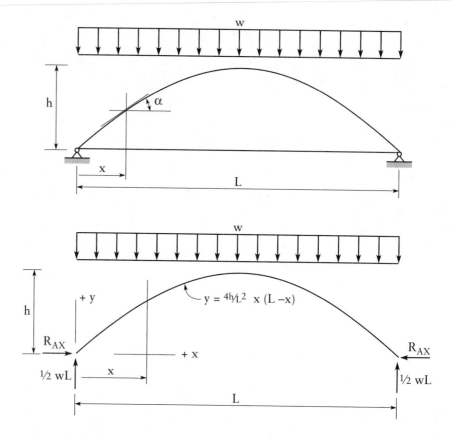

FIGURE 15-21 Parabolic arch under uniform load.

The redundant reaction R_{AX} may be found from the Castigliano theorem:

$$\Delta_{AX} = 0 = \int_0^L \frac{M_S\left(\dfrac{\partial M_S}{\partial R_{AX}}\right)ds}{EI} \qquad (15.66)$$

The moment equation and partial derivatives can now be determined. For $0 \le x \le L$:

$$M_X = \frac{1}{2}wlx - \frac{1}{2}wx^2 - R_{AX}y; \qquad \frac{\partial M_X}{\partial R_{AX}} = -y; \qquad ds = dx \sec \alpha$$

where

$$y = \frac{4h}{L^2}x(L-x)$$

$$I_x = I_0 \sec \alpha$$

These values are substituted into the Castigliano solution given by Equation 15.66:

$$0 = \int_0^L \frac{\left[\frac{1}{2}wlx - \frac{1}{2}wx^2 - R_{AX}\frac{4h}{L^2}x(L-x)\right]\left[-\frac{4h}{L^2}x(L-x)\right]dx \sec \alpha}{EI_0 \sec \alpha}$$

The denominator drops out, and the integral is then evaluated to find

$$R_{AX} = \frac{wL^2}{8h} \tag{15.67}$$

The horizontal reaction is thus a very simple expression. The moment at any point along the arch can now be found from the moment equation:

$$\begin{aligned}
M_X &= \frac{1}{2}wLx - \frac{1}{2}wx^2 - R_{AX}y \\
&= \frac{1}{2}wx(L-x) - \left[\frac{wL^2}{8h}\right]\left[\frac{4h}{L^2}(x)(L-x)\right] \\
&= 0
\end{aligned} \tag{15.68}$$

Equation 15.68 indicates that the moment anywhere along a uniformly loaded parabolic arch is zero. This remarkable feature of the parabolic arch made it exceptionally valuable in centuries past; a long-span arch could be built of brittle compressive materials such as stone or brick, and the material would not be subject to destructive tensile stresses due to bending. The masonry aqueducts of Portugal and Spain, still standing after 20 centuries, bear witness to the practical value of this feature.

It should not be inferred that there is never any bending moment on a parabolic arch. The condition of zero moment applies only to uniform loading. Unsymmetrical loads, eccentric loads, wind loads, construction misalignments, and countless other factors can introduce bending moments into a parabolic arch. In general, however, such accidental moments (and the associated tensile stresses) are relatively small in a heavy masonry or concrete arch; the uniform compressive stress created by the dead load is usually large enough to overcome any such tensile stresses.

The lateral thrust on a low arch is predictably quite large—much larger than the thrusts encountered in single-span frames. As the arch increases in height, the thrust decreases and becomes much easier to handle. A numerical example will illustrate the calculation of the thrust in a low, flat arch.

Example 15-18   Determine the reactions on the given parabolic concrete arch. EI_0 of the arch at the crown is 2.16×10^{-6} kN · m². The tie is steel, having an area of 1960 mm². For steel, $E = 200{,}000$ N/mm².

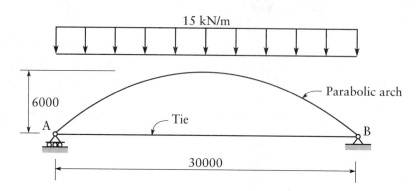

Solution   The free body of the arch is shown in the following sketch. There are four reactions as shown; so the arch is one degree indeterminate. The lateral deflection of the reaction at A is the elongation of the tie bar; the deflection at A can therefore be expressed in terms of the reaction R_{AX}. The horizontal reaction R_{AX} is chosen as the redundant. The two vertical reactions are statically determinate; they have been computed and are shown on the sketch. Due to symmetry, the horizontal reaction at B is equal and opposite to R_{AX}.

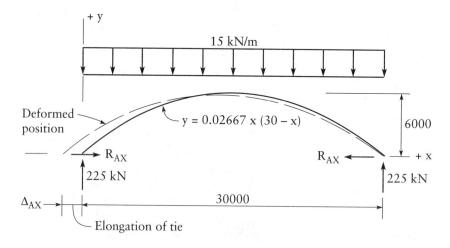

The origin of the coordinate axes is taken at A. With $h = 6$ and $L = 30$, the equation of the parabolic arch is then

$$y = 0.02667x\,(30 - x)$$

The lateral deflection at A is the elongation of the tie bar under the axial load R_{AX}:

$$\Delta_{AX} = \frac{R_{AX}L}{AE}$$
$$= (76.53 \times 10^{-6})\, R_{AX}$$

where

$L = 30$ m

$A = 1960$ mm$^2 = 0.00196$ m^2

$E = 200{,}000$ N/mm$^2 = 200 \times 10^{-6}$ kN/m^2

The lateral deflection of the arch is also given by the Castigliano theorem; this second solution is equated to the elongation of the tie bar, yielding a single equation in the redundant R_{AX}. The deflection Δ_{AX} is negative, since its direction is opposite to that of R_{AX}.

$$\Delta_{AX} = -76.53 R_{AX} = \int_0^L \frac{M_S\left(\dfrac{\partial M_S}{\partial R_{AX}}\right)ds}{EI_x} \tag{15.70}$$

The origin of the coordinate axes is taken at A, as shown on the preceding sketch. The moment equation can now be determined.

For $0 \leq x \leq 30$:

$$M_X = -R_{AX}y + 225x - 7.5x^2; \qquad ds = dx \sec \alpha$$

Notice that the relationship between ds and dx is variable, as given by Equation 15.25. For the integration, the moment equation must be expressed entirely in terms of x.

For $0 \leq x \leq 30$,

$$M_X = -R_{AX}[0.02667x\,(30-x)] + 225x - 7.5x^2;$$
$$\frac{\partial M_X}{\partial R_{AX}} = -0.02667x\,(30-x); \qquad ds = dx \sec \alpha$$

These values are substituted into Equation 15.70, with the moment of inertia I_x also varying as sec α:

$$-(76.53)\,(10^{-6})\,R_{AX} = \int_0^{30} \frac{\{-R_{AY}[0.02667x\,(30-x)] + 225x - 7.5x^2\}}{\times[-0.02667x\,(30-x)]\,dx \sec\alpha}{(2.16)(10^6)\,\sec\alpha}$$

$$R_{AX} = 219 \text{ kN} \tag{15.71}$$

For this thrust, the direct stress in the tie bar is

$$f_S = \frac{R_{AX}}{A_S} = \frac{219{,}000}{1960} = 112 \text{ N/mm}^2$$

or roughly 37% of yield stress.

The lateral thrust of 219 kN in the low flat arch of Example 15-18 is roughly equal to the vertical reaction of 225 kN. Such magnitude is much larger than any of the lateral thrust loads encountered earlier in examples involving rigid frames. For this reason, arches are very frequently tied; it is difficult to find a foundation material (other than bedrock) that can sustain these high lateral loads at a relatively shallow depth of burial, so a tie becomes one of the few reasonable alternatives.

A considerable relaxation of the lateral thrust occurs due to the deflection of the tie bar. If, for example, the base had been hinged, using rigid unyielding hinges, the reaction at A would have been $wl^2/8h$ or 281 kN rather than the 219 kN that occurs with the tie bar. This relaxation of some 20% due to the deflection in the tie bar is far larger than that encountered earlier in frames; it can best be controlled by keeping the stress in the tie bar quite low—as low as 20% of the yield stress in extreme cases.

A final example involving arches will demonstrate the solution when only a portion of the arch is loaded.

Example 15-19   Determine the reactions on the given parabolic arch.

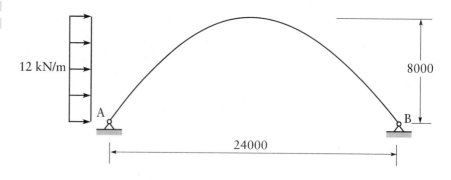

Solution   A free body of the arch, along with its four reactions, is shown in the following sketch. The arch is one degree indeterminate. Since the supports at A and B are at the same level, the vertical reactions are statically determinate. The vertical reactions have been computed and are shown on the sketch.

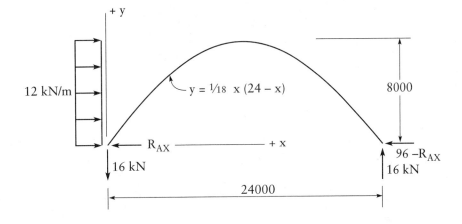

The reaction R_{AX} is selected as the redundant; its displacement Δ_{AX} is zero. The remaining reaction R_{BX} is expressed in terms of the redundant R_{AX}.

The origin of the coordinate axes is taken at A. The equation of the arch is given by

$$y = \frac{4h}{L^2}x\,(L-x) = \frac{1}{18}x\,(24-x)$$

The solution is given by the Castigliano theorem:

$$\Delta_{AX} = 0 = \int_0^L \frac{M_S\left(\dfrac{\partial M_S}{\partial R_{AX}}\right)ds}{EI} \tag{15.72}$$

The moment equation and the partial derivatives can now be determined. For $0 \le x \le 12$,

$$M_X = -16x - 6y^2 + R_{AX}y; \qquad \frac{\partial M_X}{\partial R_{AX}} = y; \qquad ds = dx\,\sec\alpha$$

For $12 \leq x \leq 24$,

$$M_X = +(96 - R_{AX})\, y - 16\,(24 - x)\, ; \qquad \frac{\partial M_X}{\partial R_{AX}} = -y\, ;$$

$$ds = dx \sec \alpha$$

These quantities are substituted into the Castigliano equation (Equation 15.72). The denominator cancels out, leaving

$$0 = \int_0^{12} \{ -16x - 6\,[0.05556x\,(24 - x)\,]^2 + R_{AX}\,(0.05556x)(24 - x)\, \}$$
$$\times [0.5556x\,(24 - x)\,]\, dx$$
$$+ \int_{12}^{24} \{ (96 - R_{AX})\,[0.05556x\,(24 - x)\,] - 16\,(24 - x)\, \}$$
$$\times [-0.5556x\,(24 - x)\,]\, dx$$

The integrals are evaluated, yielding

$$R_{AX} = 68.58 \text{ kN} \tag{15.73}$$

in the direction shown.

As a matter of interest, the moment diagram is plotted for this case of load. The plot is shown in the following sketch, drawn from the foregoing moment equations. In terms of x, the values of moment are computed at the sixth points.

x (m)	y (m)	M_x (kN · m)
0	0	0
4	4.44	122.3
8	7.11	56.3
12	8.00	−27.4
16	7.11	−67.0
20	4.44	−57.9
24	0	0

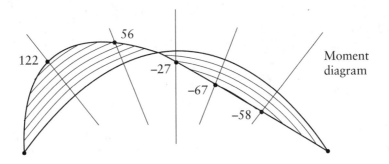

Except for the more complex integrals along the curved axis, an arch analysis is quite similar to a frame analysis. All of the arches considered here have had their supports at the same level, which simplified the algebra somewhat. Such a configuration is not necessary, however; an arch may instead have its supports at different levels, as shown in Figure 15-22.

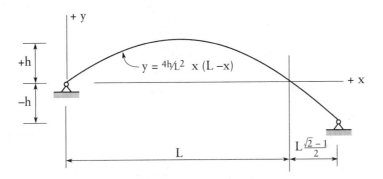

FIGURE 15-22 Arch with supports at two levels.

The vertical reactions for the arch of Figure 15-22 are not statically determinate. The algebra in the solution is therefore commensurately more involved.

Outside Problems

Determine the reactions on the given steel arches.

Problem 15-41*

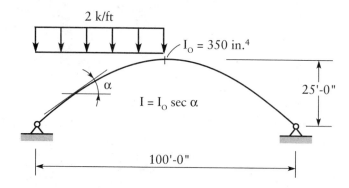

2 k/ft

$I_O = 350$ in.^{4}

α

$I = I_O \sec \alpha$

25'-0"

100'-0"

Problem 15-42

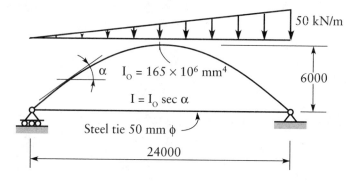

50 kN/m

α $I_O = 165 \times 10^6$ mm^4

$I = I_O \sec \alpha$

6000

Steel tie 50 mm ϕ

24000

Problem 15-43*

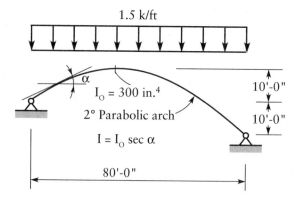

1.5 k/ft

α

$I_O = 300$ in.^{4}

2° Parabolic arch

$I = I_O \sec \alpha$

10'-0"

10'-0"

80'-0"

Problem 15-44 Determine the reactions of the arch of Problem 15-41 for a temperature increase of 100 Fahrenheit degrees. Do not include the gravity load in this analysis.

Single span utility bridge, Illinois. (Photograph courtesy of
Portland Cement Association, reprinted by permission.)

CHAPTER

16

Continuous Beams and Frames

The least work solutions for rigid frame reactions presented in Chapter 15 were intricate and laborious, even for structures with only one span. For structures with multiple spans or multiple stories, such as the rigid frame of Figure 16-1, the method of least work ceases to be practical and some other method of analysis must be used. Probably the best known and most popular such method is the method of slope deflection; this chapter is devoted entirely to the method of slope deflection.

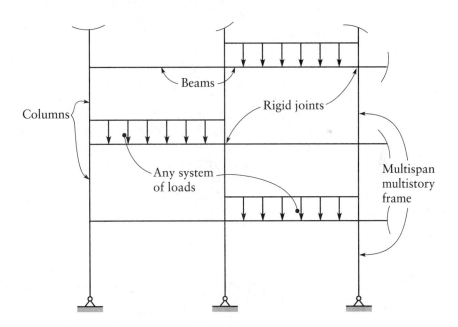

FIGURE 16-1 Multispan multistory rigid frame.

Although the method of slope deflection is itself rather laborious, much of the labor is expended in solving sets of simultaneous equations, or matrices. In years past, these sets of equations were solved by manual iterative methods; such methods are still in common use for the simpler applications. Chapter 17, in fact, examines one of the best known of these manual iterative methods, called *moment distribution*.

In recent years, the digital computer has taken the labor out of obtaining the exact solution of a matrix of simultaneous equations. To solve a matrix of equations of any appreciable size, any of numerous mathematics programs can be used. This text stops just short of introducing these matrix methods; computerized matrix solutions will follow very naturally as the next item of study in the sequence introduced here.

The applications of the slope deflection method presented in this chapter involve members that have a constant moment of inertia. While the method of slope deflection is indeed applicable to members that have a variable cross section and a variable moment of inertia, the concepts are no different; the calulations simply become more involved. Particular applications in variable moment of inertia are deferred to future studies.

16.1 DERIVATION OF THE SLOPE DEFLECTION EQUATIONS

The slope deflection method is directed toward solving for moments at the joints of a rigid frame, such as those shown earlier in Figure 16-1. The solution does not involve a direct solution for moments at the joints, however, but a solution for the rotations (the slopes) and the displacements (the deflections) at the joints. Once the slopes and the deflections are known, the redundant moments at the ends of each beam and each column can be computed.

A typical prismatic member is removed from the frame of Figure 16-1; its free body is shown in Figure 16-2. As customary, only one of the restrained joints is assumed to be capable of developing a horizontal reaction. Thus there are five reactions; the member is two degrees indeterminate. Two additional conditions must be found if a solution is to be obtained.

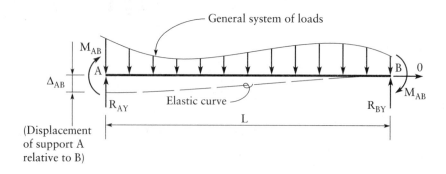

FIGURE 16-2 Typical member in a rigid frame.

The reactions M_{AB} and M_{BA} are chosen as the two redundants; the indeterminate solution is the solution for these reactions. Once the end moments are known, the vertical end reactions (actually the end shears) can readily be computed.

Some sign conventions are necessary for the slope deflection method—particularly since numerous rotations and displacements are involved. Positive directions of moments, displacements, and rotations are shown in Figure 16-3.

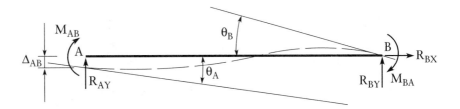

FIGURE 16-3 Positive signs for the slope deflection method.

As indicated in Figure 16-3, the following conventions are adopted:

1. Forces are positive if directed upward or to the right.

2. End moments are positive if directed clockwise.

3. End slope is positive if joint rotation is clockwise.

4. Displacement is positive if it induces positive end moments.

For vertical members, the viewer turns such that the value of x or y increases to the right; the foregoing conventions then apply.

It is elected to solve for the redundants M_{AB} and M_{BA} in Figure 16-3 by using the method of area moment. The end moments are the sums of three cases, as shown in Figure 16-4:

1. Moments that accompany applied loads. No rotations or translations of joints are permitted for this case. These moments are the fixed-end moments developed in Chapter 15, shown in Figure 16-4 as FM_{AB} and FM_{BA}.

2. Moments that accompany translation of joints. No applied loads or rotations of joints are permitted for this case. The vertical forces shown in Figure 16-4 for this case are shown in terms of the redundants TM_{AB} and TM_{BA}.

3. Moments that accompany rotation of joints, caused by loads, by translation of joints, or by both. The vertical forces shown in Figure 16-4 for this case are shown in terms of the redundants RM_{AB} and RM_{BA}.

The fixed-end moments shown in Figure 16-4 are directly those found in the solutions of Chapter 15. A tabulation of fixed-end moment for common cases of load is presented in Table 15-2. Again, there is no rotation of joints in the fixed-end condition.

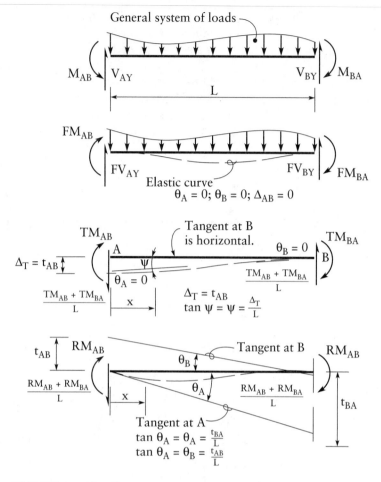

FIGURE 16-4 End moments on a prismatic beam.

The translational moments TM_{AB} and TM_{BA} may be found in terms of the translational displacement Δ_T by the method of area moment. The moment diagram for such a solution is shown in Figure 16-5. The antisymmetry of the deformations is evident.

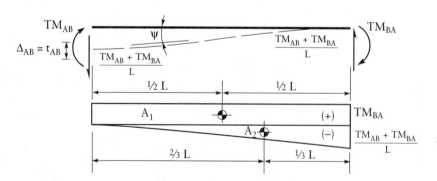

FIGURE 16-5 Moment diagram for translational moments.

The deflection Δ_T is found in the usual way:

$$\Delta_T = t_{AB} = \frac{A_M \bar{x}}{EI}$$

$$= \frac{A_1 x_1 + A_2 x_2}{EI}$$

where

$$A_1 = TM_{AB}L$$

$$A_2 = -(TM_{AB} + TM_{BA})\left(\frac{1}{2}L\right)$$

$$x_1 = \frac{1}{2}L$$

$$x_2 = \frac{2}{3}L$$

$$\Delta_T = \frac{(TM_{AB}L)\left(\frac{1}{2}L\right) - (TM_{AB} + TM_{BA})\left(\frac{1}{2}L\right)\left(\frac{2}{3}L\right)}{EI}$$

$$\Delta_T = \frac{TM_{AB}L^2}{EI} - \frac{TM_{BA}L^2}{EI}$$

It is recognized that $TM_{AB} = TM_{BA}$; hence,

$$TM_{AB} = 6Ek\psi_{AB} \qquad\qquad (16.1a)$$

$$TM_{BA} = 6Ek\psi_{BA} \qquad\qquad (16.1b)$$

where

$$\psi_{AB} = \frac{\Delta_T}{L}$$

and this variable is called the displacement angle of the member.

The angle ψ_{AB} is positive if the moments TM_{AB} and TM_{BA} are positive. No rotation of the joints is permitted when the translational moments TM_{AB} and TM_{BA} are computed.

The rotations of the joints θ_A and θ_B are found in terms of the rotational moments RM_{AB} and RM_{BA} by the method of area moment. The moment diagram by parts for this solution is shown in Figure 16-6.

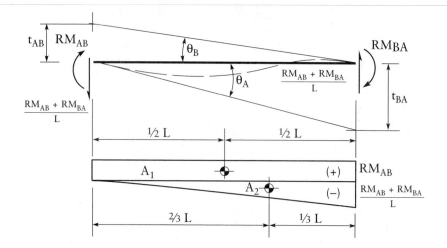

FIGURE 16-6 Moment diagram for rotational reactions.

The angle θ_A is found first:

$$\theta_A = \frac{t_{BA}}{L} = \frac{A_M \bar{x}_B}{EIL} = \frac{A_1 \bar{x}_1 + A_2 \bar{x}_2}{EIL}$$

where

$$A_1 = +RM_{AB}L$$

$$A_2 = -(RM_{AB} + RM_{BA})\left(\frac{1}{2}L\right)$$

$$\bar{x}_1 = \frac{1}{2}L$$

$$\bar{x}_2 = \frac{1}{3}L$$

$$\theta_A = \frac{(RM_{AB}L)\left(\frac{1}{2}L\right) - (RM_{AB} + RM_{BA})\left(\frac{1}{2}L\right)\left(\frac{1}{3}L\right)}{EIL}$$

$$\theta_A = \frac{RM_{AB}L}{3EI} - \frac{RM_{BA}L}{6EI} \tag{16.2a}$$

The angle θ_B is found next:

$$\theta_B = \frac{t_{AB}}{L} = \frac{A_M \bar{x}_A}{EIL} = \frac{A_1 \bar{x}_1 + A_2 \bar{x}_2}{EIL}$$

where

$$A_1 = +RM_{AB}L$$

$$A_2 = -(RM_{AB}L + RM_{BA})\left(\frac{1}{2}L\right)$$

$$\bar{x}_1 = \frac{1}{2}L$$

$$\bar{x}_2 = \frac{2}{3}L$$

$$\theta_B = \frac{(RM_{AB}L)\left(\frac{1}{2}L\right) - (RM_{AB} + RM_{BA})\left(\frac{1}{2}L\right)\left(\frac{2}{3}L\right)}{EIL}$$

$$\theta_B = \frac{RM_{AB}}{3EI} - \frac{RM_{BA}}{6EI} \tag{16.2b}$$

Equations 16.2a and b are solved simultaneously to find RM_{AB} and RM_{BA}:

$$RM_{AB} = 4Ek\theta_A + 2Ek\theta_B \tag{16.3a}$$

$$RM_{BA} = 4Ek\theta_B + 2Ek\theta_A \tag{16.3b}$$

where

$$k = \frac{I}{L} \tag{16.3c}$$

and this constant is called the stiffness factor of the member.

The final moments at A and B are equal to the sums of the three cases:

$$M_{AB} = FM_{AB} + TM_{AB} + RM_{AB}$$

$$M_{BA} = FM_{BA} + TM_{BA} + RM_{BA}$$

In final form, with constant EI,

$$M_{AB} = 4Ek\theta_A + 2Ek\theta_B + TM_{AB} + FM_{AB} \tag{16.4a}$$

$$M_{BA} = 4Ek\theta_B + 2Ek\theta_A + TM_{BA} + FM_{BA} \tag{16.4b}$$

where the translational moment $TM_{AB} = TM_{BA} = 6Ek\psi_{AB}$. The reason for retaining the identity of the translational moments TM_{AB} and TM_{BA} will become apparent in later applications.

Equations 16.4a and b are the slope deflection equations. The remainder of this chapter is devoted to applications of these equations. The procedure for applying the equations follows a rather fixed format:

1. An elastic curve is assumed, in order to determine algebraic signs of all quantities.

2. Between each two joints, the stiffness factors, fixed-end moments, and translational moments are calculated for each beam and each column, using the known loads and known displacements (if any) at each member. Algebraic signs are required.

3. Between each two joints, the slope deflection equations are written for each beam and each column.

4. Statics equations are written at each joint; that is, moments are summed to zero around each joint.

5. The slope deflection equations are substituted into the statics equations, yielding a set of n equations in the n joint rotations.

6. The n simultaneous equations are solved for the n rotations θ_A, θ_B, θ_C, . . . , θ_n.

7. The known values of the joint rotations are substituted back into the slope deflection equations to find the values of the end moments at each beam and each column.

8. The solution is completed for the remaining two statics conditions $\Sigma F_x = 0$ and $\Sigma F_y = 0$, by verifying or correcting the reactive forces at the supports.

The term *relative stiffness factor* is used in step 2 of the foregoing procedure. The reason for this term will become apparent in the examples.

Some examples can best illustrate the application of the slope deflection equations to continuous beams and frames.

16.2 CONTINUOUS BEAMS

Continuous beams, such as those used in two- and three-span bridges, are among the most common applications of the slope deflection equations. Such a beam is shown in Figure 16-7. In this beam, there is no displacement of supports, so the translational moments TM_{AB} and TM_{BA} drop out of the slope deflection equations.

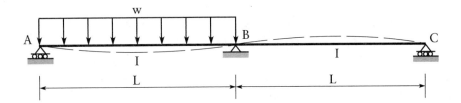

FIGURE 16-7 Two-span continuous beam.

The procedure listed earlier for applying of the slope deflection equations is used to solve for the reactions of the continuous beam of Figure 16-7:

1. As listed in the procedure, the elastic curve for the beam is shown on the sketch of Figure 16-7. The assumed curve may be incorrect, but that does not matter; the algebraic signs of the solution, as usual, will indicate the correct directions and slopes.

2. The stiffness factors and fixed-end moments are computed, with signs consistent with the assumed elastic curve:

$$k_{AB} = \frac{I_0}{L}; \qquad FM_{AB} = -\frac{1}{12}wL^2; \qquad FM_{BA} = +\frac{1}{12}wL^2$$

$$k_{BC} = \frac{I_0}{L}; \qquad FM_{BC} = 0; \qquad\qquad FM_{CB} = 0$$

3. The slope deflection equations are written for each beam:

Span AB

$$M_{AB} = 4Ek\theta_A + 2Ek\theta_B - \frac{1}{12}wL^2$$

$$M_{BA} = 4Ek\theta_B + 2Ek\theta_A + \frac{1}{12}wL^2$$

Span BC

$$M_{BC} = 4Ek\theta_B + 2Ek\theta_C$$

$$M_{CB} = 4Ek\theta_C + 2Ek\theta_B$$

Since all values of k and L in this beam are equal, no subscripts are needed for these quantities.

4. The statics equations for moment are written at each joint:

$$\Sigma M_A = 0; \qquad M_{AB} = 0$$

$$\Sigma M_B = 0; \qquad M_{BA} + M_{BC} = 0$$

$$\Sigma M_C = 0; \qquad M_{CB} = 0$$

5. The slope deflection equations are substituted into the statics equations at each joint:

(1) $\quad 0 = 4Ek\theta_A + 2Ek\theta_B - \dfrac{1}{12}wL^2$

(2) $\quad 0 = 2Ek\theta_A + 8Ek\theta_B + 2Ek\theta_C + \dfrac{1}{12}wL^2$

(3) $\quad 0 = \qquad\qquad 2Ek\theta_B + 8Ek\theta_C$

6. The set of simultaneous equations is solved for $Ek\theta_A$, $Ek\theta_B$ and $Ek\theta_C$.

$$Ek\theta_A = +\frac{1}{32}wL^2; \qquad Ek\theta_B = -\frac{1}{48}wL^2; \qquad Ek\theta_C = \frac{1}{96}wL^2$$

Notice that these are relative values.

7. The moments are computed from these known values of the relative joint rotations:

$$M_{AB} = 4\left(+\frac{1}{32}wL^2\right) + 2\left(-\frac{1}{48}wL^2\right) - \frac{1}{12}wL^2 = 0$$

$$M_{BA} = 4\left(-\frac{1}{48}wL^2\right) + 2\left(+\frac{1}{32}wL^2\right) + \frac{1}{12}wL^2 = +\frac{1}{16}wL^2 \quad \text{(clockwise)}$$

$$M_{BC} = 4\left(-\frac{1}{48}wL^2\right) + 2\left(+\frac{1}{96}wL^2\right) \qquad\qquad = -\frac{1}{16}wL^2 \quad \text{(counter-}$$

clockwise)

$$M_{CB} = 4\left(+\frac{1}{96}wL^2\right) + 2\left(-\frac{1}{48}wL^2\right) \qquad\qquad = 0$$

8. The shear and moment diagrams are drawn by the usual methods. The shears at the ends of the spans are found first. The diagrams are shown in Figure 16-8.

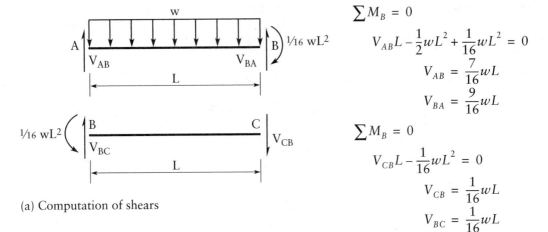

$$\sum M_B = 0$$

$$V_{AB}L - \frac{1}{2}wL^2 + \frac{1}{16}wL^2 = 0$$

$$V_{AB} = \frac{7}{16}wL$$

$$V_{BA} = \frac{9}{16}wL$$

$$\sum M_B = 0$$

$$V_{CB}L - \frac{1}{16}wL^2 = 0$$

$$V_{CB} = \frac{1}{16}wL$$

$$V_{BC} = \frac{1}{16}wL$$

(a) Computation of shears

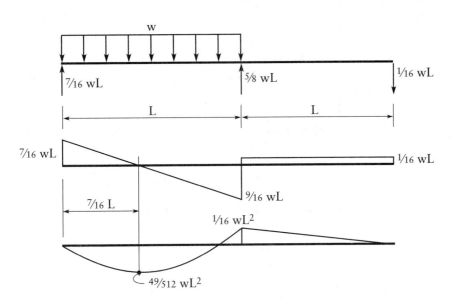

(b) Shear and moment diagrams

FIGURE 16-8 Sketching of shear and moment diagrams for two-span beam.

Some numerical examples will illustrate the application of the slope deflection equations to other types of continuous beams.

Example 16-1   Determine the moments at the supports of the given continuous beam. The smallest moment of inertia is chosen as a reference value; all other moments of inertia are shown as multiples of that reference value.

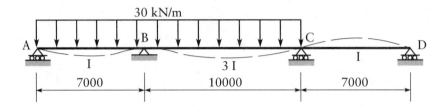

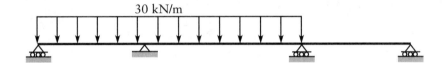

Solution   1. The shape of the elastic curve has been assumed and is shown on the preceding sketch.

2. The relative stiffness factors and fixed-end moments are determined for each span. Translational moments do not exist so those terms drop out.

$$k_{AB} = \frac{1}{7}I = 0.1429I;$$

$$FM_{AB} = -\frac{1}{12}wL^2 = -\frac{1}{12}(30)(7^2) = -122.5 \text{ kN} \cdot \text{m}$$

$$FM_{BA} = +122.5 \text{ kN} \cdot \text{m}$$

$$k_{BC} = \frac{3}{10}I = 0.300I;$$

$$FM_{BC} = -\frac{1}{12}wL^2 = -\frac{1}{12}(30)(10^2) = -250 \text{ kN} \cdot \text{m}$$

$$FM_{CB} = +250 \text{ kN}$$

$$k_{CD} = \frac{1}{7}I = 0.1429I; \qquad FM_{CD} = FM_{DC} = 0$$

3. The slope deflection equations are written for each span.

$$M_{AB} = 0.5714EI\theta_A + 0.2857EI\theta_B - 122.5$$

$$M_{BA} = 0.5714EI\theta_B + 0.2857EI\theta_A + 122.5$$

$$M_{BC} = 1.2000EI\theta_B + 0.6000EI\theta_C - 250$$
$$M_{CB} = 1.2000EI\theta_C + 0.6000EI\theta_B + 250$$

$$M_{CD} = 0.5714EI\theta_C + 0.2857EI\theta_D$$
$$M_{DC} = 0.5714EI\theta_D + 0.2857EI\theta_C$$

4. Statics equations are written at each joint.

$$\Sigma M_A = 0; \qquad 0 = M_{AB}$$
$$\Sigma M_B = 0; \qquad 0 = M_{BA} + M_{BC}$$
$$\Sigma M_C = 0; \qquad 0 = M_{CB} + M_{CD}$$
$$\Sigma M_D = 0; \qquad 0 = M_{DC}$$

5. The slope deflection equations are substituted into the statics equations, yielding one equation for each joint.

$$0.5714EI\theta_A + 0.2587EI\theta_B \qquad\qquad\qquad = +122.5$$
$$0.2857EI\theta_A + 1.7714EI\theta_B + 0.6000EI\theta_C \qquad = +127.5$$
$$0.6000EI\theta_B + 1.7714EI\theta_C + 0.2857EI\theta_D = -250.0$$
$$0.2857EI\theta_C + 0.5714EI\theta_D = 0$$

6. These four equations are solved simultaneously to find the relative joint rotations.

$$EI\theta_A = +158.13; \qquad EI\theta_B = +112.51; \qquad EI\theta_C = -194.96;$$
$$EI\theta_D = +97.48$$

7. The relative rotations are substituted back into the slope deflections to find the moments at the supports.

$$M_{AB} = 0.5714(+158.13) + 0.2857(+112.51) - 122.5 = 0$$

$$M_{BA} = 0.5714(+112.51) + 0.2857(+158.13) + 122.5$$
$$= +231.97 \text{ kN-m}$$

$$M_{BC} = 1.2000(+112.51) + 0.6000(-194.96) - 250.0$$
$$= -231.97 \text{ kN-m}$$

$$M_{CB} = 1.2000(-194.96) + 0.6000(+112.51) + 250.0$$
$$= +83.55 \text{ kN-m}$$

$$M_{CD} = 0.5714\,(-194.96) + 0.2857\,(+97.48)$$
$$= -83.55 \text{ kN-m}$$

$$M_{DC} = 0.5714\,(+97.48) \; + 0.2857\,(-194.96) \qquad\qquad = 0$$

8. The shear and moment diagrams are drawn, using the usual methods. The shears at the ends of the spans are found first.

Span *AB*

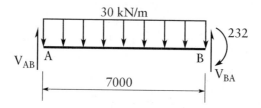

$$\Sigma M_A = 0$$
$$- V_{BA}\,(7) + (30)(7)(3.5) + 232 = 0$$
$$V_{BA} = 138 \text{ kN}$$
$$V_{AB} = 72 \text{ kN}$$

Span *BC*

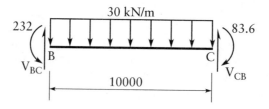

$$\Sigma M_B = 0$$
$$- 232 - (30)(10)(5) + 83.6 + V_{BC}\,(10) = 0$$
$$V_{BC} = 165 \text{ kN}$$
$$V_{CB} = 135 \text{ kN}$$

Span *CD*

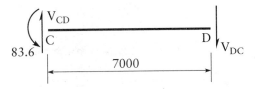

$$\Sigma M_C = 0$$
$$-83.6 + V_{DC}(7) = 0$$
$$V_{DC} = 12 \text{ kN}$$
$$V_{CD} = 12 \text{ kN}$$

Reactions are found as the sum of the two shears at a support.

$$R_{AY} = 72 \text{ kN}; \qquad R_{BY} = 303 \text{ kN}; \qquad R_{CY} = 147 \text{ kN};$$
$$R_{DY} = 12 \text{ kN (down)}$$

The shear and moment diagrams are shown in the following sketches.

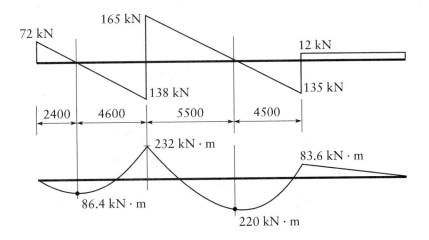

Displacement of supports can be handled routinely in the slope deflection method. In all cases, the displacement Δ_T must be known (or assumed); the moment $6Ek\psi$, with its proper sign, is then included in the calculations as a starting moment. If Δ_T is known, then the angle ψ is known, and the term $6Ek\psi$ becomes a known numerical value. Stated another way, moment due to a known displacement (translational moment) produces a known starting moment, which is comparable to a fixed-end moment.

A numerical example will illustrate a solution where displacement of supports occurs.

Example 16-2

Determine the moments and reactions at the four supports of the beam of Example 16-1 if the support at B could settle as much as 20 mm more than the other supports. The reference moment of inertia is 291×10^6 mm⁴; all other moments of inertia are shown as a multiple of that value.

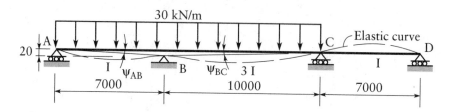

Solution

1. The shape of the elastic curve has been assumed and is shown on the preceding sketch.

2. The relative stiffness factors, fixed-end moments, and translational moments are determined for each span. The translational moments are computed for a displacement of 20 mm at support B, with all joints (including joint B) locked against rotation.

$$k_{AB} = 0.1429I;$$

$$FM_{AB} = -\frac{1}{12}wL^2 = -\frac{1}{12}(30)(7^2) = -122.5 \text{ kN-m}$$

$$FM_{BA} = +122.5 \text{ kN-m}$$

$$TM_{AB} = -6Ek\psi_{AB} = -6\,(200{,}000)\frac{(291)(10^6)}{7000}\frac{20}{7000}$$

$$= -142.5 \times 10^6 \text{ N-mm} = -142.5 \text{ kN-m}$$

$$TM_{BA} = TM_{AB} = -142.5 \text{ kN-m}$$

$$k_{BC} = 0.3000I;$$

$$FM_{BC} = -\frac{1}{12}wL^2 = -\frac{1}{12}(30)(10^2) = -250.0 \text{ kN-m}$$

$$FM_{CB} = +250.0 \text{ kN-m}$$

$$TM_{BC} = +6Ek\psi_{BC} = +6\,(200{,}000)\frac{(3)(291)(10^6)}{10{,}000}\frac{20}{10{,}000}$$

$$= +209.5 \text{ N-mm} = +209.5 \text{ kN-m}$$

$$TM_{CB} = TM_{BC} = +209.5 \text{ kN-m}$$

$$k_{CD} = 0.1429I; \qquad FM_{CD} = FM_{DC} = 0; \qquad TM_{CD} = TM_{DC} = 0$$

Notice that the signs of TM_{AB} and TM_{BA} are negative, since the moments in span AB that accompany the downward translation of joint B are counterclockwise. Similarly, the moments TM_{BC} and TM_{CB} are clockwise and are therefore positive.

3. The slope deflection equations are written for each span.

$$M_{AB} = 0.5714EI\theta_A + 0.2857EI\theta_B - 142.5 - 122.5$$
$$M_{BA} = 0.5714EI\theta_B + 0.2857EI\theta_A - 142.5 + 122.5$$

$$M_{BC} = 1.2000EI\theta_B + 0.6000EI\theta_C + 209.5 - 250$$
$$M_{CB} = 1.2000EI\theta_C + 0.6000EI\theta_B + 209.5 + 250$$

$$M_{CD} = 0.5714EI\theta_C + 0.2857EI\theta_D$$
$$M_{DC} = 0.5714EI\theta_D + 0.2857EI\theta_C$$

4. Statics equations are written at each joint.

$$\Sigma M_A = 0; \qquad 0 = M_{AB}$$

$$\Sigma M_B = 0; \qquad 0 = M_{BA} + M_{BC}$$

$$\Sigma M_C = 0; \qquad 0 = M_{CB} + M_{CD}$$

$$\Sigma M_D = 0; \qquad 0 = M_{DC}$$

5. The slope deflection equations are substituted into the statics equations, yielding one equation for each joint.

$$0.5714EI\theta_A + 0.2857EI\theta_B \qquad\qquad\qquad = +265.0$$
$$0.2857EI\theta_A + 1.7714EI\theta_B + 0.6000EI\theta_C \qquad = +60.5$$
$$0.6000EI\theta_B + 1.7714EI\theta_C + 0.2857EI\theta_D = -459.5$$
$$0.2857EI\theta_C + 0.5714EI\theta_D = 0$$

6. These four equations are solved simultaneously to find the relative joint rotations.

$$EI\theta_A = +429.21; \qquad EI\theta_B = +69.13; \qquad EI\theta_C = -307.62;$$
$$EI\theta_D = +153.81$$

7. The relative rotations are substituted back into the slope deflection equations to find the moments at the supports.

$$M_{AB} = 0.5714\,(+429.21) + 0.2857\,(+69.13) \; - 122.5 \; = \; 0$$

$$M_{BA} = 0.5714\,(+69.13) \;\; + 0.2857\,(+429.21) + 122.5$$
$$= +142.12 \text{ kN-m}$$

$$M_{BC} = 1.2000\,(+69.13) \;\; + 0.6000\,(-307.62) - 250.0$$
$$= -142.12 \text{ kN-m}$$

$$M_{CB} = 1.2000\,(-307.62) + 0.6000\,(+69.13) \;\; + 250.0$$
$$= +131.83 \text{ kN-m}$$

$$M_{CD} = 0.5714\,(-307.62) + 0.2857\,(+153.81)$$
$$= -131.83 \text{ kN-m}$$

$$M_{DC} = 0.5714\,(+153.81) + 0.2857\,(-307.62) \qquad\qquad = \; 0$$

8. The reactions at the supports are found as the sum of the shears to either side of the support. The shears at the ends of the spans are found in the usual way.

Span *AB*

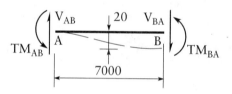

$$\Sigma M_A = 0$$
$$- V_{BA}\,(7) + (30)(7)(3.5) + 142 = 0$$
$$V_{BA} = 125 \text{ kN}$$
$$V_{AB} = 175 \text{ kN}$$

Span *BC*

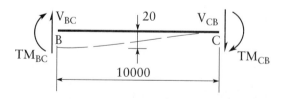

$$\Sigma M_B = 0$$

$$-142 - (30)(10)(5) + 132 + V_{CB}(10) = 0$$

$$V_{CB} = 151 \text{ kN}$$

$$V_{BC} = 149 \text{ kN}$$

Span CD

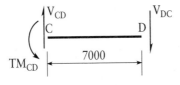

$$\Sigma M_C = 0$$

$$-132 + V_{DC}(7) = 0$$

$$V_{DC} = 19 \text{ kN}$$

$$V_{CD} = 19 \text{ kN}$$

Reactions are found as the sum of the two shears at a support.

$$R_{AY} = 125 \text{ kN}; \qquad R_{BY} = 274 \text{ kN}; \qquad R_{CY} = 168 \text{ kN};$$

$$R_{DY} = 19 \text{ kN (down)}$$

The solution of continuous beams by the method of slope deflection always follows the format of Examples 16-1 and 16-2. While the solution of the simultaneous equations may sometimes be tedious, it is nonetheless straightforward.

There is a practical limit to the number of spans that will occur in continuous beams. A continuous beam having a total length greater than about 100 ft (or about 30 m), may incur serious problems in thermal deformations. Consequently, continuous beams having more than four or five spans (five or six supports) are not commonly used. Such a practical limit on the number of spans automatically limits the size of the set of simultaneous equations normally encountered in a slope deflection solution.

Outside Problems

Determine the reactions on the given continuous steel beams.

Problem 16-1*

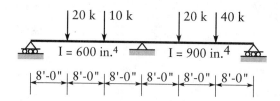

Problem 16-2

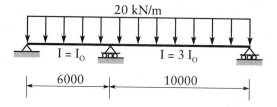

Problem 16-3*

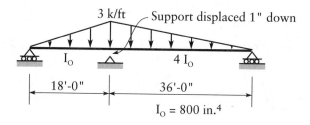

Problem 16-4

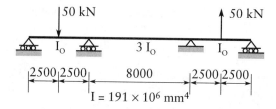

Problem 16-5*

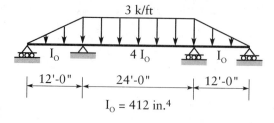

Problem 16-6

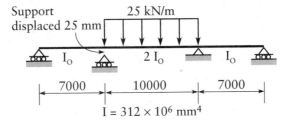

Support
displaced 25 mm

25 kN/m

I_O $2\,I_O$ I_O

7000   10000   7000

$I = 312 \times 10^6 \text{ mm}^4$

16.3 SINGLE-SPAN FRAMES

The application of the slope deflection method to symmetrical frames is very much like its application to beams. For a symmetrical frame like the one shown in Figure 16-9, the mathematics is quite similar to that of the three-span beams of the preceding section.

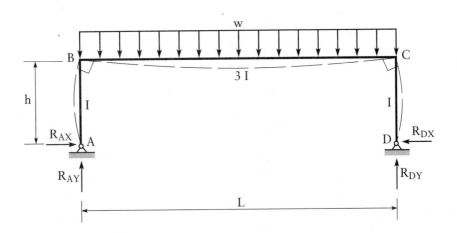

FIGURE 16-9 Symmetrical portal frame.

For symmetrical frames, the vertical reactions are statically determinate, as observed earlier in the solutions by the method of least work. The horizontal reactions must be equal and opposite, as shown in Figure 16-9, if equilibrium is to be preserved.

An example will illustrate the slope deflection solution of a symmetrical portal frame.

Example 16-3 Determine the reactions on the given symmetrical steel portal frame.
Reference $I = 153$ in.[4]

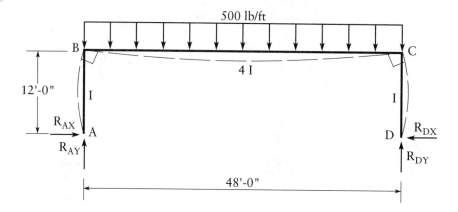

Solution 1. The shape of the elastic curve has been assumed and is shown on the preceding sketch.

2. The relative stiffness factors and the fixed-end moments are determined for each member.

For member AB,

$$k_{AB} = \frac{1}{12}; \qquad FM_{AB} = FM_{BA} = 0$$

For member BC,

$$k_{BC} = \frac{4}{48} = \frac{1}{12}; \qquad FM_{BC} = -\frac{1}{12}wL^2 = -96 \text{ kip-ft}$$

$$FM_{CB} = +\frac{1}{12}wL^2 = +96 \text{ kip-ft}$$

For member CD,

$$k_{CD} = \frac{1}{12}; \qquad FM_{CD} = FM_{DC} = 0$$

3. The slope deflection equations are written for each member, yielding the following set of six equations.

$$M_{AB} = 0.3333EI\theta_A + 0.1667EI\theta_B$$
$$M_{BA} = 0.3333EI\theta_B + 0.1667EI\theta_A$$

$$M_{BC} = 0.3333EI\theta_B + 0.1667EI\theta_C - 96$$
$$M_{CB} = 0.3333EI\theta_C + 0.1667EI\theta_B + 96$$

$$M_{CD} = 0.3333EI\theta_C + 0.1667EI\theta_D$$
$$M_{DC} = 0.3333EI\theta_D + 0.1667EI\theta_C$$

Due to symmetry,

$$EI\theta_A = -EI\theta_D \quad \text{and} \quad EI\theta_B = -EI\theta_C$$

Substituting the foregoing relationships into the slope deflection equations reduces the set of six equations to a set of three equations.

$$M_{AB} = 0.3333EI\theta_A + 0.1667EI\theta_B$$
$$M_{BA} = 0.3333EI\theta_B + 0.1667EI\theta_A$$

$$M_{BC} = 0.1667EI\theta_B - 96$$

4. The statics equations are written for joints A and B,

$$\Sigma M_A = 0; \quad M_{AB} = 0$$

$$\Sigma M_B = 0; \quad M_{BA} + M_{BC} = 0$$

5. The slope deflection equations are substituted into the statics equations:

$$0 = 0.3333EI\theta_A + 0.1667EI\theta_B$$
$$0 = 0.1667EI\theta_A + 0.5000EI\theta_B - 96$$

6. These two equations are solved simultaneously to find the relative rotations $EI\theta_A$ and $EI\theta_B$.

$$EI\theta_A = -115.2; \quad EI\theta_B = +230.4$$

7. The relative rotations are substituted back into the slope deflection equation equations to find the moments at the joints.

$$M_{AB} = 0.3333\,(-115.2) + 0.1667\,(+230.4) \qquad = 0$$

$$M_{BA} = 0.3333\,(+230.4) + 0.1667\,(-115.2) \qquad = +57.6 \text{ kip-ft}$$

$$M_{BC} = 0.1667\,(+230.4) - 96 \qquad\qquad\qquad = -57.6 \text{ kip-ft}$$

$$M_{CB} = -M_{BC} = +57.6 \text{ kip-ft} \quad \text{(due to symmetry)}$$

$$M_{CD} = -M_{BA} = -57.6 \text{ kip-ft} \quad \text{(due to symmetry)}$$

$$M_{DC} = -M_{AB} = 0$$

8. Horizontal reactions at the supports are found by taking a free body of the columns and finding the horizontal shears.

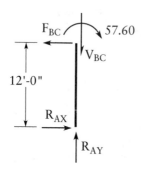

$$\Sigma M_B = 0$$
$$57.60 - R_{AX}\,(12) = 0$$
$$R_{AX} = 4.80 \text{ kips}$$
$$R_{DX} = 4.80 \text{ kips}$$

Vertical reactions are statically determinate; in a symmetrical frame such as this one, each vertical reaction is half the total load.

$$R_{AY} = \frac{1}{2}wl = 12 \text{ kips}$$

$$R_{DY} = 12 \text{ kips}$$

Final reactions and moments are summarized:

$R_{AY} = 12$ kips

$R_{AX} = 4.80$ kips   (to the right)

$R_{DY} = 12$ kips

$R_{DX} = 4.80$ kips   (to the left)

$M_{BA} = +57.6$ kip-ft

$M_{CD} = -57.6$ kip-ft

The solution of symmetrical frames is thus quite straightforward and closely resembles the solution of three-span continuous beams. Taking advantage of the symmetry to cut the number of unknowns in half is a worthwhile shortcut in such solutions. A similar shortcut can be taken in cases of antisymmetry; both of these shortcuts will be used in future examples.

In addition to having vertical loads, frames are also subject to lateral loads such as wind and earthquake. The solution for lateral loads is somewhat different from that for vertical loads. In addition to the unknown rotations at the joints, the lateral deflection is unknown; like the rotations, the deflection must be found in a way that recognizes the conditions of equilibrium. An example will demonstrate such a solution.

Example 16-4   Determine reactions at the supports and the moments at the joints of the portal frame of Example 16-3 when it is loaded laterally as shown in the accompanying drawing.

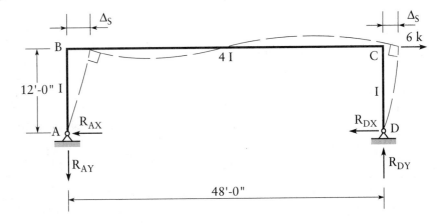

Solution
1. The shape of the elastic curve has been assumed and is shown on the preceding sketch.

2. The relative stiffness factors and translational moments are determined for each member; for this particular case of loading, there are no fixed-end moments. The lateral deflection Δ_S of the girder BC is assumed to be in inches for calculating the translational moments. Unlike in the earlier solutions for displacement of supports, the lateral deflection Δ_S is unknown; and a numerical value for this deflection cannot be found at this point. The translational moments will therefore be expressed in terms of the unknown lateral displacement Δ_S.

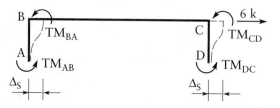

For member AB,

$$k_{AB} = \frac{1}{12};$$

$$TM_{AB} = -6Ek\psi = -(6)(29)(10^6) \times \frac{153}{(12)(12)} \times \frac{\Delta_S}{(12)(12)}$$

$$TM_{BA} = TM_{AB} = -1284\Delta_S \text{ kip-in.} = -107 \text{ kip-ft}$$

For member BC,

$$k_{AB} = \frac{1}{12}; \qquad TM_{BC} = TM_{CB} = 0$$

For member CD,

$$k_{CD} = \frac{1}{12};$$

$$TM_{CD} = TM_{DC} = -107 \text{ kip-ft} \quad \text{(identical to member } AB\text{)}$$

    One might suspect at this point that the deformations of this frame are antisymmetrical, producing $\theta_A = \theta_D$ and $\theta_B = \theta_C$. Such antisymmetry of deformations is in fact true, even though the load as currently shown is not antisymmetrical. The solution of this frame will be obtained without assuming that the deformations are antisymmetrical. The results will then be discussed further at the end of the solution.

3. The slope deflection equations are written for each member, yielding the following set of six equations.

$$M_{AB} = 0.3333EI\theta_A + 0.1667EI\theta_B - 107\Delta_S$$
$$M_{BA} = 0.3333EI\theta_B + 0.1667EI\theta_A - 107\Delta_S$$

$$M_{BC} = 0.3333EI\theta_B + 0.1667EI\theta_C$$
$$M_{CB} = 0.3333EI\theta_C + 0.1667EI\theta_B$$

$$M_{CD} = 0.3333EI\theta_C + 0.1667EI\theta_D - 107\Delta_S$$
$$M_{DC} = 0.3333EI\theta_D + 0.1667EI\theta_C - 107\Delta_S$$

4. The statics equations are written for each joint.

$$\Sigma M_A = 0; \quad M_{AB} = 0$$

$$\Sigma M_B = 0; \quad M_{BA} + M_{BC} = 0$$

$$\Sigma M_C = 0; \quad M_{CB} + M_{CD} = 0$$

$$\Sigma M_D = 0; \quad M_{DC} = 0$$

5. The slope deflection equations are substituted into the statics equations, producing four equations in the five unknowns.

$$+107\Delta_S = 0.3333EI\theta_A + 0.1667EI\theta_B$$
$$+107\Delta_S = 0.1667EI\theta_A + 0.6667EI\theta_B + 0.1667EI\theta_C$$
$$+107\Delta_S = \qquad\qquad + 0.1667EI\theta_B + 0.6667EI\theta_C + 0.1667EI\theta_D$$
$$+107\Delta_S = \qquad\qquad\qquad\qquad\qquad 0.1667EI\theta_C + 0.3333EI\theta_D$$

6. These four equations are solved simultaneously to find the relative rotations in terms of the lateral deflection Δ_S.

$$EI\theta_A = +285.6\Delta_S; \quad EI\theta_B = +71.4\Delta_S; \quad EI\theta_C = +71.4\Delta_S;$$
$$EI\theta_D = +285.6\Delta_S$$

As expected, the antisymmetry of the deformations is borne out by the full solution. To explain the apparent discrepancy, the 6-kip load (which is not antisymmetrical) can be broken into two antisymmetrical loads of 3 kips each—one located at B, and one located at C. Since any load may be applied anywhere along its line of action, the antisymmetrical loading of the two 3-kip loads is a valid case of antisymmetrical loading, equivalent to the single unsymmetrical load of 6 kips.

7. The relative values of the slopes are substituted back into the slope deflection equations to find the moments at the supports. The moments, however, are expressed in terms of the lateral displacement Δ_S.

$$M_{AB} = 0.3333\,(+285.6\Delta_S) + 0.1667\,(+71.4\Delta_S) \; - 107\Delta_S = 0$$

$$M_{BA} = 0.3333\,(+71.4\Delta_S) \; + 0.1667\,(+285.6\Delta_S) - 107\Delta_S \; = -35.7\Delta_S$$

$$M_{BC} = 0.3333\,(+71.4\Delta_S) \; + 0.1667\,(+285.6\Delta_S) - 107\Delta_S \; = +35.7\Delta_S$$

$$M_{CB} = +35.7\Delta_S \quad \text{(due to antisymmetry)}$$

$$M_{CB} = -35.7\Delta_S \quad \text{(due to antisymmetry)}$$

$$M_{DC} = 0 \quad \text{(due to antisymmetry)}$$

8. The foregoing moments are expressed in terms of the lateral displacement Δ_S, which is unknown. An additional condition beyond those already used is required for a solution. For this solution, an additional condition of statics, $\Sigma F_X = 0$, will be applied to the overall frame. The two horizontal reactions at A and D are found as before, by taking the columns as free bodies and solving for the end shears.

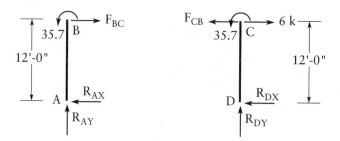

$$\Sigma M_B = 0$$

$$- 35.7 + R_{AX}(12) = 0$$

$$R_{AX} = 2.975\Delta_S$$

$$\Sigma M_C = 0$$

$$- 35.7 + R_{AX}(12) = 0$$

$$R_{AX} = 2.975\Delta_S$$

Horizontal forces are now summed on the entire frame; all forces involved in such a summation are shown in the following sketch. (The vertical reactions are statically determinate and are included in the sketch for reference.)

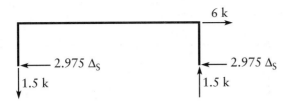

The sum of horizontal forces yields a solution for the displacement Δ_S.

$$\Sigma F_X = 0; \qquad 6 - 2.975\Delta_S - 2.975\Delta_S = 0$$
$$\Delta_S = 1.008 \text{ in.}$$

The final values of moments and reactions can now be computed:

$M_{AB} = 0$ $M_{DC} = 0$

$M_{BA} = -35.7\Delta_S = -36 \text{ kip-ft}$ $M_{CD} = -36 \text{ kip-ft}$

$M_{BC} = +35.7\Delta_S = +36 \text{ kip-ft}$ $M_{CB} = +36 \text{ kip-ft}$

$R_{AX} = 3.0 \text{ kips}$ (to the left) $R_{DX} = 3.0 \text{ kips}$ (to the left)

$R_{AY} = 1.5 \text{ kips}$ (down) $R_{DY} = 1.5 \text{ kips}$ (down)

Intuitively, one might have anticipated the final results of this particular case due to the simple antisymmetry of the system. For completely unsymmetrical frames, however, the solution cannot be anticipated so easily.

The application of the slope deflection method to unsymmetrical frames is much like its application to symmetrical frames, but with a notable difference: unsymmetrical frames are subject to sidesway, or drift. The moments produced by rotations of the joints can produce an imbalance in horizontal forces. Under such an imbalance, the frame sways laterally; the swaying equalizes horizontal forces and maintains horizontal equilibrium in the system.

A typical case of sidesway is shown in the portal frame of Figure 16-10. In that frame, the sidesway equalizes the reactions R_{AX} and R_{DX}; equilibrium requires that these reactions be equal and opposite if the sum of horizontal forces is to be zero. In this case, as in all cases, sidesway is the mechanism that maintains horizontal equilibrium.

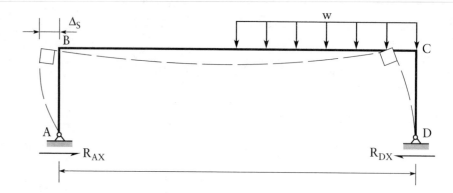

FIGURE 16-10 Portal frame subject to sidesway.

The horizontal displacement Δ_S defines the amount of sidesway in the frame. The displacement Δ_S that occurs at one end of the columns is much like the displacement that occurred due to the known lateral load in the preceding example. Like that displacement, the sidesway displacement Δ_S is an unknown quantity and must be found as a part of the solution.

The total solution of a frame subject to sidesway consists of the sum of two parts, as shown in Figure 16-11. The two parts may be described as follows:

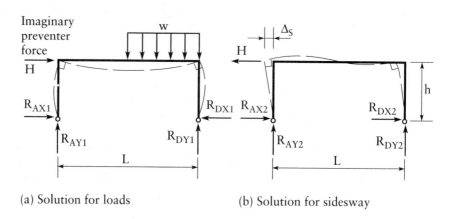

(a) Solution for loads   (b) Solution for sidesway

FIGURE 16-11 Two parts of a sidesway solution.

1. Solution due to applied loads (and displacements of supports, if applicable) with sidesway prevented. For this solution, an imaginary "preventer" force is located at some appropriate point to prevent any unwanted sidesway; such a preventer force H is indicated at point B in Figure 16-10(a). The analysis is then completed for moments and reactions for this configuration, without any further regard for sidesway.

2. Solution due to the release of the preventer force H. The magnitude of the preventer force H is found by summing the horizontal forces resulting from the first solution; the force H is the imbalance in these forces. The force H is "released" by applying an equal and opposite force at the same point. The solution is then performed to identify how much sidesway occurs due to the release of the force H, and to find the moments at the joints that occur as a consequence of that sidesway. No forces or loads other than H are included in this solution. (For portal frames, this load case follows the antisymmetrical load pattern of Example 16-4.)

The solution for sidesway shown in Figure 16-11 will be a solution in terms of the unknown displacement Δ_S, similar to the procedure used in Example 16-4. And as with the procedure used in Example 16-4, the magnitude of Δ_S is found from the condition of horizontal equilibrium, $\Sigma F_x = 0$.

An example will illustrate the analysis of an unsymmetrical frame subject to sidesway.

Example 16-5   Determine the reactions on the given unsymmetrical steel frame.

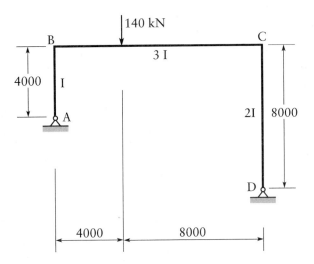

Reference $I = 300 \times 10^6$ mm^4

Solution   The solution will be performed in two parts. The first part will produce a solution with sidesway prevented. For this solution, an imaginary preventer force is placed at point C to prevent any sidesway of the girder BC, as shown in the following sketch.

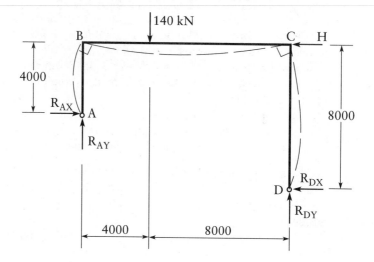

The slope deflection solution is now performed for the frame with sidesway prevented.

1. The shape of the elastic curve has been assumed and is shown on the preceding sketch.

2. The relative stiffness factors and fixed-end moments are determined for each member.

For member AB,

$$k_{AB} = 0.250; \qquad FM_{AB} = FM_{BA} = 0$$

For member BC,

$$k_{BC} = 0.250;$$

$$FM_{AB} = -\frac{Pab^2}{L^2} = -\frac{(140)(4)(8^2)}{12^2} = -248.8 \text{ kN-m}$$

$$FM_{BA} = +\frac{Pa^2b}{L^2} = +\frac{(140)(4^2)(8)}{12^2} = +124.4 \text{ kN-m}$$

For member CD,

$$k_{CD} = 0.250; \qquad FM_{CD} = FM_{DC} = 0$$

3. The slope deflection equations are written for each member.

$$M_{AB} = 1.000EI\theta_A + 0.5000EI\theta_B$$
$$M_{BA} = 1.000EI\theta_B + 0.5000EI\theta_A$$

$$M_{BC} = 1.000EI\theta_B + 0.5000EI\theta_C - 124.4$$
$$M_{CB} = 1.000EI\theta_C + 0.5000EI\theta_B + 124.4$$

$$M_{CD} = 1.000EI\theta_C + 0.5000EI\theta_D$$
$$M_{DC} = 1.000EI\theta_D + 0.5000EI\theta_C$$

4. The statics equations are written for each joint.

$$\Sigma M_A = 0; \qquad M_{AB} = 0$$

$$\Sigma M_B = 0; \qquad M_{BA} + M_{BC} = 0$$

$$\Sigma M_C = 0; \qquad M_{CB} + M_{CD} = 0$$

$$\Sigma M_D = 0; \qquad M_{DC} = 0$$

5. The slope deflection equations are substituted into the statics equations, yielding four equations in the four unknown rotations.

$$0 = 1.0000EI\theta_A + 0.5000EI\theta_B$$
$$+248.8 = 0.5000EI\theta_A + 0.2000EI\theta_B + 0.5000EI\theta_C$$
$$-124.4 = \qquad\qquad 0.5000EI\theta_B + 2.0000EI\theta_C + 0.5000EI\theta_D$$
$$0 = \qquad\qquad\qquad\qquad 0.5000EI\theta_C + 1.0000EI\theta_D$$

6. These four equations are solved simultaneously to find the relative rotations.

$$EI\theta_A = -88.46; \qquad EI\theta_B = +176.92; \qquad EI\theta_C = -121.64;$$
$$EI\theta_D = +60.82$$

7. The known rotations are substituted back into the slope deflection equations to find the moments at the rigid joints.

$$M_{AB} = 1.0000\,(-88.46) \;\; + 0.5000\,(+176.92) \qquad\qquad = 0$$

$$M_{BA} = 1.0000\,(+176.92) + 0.5000\,(-88.46)$$
$$= +132.7 \text{ kN-m}$$

$$M_{BC} = 1.0000\,(+176.92) + 0.5000\,(-121.64) - 248.8$$
$$= -132.7 \text{ kN-m}$$

$$M_{CB} = 1.0000\,(-121.64) + 0.5000\,(+176.92) + 124.4$$
$$= +91.2 \text{ kN-m}$$

$$M_{CD} = 1.0000\,(-121.64) + 0.5000\,(+60.82)$$
$$= -91.2 \text{ kN-m}$$

$$M_{DC} = 1.0000\,(+60.82) \;\; + 0.5000\,(-121.64) \qquad\qquad = 0$$

8. Horizontal reactions at the bases of the columns are found as before. The columns are removed as free bodies and are shown in the following sketches.

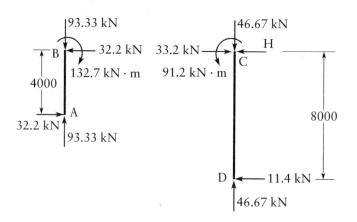

$$\Sigma M_B = 0$$
$$+132.7 - R_{AX}(4) = 0$$
$$R_{AX} = 33.2 \text{ kN}$$

$$\Sigma M_C = 0$$
$$-91.2 + R_{DX}(8) = 0$$
$$R_{DX} = 11.4 \text{ kN}$$

Reactions on the frame are shown in the following sketch.

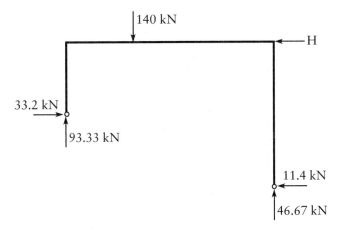

The sum of horizontal forces yields the magnitude of the preventer force H that is needed to prevent sidesway.

$$\Sigma F_X = 0; \qquad 0 = 33.2 - 11.4 - H$$
$$H = 21.8 \text{ kN} \quad \text{(in the direction shown)}$$

The second part of the solution is for the reactions when the preventer force is released, as shown in the following sketch. As always in a slope deflection solution, the starting moments are determined with zero rotation at the joints.

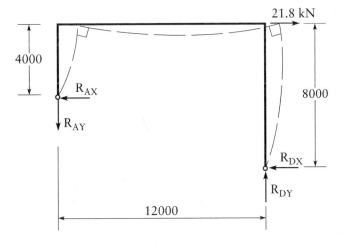

1. The shape of the elastic curve for this case has been assumed and is shown in the foregoing sketch.

2. The relative stiffness factors and translational moments are determined for each member. Translational moments are expressed in terms of the unknown sidesway displacement Δ_S, as shown in the following sketch. The value of Δ_S is assumed to be in millimeters.

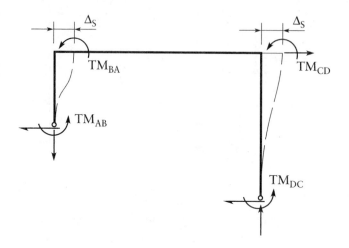

For member AB,

$$k_{AB} = 0.250;$$

$$TM_{AB} = -6Ek\psi_{AB} = -6\,(200{,}000) \times \frac{(300)(10^6)}{4000} \times \frac{\Delta_S}{4000}$$

$$= (-22.5 \times 10^6)\,\Delta_S \text{ N-mm} = (-22.5 \times 10^6)\,\Delta_S \text{ kN-m}$$

$$TM_{BA} = (-22.5 \times 10^6)\,\Delta_S \text{ kN-m}$$

For member BC,

$$k_{BC} = 0.250; \qquad TM_{AB} = TM_{BA} = 0$$

For member CD,

$$k_{CD} = 0.250;$$

$$TM_{CD} = -6Ek\psi_{CD} = -6\,(200{,}000) \times \frac{(2)(300)(10^6)}{8000} \times \frac{\Delta_S}{8000}$$

$$= (-11.25 \times 10^6)\,\Delta_S \text{ N-mm} = -11.25 \times 10^6 \text{ kN-m}$$

$$TM_{DC} = (-11.25 \times 10^6)\,\Delta_S \text{ kN-m}$$

3. The slope deflection equations are written for each member.

$$M_{AB} = 1.000EI\theta_A + 0.5000EI\theta_B - 22.5\Delta_S$$
$$M_{BA} = 1.000EI\theta_B + 0.5000EI\theta_A - 22.5\Delta_S$$

$$M_{BC} = 1.000EI\theta_B + 0.5000EI\theta_C$$
$$M_{CB} = 1.000EI\theta_C + 0.5000EI\theta_B$$

$$M_{CD} = 1.000EI\theta_C + 0.5000EI\theta_D - 11.25\Delta_S$$
$$M_{DC} = 1.000EI\theta_D + 0.5000EI\theta_C - 11.25\Delta_S$$

4. The statics equations are written for each joint.

$$\Sigma M_A = 0; \quad M_{AB} = 0$$

$$\Sigma M_B = 0; \quad M_{BA} + M_{BC} = 0$$

$$\Sigma M_C = 0; \quad M_{CB} + M_{CD} = 0$$

$$\Sigma M_D = 0; \quad M_{DC} = 0$$

5. The slope deflection equations are substituted into the statics equations, yielding four equations in the five unknowns.

$$+22.50\Delta_S = 1.00EI\theta_A + 0.50EI\theta_B$$
$$+22.50\Delta_S = 0.50EI\theta_A + 2.00EI\theta_B + 0.50EI\theta_C$$
$$+11.25\Delta_S = \qquad 0.50EI\theta_B + 2.00EI\theta_C + 0.50EI\theta_D$$
$$+11.25\Delta_S = \qquad\qquad 0.50EI\theta_C + 1.00EI\theta_D$$

6. These four equations are solved simultaneously to find the relative rotations in terms of the sidesway displacement Δ_S.

$$EI\theta_A = +19.50\Delta_S; \quad EI\theta_B = +6.00\Delta_S; \quad EI\theta_C = +1.50\Delta_S;$$
$$EI\theta_D = +10.50\Delta_S$$

7. The known rotations are now substituted back into the slope deflection equations to find the moments at the joints; these moments are expressed in terms of the sidesway displacement Δ_S.

$$M_{AB} = 1.00\,(+19.50\Delta_S) + 0.50\,(+6.00\Delta_S) - 22.50\Delta_S = 0$$

$$M_{BA} = 1.00\,(+6.00\Delta_S) + 0.50\,(+19.50\Delta_S) - 22.50\Delta_S = -6.75\Delta_S$$

$$M_{BC} = 1.00\,(+6.00\Delta_S) + 0.50\,(+1.50\Delta_S) \qquad\qquad = +6.75\Delta_S$$

$$M_{CB} = 1.00\,(+1.50\Delta_S) + 0.50\,(+6.00\Delta_S) \qquad\qquad = +4.50\Delta_S$$

$$M_{CD} = 1.00\,(+1.50\Delta_S) + 0.50\,(+10.50\Delta_S) - 11.25\Delta_S = -4.50\Delta_S$$

$$M_{DC} = 1.00\,(+10.50\Delta_S) + 0.50\,(+1.50\Delta_S) - 11.25\Delta_S = 0$$

8. The horizontal reactions at A and B are found in terms of the sidesway displacement Δ_S in the usual way. The columns are removed as free bodies, and the horizontal shears are found by simple statics.

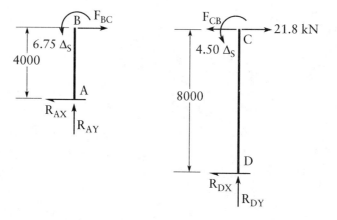

$$\Sigma M_B = 0$$
$$-6.75\Delta_S + 4R_{AX} = 0$$
$$R_{AX} = 1.69\Delta_S$$

$$\Sigma M_C = 0$$
$$-4.50\Delta_S + 8R_{DX} = 0$$
$$R_{DX} = 0.56\Delta_S$$

The sidesway displacement Δ_S is found by summing horizontal forces on the entire frame; the frame and its reactions are shown in the following sketch.

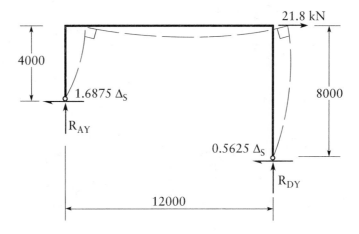

The sum of horizontal forces yields

$$\Sigma F_X = 0; \qquad 21.8 - 1.69\Delta_S - 0.56\Delta_S = 0$$
$$\Delta_S = 9.69 \text{ mm}$$

With the magnitude of the sidesway displacement now known, the final moments and reactions due to sidesway can be computed.

$M_{AB} = 0$ $\qquad\qquad\qquad$ $M_{DC} = 0$

$M_{BA} = -6.75\Delta_S = -65.4$ kN-m $\qquad$ $M_{CD} = -4.50\Delta_S = -43.6$ kN-m

$M_{BC} = +6.75\Delta_S = +65.4$ kN-m $\qquad$ $M_{CB} = +0.56\Delta_S = +43.6$ kN-m

$R_{AX} = 1.68\Delta_S = 16.4$ kN $\qquad\quad$ $R_{DX} = 0.56\Delta_S = 5.5$ kN

The total reactions and moments due to loads and sidesway are the sum of the two cases.

$$M_{AB} = 0$$

$$M_{BA} = +132.7 - 65.4 = +67.3 \text{ kN-m}$$

$$M_{BC} = -132.7 + 65.4 = -67.3 \text{ kN-m}$$

$$M_{CB} = +91.2 + 43.6 = +134.8 \text{ kN-m}$$

$$M_{CD} = -91.2 - 43.6 = -134.8 \text{ kN-m}$$

$$M_{DC} = 0$$

$$R_{AX} = +33.2 - 16.4 = +16.8 \text{ kN} \quad \text{(to the right)}$$

$$R_{DX} = -11.4 - 5.5 = -16.8 \text{ kN} \quad \text{(to the left)}$$

The vertical reactions R_{AY} and R_{DY} can now be found by simple statics. The final results are shown in the following sketches. Moments are drawn on the tension side.

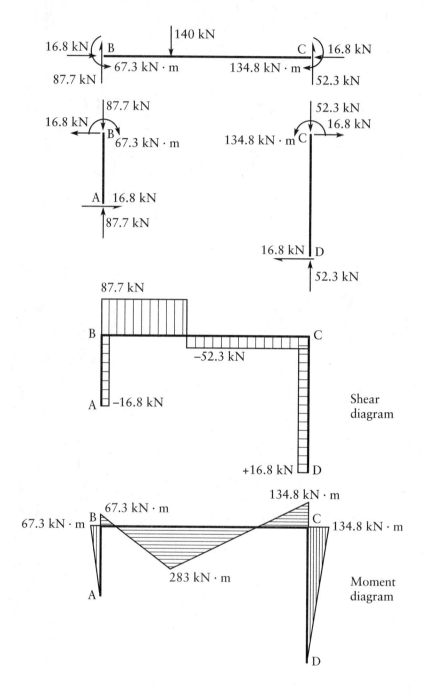

Shear diagram

Moment diagram

A moment's reflection on the results of Example 16-5 is in order. Notice that the columns *AB* and *CD* are subject both to axial loads and to flexural loads, which is to be expected. Notice also, however, that the girder *BC* has an axial load of 16.8 kN, in addition to its large moment of 283 kN-m. In the design codes, this case is identified as "a beam subject to a dominant flexural load plus a small axial load." The design of such members can be quite troublesome, especially in concrete. At this point, it is simply noted that the case of "a small axial load" can sometimes arise in unexpected places, such as in the beams and girders of a rigid frame.

A further reflection relates to a possible solution of Example 16-5 by the method of least work, as developed in Chapter 15. Such a solution is indeed possible and may even be preferred by some analysts (including the author). In fact, all of the portal frames considered in this section could have been solved by the method of least work. In frames, the method of least work has the advantage of producing a solution that inherently includes the effects of sidesway; there is no need for a separate solution for sidesway in the method of least work.

In addition to its applications in portal frames, the slope deflection method may also be applied to gable frames and clerestory frames. In these frames, however, the slope deflection method is unreasonably cumbersome, requiring two or more preventer forces and then the release of each preventer force separately. Detailed treatments exist in the literature for the solution of such frames; interested readers should consult these. In this text, the solution of gable frames and clerestory frames is done only by the method of least work, as presented in Chapter 15.

Outside Problems

Problem 16-7* Solve Problem 15-25, using the method of slope deflection.

Problem 16-8 Solve Problem 15-27, using the method of slope deflection.

Problem 16-9* Solve Problem 15-28, using the method of slope deflection.

Problem 16-10 Solve Problem 15-31, using the method of slope deflection.

Problem 16-11* Solve Problem 15-32, using the method of slope deflection.

Problem 16-12 Solve Problem 15-33, using the method of slope deflection. Ignore elongation of the tie.

Problem 16-13* Solve for reactions.   Problem 16-14 Solve for reactions.

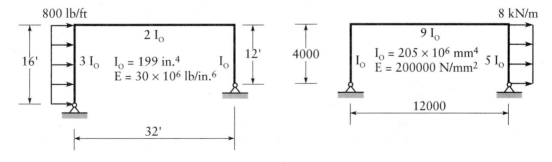

16.4 MULTISPAN FRAMES

The solution for moments and reactions in multispan frames is simply an extension of the solutions already presented. Here, the method of slope deflection dominates. Other than fully computerized high-level methods (such as the finite element method), there are no practical alternatives to the slope deflection method for the analysis of multispan multistory frames.

The primary difficulty in the slope deflection method consists in solving the simultaneous equations. As the number of members increases, the number of equations increases, and the labor needed to perform the solution increases significantly. If one has access to mathematics software that can process matrix equations, this particular disadvantage disappears, and the method of slope deflection becomes relatively easy to handle.

All of the beams and frames considered in earlier solutions have had hinged supports. Where foundation conditions permit, however, supports for rigid frames might also be fixed, in which case the slope deflection method remains a viable solution. The solution becomes somewhat more involved, however, since a fixed base has more redundants than does a hinged base. An example of a multispan frame with fixed supports will demonstrate such a solution.

Example 16-6   Determine the reactions for the given multispan steel frame.

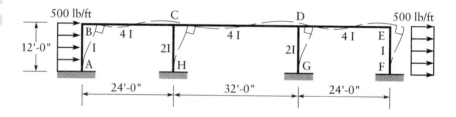

Reference $I = 240$ in.^{4}

Solution   The antisymmetry of the system is noted. As a consequence of the antisymmetry, the following relationships occur at the joints:

$$\theta_B = \theta_E \qquad \theta_C = \theta_D$$

As a consequence of the fixed bases,

$$\theta_A = 0; \qquad \theta_H = 0; \qquad \theta_G = 0; \qquad \theta_F = 0$$

The solution is thus reduced to finding the relative rotations at two joints— $EI\theta_B$ and $EI\theta_C$—plus the sidesway displacement Δ_S.

The first solution is, as usual, the solution for rotational moments with sideway prevented. Preventer forces are placed antisymmetrically at B and C, as shown in the following sketch. (It was demonstrated in Example 16-4 that the preventer forces could be reduced to only one force at B or at C, but in this solution it is preferred to accent the antisymmetry.)

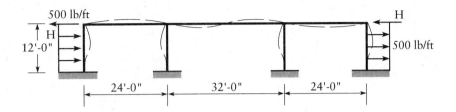

1. The shape of the elastic curve has been assumed and is shown in the sketch.

2. The relative stiffness factors and fixed-end moments are determined for each member.

For member AB,

$$k_{AB} = \frac{1}{12}; \qquad FM_{AB} = -\frac{1}{12}wL^2 = -6 \text{ kip-ft}$$

$$FM_{BA} = +\frac{1}{12}wL^2 = +6 \text{ kip-ft}$$

For member BC,

$$k_{BC} = \frac{1}{6}; \qquad FM_{BC} = FM_{CB} = 0$$

For member CH,

$$k_{CH} = \frac{1}{6}; \qquad FM_{CH} = FM_{HC} = 0$$

For member CD,

$$k_{CD} = \frac{1}{8}; \qquad FM_{CD} = FM_{DC} = 0$$

Due to the antisymmetry, these spans are the only ones needed for a solution.

3. The slope deflection equations are written for each member. In these equations, the condition that $\theta_A = \theta_H = \theta_G = \theta_F = 0$ is included, as is the condition that $\theta_C = \theta_D$.

$$M_{AB} = 0.3333EI\theta_A + 0.1667EI\theta_B - 6 = 0.1667EI\theta_B - 6$$
$$M_{BA} = 0.3333EI\theta_B + 0.1667EI\theta_A + 6 = 0.3333EI\theta_B + 6$$

$$M_{BC} = 0.6667EI\theta_B + 0.3333EI\theta_C \quad = 0.6667EI\theta_B + 0.3333EI\theta_C$$
$$M_{CB} = 0.6667EI\theta_C + 0.3333EI\theta_B \quad = 0.6667EI\theta_C + 0.3333EI\theta_B$$

$$M_{CH} = 0.6667EI\theta_C + 0.3333EI\theta_H \quad = 0.6667EI\theta_C$$
$$M_{HC} = 0.6667EI\theta_H + 0.3333EI\theta_C \quad = 0.3333EI\theta_C$$

$$M_{CD} = 0.5000EI\theta_C + 0.2500EI\theta_D \quad = 0.7500EI\theta_C$$

4. The statics equations are written for joints B and C.

$$\Sigma M_B = 0; \qquad M_{BA} + M_{BC} = 0$$

$$\Sigma M_C = 0; \qquad M_{CB} + M_{CH} + M_{CD} = 0$$

5. The slope deflection equations are substituted into the statics equations, yielding two equations in the two unknown rotations.

$$-6 = 1.0000EI\theta_B + 0.3333EI\theta_C$$
$$0 = 0.3333EI\theta_B + 2.0833EI\theta_C$$

6. These two equations are solved simultaneously to find the relative rotations with sidesway prevented.

$$EI\theta_B = -6.3380; \qquad EI\theta_C = +1.0141$$

7. These known values of the relative rotations are substituted back into the slope deflection equations to find the moments at the supports and at the joints.

$$M_{AB} = 0.1667EI\theta_B - 6 \qquad\qquad = -7.056 \text{ kip-ft} = M_{FE}$$

$$M_{BA} = 0.3333EI\theta_B + 6 \qquad\qquad = +3.887 \text{ kip-ft} = M_{EF}$$

$$M_{BC} = 0.6667EI\theta_B + 0.3333EI\theta_C = -3.887 \text{ kip-ft} = M_{ED}$$

$$M_{CB} = 0.6667EI\theta_C + 0.3333EI\theta_B = -1.437 \text{ kip-ft} = M_{DE}$$

$$M_{CH} = 0.6667EI\theta_C \qquad\qquad = +0.676 \text{ kip-ft} = M_{DG}$$

$$M_{HC} = 0.6667EI\theta_C \qquad\qquad = +0.338 \text{ kip-ft} = M_{GD}$$

$$M_{CD} = 0.7500EI\theta_C \qquad\qquad = +0.761 \text{ kip-ft} = M_{DC}$$

8. Reactions at the fixed supports are found from the statics relationships. Horizontal reactions are found by taking the columns as free bodies and finding the horizontal shears on the columns.

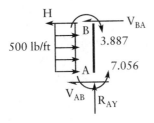

$$\Sigma M_B = 0$$

$$V_{AB}(12) - 7.056 - 0.5(12)(6) + 3.887 = 0$$

$$V_{AB} = 3.264 \text{ kips} \quad \text{(to the left)}$$

$$V_{FE} = 3.264 \text{ kips} \quad \text{(to the left)}$$

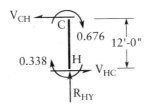

$$\Sigma M_C = 0$$

$$-V_{HC}(12) + 0.338 + 0.676 = 0$$

$$V_{HC} = 0.0845 \text{ kips} \quad \text{(to the right)}$$

$$V_{GD} = 0.0845 \text{ kips} \quad \text{(to the right)}$$

The preventer forces at B and at E are found by summing horizontal forces.

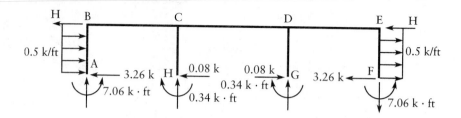

$$\Sigma F_X = 0; \qquad 6 + 6 - 3.26 - H - H + 0.08 + 0.08 = 0$$

$$H = 2.82 \text{ kips} \quad \text{(to the left)}$$

One way to find the vertical reactions is to find the end shears on the girders.

$$\Sigma M_C = 0$$

$$V_{BC}(24) - 3.89 - 1.43 = 0$$

$$V_{BC} = 0.22 \text{ kips} \quad \text{(up)}$$

$$V_{CB} = 0.22 \text{ kips} \quad \text{(down)}$$

$$R_{AY} = V_{BC} = 0.22 \text{ kips} \quad \text{(up)}$$

$$R_{FY} = 0.22 \text{ kips} \quad \text{(down)}$$

$$\Sigma M_D = 0$$

$$-V_{CD}(32) + 0.761 + 0.761 = 0$$

$$V_{CD} = 0.05 \text{ kips} \quad \text{(down)}$$

$$V_{DC} = 0.05 \text{ kips} \quad \text{(up)}$$

$$R_{HY} = -V_{CB} - V_{CD} = 0.27 \text{ kips} \quad \text{(down)}$$

$$R_{GY} = 0.27 \text{ kips} \quad \text{(up)}$$

The final results of the first part of the solution (with sidesway prevented) are shown in the following sketch.

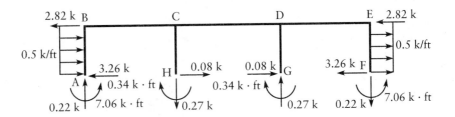

The second part of the solution is for the reactions when the preventer forces at *B* and *E* are released. This case of load is given in the following sketch. The antisymmetry of the loads is noted.

The solution follows the usual procedure for a slope deflection solution.

1. The shape of the elastic curve has been assumed and is shown on the preceding sketch. Due to the antisymmetry,

$$\theta_B = \theta_E \quad \text{and} \quad \theta_C = \theta_D$$

Further, due to the fixed bases on the columns,

$$\theta_A = \theta_H = \theta_G = \theta_F = 0$$

2. The relative stiffness factors and translational moments are determined for each member.

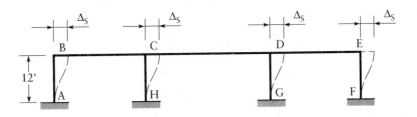

For member AB,

$$k_{AB} = \frac{1}{12}; \qquad TM_{AB} = -6Ek\psi = -6(29 \times 10^6) \times \frac{240}{144} \times \frac{\Delta_S}{144}$$

$$= -168\Delta_S \text{ kip-ft}$$

$$TM_{BA} = -168\Delta_S \text{ kip-ft}$$

For member BC,

$$k_{BC} = \frac{1}{6}; \qquad TM_{BC} = TM_{CB} = 0$$

For member CH,

$$k_{CH} = \frac{1}{6}; \qquad TM_{CH} = TM_{HC} = -336\Delta_S \text{ kip-ft}$$

For member CD,

$$k_{CD} = \frac{1}{8}; \qquad TM_{CD} = TM_{DC} = 0$$

3. The slope deflection equations are written for each member.

$$M_{AB} = 0.3333EI\theta_A + 0.1667EI\theta_B - 168\Delta_S = 0.1667EI\theta_B - 168\Delta_S$$
$$M_{BA} = 0.3333EI\theta_B + 0.1667EI\theta_A - 168\Delta_S = 0.3333EI\theta_B - 168\Delta_S$$

$$M_{BC} = 0.6667EI\theta_B + 0.3333EI\theta_C = 0.6667EI\theta_B + 0.3333EI\theta_C$$
$$M_{CB} = 0.6667EI\theta_C + 0.3333EI\theta_B = 0.6667EI\theta_C + 0.3333EI\theta_B$$

$$M_{CH} = 0.6667EI\theta_C + 0.3333EI\theta_H - 336\Delta_S = 0.6667EI\theta_C - 336\Delta_S$$
$$M_{HC} = 0.6667EI\theta_H + 0.3333EI\theta_C - 336\Delta_S = 0.3333EI\theta_C - 336\Delta_S$$

$$M_{CD} = 0.5000EI\theta_C + 0.2500EI\theta_D = 0.7500EI\theta_C$$

4. The statics equations are written for joints B and C.

$$\Sigma M_B = 0; \qquad M_{BA} + M_{BC} = 0$$

$$\Sigma M_C = 0; \qquad M_{CB} + M_{CH} + M_{CD} = 0$$

5. The slope deflection equations are substituted into the statics equations, yielding two equations in the two unknown rotations.

$$168\Delta_S = 1.0000EI\theta_B + 0.3333EI\theta_C$$
$$336\Delta_S = 0.3333EI\theta_B + 2.0833EI\theta_C$$

6. These two equations are solved simultaneously to find the relative rotation in terms of the sidesway displacement Δ_S.

$$EI\theta_B = +120.68\Delta_S; \qquad EI\theta_C = +141.79\Delta_S$$

7. The values of the relative rotations are substituted back into the slope deflection equations to find the values of the moments at the joints and at the supports.

$$M_{AB} = 0.1667\,(+120.68\Delta_S) - 168\Delta_S \qquad\qquad = -147.89\Delta_S$$

$$M_{BA} = 0.3333\,(+120.68\Delta_S) - 168\Delta_S \qquad\qquad = -127.77\Delta_S$$

$$M_{BC} = 0.6667\,(+120.68\Delta_S) + 0.3333\,(+141.97\Delta_S) = +127.77\Delta_S$$

$$M_{CB} = 0.6667\,(+141.97\Delta_S) + 0.3333\,(+120.68\Delta_S) = +134.87\Delta_S$$

$$M_{CH} = 0.6667\,(+141.97\Delta_S) - 336\Delta_S \qquad\qquad = -241.35\Delta_S$$

$$M_{HC} = 0.3333\,(+141.97\Delta_S) - 336\Delta_S \qquad\qquad = -288.68\Delta_S$$

$$M_{CD} = 0.7500\,(+141.97\Delta_S) \qquad\qquad\qquad\;\; = +106.48\Delta_S$$

8. Horizontal reactions are found, as usual, from the statics relationships.

$$\Sigma M_B = 0$$
$$-127.77\Delta_S + V_{AB}\,(12) - 147.89\Delta_S = 0$$
$$V_{AB} = 22.97\Delta_S$$

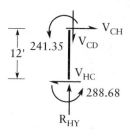

$$\Sigma M_C = 0$$

$$-241.35\Delta_S + V_{HC}(12) - 288.68\Delta_S = 0$$

$$V_{HC} = 44.17\Delta_S$$

Other reactions are antisymmetric. The final results are shown on the following sketch.

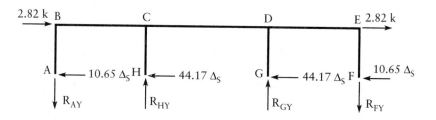

The sum of horizontal forces yields a solution for the sidesway displacement Δ_S.

$$\Sigma F_X = 0;$$

$$2.82 + 2.82 - 10.65\Delta_S - 10.65\Delta_S - 44.17\Delta_S - 44.17\Delta_S = 0$$

$$\Delta_S = 0.0514 \text{ in.}$$

Final moments due to sidesway can now be computed.

$$M_{AB} = -7.61 \text{ kip-ft} = M_{FE}$$

$$M_{BA} = -6.57 \text{ kip-ft} = M_{EF}$$

$$M_{BC} = +6.57 \text{ kip-ft} = M_{ED}$$

$$M_{CB} = +6.94 \text{ kip-ft} = M_{DE}$$

$$M_{CH} = -12.42 \text{ kip-ft} = M_{DG}$$

$$M_{HC} = -14.85 \text{ kip-ft} = M_{GD}$$

$$M_{CD} = +5.48 \text{ kip-ft} = M_{DC}$$

Final horizontal reactions can also be computed.

$$R_{AX} = 0.55 \text{ kips;} \qquad R_{HX} = 2.27 \text{ kips;} \qquad R_{GX} = 2.27 \text{ kips;}$$
$$R_{FX} = 0.55 \text{ kips}$$

Vertical reactions are found by simple statics.

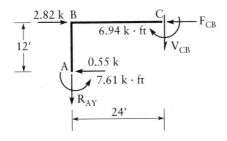

$$\Sigma M_C = 0$$
$$6.94 - 7.61 + (0.55)(12) - R_{AY}(24) = 0$$
$$R_{AY} = 0.25 \text{ kips} \quad \text{(down)}$$

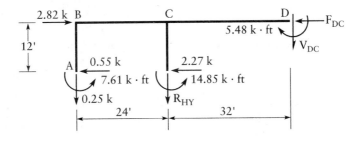

$$\Sigma M_D = 0$$
$$5.48 - 14.85 - 7.61 + (2.27)(12) + (0.55)(12)$$
$$- (0.25)(56) - R_{HY}(32) = 0$$
$$R_{HY} = 0.09 \text{ kips}$$

The results of the sidesway solution are shown in the following sketch.

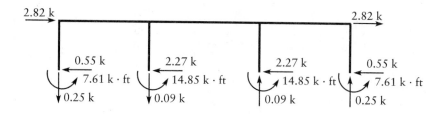

The results from the sidesway solution are summed with the results from the first solution (with sidesway prevented) to obtain the final reactions, which are shown in the following sketch.

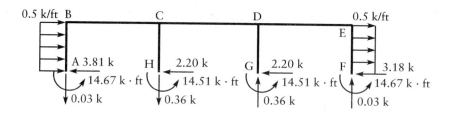

The magnitude of the sidesway displacement in the foregoing example was only 0.0514 inches (1.3 mm)—less than 1/16 inch. The low height of the frame, 12 ft, in combination with the fixed column bases, served to produce a very stiff structure. Fixed column bases are sometimes used for just that reason: to stiffen a structure against lateral deflections.

Another example in single-story frames involves a completely unsymmetrical case. The frame here is subject to both an unsymmetrical load and an unsymmetrical displacement of supports. The solution, however, follows the same format as always.

Example 16-7 Determine the reactions at the supports of the given steel frame. The support at E could settle as much as 25 mm more than the other two supports.

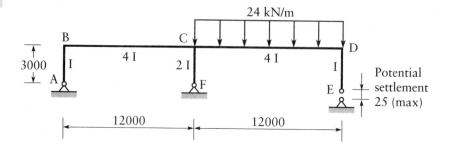

Reference $I = 125 \times 10^6$ mm^4

Solution

As was established earlier, the solution consists of two parts. The first part is the solution for reactions due to loads and to displacement of supports, with sidesway prevented. The second part is the solution for reactions due to sidesway. The sum of the two parts yields the total solution for the reactions.

The solution for the reactions due to loads and to displacement of supports is undertaken first.

1. The shape of the elastic curve has been assumed and is shown on the following sketch. A force H is placed at point D to prevent sidesway.

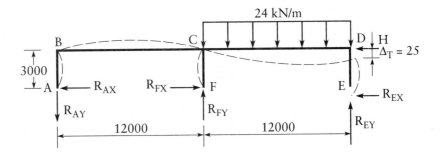

2. The relative stiffnesses, fixed-end moments, and translational moments are determined for each member. Fixed-end moments and translational moments are determined with all joints locked against rotation.

$$TM_{CH} = TM_{HC} = -6Ek\psi = -6 \times 200{,}000 \times \frac{4 \times 125 \times 10^6}{12{,}000} \times \frac{25}{12{,}000}$$

$$= -104 \times 10^6 \text{ N-mm} = -104 \text{ kN-m}$$

Fixed-end moments are computed in the usual way.

$$FM_{CH} = -\frac{1}{12}wL^2 = -228 \text{ kN-m}$$

$$FM_{HC} = +\frac{1}{12}wL^2 = +228 \text{ kN-m}$$

Relative stiffnesses are taken at a convenient size to avoid lengthy decimal fractions.

$$k_{AB} = 1; \qquad FM_{AB} = FM_{BA} = 0$$

$$k_{BC} = 1; \qquad FM_{BC} = FM_{CB} = 0$$

$$k_{CF} = 2; \qquad FM_{CF} = FM_{FC} = 0$$

$$k_{CD} = 1; \qquad FM_{CD} = -288 \text{ kN-m}; \qquad FM_{DC} = +288 \text{ kN-m}$$

$$\qquad\qquad\qquad TM_{CD} = -104 \text{ kN-m}; \qquad TM_{DC} = -104 \text{ kN-m}$$

$$k_{DE} = 1; \qquad FM_{DE} = FM_{ED} = 0$$

3. The slope deflection equations are written for each member.

$$M_{AB} = 4EI\theta_A + 2EI\theta_B$$

$$M_{BA} = 4EI\theta_B + 2EI\theta_A$$

$$M_{BC} = 4EI\theta_B + 2EI\theta_C$$

$$M_{CB} = 4EI\theta_C + 2EI\theta_B$$

$$M_{CF} = 8EI\theta_C + 4EI\theta_F$$

$$M_{CD} = 4EI\theta_C + 2EI\theta_D - 104 - 288$$

$$M_{DC} = 4EI\theta_D + 2EI\theta_C - 104 + 288$$

$$M_{DE} = 4EI\theta_D + 2EI\theta_E$$

$$M_{ED} = 4EI\theta_E + 2EI\theta_D$$

$$M_{FC} = 8EI\theta_F + 4EI\theta_C$$

4. The statics equations are written for each joint.

$$\Sigma M_A = 0; \qquad M_{AB} = 0$$

$$\Sigma M_B = 0; \qquad M_{BA} + M_{BC} = 0$$

$$\Sigma M_C = 0; \qquad M_{CB} + M_{CF} + M_{CD} = 0$$

$$\Sigma M_D = 0; \qquad M_{DC} + M_{DE} = 0$$

$$\Sigma M_E = 0; \qquad M_{ED} = 0$$

$$\Sigma M_F = 0; \qquad M_{FE} = 0$$

5. The slope deflection equations are substituted into the statics equations, yielding a set of simultaneous equations in the relative rotations. The set of equations falls in a classical diagonal pattern.

$$0 = 4EI\theta_A + 2EI\theta_B$$
$$0 = 2EI\theta_A + 8EI\theta_B + 2EI\theta_C$$
$$+392 = \quad\quad 2EI\theta_B + 16EI\theta_C + 2EI\theta_D \quad\quad\quad + 4EI\theta_F$$
$$-184 = \quad\quad\quad\quad\quad 2EI\theta_C + 8EI\theta_D + 2EI\theta_E$$
$$0 = \quad\quad\quad\quad\quad\quad\quad\quad 2EI\theta_D + 4EI\theta_E$$
$$0 = \quad\quad\quad 4EI\theta_C \quad\quad\quad\quad\quad + 8EI\theta_F$$

6. These six equations are solved simultaneously to find the relative rotations.

$$EI\theta_A = +4.9397; \quad EI\theta_B = -9.8794; \quad EI\theta_C = +34.5777$$

$$EI\theta_D = -36.1651; \quad EI\theta_E = +18.0825; \quad EI\theta_F = -17.2889$$

7. The values of the relative rotations are substituted back into the slope deflection equations to find the moments at the joints.

$$M_{AB} = 0 \quad\quad\quad\quad\quad M_{BA} = -29.64 \text{ kN-m}$$

$$M_{BC} = +29.64 \text{ kN-m} \quad\quad M_{CB} = +118.55 \text{ kN-m}$$

$$M_{CF} = +207.47 \text{ kN-m} \quad\quad M_{FC} = 0$$

$$M_{CD} = -326.02 \text{ kN-m} \quad\quad M_{DC} = +108.50 \text{ kN-m}$$

$$M_{DE} = -108.50 \text{ kN-m} \quad\quad M_{ED} = 0$$

8. The horizontal reactions are found as usual, by removing the columns as free bodies and finding the horizontal shears at their ends.

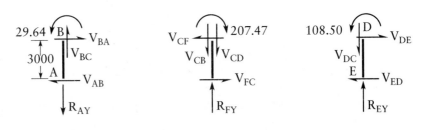

$$\Sigma M_B = 0 \quad\quad\quad \Sigma M_C = 0 \quad\quad\quad \Sigma M_D = 0$$
$$V_{AB} = 9.88 \text{ kN} \quad\quad V_{FC} = 69.19 \text{ kN} \quad\quad V_{ED} = 36.17 \text{ kN}$$

The vertical reactions are found similarly.

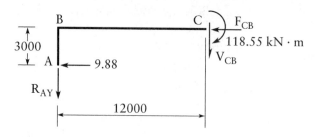

$$\Sigma M_C = 0$$

$$118.55 + 9.88\,(3) - R_{AY}(12) = 0$$

$$R_{AY} = 12.35 \text{ kN}$$

The final reactions due to loads and to displacement of supports (with sidesway prevented) are shown in the following sketch. The preventer force H is found by summing horizontal forces.

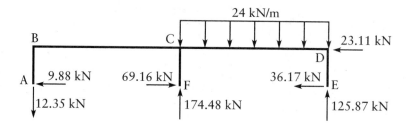

The first part of the solution is now complete. The second part of the solution is for the reactions due to sidesway, which occur when the preventer force is released. The preventer force is released by adding a force of 23.11 kN equal and opposite to it, as shown in the following sketch.

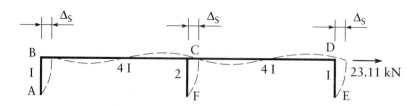

The solution for the reactions due to sidesway follow the usual format.

1. The shape of the elastic curve has been assumed and is shown in the preceding sketch. The antisymmetry is noted.

$$\theta_A = \theta_E \qquad \theta_B = \theta_D$$

2. The relative stiffness factors and translational moments are determined for each member. The translational moments are determined for all columns undergoing the translation, with all joints locked against rotation.

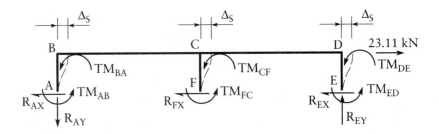

In terms of the sidesway displacement Δ_S, with Δ_S expressed in millimeters, the translational moments are

$$TM_{AB} = TM_{BA} = -6Ek\psi_{AB} = -6 \times 200,000 \times \frac{125 \times 10^6}{3000} \times \frac{\Delta_S}{3000}$$
$$= (-16.7 \times 10^6)\Delta_S \text{ N-mm} = -16.7\Delta_S \text{ kN-m}$$

$$TM_{FC} = TM_{CF} = -6Ek\psi_{CF} = -6 \times 200,000 \times \frac{2 \times 125 \times 10^6}{3000} \times \frac{\Delta_S}{3000}$$
$$= (-33.3 \times 10^6)\Delta_S \text{ N-mm} = -33.3\Delta_S \text{ kN-m}$$

$$TM_{DE} = TM_{ED} = -16.7\Delta_S \text{ kN-m}$$

The relative stiffnesses are the same as those computed earlier for the solution with sidesway prevented.

$$k_{AB} = 1; \qquad k_{BC} = 1; \qquad k_{CF} = 2; \qquad k_{CD} = 1; \qquad k_{DE} = 1$$

3. The slope deflection equations are written for each span, to include the antisymmetrical relationships noted earlier.

$$M_{AB} = 4EI\theta_A + 2EI\theta_B - 16.7\Delta_S$$
$$M_{BA} = 4EI\theta_B + 2EI\theta_A - 16.7\Delta_S$$

$$M_{BC} = 4EI\theta_B + 2EI\theta_C$$
$$M_{CB} = 4EI\theta_C + 2EI\theta_B$$

$$M_{CF} = 8EI\theta_C + 4EI\theta_F - 33.3\Delta_S$$
$$M_{CD} = 4EI\theta_C + 2EI\theta_B$$

$$M_{FC} = 8EI\theta_F + 4EI\theta_C - 33.3\Delta_S$$

4. The statics equations are written for each joint.

$$\Sigma M_A = 0; \qquad M_{AB} = 0$$

$$\Sigma M_B = 0; \qquad M_{BA} + M_{BC} = 0$$

$$\Sigma M_C = 0; \qquad M_{CB} + M_{CF} + M_{CD} = 0$$

$$\Sigma M_F = 0; \qquad M_{FC} = 0$$

5. The slope deflection equations are substituted into the statics equations, yielding four equations in the five unknowns.

$$16.7\Delta_S = 4EI\theta_A + 2EI\theta_B$$
$$16.6\Delta_S = 2EI\theta_A + 8EI\theta_B + 2EI\theta_C$$
$$33.3\Delta_S = \qquad 4EI\theta_B + 16EI\theta_C + 4EI\theta_F$$
$$33.3\Delta_S = \qquad\qquad 4EI\theta_C + 8EI\theta_F$$

6. These equations are solved simultaneously to find the relative rotations in terms of the sidesway displacement Δ_S.

$$EI\theta_A = +3.7037\Delta_S; \qquad EI\theta_B = +0.9259\Delta_S$$

$$EI\theta_C = +0.9259\Delta_S; \qquad EI\theta_F = +3.7037\Delta_S$$

$$EI\theta_D = +0.9259\Delta_S; \qquad EI\theta_E = +3.7037\Delta_S$$

(It is not due to antisymmetry that $EI\theta_C$ is equal to the other rotations. It is a coincidence of numbers, produced because I_{CF} is exactly twice I_{AB}.)

7. The relative rotations are substituted back into the slope deflection equations to find the moments at the joints. At this point, the moments are expressed in terms of the sidesway displacement Δ_S.

$$M_{AB} = 0; \qquad M_{BA} = -5.5555\Delta_S \qquad M_{BC} = +5.5555\Delta_S$$

$$M_{CB} = +5.5555\Delta_S; \qquad M_{CF} = -11.111\Delta_S \qquad M_{CD} = +5.5555\Delta_S$$

$$M_{DC} = +5.5555\Delta_S; \qquad M_{DE} = -5.5555\Delta_S; \qquad M_{ED} = M_{FC} = 0$$

8. The lateral forces at the base of the columns are found, as usual, by removing the columns as free bodies and finding the horizontal shears.

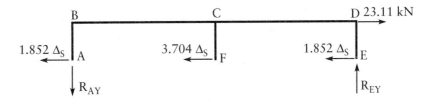

$$V_{AB} = 1.852\Delta_S \qquad\qquad V_{FC} = 3.704\Delta_S \qquad\qquad V_{ED} = 1.852\Delta_S$$

The horizontal loads on the frame are shown on the following sketch.

The sum of horizontal forces yields a solution for the sidesway displacement Δ_S.

$$\Sigma F_X = 0; \qquad -1.852\Delta_S - 3.704\Delta_S - 1.852\Delta_S + 23.11 = 0$$

$$\Delta_S = 3.12 \text{ mm} \quad \text{(to the right)}$$

This value of Δ_S is substituted into the equations for moment given in step 7 to find the values of moment at the joints.

$$M_{AB} = 0; \qquad\qquad M_{BA} = -17.33 \text{ kN-m}; \quad M_{BC} = +17.33 \text{ kN-m}$$

$$M_{CB} = +17.33 \text{ kN-m}; \quad M_{CF} = -34.67 \text{ kN-m}; \quad M_{CD} = +17.33 \text{ kN-m}$$

$$M_{DC} = +17.33 \text{ kN-m}; \quad M_{DE} = +17.33 \text{ kN-m}; \quad M_{ED} = M_{FC} = 0$$

The vertical reaction at A is found by simple statics.

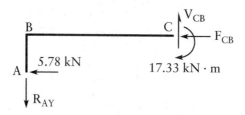

$$\Sigma M_C = 0; \quad -R_{AY}(12) + 5.78\,(3) + 17.33 = 0$$

$$R_{AY} = 2.89 \text{ kN} \quad \text{(down)}$$

The reaction at E is found similarly.

The solution for the reactions due to sidesway is shown in the following sketch.

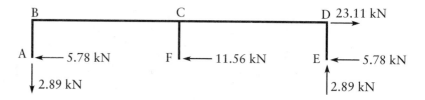

This solution is summed with the solution for reactions with sidesway prevented, to produce the final solution for the reactions, as shown in the following sketch.

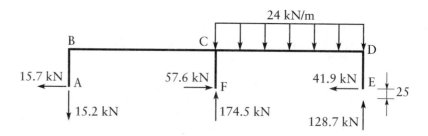

Like single-span frames, multispan frames are subject to thermal loads. The analysis of multispan frames for thermal loads is quite similar to that for single-span frames. An example will illustrate the procedure for a very general case—that of an unsymmetrical two-span frame.

Example 16-8 Determine the reactions on the given steel frame due to a temperature rise of 100°F.

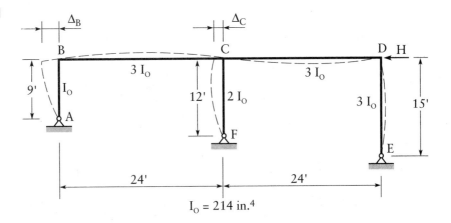

$$I_O = 214 \text{ in.}^4$$

Solution As in the analysis of other unsymmetrical frames by the slope deflection method, the analysis of this frame will consist of two parts—the first with sidesway prevented, and the second for the effects of sidesway.

The solution with sidesway prevented is taken first.

1. The shape of the elastic curve has been assumed and is shown on the preceding sketch. A preventer force H has been placed at D to prevent sidesway.

2. The relative stiffnesses and starting moments are determined for each member. As always, the translational moments are determined with all joints locked against rotation.

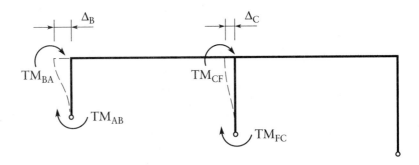

The displacements Δ_B and Δ_C are found relative to the end member DE, where displacement is assumed to be zero due to the preventer force H.

$$\Delta_C = \alpha(\Delta T) L = 6.5 \times 10^{-6}(100)(24 \times 12) = 0.187 \text{ in.}$$

$$\Delta_D = \alpha(\Delta T) L = 6.5 \times 10^{-6}(100)(48 \times 12) = 0.374 \text{ in.}$$

The translational moments are determined as usual.

$$TM_{AB} = TM_{BA} = +6Ek\psi = (6 \times 30 \times 10^6)\frac{214}{108} \times \frac{0.374}{108}$$
$$= 1235 \text{ kip-in.} = +103 \text{ kip-ft}$$

$$TM_{FC} = TM_{CF} = +6Ek\psi = (6 \times 30 \times 10^6)\frac{2 \times 214}{144} \times \frac{0.187}{144}$$
$$= 695 \text{ kip-in.} = +58 \text{ kip-ft}$$

Relative stiffnesses are taken at a convenient size to avoid lengthy decimal fractions.

$k_{AB} = 40;$ $\qquad TM_{AB} = TM_{BA} = +102 \text{ kip-ft}$

$k_{BC} = 45;$ $\qquad TM_{BC} = TM_{CB} = 0$

$k_{CF} = 60;$ $\qquad TM_{CF} = TM_{FC} = +58 \text{ kip-ft}$

$k_{CD} = 45;$ $\qquad TM_{CD} = TM_{DC} = 0$

$k_{DE} = 72;$ $\qquad TM_{DE} = TM_{ED} = 0$

3. The slope deflection equations are written for each member.

$$M_{AB} = 160EI\theta_A + 80EI\theta_B + 102$$

$$M_{BA} = 160EI\theta_B + 80EI\theta_A + 102$$

$$M_{BC} = 180EI\theta_B + 90EI\theta_C$$

$$M_{CB} = 180EI\theta_C + 90EI\theta_B$$

$$M_{CF} = 240EI\theta_C + 120EI\theta_F + 58$$

$$M_{FC} = 240EI\theta_F + 120EI\theta_C + 58$$

$$M_{CD} = 180EI\theta_C + 90EI\theta_D$$

$$M_{DC} = 180EI\theta_D + 90EI\theta_C$$

$$M_{DE} = 288EI\theta_D + 144EI\theta_E$$

$$M_{ED} = 288EI\theta_E + 144EI\theta_D$$

4. The statics equations are written for each joint.

$$\Sigma M_A = 0; \qquad M_{AB} = 0$$

$$\Sigma M_B = 0; \qquad M_{BA} + M_{BC} = 0$$

$$\Sigma M_C = 0; \qquad M_{CB} + M_{CF} + M_{CD} = 0$$

$$\Sigma M_D = 0; \qquad M_{DC} + M_{DE} = 0$$

$$\Sigma M_E = 0; \qquad M_{ED} = 0$$

$$\Sigma M_F = 0; \qquad M_{FC} = 0$$

5. The slope deflection equations are substituted into the statics equations, yielding a set of six equations in the six unknown rotations.

$$-102 = 160EI\theta_A + 80EI\theta_B$$
$$-102 = 80EI\theta_A + 340EI\theta_B + 90EI\theta_C$$
$$-58 = 90EI\theta_B + 600EI\theta_C + 90EI\theta_D + 120EI\theta_F$$
$$0 = 90EI\theta_C + 468EI\theta_D + 144EI\theta_E$$
$$0 = 144EI\theta_D + 288EI\theta_E$$
$$-58 = 120EI\theta_C + 24EI\theta_F$$

6. These six equations are solved simultaneously to find the relative rotations.

$$EI\theta_A = -0.5567; \qquad EI\theta_B = -0.1617; \qquad EI\theta_C = -0.0278$$

$$EI\theta_D = +0.0063; \qquad EI\theta_E = -0.0032; \qquad EI\theta_F = -0.2278$$

7. These values of relative rotations are substituted into the slope deflection equations to find the moments at the joints.

$$M_{AB} = 0; \qquad\qquad M_{BA} = +31.59 \text{ kip-ft}$$

$$M_{BC} = -31.60 \text{ kip-ft}; \qquad M_{CB} = -19.56 \text{ kip-ft}$$

$$M_{CF} = +23.99 \text{ kip-ft}; \qquad M_{FC} = 0$$

$$M_{CD} = -4.44 \text{ kip-ft}; \qquad M_{DC} = -1.36 \text{ kip-ft}$$

$$M_{DE} = +1.36 \text{ kip-ft}; \qquad M_{ED} = 0$$

8. The horizontal reactions at the supports are found as usual.

$$R_{AX} = \frac{M_{BA}}{9} = 3.51 \text{ kips} \quad \text{(to the right)}$$

$$R_{FX} = \frac{M_{CF}}{12} = 2.00 \text{ kips} \quad \text{(to the right)}$$

$$R_{EX} = \frac{M_{DE}}{15} = 0.09 \text{ kips} \quad \text{(to the left)}$$

The sum of horizontal force on the overall frame yields the preventer force H.

$$-H + 3.51 + 2.00 - 0.09 = 0$$
$$H = 5.60 \text{ kips} \quad \text{(to the left)}$$

The first part of the solution is now complete. The second part of the solution is for the effects of sidesway, which will occur when the preventer force is released. This load case is shown in the following sketch.

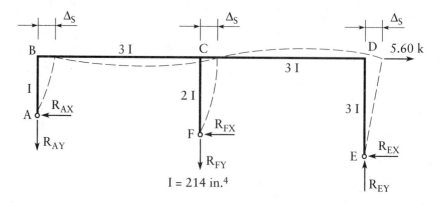

1. The shape of the elastic curve is shown on the preceding sketch.
2. Translational moments are expressed in terms of the sidesway displacement Δ_S, with Δ_S in inches.

$$TM_{AB} = TM_{BA} = -6Ek\psi = (-6 \times 30 \times 10^6)\frac{214}{108} \times \frac{\Delta_S}{108}$$
$$= -3302\Delta_S \text{ kip-in.} = -275\Delta_S \text{ kip-ft}$$

$$TM_{CF} = TM_{FC} = -6Ek\psi = (-6 \times 30 \times 10^6)\frac{2 \times 214}{144} \times \frac{\Delta_S}{144}$$
$$= -3715\Delta_S \text{ kip-in.} = -310\Delta_S \text{ kip-ft}$$

$$TM_{ED} = TM_{DE} = -6Ek\psi = (-6 \times 30 \times 10^6)\frac{3 \times 214}{180} \times \frac{\Delta_S}{180}$$
$$= -3567\Delta_S \text{ kip-in.} = -297\Delta_S \text{ kip-ft}$$

The relative stiffnesses are those computed earlier.

$$k_{AB} = 40; \quad k_{BC} = 45; \quad k_{CF} = 60; \quad k_{CD} = 45;$$
$$k_{DE} = 72$$

3. The slope deflection equations are written for each span,

$$M_{AB} = 160EI\theta_A + 80EI\theta_B - 275\Delta_S$$
$$M_{BA} = 160EI\theta_B + 80EI\theta_A - 275\Delta_S$$
$$M_{BC} = 180EI\theta_B + 90EI\theta_C$$
$$M_{CB} = 180EI\theta_C + 90EI\theta_B$$
$$M_{CF} = 240EI\theta_C + 120EI\theta_F - 310\Delta_S$$
$$M_{FC} = 240EI\theta_F + 120EI\theta_C - 310\Delta_S$$
$$M_{CD} = 180EI\theta_C + 90EI\theta_D$$
$$M_{DC} = 180EI\theta_D + 90EI\theta_C$$
$$M_{DE} = 288EI\theta_D + 144EI\theta_E - 297\Delta_S$$
$$M_{ED} = 288EI\theta_E + 144EI\theta_D - 297\Delta_S$$

4. The statics equations are written for each joint

$$\Sigma M_A = 0; \qquad M_{AB} = 0$$

$$\Sigma M_B = 0; \qquad M_{BA} + M_{BC} = 0$$

$$\Sigma M_C = 0; \qquad M_{CB} + M_{CF} + M_{CD} = 0$$

$$\Sigma M_D = 0; \qquad M_{DC} + M_{DE} = 0$$

$$\Sigma M_E = 0; \qquad M_{ED} = 0$$

$$\Sigma M_F = 0; \qquad M_{FC} = 0$$

5. The slope deflection equations are substituted into the statics equations, yielding a set of six equations in the six unknown rotations.

$$275\Delta_S = 160EI\theta_A + 80EI\theta_B$$
$$275\Delta_S = 80EI\theta_A + 340EI\theta_B + 90EI\theta_C$$
$$310\Delta_S = \qquad\qquad 90EI\theta_B + 600EI\theta_C + 90EI\theta_D \qquad\qquad + 120EI\theta_F$$
$$297\Delta_S = \qquad\qquad\qquad\qquad 90EI\theta_C + 468EI\theta_D + 144EI\theta_E$$
$$297\Delta_S = \qquad\qquad\qquad\qquad\qquad\qquad 144EI\theta_D + 288EI\theta_E$$
$$310\Delta_S = \qquad\qquad\qquad\qquad 120EI\theta_C \qquad\qquad\qquad + 240EI\theta_F$$

6. These six equations are solved simultaneously to find the relative rotations in terms of the sidesway displacement Δ_S.

$$EI\theta_A = +1.5140\Delta_S; \qquad EI\theta_B = +0.4096\Delta_S; \qquad EI\theta_C = +0.1624\Delta_S$$

$$EI\theta_D = +0.3381\Delta_S; \qquad EI\theta_E = +0.8622\Delta_S; \qquad EI\theta_F = +1.2105\Delta_S$$

7. The relative rotations are substituted into the slope deflection equations to find the moments at the joints in terms of the sidesway displacement Δ_S.

$$M_{AB} = 0; \qquad\qquad M_{BA} = -88.34\Delta_S$$

$$M_{BC} = +88.34\Delta_S; \qquad M_{CB} = +66.10\Delta_S$$

$$M_{CF} = -125.76\Delta_S; \qquad M_{FC} = 0$$

$$M_{CD} = +59.66\Delta_S; \qquad M_{DC} = +75.47\Delta_S$$

$$M_{DE} = -75.47\Delta_S; \qquad M_{ED} = 0$$

8. The lateral forces at the supports are found in the usual way,

$$R_{AX} = \frac{M_{BA}}{9} = 9.82\Delta_S \text{ kips} \quad \text{(to the left)}$$

$$R_{FX} = \frac{M_{CF}}{12} = 10.48\Delta_S \text{ kips} \quad \text{(to the left)}$$

$$R_{EX} = \frac{M_{DE}}{15} = 5.03\Delta_S \text{ kips} \quad \text{(to the left)}$$

The sum of horizontal forces on the overall frame yields the value of Δ_S.

$$5.60 - 9.82\Delta_S - 10.48\Delta_S - 5.03\Delta_S = 0$$
$$\Delta_S = 0.221 \text{ in.}$$

This value of Δ_S is substituted back into the earlier solutions to find the values of the moments at the joint and of the reactions at the supports.

$M_{AB} = 0;$ $\qquad M_{BA} = -19.52$

$M_{BC} = +19.52;$ $\qquad M_{CB} = +14.61$

$M_{CF} = -27.80;$ $\qquad M_{FC} = 0$

$M_{CD} = +13.19;$ $\qquad M_{DC} = +16.69$

$M_{DE} = -16.69;$ $\qquad M_{ED} = 0$

$R_{AX} = 2.17 \text{ kips} \quad \text{(to the left)}$

$R_{FX} = 2.32 \text{ kips} \quad \text{(to the left)}$

$R_{EX} = 1.11 \text{ kips} \quad \text{(to the left)}$

The sum of the two cases yields the final results, shown in the following sketch.

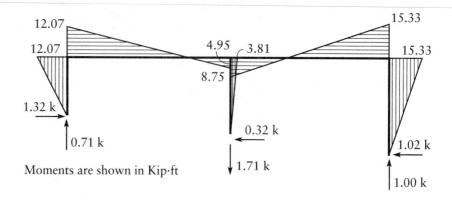

Moments are shown in Kip·ft

Outside Problems

Problem 16-15* Determine the reactions on the given steel frame.

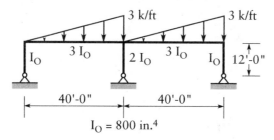

$I_O = 800$ in.^{4}

Problem 16-16 Solve Problem 16-15 for the case where the center support is displaced downward 1 inch. Do not include gravity loads in this solution.

Problem 16-17* Determine the reactions on the given steel frame.

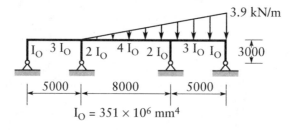

$I_O = 351 \times 10^6$ mm^4

Problem 16-18 Solve Problem 16-17 for the case where the rightmost support is displaced downward 20 mm. Do not include gravity loads in this solution.

Problem 16-19* Solve the frame of Problem 16-15 for a temperature rise of 100 Fahrenheit degrees. Do not include the gravity load in this solution. The thermal coefficient of expansion for steel is 6.5×10^{-6} in./in./°F.

Problem 16-20 Solve the frame of Problem 16-17 for a temperature drop of 70 Celsius degrees. Do not include the gravity load in this solution. The thermal coefficient of contraction for steel is 11×10^{-6} m/m/°C.

16.5 MULTISTORY FRAMES

The application of the slope deflection method to multistory frames is much like its application to single-story frames. The solution becomes somewhat more complex, however, due to the increase in the number of sidesway displacements. A typical pattern of sidesway displacements is shown in the sketch of Figure 16-12.

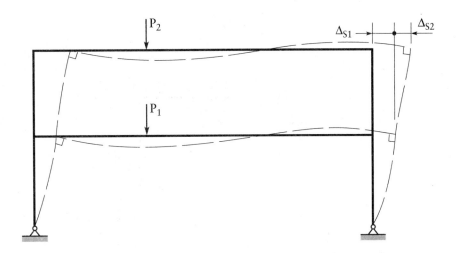

FIGURE 16-12 Sidesway in a multistory frame.

Each story of the frame of Figure 16-12 has its own sidesway displacement relative to the floor below; these displacements are shown in the sketch as Δ_{S1} and Δ_{S2}. The procedure to be used in the solution is relatively straightforward:

1. Solve for loads and any known displacements Δ_T, with sidesway prevented.

2. Solve for each of the n preventer forces, where n is the number of stories.

3 Solve for moments at the rigid joints in each of the n cases of sidesway that occur when each of the n preventer forces is released.

4. Total moment at a joint is the sum of these $n + 1$ cases, expressed in terms of the unknown sidesway displacements $\Delta_{S1}, \Delta_{S2}, \Delta_{S3}, \ldots, \Delta_{Sn}$.

5. Solve for horizontal forces at each level in terms of these sidesway displacements, yielding n equations in these n unknown displacements.

6. Simultaneously solve for the *n* sidesway displacements.

7. Substitute known sidesway displacements back into the equations of step 2 to find the final values for moments at the joints.

In the foregoing procedure, *it is essential that the moments be summed* (step 4) *before the shears are balanced* (steps 5 and 6). The rationale for this requirement will become apparent in the following examples. Further discussion of this requirement follows Example 16-10.

A simple case involving only lateral loads will demonstrate the procedure.

Example 16-9   Determine the moments at the joints and the reactions at the supports in the given two-story steel frame.

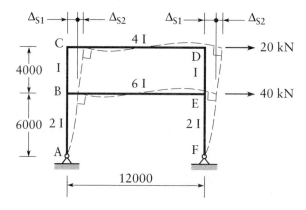

Reference $I = 80 \times 10^6$ mm^4

Solution   This solution could be made by solving with both forces applied simultaneously or by solving for each force separately and then summing the results. For the sake of demonstration, this example is solved with both forces applied simultaneously; in the next example, separate solutions will be demonstrated.

1. The shape of the elastic curve has been assumed and is shown on the sketch. Due to the antisymmetry,

$$\theta_A = \theta_F; \qquad \theta_B = \theta_E; \qquad \theta_C = \theta_D$$

2. The stiffness factors and translational moments are determined for each member. Translational moments are determined only for columns undergoing the specific translation; no other columns undergo translation between joints. As usual, all joints are locked against rotation.

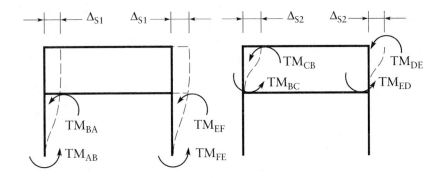

For the lower-level translation, with Δ_{S1} in mm,

$$TM_{AB} = TM_{BA} = -6Ek\psi_{AB} = (-6 \times 200,000)\frac{80 \times 10^6}{4000} \times \frac{\Delta_{S1}}{4000}$$
$$= (-5.3333 \times 10^6)\Delta_{S1} \text{ N-mm} = -5.3333\Delta_{S1} \text{ kN-m}$$

For the upper-level translation, with Δ_{S2} in mm,

$$TM_{BC} = TM_{CB} = -6Ek\psi_{BC} = (-6 \times 200,000)\frac{2 \times 80 \times 10^6}{6000} \times \frac{\Delta_{S2}}{6000}$$
$$= (-6.0000 \times 10^6)\Delta_{S2} \text{ N-mm} = -6.0000\Delta_{S2} \text{ kN-m}$$

Relative rotational stiffnesses are set at some convenient relative size to avoid lengthy decimal fractions. For member AB,

$$k_{AB} = 4; \qquad TM_{AB} = TM_{BA} = -5.3333\Delta_{S1}$$

For member BE,

$$k_{BE} = 6; \qquad TM_{BE} = TM_{EB} = 0$$

For member BC,

$$k_{BC} = 3; \qquad TM_{BC} = TM_{CB} = -6.0000\Delta_{S2}$$

For member CD,

$$k_{CD} = 4; \qquad TM_{CD} = TM_{DC} = 0$$

3. The slope deflection equations are written for each member, to include antisymmetry.

$$M_{AB} = 16EI\theta_A + 8EI\theta_B - 5.3333\Delta_{S1}$$
$$M_{BA} = 16EI\theta_B + 8EI\theta_A - 5.3333\Delta_{S1}$$

$$M_{BE} = 24EI\theta_B + 12EI\theta_E \qquad = 36EI\theta_B$$

$$M_{BC} = 12EI\theta_B + 6EI\theta_C - 6.0000\Delta_{S2}$$
$$M_{CB} = 12EI\theta_C + 6EI\theta_B - 6.0000\Delta_{S2}$$

$$M_{CD} = 16EI\theta_C + 8EI\theta_D \qquad = 24EI\theta_C$$

4. The statics equations are written for each joint.

$$\Sigma M_A = 0; \qquad M_{AB} = 0$$

$$\Sigma M_B = 0; \qquad M_{BA} + M_{BE} + M_{BC} = 0$$

$$\Sigma M_C = 0; \qquad M_{CB} + M_{CD} = 0$$

5. The slope deflection equations are substituted into the statics equations, yielding three equations in the three unknown rotations, expressed in terms of the sidesway displacements Δ_{S1} and Δ_{S2}.

$$5.3333\Delta_{S1} \qquad\qquad = 16EI\theta_A + 8EI\theta_B$$
$$5.3333\Delta_{S1} + 6.0000\Delta_{S2} = 8EI\theta_A + 64EI\theta_B + 6EI\theta_C$$
$$\qquad\qquad + 6.0000\Delta_{S2} = \qquad\qquad 6EI\theta_B + 36EI\theta_C$$

6. The three equations are solved simultaneously to find the relative rotations.

$$EI\theta_A = +0.31073\Delta_{S1} - 0.04237\Delta_{S2}$$

$$EI\theta_B = +0.04520\Delta_{S1} + 0.08475\Delta_{S2}$$

$$EI\theta_C = -0.00753\Delta_{S1} + 0.15254\Delta_{S2}$$

7. These rotations are substituted back into the slope deflection equations of step 3, yielding the moments at each joint in terms of the sidesway displacements.

$$M_{AB} = 0$$

$$M_{BA} = -2.1243\Delta_{S1} + 1.0170\Delta_{S2}$$

$$M_{BE} = +1.6271\Delta_{S1} + 3.0509\Delta_{S2}$$

$$M_{BC} = +0.4972\Delta_{S1} - 4.0678\Delta_{S2}$$

$$M_{CB} = +0.1808\Delta_{S1} - 3.6610\Delta_{S2}$$

$$M_{CD} = -0.1808\Delta_{S1} + 3.6610\Delta_{S2}$$

8. Horizontal shears at the bases of the columns are determined as usual; the columns are removed as free bodies, and the horizontal shears are computed by simple statics.

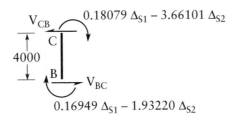

$$\Sigma M_C = 0$$

$$V_{BC} = \frac{M_{CB} + M_{BC}}{4}$$

$$= 0.1695\Delta_{S1} - 1.9322\Delta_{S2} = V_{ED}$$

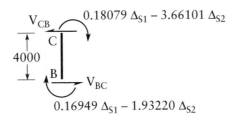

$$\Sigma M_B = 0$$

$$V_{AB} = \frac{M_{BA}}{6}$$

$$= -0.3541\Delta_{S1} + 0.1695\Delta_{S2} = V_{FE}$$

The shears at the upper level are shown in the following sketch.

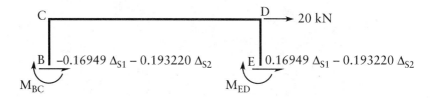

The sum of horizontal forces yields one equation in the two unknown displacements Δ_{S1} and Δ_{S2}.

$$\Sigma F_X = 0; \qquad (0.1695\Delta_{S1} - 1.9322\Delta_{S2})\,2 + 20 = 0$$

The shears on the overall frame are shown in the following sketch.

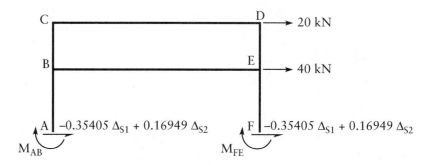

The sum of horizontal forces yields a second equation in the two unknown displacements Δ_{S1} and Δ_{S2}.

$$\Sigma F_X = 0; \qquad (-0.3541\Delta_{S1} + 0.1695\Delta_{S2})\,2 + 60 = 0$$

The two equations in Δ_{S1} and Δ_{S2} are solved simultaneously to find

$$\Delta_{S1} = 91.0341 \text{ mm}; \qquad \Delta_{S2} = 13.1608 \text{ mm}$$

These values are substituted back into the equations for moment developed in step 7 to find the moments at the joints with sidesway prevented.

$$M_{AB} = 0 \qquad\qquad = M_{FE}$$

$$M_{BA} = -180.00 \text{ kN-m} = M_{EF}$$

$$M_{BE} = +188.28 \text{ kN-m} = M_{FB}$$

$$M_{BC} = \quad -8.28 \text{ kN-m} = M_{ED}$$

$$M_{CB} = \quad -31.72 \text{ kN-m} = M_{DE}$$

$$M_{CD} = \quad +31.72 \text{ kN-m} = M_{DC}$$

$$V_{BC} = -10.00 \text{ kN} \qquad = V_{ED}$$

$$V_{AB} = -30.00 \text{ kN} \qquad = V_{FE}$$

Reactions R_{AY} and R_{FY} are statically determinate and are found in the usual way. Final results are shown in the following sketches; the moment diagram is drawn on the tension side.

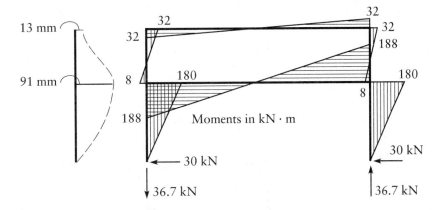

The next example is for a more general case in which an eccentric load creates sidesway in a three-story frame. The procedure demonstrates the use of individual solutions for each of the preventer forces.

Example 16-10   Determine the moments at the joints and the reactions at the supports for the given steel frame.

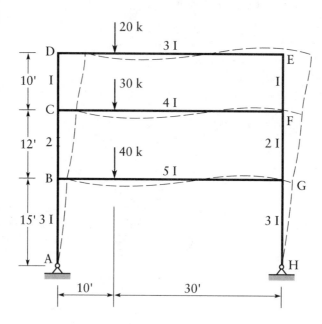

Reference $I = 300$ in.^{4}

Solution   Four separate solutions are required—one solution for the loads, and one for each of the three preventer forces. The solution for the applied loads is taken first.

1. The shape of the elastic curve has been assumed and is shown on the following sketch.

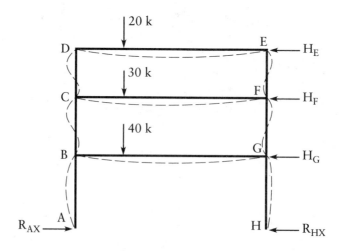

2. The relative stiffnesses and fixed-end moments are determined for each
member. The relative stiffnesses are set at some convenient size to avoid
cumbersome decimal fractions.

Fixed-end moments are determined first, with all joints locked against
rotations.

$$FM_{DE} = -\frac{Pab^2}{L^2} = -\frac{20 \times 10 \times 30^2}{40^2} = -225 \text{ kip-ft}$$

$$FM_{ED} = +\frac{Pa^2b}{L^2} = +\frac{20 \times 10^2 \times 30}{40^2} = +75 \text{ kip-ft}$$

$$FM_{CF} = -\frac{Pab^2}{L^2} = -\frac{30 \times 10 \times 30^2}{40^2} = -169 \text{ kip-ft}$$

$$FM_{FC} = +\frac{Pa^2b}{L^2} = +\frac{30 \times 10^2 \times 30}{40^2} = +56 \text{ kip-ft}$$

$$FM_{BG} = -\frac{Pab^2}{L^2} = -\frac{40 \times 10 \times 30^2}{40^2} = -113 \text{ kip-ft}$$

$$FM_{GB} = +\frac{Pa^2b}{L^2} = +\frac{40 \times 10^2 \times 30}{40^2} = +38 \text{ kip-ft}$$

The stiffnesses and starting moments are:

$k_{AB} = 24;$ $FM_{AB} = 0;$ $FM_{BA} = 0$

$k_{BG} = 15;$ $FM_{BG} = -225 \text{ kip-ft};$ $FM_{GB} = +75 \text{ kip-ft}$

$k_{BC} = 20;$ $FM_{BC} = 0;$ $FM_{CB} = 0$

$k_{CF} = 12;$ $FM_{CF} = -169 \text{ kip-ft};$ $FM_{FC} = +56 \text{ kip-ft}$

$k_{CD} = 12;$ $FM_{CD} = 0;$ $FM_{DC} = 0$

$k_{DE} = 9;$ $FM_{DE} = -113 \text{ kip-ft};$ $FM_{ED} = +38 \text{ kip-ft}$

$k_{EF} = 12;$ $FM_{EF} = 0;$ $FM_{FE} = 0$

$k_{FG} = 20;$ $FM_{FG} = 0;$ $FM_{GF} = 0$

$k_{GH} = 24;$ $FM_{GH} = 0;$ $FM_{HG} = 0$

3. The slope deflection equations are written for each span.

$$M_{AB} = 96EI\theta_A + 48EI\theta_B \qquad\qquad M_{HG} = 96EI\theta_H + 48EI\theta_G$$

$$M_{BA} = 96EI\theta_B + 48EI\theta_A \qquad\qquad M_{GH} = 96EI\theta_G + 48EI\theta_H$$

$$M_{BG} = 60EI\theta_B + 30EI\theta_G - 225 \qquad M_{GB} = 60EI\theta_G + 30EI\theta_B + 75$$

$$M_{BC} = 80EI\theta_B + 40EI\theta_C \qquad\qquad M_{GF} = 80EI\theta_G + 40EI\theta_F$$

$$M_{CB} = 80EI\theta_C + 40EI\theta_B \qquad\qquad M_{FG} = 80EI\theta_F + 40EI\theta_G$$

$$M_{CF} = 48EI\theta_C + 24EI\theta_F - 169 \qquad M_{FC} = 48EI\theta_F + 24EI\theta_C + 56$$

$$M_{CD} = 48EI\theta_C + 24EI\theta_D \qquad\qquad M_{FE} = 48EI\theta_F + 24EI\theta_E$$

$$M_{DC} = 48EI\theta_D + 24EI\theta_C \qquad\qquad M_{EF} = 48EI\theta_E + 24EI\theta_F$$

$$M_{DE} = 36EI\theta_D + 18EI\theta_E - 113 \qquad M_{ED} = 36EI\theta_E + 18EI\theta_D + 38$$

4. The statics equations are written for each joint.

$$\Sigma M_A = 0; \qquad M_{AB} = 0$$

$$\Sigma M_H = 0; \qquad M_{HG} = 0$$

$$\Sigma M_B = 0; \qquad M_{BA} + M_{BG} + M_{BC} = 0$$

$$\Sigma M_G = 0; \qquad M_{GF} + M_{GB} + M_{GH} = 0$$

$$\Sigma M_C = 0; \qquad M_{CB} + M_{CF} + M_{CD} = 0$$

$$\Sigma M_F = 0; \qquad M_{FE} + M_{FC} + M_{FG} = 0$$

$$\Sigma M_D = 0; \qquad M_{DC} + M_{DE} = 0$$

$$\Sigma M_E = 0; \qquad M_{ED} + M_{EF} = 0$$

5. The slope deflection equations are substituted into the statics equations, yielding eight equations in the eight unknown rotations. The resulting set of equations forms a classical diagonal matrix.

$$0 = 96EI\theta_A + 48EI\theta_B$$

$$225 = 48EI\theta_A + 236EI\theta_B + 40EI\theta_C \qquad\qquad + 30EI\theta_G$$

$$169 = \qquad\quad 40EI\theta_B + 176EI\theta_C + 24EI\theta_D \qquad + 24EI\theta_F$$

$$113 = \qquad\qquad\qquad 24EI\theta_C + 84EI\theta_D + 18EI\theta_E$$

$$-38 = \qquad\qquad\qquad\qquad\quad 18EI\theta_D + 84EI\theta_E + 24EI\theta_F$$

$$-56 = \qquad\qquad 24EI\theta_C \qquad\quad + 24EI\theta_E + 176EI\theta_F + 40EI\theta_G$$

$$-75 = \qquad 30EI\theta_B \qquad\qquad\qquad\quad + 40EI\theta_F + 236EI\theta_G + 48EI\theta_H$$

$$0 = \qquad\qquad\qquad\qquad\qquad\qquad\qquad\qquad 48EI\theta_G + 96EI\theta_H$$

6. The eight equations are solved simultaneously to find the values of the relative rotations.

$$EI\theta_A = -0.50896$$

$$EI\theta_B = +1.01792$$

$$EI\theta_C = +0.57517$$

$$EI\theta_D = +1.32655$$

$$EI\theta_E = -0.67969$$

$$EI\theta_F = -0.19934$$

$$EI\theta_G = -0.46021$$

$$EI\theta_H = +0.23010$$

7. These values are substituted back into the slope deflection equations of step 3 to find the moments at the joints when sidesway is prevented.

$$M_{AB} = 0 \qquad\qquad\qquad M_{ED} = +37.41 \text{ kip-ft}$$

$$M_{BA} = +73.29 \text{ kip-ft} \qquad M_{EF} = -37.41 \text{ kip-ft}$$

$$M_{BG} = -177.73 \text{ kip-ft} \qquad M_{FE} = -25.88 \text{ kip-ft}$$

$$M_{BC} = +104.44 \text{ kip-ft} \qquad M_{FC} = +60.24 \text{ kip-ft}$$

$$M_{CB} = +86.73 \text{ kip-ft} \qquad M_{FG} = -34.36 \text{ kip-ft}$$

$$M_{CF} = -146.18 \text{ kip-ft} \qquad M_{GF} = -44.79 \text{ kip-ft}$$

$$M_{CD} = +59.45 \text{ kip-ft} \qquad M_{GB} = +77.93 \text{ kip-ft}$$

$$M_{DC} = +77.48 \text{ kip-ft} \qquad M_{GH} = -33.14 \text{ kip-ft}$$

$$M_{DE} = -77.48 \text{ kip-ft} \qquad M_{HG} = 0$$

8. The horizontal shears at the bases of the columns are found, as usual, by removing the columns as free bodies and finding the end shears by statics. The top story is taken first, with columns DC and EF.

$$\Sigma M_D = 0$$
$$-V_{CD}(10) + 77.48 + 59.45 = 0$$
$$V_{CD} = 13.69 \text{ kips}$$

$$\Sigma M_F = 0$$
$$+V_{FE}(10) - 37.41 - 25.88 = 0$$
$$V_{FE} = 6.33 \text{ kips}$$

The top level is now taken as a free body with these base shears shown at the bases of the columns.

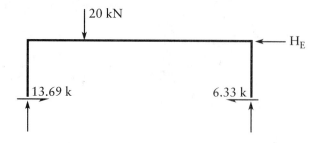

The preventer force H_E is found by summing horizontal forces on the free body.

$$\Sigma F_X = 0; \qquad 13.69 - 6.33 - H_E = 0$$
$$H_E = 7.63 \text{ kips} \quad \text{(to the right)}$$

The horizontal shears at the bases of the columns CB and FG are found similarly.

$$V_{BC} = 15.93 \text{ kips} \quad \text{(to the right)}$$

$$V_{GF} = 6.60 \text{ kips} \quad \text{(to the left)}$$

The preventer force H_F is found by removing the top two floors as a free body and summing horizontal forces.

$$H_F = 1.97 \text{ kips} \quad \text{(to the left)}$$

The horizontal shears at the bases of the columns AB and GH are found similarly.

$$V_{AB} = 4.89 \text{ kips} \quad \text{(to the right)}$$

$$V_{HG} = 2.21 \text{ kips} \quad \text{(to the left)}$$

The preventer force H_G is found by taking the entire frame as a free body and summing horizontal forces.

$$H_G = 6.65 \text{ kips} \quad \text{(to the right)}$$

The final reactions (with sidesway prevented) are shown on the following sketch.

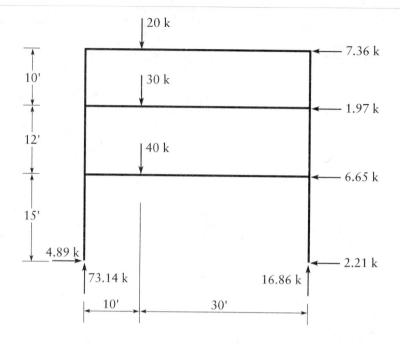

Notice that without the preventer forces, the vertical reaction at *A* would be 67.5 kips; the prevention of sidesway thus creates a significant difference in reactions—in this case about 8%.

The next solution is for the release of the preventer force H_G. A force of 6.65 kips is applied at *G*, equal and opposite to H_G, as shown in the following sketch. The vertical reactions are statically determinate; they have been computed and are also shown on the sketch.

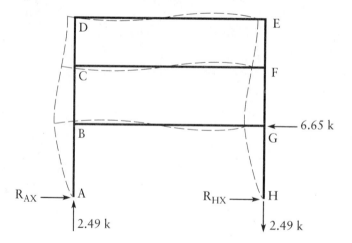

1. The shape of the elastic curve has been assumed and is shown on the pre- ceding sketch. The antisymmetry is noted.

$$\theta_A = \theta_H; \qquad \theta_B = \theta_G; \qquad \theta_C = \theta_F; \qquad \theta_D = \theta_E$$

2. The stiffness factors and translational moments are determined with all joints locked against rotations. Only the columns undergoing the transla- tion Δ_{SG} develop a translational moment. The sidesway displacement Δ_{SG} is assumed to be in inches.

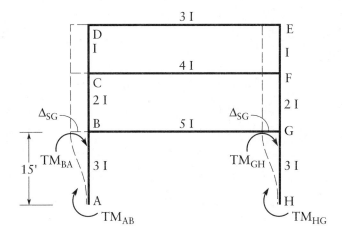

$$TM_{AB} = TM_{BA} = +6Ek\psi_{AB} = (+6 \times 29 \times 10^6) \frac{3 \times 300}{15 \times 12} \times \frac{\Delta_{SG}}{15 \times 12}$$

$$= (+4.833 \times 10^6)\,\Delta_{SG}\text{lb-in.} = +402.78\Delta_{SG} \text{ kip-ft}$$

$$TM_{HG} = TM_{GH} = +402.78\Delta_{SG} \text{ kip-ft}$$

Relative stiffness factors for rotations are taken at the same values used earlier.

$$k_{AB} = 24; \qquad k_{BG} = 15; \qquad k_{BC} = 20$$

$$k_{CF} = 12; \qquad k_{CD} = 12; \qquad k_{DE} = 9$$

3. The slope deflection equations are written for each member, to include the antisymmetry.

$$M_{AB} = 96EI\theta_A + 48EI\theta_B + 402.78\Delta_{SG}$$

$$M_{BA} = 96EI\theta_B + 48EI\theta_A$$

$$M_{BG} = 60EI\theta_B + 30EI\theta_G \qquad\qquad = 90EI\theta_B$$

$$M_{BC} = 80EI\theta_B + 40EI\theta_C$$

$$M_{CB} = 80EI\theta_C + 40EI\theta_B$$

$$M_{CF} = 48EI\theta_C + 24EI\theta_F \qquad\qquad = 72EI\theta_C$$

$$M_{CD} = 48EI\theta_C + 24EI\theta_D$$

$$M_{DC} = 48EI\theta_D + 24EI\theta_D$$

$$M_{DE} = 36EI\theta_D + 18EI\theta_E \qquad\qquad = 54EI\theta_D$$

4. The statics equations are written for each joint.

$$\Sigma M_A = 0; \qquad M_{AB} = 0$$

$$\Sigma M_B = 0; \qquad M_{BA} + M_{BG} + M_{BC} = 0$$

$$\Sigma M_C = 0; \qquad M_{CB} + M_{CF} + M_{CD} = 0$$

$$\Sigma M_D = 0; \qquad M_{DC} + M_{DE} = 0$$

5. The slope deflection equations are substituted into the statics equations, yielding four equations in the four unknown rotations.

$$-402.78\Delta_{SG} = 96EI\theta_A + 48EI\theta_B$$

$$0 = 48EI\theta_A + 266EI\theta_B + 40EI\theta_C$$

$$0 = 40EI\theta_B + 200EI\theta_C + 24EI\theta_D$$

$$0 = 24EI\theta_C + 102EI\theta_D$$

6. These four equations are solved simultaneously to find the relative rotations in terms of the sidesway displacement Δ_{SG}.

$$EI\theta_A = -4.6264\Delta_{SG}$$

$$EI\theta_B = +0.8615\Delta_{SG}$$

$$EI\theta_C = -0.1773\Delta_{SG}$$

$$EI\theta_D = +0.0417\Delta_{SG}$$

7. The relative rotations are substituted back into the slope deflection equations of step 2 to find the moments at the joints in terms of the sidesway displacement Δ_{SG}.

$$M_{AB} = 0 \qquad\qquad = M_{HG}$$

$$M_{BA} = -139.36\Delta_{SG} = M_{GH}$$

$$M_{BG} = +77.53\Delta_{SG} = M_{GB}$$

$$M_{BC} = +61.83\Delta_{SG} = M_{GF}$$

$$M_{CB} = +20.28\Delta_{SG} = M_{FG}$$

$$M_{CF} = -12.77\Delta_{SG} = M_{FC}$$

$$M_{CD} = -7.51\Delta_{SG} \quad = M_{FE}$$

$$M_{DC} = -2.25\Delta_{SG} \quad = M_{EF}$$

$$M_{DE} = +2.25\Delta_{SG} \quad = M_{ED}$$

Similarly, when the preventer force H_F is released, the relative rotations at the joints (in terms of the sidesway displacement Δ_{SF} at point F) are found by the same procedure to be

$$EI\theta_A = -0.8974\Delta_{SF}$$

$$EI\theta_B = +1.7948\Delta_{SF}$$

$$EI\theta_C = -0.3694\Delta_{SF}$$

$$EI\theta_D = +0.0869\Delta_{SF}$$

For these values of the relative rotations, the moments at the joints (in terms of the sidesway displacement Δ_{SF}) are

$$M_{AB} = 0 \qquad\qquad = M_{HG}$$

$$M_{BA} = +129.22\Delta_{SF} = M_{GH}$$

$$M_{BG} = +161.53\Delta_{SF} = M_{GB}$$

$$M_{BC} = -290.75\Delta_{SF} = M_{GF}$$

$$M_{CB} = +42.24\Delta_{SF} = M_{FG}$$

$$M_{CF} = -26.60\Delta_{SF} = M_{FC}$$

$$M_{CD} = -15.64\Delta_{SF} = M_{FE}$$

$$M_{DC} = -4.69\Delta_{SF} = M_{EF}$$

$$M_{DE} = +4.69\Delta_{SF} = M_{ED}$$

Finally, when the preventer force H_E is released, the relative rotations at the joints (in terms of the sidesway displacement Δ_{SE} at point E) are found by the same procedure to be

$$EI\theta_A = +0.1330\Delta_{SE}$$

$$EI\theta_B = -0.2660\Delta_{SE}$$

$$EI\theta_C = +1.6090\Delta_{SE}$$

$$EI\theta_D = -0.3786\Delta_{SE}$$

For these values of the relative rotations, the moments at the joints (in terms of the sidesway displacement Δ_{SE}) are

$$M_{AB} = 0 \qquad\qquad = M_{HG}$$

$$M_{BA} = -19.15\Delta_{SE} = M_{GH}$$

$$M_{BG} = -23.94\Delta_{SE} = M_{GB}$$

$$M_{BC} = +43.08\Delta_{SE} = M_{GF}$$

$$M_{CB} = +118.08\Delta_{SE} = M_{FG}$$

$$M_{CF} = +115.85\Delta_{SE} = M_{FC}$$

$$M_{CD} = -233.93\Delta_{SE} = M_{FE}$$

$$M_{DC} = +20.44\Delta_{SE} = M_{EF}$$

$$M_{DE} = -20.44\Delta_{SE} = M_{ED}$$

The total moment at a joint is the sum of the four cases: Loads + H_G + H_F + H_E.

$$M_{AB} = 0$$

$$M_{BA} = +73.29 \quad - 139.36\Delta_{SG} + 129.22\Delta_{SF} - 19.15\Delta_{SE}$$

$$M_{BG} = -177.73 \quad + 77.53\Delta_{SG} \quad + 161.53\Delta_{SF} - 23.94\Delta_{SE}$$

$$M_{BC} = +104.44 + 61.83\Delta_{SG} \quad - 290.75\Delta_{SF} + 43.08\Delta_{SE}$$

$$M_{CB} = +86.73 \quad + 20.28\Delta_{SG} \quad + 42.24\Delta_{SF} \quad + 118.08\Delta_{SE}$$

$$M_{CF} = -146.18 - 12.77\Delta_{SG} \quad - 26.60\Delta_{SF} \quad + 115.85\Delta_{SE}$$

$$M_{CD} = +59.45 \quad - 7.51\Delta_{SG} \quad - 15.64\Delta_{SF} - 233.93\Delta_{SE}$$

$$M_{DC} = +77.48 \quad - 2.25\Delta_{SG} \quad - 4.69\Delta_{SF} \quad + 20.44\Delta_{SE}$$

$$M_{DE} = -77.48 \quad + 2.25\Delta_{SG} \quad + 4.69\Delta_{SF} \quad - 20.44\Delta_{SE}$$

$$M_{ED} = +37.41 \quad + 2.25\Delta_{SG} \quad + 4.69\Delta_{SF} \quad - 20.44\Delta_{SE}$$

$$M_{EF} = -37.41 \quad - 2.25\Delta_{SG} \quad - 4.69\Delta_{SF} \quad + 20.44\Delta_{SE}$$

$$M_{FE} = -25.88 \quad - 7.51\Delta_{SG} \quad - 15.64\Delta_{SF} - 233.93\Delta_{SE}$$

$$M_{FC} = +60.24 \quad - 12.77\Delta_{SG} \quad - 26.60\Delta_{SF} \quad + 115.85\Delta_{SE}$$

$$M_{FG} = -34.36 \quad + 20.28\Delta_{SG} \quad + 42.24\Delta_{SF} \quad + 118.08\Delta_{SE}$$

$$M_{GF} = -44.79 \quad + 61.83\Delta_{SG} \quad - 290.75\Delta_{SF} + 43.08\Delta_{SE}$$

$$M_{GB} = +77.93 \quad + 77.53\Delta_{SG} \quad + 161.53\Delta_{SF} - 23.94\Delta_{SE}$$

$$M_{GH} = -33.14 \quad - 139.36\Delta_{SG} + 129.22\Delta_{SF} - 19.15\Delta_{SE}$$

$$M_{HG} = 0$$

8. Reactions at the bases of the columns are found, as usual, by taking the columns as free bodies and finding the horizontal shears at the ends. At the top level,

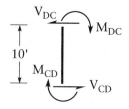 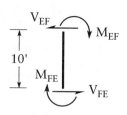

$$V_{CD} = +13.69 - 0.98\Delta_{SG} - 2.03\Delta_{SF} - 21.35\Delta_{SE}$$

$$V_{FE} = -6.33 - 0.98\Delta_{SG} - 2.03\Delta_{SF} - 21.35\Delta_{SE}$$

Notice that the preventer force no longer exists; the sum of these shears must therefore be zero.

$$0 = 7.36 - 1.96\Delta_{SG} - 4.06\Delta_{SF} - 42.70\Delta_{SE}$$

Similarly, at the second level,

$$0 = +9.33 + 13.68\Delta_{SG} - 41.42\Delta_{SF} + 26.86\Delta_{SE}$$

And at the support level,

$$0 = 2.68 - 18.58\Delta_{SG} + 17.22\Delta_{SF} - 2.56\Delta_{SE}$$

These three equations are solved simultaneously for the three sidesway displacements.

$$\Delta_{SG} = +0.5724 \text{ in.}; \qquad \Delta_{SF} = +0.4803 \text{ in.}; \qquad \Delta_{SE} = +0.1004 \text{ in.}$$

These known sidesway displacements are substituted back into the foregoing equations for moment to obtain the final redundant moments at the joints.

$$M_{AB} = 0; \qquad\qquad M_{ED} = +38.90 \text{ kip-ft}$$

$$M_{BA} = +53.66 \text{ kip-ft}; \qquad M_{EF} = -38.90 \text{ kip-ft}$$

$$M_{BG} = -58.17 \text{ kip-ft}; \qquad M_{FE} = -61.18 \text{ kip-ft}$$

$$M_{BC} = +4.51 \text{ kip-ft}; \qquad M_{FC} = +51.79 \text{ kip-ft}$$

$$M_{CB} = +130.48 \text{ kip-ft}; \qquad M_{FG} = +9.39 \text{ kip-ft}$$

$$M_{CF} = -154.63 \text{ kip-ft};\quad M_{GF} = -144.74 \text{ kip-ft}$$

$$M_{CD} = +24.15 \text{ kip-ft};\quad M_{GB} = +197.49 \text{ kip-ft}$$

$$M_{DC} = +75.99 \text{ kip-ft};\quad M_{GH} = -52.76 \text{ kip-ft}$$

$$M_{DE} = -75.99 \text{ kip-ft};\quad M_{HG} = 0$$

Final results are shown in the following sketches. The moment diagram is drawn on the tension side.

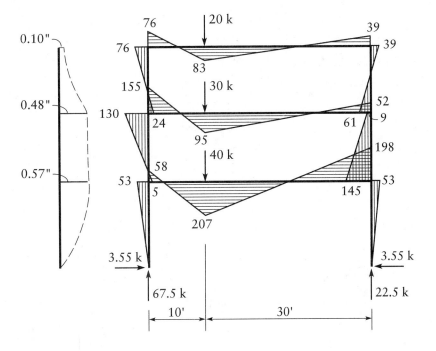

The solution of Example 16-10 is complete as it is shown in the sketch. Any further calculations concerning deflections, shears, or displacements can be made by using the given results.

It was noted earlier that a rather subtle source of error can arise when the preventer forces are released, making it essential that all moments produced by the preventer forces be summed before the horizontal imbalances are found, as was done in Example 16-10. The reason for such a requirement is that the release of a preventer force by itself creates secondary sideways, with their secondary unbalanced forces at the other levels. In Example 16-10, for example, the release of preventer force H_G by itself would create a secondary sideway with a secondary horizontal imbalance at the other levels (E and F), which in turn would require that secondary preventer forces be added at those levels. All such secondary effects can be included in the solution, however, simply by summing all moments (as in step 8 of Example 16-10) before finding the imbalance at each level. The result will always be a set of n simultaneous equations—one equation for each level—whose solution automatically includes the interdependence among the n unknowns.

Outside Problems   Determine the reactions on the given steel frames, and sketch the moment diagrams.

Problem 16-21*

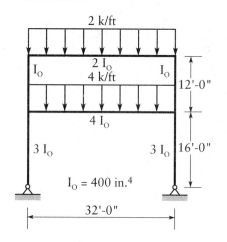

Problem 16-22

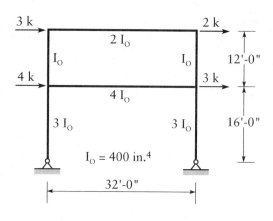

Problem 16-23*

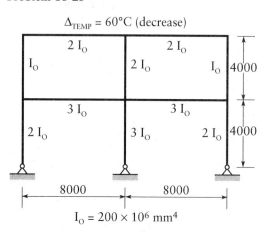

Problem 16-24

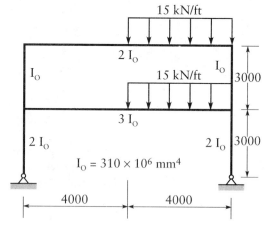

16.6 DISCUSSION OF THE SLOPE DEFLECTION METHOD

The presentation of the slope deflection method given in this chapter constitutes the barest of introductions to the method. As has been noted, the biggest drawback of the method involves the difficulty inherent in solving the large sets of simultaneous equations. A solution for sets of equations having more than about four unknowns rapidly becomes impractical. Clearly, some better way to perform these solutions is essential if the method is to be used on structures of any significant size.

One way to obtain a solution to these equations is through the use of numerical methods, also called *iterative methods* or *methods of successive approximations*. Several such methods have been developed, the most popular of which is that of moment distribution, presented in the next chapter. In addition to these manual methods, mathematics software at modest cost has been developed for computerized methods that can handle arrays of hundreds of unknowns; this alternative, if available, is by far the most convenient way to obtain a solution to the sets of equations.

Several very good (but very expensive) programs perform a complete analysis of rigid frames. Such software does nothing, however, to help one understand the structural response to loads; they simply produce the final numerical results. Most responsible instructors do not permit their students to use such programs until the students have exhibited a firm understanding of the ways in which a structure responds to load.

A few points concerning the method of slope deflection warrant further discussion. One such point involves recognizing the diagonal pattern formed by the set of simultaneous equations. In the preceding examples, diagonal arrays always appeared in the solution for the relative rotations. This type of diagonal array is particularly susceptible to solution by successive approximations; the solution of these diagonal arrays usually converges in only a few cycles. It is no coincidence that the method of moment distribution, presented in the next chapter, relies heavily on this property of diagonal matrices.

A second point in the slope deflection method that bears repeating relates to the distinction between displacement due to settlement of supports and displacement due to sidesway. Both of these deformations produce translational moments, but they have been treated as separate cases in the foregoing examples. In general, the distinction may be drawn that, if the magnitude of a translational displacement is known, the displacement will be included in the starting translational moments TM_{AB} or TM_{BA}; if the translation is unknown and its magnitude must be found as part of the solution, the displacement will be treated as sidesway.

Sidesway, however, need not always be horizontal, although it was in fact horizontal in all of the examples presented heretofore. Consider the frame of Figure 16-13, for example, where the column CD is subject to downward displacement due to flexure in beam BCF.

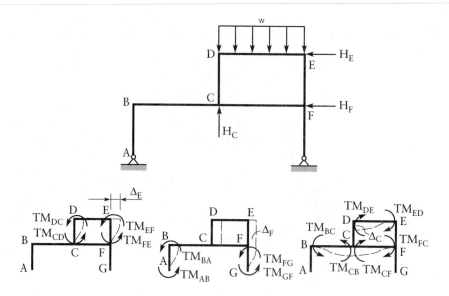

FIGURE 16-13 Alternative cases of sidesway.

The solution of the frame shown in Figure 16-13 resembles the solution of other examples involving slope deflection, once the patterns of sidesway (or downsway) are recognized. The downward displacement Δ_C of column *DC* is of unknown magnitude, and it exists to satisfy vertical equilibrium. Its magnitude must be found as part of the overall solution; it is therefore classified as sidesway (or downsway).

Another point concerning the slope deflection method has to do with refinements, special applications, and special cases. Any procedure that is as widely used as the slope deflection method is will be subject to special tricks, gimmicks, and shortcuts. There are, of course, many such refinements and additions to the slope deflection method; more often than not, such additions tend to obscure what is essentially a rather straightforward (though tedious) procedure.

One popular refinement is a "modified stiffness factor," intended to be used when the support at the outer end of a member is a hinge. The use of the modified stiffness factor eliminates the rotation $EI\theta$ at that hinge from the array of equations; it must be used with a propped-end moment, however, rather than a fixed-end moment. Other modifications apply at the midpoint of a symmetrical system or at the midpoint of an antisymmetrical system. Each has its own peculiarities regarding starting moments and algebraic signs that must be memorized and kept straight. Many of these modified methods are applicable only in situations where sidesway is prevented; they fall apart when sidesway is introduced.

Such refinements seem especially popular among people in the academic world who deal with the slope deflection equations almost daily. For those in practice, who might use the method once a year (or less), such refinements are rarely worth memorizing and keeping straight. The general procedures presented in this chapter will serve the long-term user quite adequately, without creating any unnecessary clutter.

For high-rise buildings, the continuous rigid frame (with its slope deflection analysis) is the dominant structure in today's technology, although the trussed frame is gaining acceptance in areas subject to high earthquake risk. For low buildings—buildings less than about six or seven stories high—the shearwall and diaphragm structure (with its statically determinate analysis) is the dominant structural system, primarily because it offers real advantages in cost, ease of fabrication, and ease of construction. For buildings of more than seven or eight stories, however, the foundation problems under shearwalls rapidly become insurmountable, and the rigid frame becomes more practical. Familiarity with both structural systems (and both methods of analysis) is recommended to anyone who plans to enter general practice.

Medium span steel arch, Alsea Bay, Waldport, Oregon.
(Photograph courtesy American Institute of Steel
Construction, reprinted by permission.)

CHAPTER 17

Moment Distribution

Moment distribution is an iterative technique for solving the sets of simultaneous equations that occur in the slope deflection method. It has several advantages over the algebraically exact solutions that were used in Chapter 16:

1. The solution is made directly for moments, rather than for a slope that is used later in computing the moments.
2. There is a physical interpretation for each numerical operation.
3. The technique is self-correcting for some types of numerical error.
4. The solution is much faster than the algebraically exact solution.

The technique also has some disadvantages:

1. Good "bookkeeping" practices must be rigorously observed.
2. The accuracy of the final results is reduced (not seriously).
3. The calculations can be quite confusing to pick up again after an interruption.

The technique of moment distribution was introduced by Hardy Cross in 1932. In the years since its introduction, it has had a profound influence on calculation techniques in all fields of civil engineering. The advent of the computerized solution of rigid frames has reduced its use appreciably, but in manual solutions it remains probably the most widely used solution. It seems likely to continue to be widely used for many years to come.

Moment distribution may be completely derived from the slope deflection method. It is a repetitive joint-by-joint solution of the set of simultaneous equations, rather than a one-time algebraic solution of a single large array. It converges rapidly; a final solution is usually developed in only a few cycles.

Consider the joint C in Figure 17-1, taken as a typical joint from a rigid frame. The adjacent joints are labeled as left, right, top, and bottom, but the number of joints is not limited to four; any number of members may be framed into the joint.

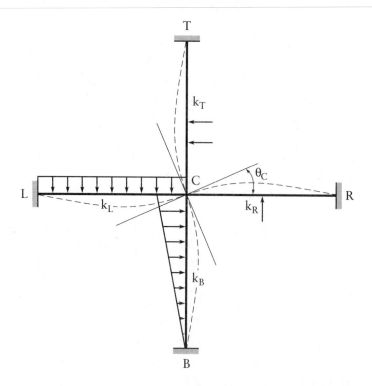

FIGURE 17-1 Rotation of a joint.

The value of k is given for each member, as shown, and includes the effects of both moment of inertia and length of span, where $k = I/L$. The starting moments are either fixed-end moments or translational moments with all joints locked against rotation—just as in the method of slope deflection. The joint C is then released and allowed to rotate. The resulting moments in the other joints (still locked against rotation) are found in the following solution, using the usual slope deflection procedures.

1. The elastic curves resulting from the release of joint C have been included in the sketch of Figure 17-1.

2. The stiffness factors and starting moments are determined for each span. The starting moments (denoted here as SM) are determined, as usual, with all joints locked against rotation. For member LC,

$$k_{LC} = k_L; \quad \text{starting moments are } SM_{LC} \text{ and } SM_{CL}$$

For member RC,

$$k_{RC} = k_R; \quad \text{starting moments are } SM_{RC} \text{ and } SM_{CR}$$

For member TC,

$k_{TC} = k_T;$ starting moments are SM_{TC} and SM_{CT}

For member BC,

$k_{BC} = k_B;$ starting moments are SM_{BC} and SM_{CB}

3. The slope deflection equations are written for each member, recognizing that only joint C is being released; the other joints remain locked against rotation and their rotations are zero:

$$M_{LC} = 2Ek_L\theta_C + SM_{LC}$$

$$M_{CL} = 4Ek_L\theta_C + SM_{CL}$$

$$M_{RC} = 2Ek_R\theta_C + SM_{RC}$$

$$M_{CR} = 4Ek_R\theta_R + SM_{CR}$$

$$M_{TC} = 2Ek_T\theta_C + SM_{TC}$$

$$M_{CT} = 4Ek_T\theta_C + SM_{CT}$$

$$M_{BC} = 2Ek_B\theta_C + SM_{BC}$$

$$M_{CB} = 4Ek_B\theta_C + SM_{CB}$$

4. The statics equation is written for joint C, the only joint being released:

$$\Sigma M_C = 0;   M_{CL} + M_{CT} + M_{CR} + M_{CB} = 0$$

5. The slope deflection equations are substituted into the statics equations:

$$4E\,(k_L + k_T + k_R + k_B) + \Sigma SM_C = 0$$

Notice that the sum of the starting moments around joint C, ΣSM_C, yields the *imbalance* in the moment around the joint, denoted here as ΔM.

6. The foregoing equation is solved for the rotation $E\theta_C$:

$$E\theta_C = -\Delta M \frac{1}{4\Sigma k}$$

where

$$\Sigma k = k_L + k_R + k_T + k_B$$

7. This value of the rotation is substituted back into the slope deflection equations to find the final moments at the ends of each of the four members:

$$M_{LC} = SM_{LC} - \frac{1}{2}\frac{k_L}{\Sigma k}\Delta M = SM_{LC} - \frac{1}{2}\Delta M_{CL}$$

$$M_{CL} = SM_{CL} - \frac{k_L}{\Sigma k}\Delta M = SM_{CL} - \Delta M_{CL}$$

$$M_{RC} = SM_{RC} - \frac{1}{2}\frac{k_R}{\Sigma k}\Delta M = SM_{RC} - \frac{1}{2}\Delta M_{CR}$$

$$M_{CR} = SM_{CR} - \frac{k_R}{\Sigma k}\Delta M = SM_{CR} - \Delta M_{CR}$$

$$M_{TC} = SM_{TC} - \frac{1}{2}\frac{k_T}{\Sigma k}\Delta M = SM_{TC} - \frac{1}{2}\Delta M_{CT}$$

$$M_{CT} = SM_{CT} - \frac{k_T}{\Sigma k}\Delta M = SM_{CT} - \Delta M_{CT}$$

$$M_{BC} = SM_{BC} - \frac{1}{2}\frac{k_B}{\Sigma k}\Delta M = SM_{BC} - \frac{1}{2}\Delta M_{CB}$$

$$M_{CB} = SM_{CB} - \frac{k_B}{\Sigma k}\Delta M = SM_{CB} - \Delta M_{CB}$$

The foregoing solution has yielded the moments at the joints adjacent to joint C when joint C is unlocked and allowed to rotate to its equilibrium position. A physical interpretation of the solution is readily possible:

1. When joint C was released and allowed to rotate, the *imbalance* in moments at joint C, ΔM, was distributed proportionally to the four members framed into the joint. Each member received moment according to a distribution factor DF, where

$$DF_L = -\frac{k_L}{k_L + k_R + k_T + k_B}$$

$$DF_R = -\frac{k_R}{k_L + k_R + k_T + k_B}$$

$$DF_T = -\frac{k_T}{k_L + k_R + k_T + k_B}$$

$$DF_B = -\frac{k_B}{k_L + k_R + k_T + k_B}$$

Notice that the distribution factor is always negative.

2. The resulting *change* in the moment at the near end of the member (nearest to joint C) was immediately carried by half (with the same sign) to the far end of the member.

3. The final moment at every joint, including joint C, is the algebraic sum of the starting moment plus all added increments.

A procedure for solving a system of several joints can be formulated, using the foregoing interpretation:

1. For each span, determine stiffnesses and starting moments exactly as in the slope deflection method.

2. At each joint, determine the distribution factor DF to each member framed into the joint, where $DF = k/\Sigma k$.

3. On a schematic of the structure, enter the starting moments for each member and the distribution factors for each member.

4. Beginning at some convenient joint in the structure, sum moments around the joint to find the imbalance ΔM. Unlock the joint and allow it to rotate, distributing the imbalance ΔM to each member framed into the joint according to its distribution factor DF.

5. Carry half of this distributed imbalance to the far end of the member.

6. Move to the next joint and repeat the procedure for that joint; then continue to the next joint; and so on. Repeat until every joint in the structure has been "relaxed," which constitutes one cycle of relaxation.

7. At this point, the imbalances in the starting moments at every joint will have been balanced to zero. However, additional moments will have been

carried into the joint when surrounding joints were relaxed. The relaxation cycle must now be repeated, but this time only for any new imbalances that were created by the carryover moments.

8. Repeat the cycle until the carryover values become negligible (usually four or five cycles).

9. Sum all moments at each end of each member algebraically to obtain the final moment there.

Moment distribution is simply a technique for solving the set of equations obtained in a slope deflection solution. All of the characteristics of the slope deflection method—including fixed-end moments, translational moments, sidesway, sign conventions, and so on—therefore apply to moment distribution. Moment distribution constitutes a numerical technique that can be applied to a part of the slope deflection method; it is not by itself a method of analysis.

17.1 CONTINUOUS BEAMS

The applications of moment distribution are best illustrated by examples. The two-span continuous beam of Figure 17-2 will be considered as a first example.

As shown in the schematic of Figure 17-2, the fixed-end moment $1/12wL^2 = 9$ kN-m was computed aside and entered with its proper sign at each end of span AB. A starting moment of zero is entered for the span BC.

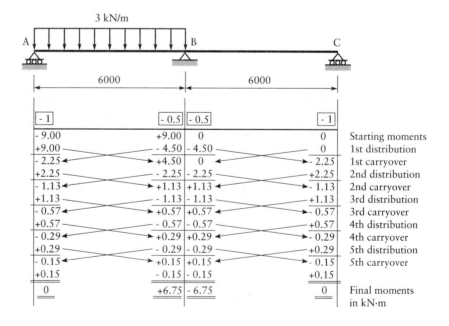

FIGURE 17-2 Moment distribution on a two-span beam.

A distribution factor of -1 is computed for the hinges at joint A and at joint C and is entered on the schematic as shown in Figure 17-2. For joint B, a distribution factor $DF_B = k/\Sigma k = 1/6/(1/6 + 1/6) = 1/2$ is computed and entered on either side of joint B, as shown in the figure.

The first distribution is made, as indicated, by finding the imbalance ΔM at each joint, multiplying that imbalance by the distribution factor, and reapplying it. A line is drawn under each of the distributed moments to indicate that the joint was "balanced" at that point. To reduce the likelihood of error, all distributions are completed for the entire structure before any carryovers are made.

When the distributions have been completed, each distributed value on a beam is carried over to the other end of the beam, as shown by the arrows in Figure 17-2. The carryover moment is 1/2 the distributed moment, with the same algebraic sign. Again, to reduce the likelihood of error, all carryovers are completed before the next distribution cycle is started.

When the carryover cycle is completed, any imbalance created by the carryover values is found by summing the moments that have entered the joint since the last distribution; the imbalance is distributed, as before, by multiplying it by the distribution factor and reapplying it. Once again, a line is drawn under the number to indicate that the joint was rebalanced at that point.

The procedure is repeated until the carryover is considered to be negligible or (in this case) repetitive. The final moment at each end of the beam is the algebraic sum of all moments at that end, including starting moments, distributed imbalances, and carryover moments.

The exact answer to the foregoing beam problem can be found in Chapter 16, for the beam of Figure 16-7; the exact moment is $wL^2/16$ or 6.75 kN-m. In this case, the result obtained by the moment distribution technique turns out to be exactly correct.

A second example includes varying moments of inertia and varying span lengths.

Example 17-1   Determine the moments at the supports of the given continuous beam, using moment distribution.

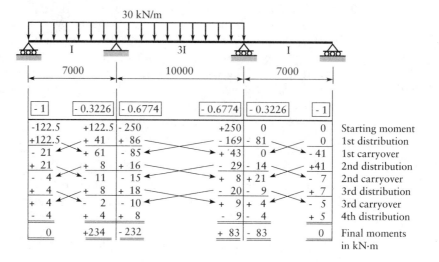

Solution   The supporting calculations are performed first.

The starting moments in the table are fixed-end moments, $1/12wL^2$:

$$FM_{AB} = -\frac{1}{12}wL^2 = -122.5 \text{ kN-m}; \qquad FM_{BA} = +122.5 \text{ kN-m}$$

$$FM_{BC} = -\frac{1}{12}wL^2 = -250.0 \text{ kN-m}; \qquad FM_{CB} = +250.0 \text{ kN-m}$$

Starting moments are entered where shown in the preceding schematic table. Distribution factors at joints B and C are computed as

$$DF_{BA} = -\frac{\frac{1}{7}}{\frac{1}{7} + \frac{3}{10}} = -0.3226$$

$$DF_{BC} = -\frac{\frac{3}{10}}{\frac{1}{7} + \frac{3}{10}} = -0.6774$$

In the preceding table, the distribution factors are shown as the boxed values.

All distributions are made first; no carryovers are made at this point. The first imbalance at joint A is -122.5 kN-m. It is multiplied by the distribution factor −1 and reentered and underlined, indicating that the sum of moments at A is now zero.

The first imbalance at joint B is −127.5 kN-m. It is multiplied by the distribution factors to each side of joint B, and the results are entered as positive moments and underlined as shown, indicating that the sum of moments around joint B is now zero.

The first imbalance at joint C is +250 kN-m. It is multiplied by the distribution factors to either side of joint C, and the results are entered and underlined as shown; the sum of moments around joint C is now zero.

The first imbalance at joint D is zero. No further calculation is necessary, but the value of zero is entered and underlined anyway, to ensure that the same number of lines are used at D as at the other joints (a bookkeeping indicator).

When all distributions have been completed, the carryovers are begun. The moments just distributed are carried over to the far end of the beam by a factor of half (with the same sign). These carryovers are indicated on the preceding schematic by the arrows. No distributions are made while the carryover cycle is underway.

When the carryover cycle is completed for all joints, a new cycle of distribution is begun. All new increments of carryover moment (those entered since the last underlined values) are summed to find any new imbalance; then the imbalance is distributed to each member by its distribution factor, as before. No carryovers are made while this next distribution cycle is underway.

The second imbalance at joint A, for example, is +21 kN-m. It is distributed as +21 and then underlined as shown in the schematic. Similarly, the second imbalance at joint B is −24 kN-m. It is distributed as before, by multiplying by the distribution factors, entering these new values, and underlining them.

The procedure continues in this way until the carryover values are negligible or until they start repeating, as in the earlier example.

The exact values for the moments in Example 17-1 are those found in Chapter 16 in the slope deflection solution of Example 16-1. There, the exact solution was found to be

$$M_{BA} = -M_{BC} = +232.0 \text{ kN-m}$$

$$M_{CB} = -MCD = +83.6 \text{ kN-m}$$

In comparison, the values found here by moment distribution are 233 kN-m (average) and 83 kN-m, respectively—a very good agreement of results.

The next example includes a displaced support. As in any slope deflection solution, a known displacement produces a starting moment of known magnitude; thereafter, the solution is the same as before.

Example 17-2

Determine the moments at the supports of the steel beam of Example 17-1 for the case where the support at B could settle as much as 20 mm more than the other supports. The reference moment of inertia is 291×10^6 mm⁴

The reference moment of inertia is 291×10^6 mm⁴.

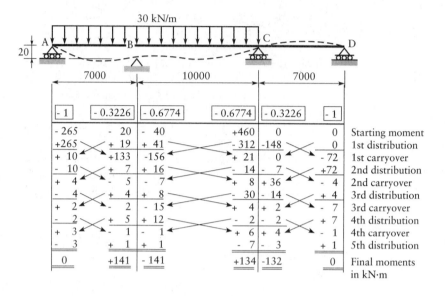

-1	-0.3226	-0.6774	-0.6774	-0.3226	-1	Starting moment
-265	-20	-40	+460	0	0	Starting moment
+265	+19	+41	-312	-148	0	1st distribution
+10	+133	-156	+21	0	-72	1st carryover
-10	+7	+16	-14	-7	+72	2nd distribution
+4	-5	-7	+8	+36	-4	2nd carryover
-4	+4	+8	-30	-14	+4	3rd distribution
+2	-2	-15	+4	+2	-7	3rd carryover
-2	+5	+12	-2	-2	+7	4th distribution
+3	-1	-1	+6	+4	-1	4th carryover
-3	+1	+1	-7	-3	+1	5th distribution
0	+141	-141	+134	-132	0	Final moments in kN·m

Solution

The supporting calculations are performed first.

The starting fixed-end moments are the same as those found earlier:

$$FM_{AB} = -122.5 \text{ kN-m}; \qquad FM_{BA} = +122.5 \text{ kN-m}$$

$$FM_{BC} = -250.0 \text{ kN-m}; \qquad FM_{CB} = +250.0 \text{ kN-m}$$

The starting translational moments are found as usual:

$$TM_{AB} = -6Ek\psi_{AB} = (-6 \times 200{,}000) \times \frac{291 \times 10^6}{7000} \times \frac{20}{7000}$$

$$= -143 \text{ kN-m}$$

$$TM_{BA} = TM_{AB} = -143 \text{ kN-m}$$

$$TM_{BC} = +6Ek\psi_{BC} = (+6 \times 200{,}000) \times \frac{3 \times 291 \times 10^6}{10{,}000} \times \frac{20}{10{,}000}$$

$$= +210 \text{ kN-m}$$

$$TM_{CB} = TM_{BC} = +210 \text{ kN-m}$$

The distribution factors are the same as those found earlier. For the hinges at A and D,

$$DF_{AB} = -1; \qquad DF_{DC} = -1$$

For joints B and C,

$$DF_{AB} = -0.3226; \qquad DF_{BC} = -0.6774$$

$$DF_{CD} = -0.3226; \qquad DF_{CB} = -0.6774$$

The distribution factors are entered on the preceding schematic table as shown.

The starting moments are the sum of the fixed-end moment and the translational moment at each end of the span. These sums are entered on the schematic table on the first line. From this point onward, the distributions and carryovers are performed exactly as before. The final values are double-underlined.

The exact values for the moments in Example 17-2 are those found in Chapter 16 in the slope deflection solution of Example 16-2. The exact values are

$$M_{BA} = -M_{BC} = +142.12 \text{ kN-m}$$

$$M_{CB} = -M_{CD} = +131.83 \text{ kN-m}$$

In comparison, the values just obtained by moment distribution are 141 kN-m and 133 kN-m (average), respectively—a very good agreement of results.

Outside Problems

Problem 17-1 Solve Problem 16-1 using moment distribution.

Problem 17-2 Solve Problem 16-2 using moment distribution.

Problem 17-3 Solve Problem 16-3 using moment distribution.

Problem 17-4 Solve Problem 16-4 using moment distribution.

Problem 17-5 Solve Problem 16-5 using moment distribution.

Problem 17-6 Solve Problem 16-6 using moment distribution.

17.2 SINGLE-SPAN FRAMES

The procedure for using moment distribution to solve single-span frames is like the procedure for continuous beams. One notable difference, however, is that carryover moments are carried vertically as well as horizontally. The "bookkeeping" part of the solution becomes somewhat harder to control, so it becomes even more important to follow a rigid, fixed procedure. An example of a symmetrically loaded portal frame will illustrate the application of moment distribution to single-span frames.

Example 17-3 Determine the moments at the joints of the given steel portal frame.

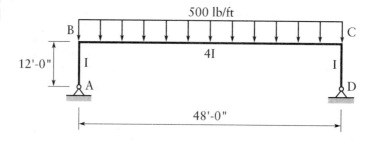

Reference $I = 153$ in.^{4}

Solution The schematic table becomes somewhat distorted, as shown in the following table.

The starting values are

$$FM_{BC} = -\frac{1}{12}wL^2 = -96 \text{ kip-ft}; \qquad FM_{CB} = +96 \text{ kip-ft}$$

The distribution factors are

$$DF_{AB} = -1; \qquad\qquad DF_{DC} = -1$$

$$DF_{BA} = -\frac{\dfrac{1}{12}}{\dfrac{1}{12}+\dfrac{4}{48}} = -\frac{1}{2}; \qquad DF_{BC} = -\frac{\dfrac{4}{48}}{\dfrac{1}{12}+\dfrac{4}{48}} = -\frac{1}{2}$$

$$DF_{CD} = -\frac{1}{2}; \qquad\qquad DF_{DC} = -\frac{1}{2}$$

The distribution factors and starting moments are entered on the frame as shown in the following sketch. On frames, it is well also to identify each member for continuing reference. It becomes even more important to underline the moments following each distribution and to include all entries, even if an entry is zero.

-0.5	-0.5		-0.5	-0.5	
B ↓BA	**BC →**		**← CB**	**CD ↓ C**	
0	-96		+96	0	Starting moments
+48	+48		-48	-48	1st distribution
0	-24		+24	0	1st carryover
+12	+12		-12	-12	2nd distribution
-12	-6		+6	+12	2nd carryover
+9	+9		-9	-9	3rd distribution
-3	-5		+5	+3	3rd carryover
+4	+4		-4	-4	4th distribution
-3	-2		+2	+3	4th carryover
+2	+2		-2	-2	5th distribution
+57	-58		-58	+57	Final moments in kip·ft

-1	-1	
A ↑ AB	**DC ↑ D**	
0	0	Starting moments
0	0	1st distribution
+24	-24	1st carryover
-24	+24	2nd distribution
+6	-6	2nd carryover
-6	+6	3rd distribution
+5	-5	3rd carryover
-5	+5	4th distribution
+2	-2	4th carryover
-2	+2	5th distribution
0	0	Final moments in kip·ft

The final average moment of 57.5 kip-ft at B and at C compares very well to the exact solution of 57.6 kip-ft obtained by the slope deflection method (Example 16-3).

The next example shows the application of moment distribution to frames under lateral loading. As might be expected, the procedure follows the slope deflection method, except that the set of simultaneous equations are solved by moment distribution rather than by algebraic means.

Example 17-4   Determine the moments at the joints of the steel frame of Example 17-3 for the case where the frame is loaded laterally, as shown.

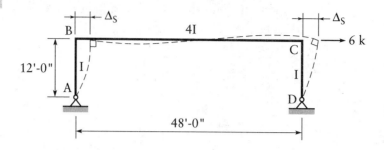

Reference $I = 153$ in.^{4}

Solution   As before, the schematic table becomes somewhat distorted.

The supporting calculations include the translational moments and the distribution factors. The sidesway displacement Δ_S is assumed to be in inches:

$$TM_{AB} = -6Ek\psi_{AB} = (-6 \times 29 \times 10^3) \times \frac{153}{144} \times \frac{\Delta_S}{144} = -1284\Delta_S \text{ kip-in.}$$

$$TM_{BA} = TM_{AB} = -107 \text{ kip-ft}$$

$$TM_{CD} = TM_{DC} = -107 \text{ kip-ft}$$

The distribution factors are those found in Example 17-3:

$$DF_{AB} = -1; \qquad DF_{BA} = -\frac{1}{2}; \qquad DF_{BC} = -\frac{1}{2}$$

$$DF_{CB} = -\frac{1}{2}; \qquad DF_{DC} = -1; \qquad DF_{CD} = -\frac{1}{2}$$

The starting values of the translational moments are not moments, but a coefficient times a common unknown displacement Δ_S. Since *all* starting values are linear multiples of Δ_S, the moment distribution remains valid when only the coefficient is used.

	$\boxed{-0.5}$ $\boxed{-0.5}$			$\boxed{-0.5}$ $\boxed{-0.5}$	
B ↓ BA	BC →		← CB	CD ↓ **C**	
-107	0		0	-107	Starting moment
+ 54	+ 54		+ 54	+ 54	1st distribution
+ 54	+ 27		+ 27	+ 54	1st carryover
- 41	- 41		- 41	- 41	2nd distribution
- 14	- 21		- 21	- 14	2nd carryover
+ 18	+ 18		+ 18	+ 18	3rd distribution
+ 11	+ 9		+ 9	+ 11	3rd carryover
- 10	- 10		- 10	- 10	4th distribution
- 35	+ 36		+ 36	- 35	Final coefficient

$\boxed{-1}$	$\boxed{-1}$	
A ↑ AB	DC ↑ **D**	
- 107	- 107	Starting moment
+107	+107	1st distribution
- 27	- 27	1st carryover
+ 27	+ 27	2nd distribution
- 21	- 21	2nd carryover
+ 21	+ 21	3rd distribution
- 9	- 9	3rd carryover
+ 9	+ 9	4th distribution
0	0	Final coefficient

The exact solution for these coefficients (see Example 16-4) is $35.7\Delta_S$ kip-ft, which compares very closely to the value of $35.5\Delta_S$ kip-ft found here.

From this point onward, the solution is a slope deflection solution; the moment distribution part of the solution is over.

The horizontal shears at the base of the columns are found in exactly the same way as in slope deflection. The columns are removed as free bodies, and the horizontal couple is found in the usual way.

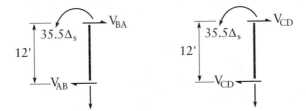

$$\Sigma M_B = 0$$

$$-35.5\Delta_S + V_{AB}(12) = 0$$

$$V_{AB} = 2.96\Delta_S$$

$$\Sigma M_C = 0$$

$$-35.5\Delta_S + V_{DC}(12) = 0$$

$$V_{DC} = 2.96\Delta_S$$

These horizontal shears are shown on the frame as indicated in the following sketch. (Vertical reactions are statically determinate; they were found separately and entered on the sketch.)

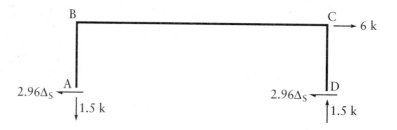

The sum of horizontal forces yields a solution for Δ_S:

$$\Sigma F_X = 0; \qquad -2.96\Delta_S - 2.96\Delta_S + 6 = 0$$

$$\Delta_S = 1.014 \text{ in.}$$

The final values of the moments at the joints are found to be

$$M_{AB} = 0$$

$$M_{BA} = -35.5\Delta_S = -36 \text{ kip-ft}$$

$$M_{BC} = +35.5\Delta_S = +36 \text{ kip-ft}$$

$$M_{CD} = 0$$

This final value of 36 kip-ft is identical to the one in the exact solution, given by the slope deflection solution of Example 16-4.

The next example deals with an unsymmetrical frame subject to sidesway. As in all slope deflection solutions of such cases, the solution consists of two parts—the first with sidesway prevented, and the second for the results of the sidesway.

Example 17-5 Determine the moments at the joints of the given steel frame.

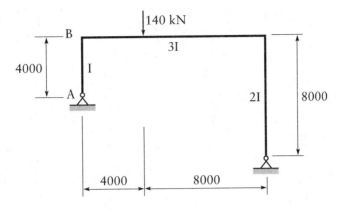

Reference $I = 300 \times 10^6$ mm^4

Solution The first part of the solution to be performed is that with sidesway prevented. The preventer force H is applied at joint C, as shown in the following sketch.

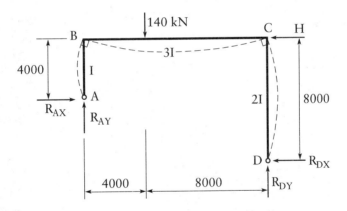

The starting moments are fixed-end moments:

$$FM_{BC} = -\frac{Pab^2}{L^2} = -\frac{140 \times 4 \times 8^2}{12^2} = -249 \text{ kN-m}$$

$$FM_{CB} = +\frac{Pa^2b}{L^2} = +\frac{140 \times 4^2 \times 8}{12^2} = +124 \text{ kN-m}$$

The distribution factors are found as usual:

$$D_{AB} = -1; \quad D_{BA} = -\frac{\frac{1}{4}}{\frac{1}{4}+\frac{3}{12}} = -\frac{1}{2}; \quad D_{BC} = -\frac{\frac{3}{12}}{\frac{1}{4}+\frac{3}{12}} = -\frac{1}{2}$$

$$D_{CB} = -\frac{\frac{3}{12}}{\frac{3}{12}+\frac{2}{8}} = -\frac{1}{2}; \quad D_{CD} = -\frac{\frac{2}{8}}{\frac{3}{12}+\frac{2}{8}} = -\frac{1}{2}; \quad D_{DC} = -1$$

These values are entered on the following schematic table, and the moment distribution solution is made.

$\boxed{-0.5}$	$\boxed{-0.5}$		$\boxed{-0.5}$	$\boxed{-0.5}$	
B ↓ BA	BC →		← CB	CD ↓ C	
0	-249		+124	0	Starting moment
+125	+125		- 62	- 62	1st distribution
0	- 31		+ 63	0	1st carryover
+ 16	+ 16		- 32	- 32	2nd distribution
- 32	- 16		+ 16	+ 16	2nd carryover
+ 24	+ 24		- 16	- 16	3rd distribution
- 4	- 8		+ 12	+ 4	3rd carryover
+ 6	+ 6		- 8	- 8	4th distribution
- 6	- 4		+ 3	+ 4	4th carryover
+ 5	+ 5		- 4	- 4	5th distribution
+134	- 132		+ 96	- 98	Final moment in kN·m (sidesway prevented)

$\boxed{-1}$			$\boxed{-1}$		
A ↑ AB			DC ↑ D		
0			0		Starting moment
0			0		1st distribution
+ 63			- 31		1st carryover
- 63			+ 31		2nd distribution
+ 8			- 8		2nd carryover
- 8			+ 8		3rd distribution
+ 12			- 8		3rd carryover
- 12			+ 8		4th distribution
+ 3			- 4		4th carryover
- 3			+ 4		5th distribution
0			0		Final moment in kN·m (sidesway prevented)

The horizontal reactions at the bases of the columns are found by removing the columns as free bodies and finding the horizontal shears. The results of such a solution are entered in the following sketches.

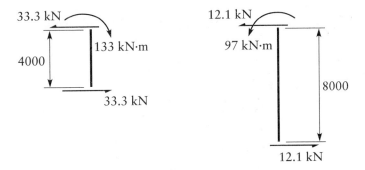

Frame reactions are shown in the following sketch, for the case of loads with sidesway prevented.

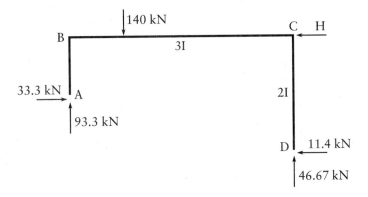

The sum of horizontal forces provides a solution for the preventer force H:

$$\Sigma F_X = 0; \quad +33.3 - 11.4 - H = 0$$
$$H = 21.9 \text{ kN}$$

The second part of the solution is that for sidesway only, with no loads being applied. The translational moments due to sidesway, with H directed toward the right, are

$$TM_{AB} = -6Ek\psi_{AB} = (-6 \times 200,000) \times \frac{300 \times 10^6}{4000} \times \frac{\Delta_S}{4000}$$

$$= -22.5\Delta_S \text{ kN-m}$$

$$TM_{BA} = -22.5\Delta_S \text{ kN-m}$$

$$TM_{CD} = -6Ek\psi_{CD} = (-6 \times 200,000) \times \frac{2 \times 300 \times 10^6}{8000} \times \frac{\Delta_S}{8000}$$

$$= -11.25 \text{ kN-m}$$

$$TM_{DC} = -11.25 \text{ kN-m}$$

The distribution factors are the same as those computed for the case with sidesway prevented. The moment distribution is performed for the coefficients of Δ_S as in the earlier example.

-0.5	-0.5		-0.5	-0.5	
B ↓ BA	BC →		← CB	CD ↓ C	
-22.50	0		0	-11.25	Starting moment
+11.25	+11.25		+5.63	+5.63	1st distribution
+11.25	+2.82		+5.63	+5.63	1st carryover
-7.04	-7.04		-5.63	-5.63	2nd distribution
-2.82	-2.82		-3.52	-1.41	2nd carryover
+2.82	+2.82		+2.47	+2.47	3rd distribution
+1.76	+1.24		+1.24	+1.41	3rd carryover
-1.50	-1.50		-1.33	-1.33	4th distribution
-6.78	+6.77		-6.77	+4.49	Final coefficient

-1		-1
A ↑ AB		DC ↑ D
-22.50		-11.25	Starting moment
+22.50		+11.25	1st distribution
+5.63		+2.82	1st carryover
-5.63		-2.82	2nd distribution
-3.52		-2.82	2nd carryover
+3.52		+2.82	3rd distribution
+1.41		+1.24	3rd carryover
-1.41		-1.24	4th distribution
0		0	Final coefficient

The moments at the joints are

$$M_{AB} = 0 \qquad\qquad M_{DC} = 0$$

$$M_{BA} = -6.78\Delta_S \text{ kN-m} \qquad M_{CD} = -4.48\Delta_S \text{ kN-m}$$

$$M_{BC} = +6.77\Delta_S \text{ kN-m} \qquad M_{CB} = +4.49\Delta_S \text{ kN-m}$$

This result is identical to the exact solution found by slope deflection in Example 16-5. The remainder of the solution to this example matches that given in Example 16-5 and is not repeated here.

Outside Problems

Problem 17-7 Solve Problem 15-17 using moment distribution.

Problem 17-8 Solve Problem 15-18 using moment distribution.

Problem 17-9 Solve Problem 15-19 using moment distribution.

Problem 17-10 Solve Problem 15-20 using moment distribution.

Problem 17-11 Solve Problem 15-21 using moment distribution.

Problem 17-12 Solve Problem 15-22 using moment distribution.

Problem 17-13 Solve Problem 15-23 using moment distribution.

Problem 17-14 Solve Problem 15-24 using moment distribution.

17.3 MULTISPAN AND MULTISTORY FRAMES

As one might expect, the applications of moment distribution in multispan and multistory frames are simply an extension of the applications to single-span frames. Of course, the extension gets progressively more complex and more difficult to control. Possibly the most difficult aspect of applying moment distribution to the larger frames involves trying to maintain orderly "bookkeeping" practices.

In all of the earlier examples, no more than two vertical lines of moments occurred at any one joint. In multispan multistory frames, as many as four lines (or more, if the frame is pentagonal or hexagonal) can occur. In larger structures, the sheer size of the schematic table with its four columns of numbers at each joint can easily become a problem. In years past (before computerized solutions), it was common practice on larger frames to perform the moment distribution on a drawing board, using a full-size 24 in. × 36 in. sheet of drawing paper as the worksheet.

Just trying to keep distributions and carryovers in their proper places in the schematic table can become quite confusing on such large projects. The problem is compounded by telephone calls, lunch periods, scheduled meetings, and other interruptions that force one to leave the schematic table and come back to it later, thereby losing one's place in the cycle. A rigidly maintained, orderly, and regular procedure is the best insurance against getting lost as a result of such interruptions.

One popular arrangement of the schematic table applies to the two-story, two-bay frame of Figure 17-3. The schematic table is shown separately in Figure 17-4, with distribution factors and starting moments arranged in their correct positions. Moments are recorded above the beam or column at its left end and below the beam or column at its right end. Distribution factors are entered in a box, providing an indicator of the place where moments are to be entered.

It should be apparent by now that, for smaller frames, moment distribution offers a real advantage in performing a solution of the slope deflection equations. As the size of the frame increases, however, moment distribution becomes more and more cumbersome until it, too, loses its value. For solving large arrays of unknowns generated by the slope deflection method, the matrix methods of solution come into prominence.

This text stops here, at the threshhold of the matrix methods of analysis. The matrix methods represent a relatively new approach in structural analysis and depend heavily on computerized solutions of the matrices. Solution of the large arrays of equations encountered in the matrix solutions is possible—even common—using modestly priced software that has been specially developed for personal computers. For any array having more than about six unknowns, manual methods of solution cease to be economically viable; using computerized methods in such cases is strongly recommended.

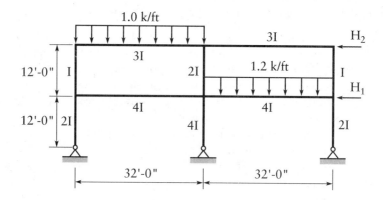

FIGURE 17-3 Two-story two-bay rigid frame.

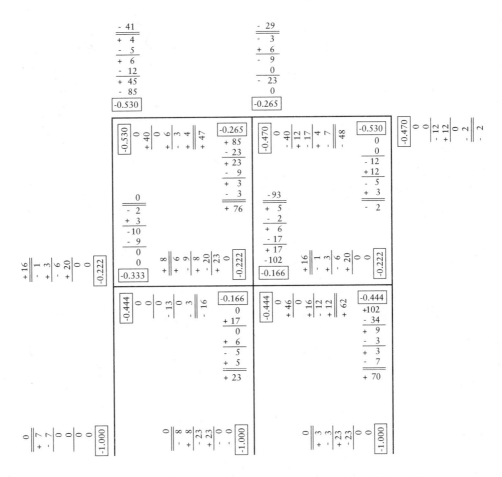

FIGURE 17-4 Moment distribution in a multispan multistory frame.

Outside Problems

Problem 17-15 Solve Problem 16-15 using moment distribution.

Problem 17-16 Solve Problem 16-16 using moment distribution.

Problem 17-17 Solve Problem 16-17 using moment distribution.

Problem 17-18 Solve Problem 16-18 using moment distribution.

Problem 17-19 Solve Problem 16-19 using moment distribution.

Problem 17-20 Solve Problem 16-20 using moment distribution.

Problem 17-21 Solve Problem 16-21 using moment distribution.

Problem 17-22 Solve Problem 16-22 using moment distribution.

Problem 17-23 Solve Problem 16-23 using moment distribution.

Problem 17-24 Solve Problem 16-24 using moment distribution.

Review of Hinged Beams and Three-hinged Arches

In the preparation of this text, it was assumed that the reader has completed the usual preparatory coursework in elementary statics and elementary strength of materials. The more popular texts on statics and strength usually include a few problems involving hinged beams and three-hinged arches, but little emphasis is placed on these configurations. The following discussions are included here for students who may want to review these topics.

A.1 HINGED BEAMS

A beam may be extended over several support points and nonetheless remain statically determinate if hinge points are judiciously placed at interior points along the span. Typical hinged beams are shown in Figure A-1 for two- and three-span beams. Additional spans could be treated similarly, but members longer than about four spans begin to encounter problems with thermal expansion and contraction.

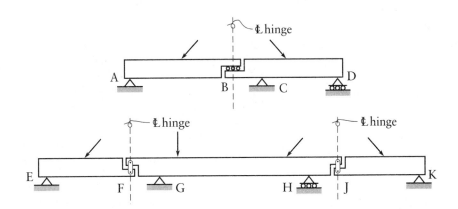

FIGURE A-1 Hinged beams.

The reactions for hinged beams can readily be computed by simple statics. To begin, one looks for segments of the overall beam that have only two
hinge points; in the beams of Figure A-1, for example, such segments are
beams AB, EF, and JK. These segments may be solved as simple beams. The
reactions computed for these segments are then placed as known loads on
the remaining spans. Some examples will illustrate the procedure.

Example A-1   Determine the reactions for the given hinged beam.

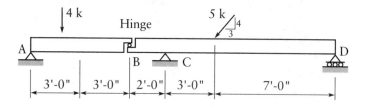

Solution   The segment AB has only two hinged supports. It does not matter that one
of the hinges is located internally; it still functions as a hinged support. A
free body of AB is shown in the following sketch.

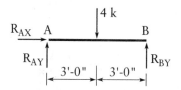

The reaction R_{BY} is found by summing moments about A:

$$\Sigma M_A = 0 = (4 \times 3) - (R_{BY} \times 6)$$
$$R_{BY} = 2 \text{ kips}$$

The reaction R_{AY} is found by summing moments about B:

$$\Sigma M_B = 0 = (-4 \times 3) + (R_{AY} \times 6)$$
$$R_{AY} = 2 \text{ kips}$$

The reaction R_{AX} is found by summing forces horizontally:

$$\Sigma F_H = 0 = R_{AX}$$

The free body of segment BCD can now be drawn, with the reaction at B shown as a known load.

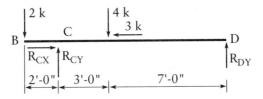

The reactions for beam BCD are found in the same way as those for any other simply supported beam:

$$\Sigma M_C = 0 = (-2 \times 2) + (4 \times 3) - (R_{DY} \times 10)$$
$$R_{DY} = 0.8 \text{ kips}$$

$$\Sigma M_D = 0 = (-2 \times 12) - (4 \times 7) + (R_{CY} \times 10)$$
$$R_{CY} = 5.2 \text{ kips}$$

$$\Sigma F_H = 0 = +R_{CX} - 3$$
$$R_{CX} = 3 \text{ kips}$$

The final external reactions are shown in the following sketch.

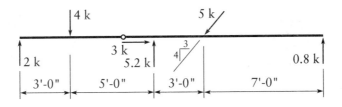

Example A-2   Determine the reactions for the given hinged beam.

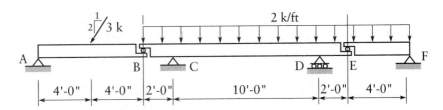

Solution   Two segments of the beam have only two hinged supports: segment AB and segment EF. These two segments will be solved first. The following free body sketch of segment AB is drawn.

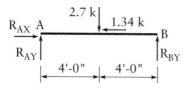

The beam reactions are found in the same way as any other simply supported beam:

$$\Sigma M_A = 0 = (2.7 \times 4) - (R_{BY} \times 8)$$
$$R_{BY} = 1.35 \text{ kips}$$

$$\Sigma M_B = 0 = (R_{AY} \times 8) - (2.7 \times 4)$$
$$R_{AY} = 1.35 \text{ kips}$$

$$\Sigma F_H = 0 = R_{AX} - 1.34$$
$$R_{AX} = 1.34 \text{ kips}$$

A freebody sketch of segment EF is drawn as shown in the following sketch.

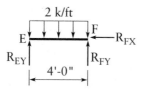

Reactions are found by the usual methods:

$$\Sigma M_E = 0 = (2 \times 4)\left(\frac{4}{2}\right) - (R_{FY} \times 4)$$
$$R_{FY} = 4 \text{ kips}$$

$$\Sigma M_F = 0 = -(2 \times 4)\left(\frac{4}{2}\right) + (R_{EY} \times 4)$$
$$R_{EY} = 4 \text{ kips}$$

$$\Sigma F_H = 0 = R_{EY}$$

A free body sketch of segment *BCDE* is now drawn, with the forces at *B* and *E* shown simply as known loads.

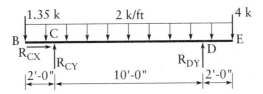

Reactions are found by the usual methods:

$$\Sigma M_C = 0 = (-1.35 \times 2) + (2 \times 14 \times 5) - (R_{DY} \times 10) + (4 \times 12)$$
$$R_{DY} = 18.53 \text{ kips}$$

$$\Sigma M_D = 0 = (-1.35 \times 12) + (R_{CY} \times 10) - (2 \times 14 \times 5) + (4 \times 2)$$
$$R_{CY} = 14.82 \text{ kips}$$

$$\Sigma F_H = 0 = R_{CX}$$

Final reactions are shown in the following sketch.

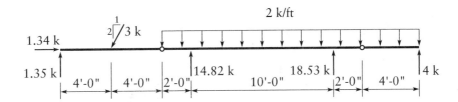

A.2 THREE-HINGED ARCHES

The feature that makes hinged beams statically determinate (and therefore solvable by simple statics) is the fact that such beams contain points where the moment is known to be zero. These points are, of course, the internal hinges. The three-hinged arch is another structure that falls into the same general category of configurations.

The three-hinged arch receives little emphasis in coursework on statics and strength of materials; yet it is one of our more commonly used structures. Manufacturers of prefabricated steel buildings frequently use the three-hinged arch, not only because it is easy to fabricate and erect, but because it is insensitive to changes in temperature. Some typical three-hinged arches are shown in Figure A-2.

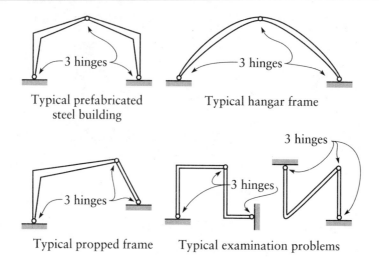

FIGURE A-2 Typical three-hinged arches.

A three-hinged arch may be viewed as consisting of two beams—straight, curved, or bent—whose hinged supports form a triangle. If the three hinges ever align into a straight line, the configuration becomes unstable and will collapse under load. A comparison is shown in Figure A-3.

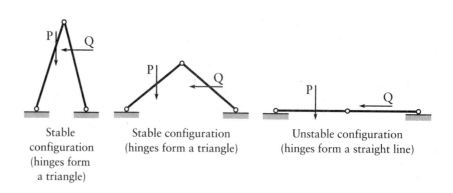

FIGURE A-3 Stable and unstable three-hinged arches.

The solution for the reactions in a three-hinged arch is somewhat like that for reactions in a hinged beam. There are two distinctive cases—one in which the supports are situated at the same level, and one in which the supports are situated at different levels. Some examples will illustrate the solution for reactions.

Example A-3   Determine the reactions for the given structure.

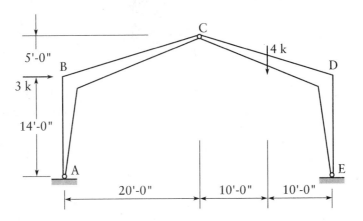

Solution   The structure is a three-hinged arch, formed by two bent beams *ABC* and *CDE*. Its three hinges form a discrete triangle, so it is stable. Its supports are situated at the same level, which simplifies the solution somewhat.

The entire structure is taken as a free body, as shown in the following sketch.

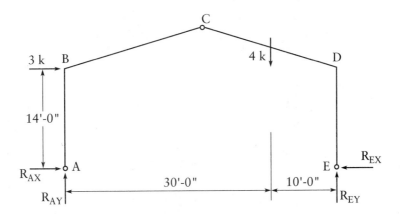

Moments are summed about point *E*. Where supports occur at the same level, such a procedure eliminates three of the four unknowns:

$$\Sigma M_E = 0 = (R_{AY} \times 40) + (3 \times 14) - (4 \times 10)$$
$$R_{AY} = -0.05 \text{ kips} \quad \text{(downward)}$$

Similarly, summing moments about point A eliminates three of the four unknowns, allowing a solution for R_{EY}:

$$\Sigma M_A = 0 = (3 \times 14) + (4 \times 30) - (R_{EY} \times 40)$$
$$R_{EY} = 4.05 \text{ kips} \quad \text{(upward)}$$

The solution for the remaining reactions is obtained by taking the two bent beams as separate free bodies. The two known reactions are shown in the following sketch simply as known loads.

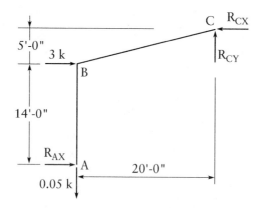

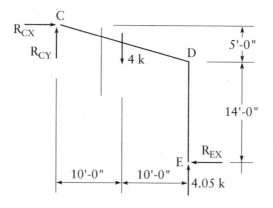

For segment ABC, summing moments about C eliminates the unknown forces at C, yielding a solution for R_{AX}:

$$\Sigma M_C = 0 = (-0.05 \times 20) - (R_{AX} \times 19) - (3 \times 5)$$
$$R_{AX} = -0.84 \text{ kips} \quad \text{(opposite to direction shown)}$$

Similarly for segment *CDE*, the sum of moments about *C* yields a solution for R_{EX}:

$$\Sigma M_C = 0 = (4 \times 10) + (R_{EX} \times 19) - (4.05 \times 20)$$
$$R_{EX} = +2.16 \text{ kips} \quad \text{(in direction shown)}$$

Final reactions are shown on the following sketch.

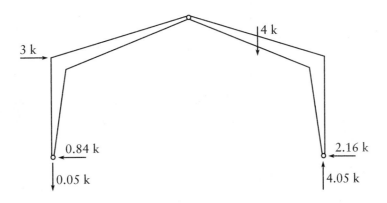

Example A-4   Determine the reactions for the given structure.

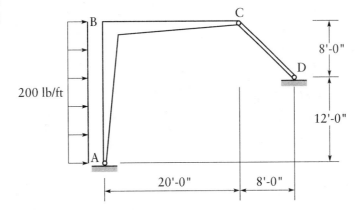

Solution   The structure is a three-hinged arch, formed by the bent beam *ABC* and the straight beam *CD*. Its three hinges form a discrete triangle, so it is stable. Its supports are at two levels, complicating the solution somewhat.

The entire structure is taken as a free body, as shown in the following sketch.

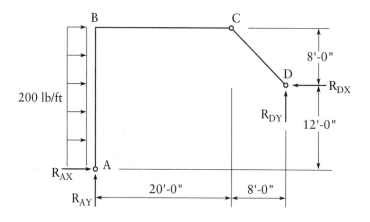

Moments are summed about point D:

$$\Sigma M_D = 0 = (-200 \times 20 \times 2) - (R_{AX} \times 12) + (R_{AY} \times 28)$$
$$= -8000 - 12R_{AX} + 28R_{AY}$$

The resulting equation contains two unknowns and is not solvable.

Segment ABC is now taken as a free body, which introduces the two additional unknowns that occur at C.

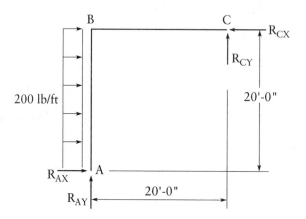

Moments are summed about point C, eliminating the two new unknowns at C:

$$\Sigma M_C = 0 = (R_{AY} \times 20) - (R_{AX} \times 20) - (200 \times 20 \times 10)$$
$$= -2000 - R_{AX} + R_{AY}$$

There are now two equations in two unknowns:

$$0 = -8000 - 12R_{AX} + 28R_{AY}$$

$$0 = -2000 - R_{AX} + R_{AY}$$

The simultaneous solution yields the unknowns:

$R_{AX} = -3$ kips   (opposite to direction shown)

$R_{AY} = -1$ kip   (opposite to direction shown)

The sum of forces vertically and horizontally yields the reactions at D:

$R_{DX} = +1$ kip   (in the direction shown)

$R_{DY} = +1$ kip   (in the direction shown)

The final reactions are shown on the following sketch.

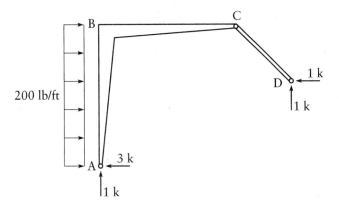

Answers to Selected Problems

Review Questions

1. The two broad classifications of structures according to their methods of analysis are statically determinate structures and statically indeterminate structures.

3. Long columns fail by buckling; short columns fail by crushing.

5. Rigid frames are commonly built of steel or of reinforced concrete.

7. The loads to be expected on a shear panel are shown in the following sketch:

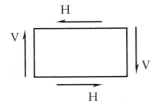

9. Rigid frames carry their loads in the plane of the frame; space frames include loads from the third dimension.

11. Shear in a member is positive if the left side of the member moves upward with respect to the right.

13. The slope at any point in a member is positive if a tangent to the elastic curve at that point slopes upward to the right.

15. If a member is vertical, the viewer turns such that the coordinate distance along the member increases to the right. Top, bottom, left, and right, as given in the answers to questions 11, 12, 13, and 14 are then in their correct orientation.

17. In the structural analysis of buildings, the friction loads created at bearings are usually ignored.

19. Generally, structures are conscientiously designed and detailed to prevent thermal loads from ever occurring. Random or unpredictable loads or stresses due to temperature effects are then relegated to the overall factor of safety for the design. A separate thermal analysis is rarely performed.

CHAPTER 2 LOADS AND REACTIONS ON BEAMS

Outside Problems

2-1 This beam is statically determinate.

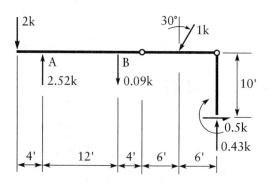

2-3 This beam is statically determinate.

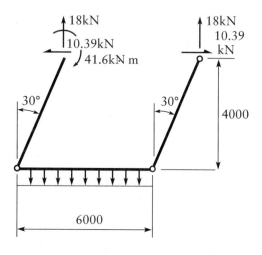

2-5 This beam is statically indeterminate.

2-7 This beam is statically determinate.

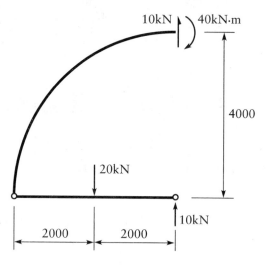

2-9 This arch is statically determinate.

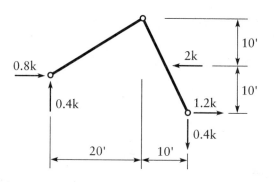

2-11 This beam is statically determinate.

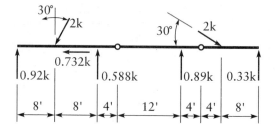

2-13 This beam is statically determinate.

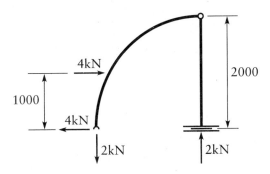

Review Questions

1. In a building design, the structural members constitute the primary load-carrying system for the overall building; the collapse of a member that is classified as structural would contribute to the collapse of the building. All other members are classified as nonstructural.

3.

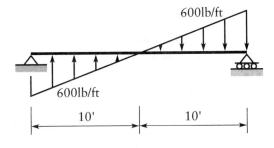

5. When showing beam reactions on a sketch, it is advisable to show all reactions that can occur, even if one intuitively sees that a particular load is zero; intuition can be wrong.

7. A link mechanism is formed by placing too many hinges in a load-carrying set of hinged beams.

9. The structural system of Example 2-5 would form horizontal reactions and moments at the fixed bases if the system were subjected to a temperature change. The structural system of Example 2-6 would be unaffected by a temperature change.

11. Statically determinate systems are unaffected by temperature changes.

CHAPTER 3 SHEAR AND MOMENT IN BEAMS

Outside Problems

3-1

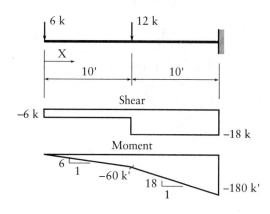

$0 \le x \le 10$

$$V_x = -6$$

$$M_x = -6x$$

$0 \le x \le 20$

$$V_x = -18 \text{ kips}$$

$$M_x = -6x - 12(x - 10)$$

3-3

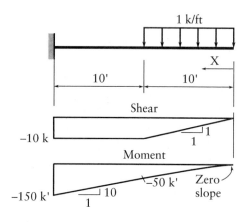

$0 \le x \le 10$

$$V_x = -x$$

$$M_x = \frac{1}{2}x^2$$

$10 \le x \le 20$

$$V_x = -10 \text{ kips}$$

$$M_x = -10(x - 5)$$

3-5

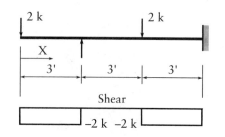

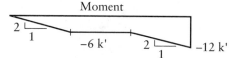

$0 \le x \le 3$

$$V_x = -2$$

$$M_x = -2x$$

$3 \le x \le 6$

$$V_x = 0$$

$$M_x = -2x + 2(x - 3)$$

$6 \le x \le 9$

$$V_x = -2$$

$$M_x = -2x + 2(x - 3) - 2(x - 6)$$

3-7

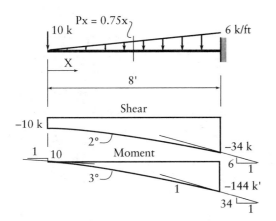

$$0 \le x \le 8$$
$$V_x = -10 - 0.375x^2$$
$$M_x = -10x - 0.125x^3$$

3-9

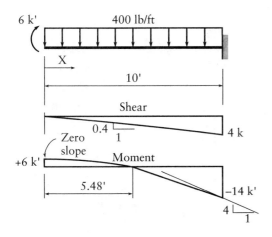

$$0 \le x \le 10$$
$$V_x = -0.4x$$
$$M_x = +6 - 0.2x^2$$

3-11

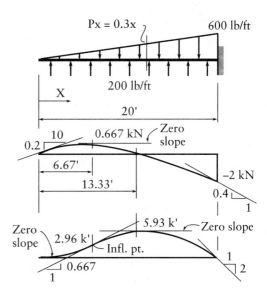

$$0 \le x \le 20$$
$$V_x = +0.2x - 0.015x^2$$
$$M_x = +0.1x^2 - 0.005x^3$$

3-13

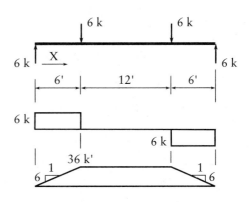

$$0 \le x \le 6$$
$$V_x = +6 \text{ kips}$$
$$M_x = +6x$$

$6 \leq x \leq 18$

$\quad V_x = 0$

$\quad M_x = +6x - 6(x - 6)$

$18 \leq x \leq 24$

$\quad V_x = -6$ kips

$\quad M_x = +6x - 6(x - 6) - 6(x - 18)$

3-15

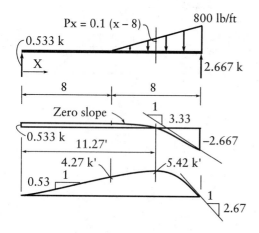

$0 \leq x \leq 8$

$\quad V_x = 0.5333$

$\quad M_x = 0.533x$

$8 \leq x \leq 16$

$\quad V_x = 0.5333 - 0.05(x - 8)^2$

$\quad M_x = 0.533x - 0.0167(x - 8)^3$

3-17

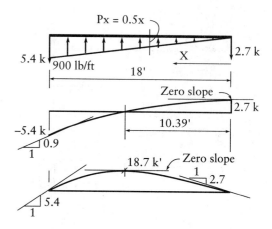

$0 \leq x \leq 18$

$\quad V_x = +2.7 - 0.025x^2$

$\quad M_x = -2.7x + 0.00833x^3$

3-19

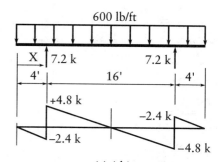

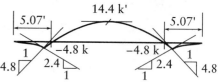

$0 \leq x \leq 4$

$\quad V_x = -0.6x$

$\quad M_x = -0.3x^2$

$4 \leq x \leq 20$

$\quad V_x = -0.6x + 7.2$

$\quad M_x = -0.3x^2 + 7.2(x - 4)$

$20 \leq x \leq 24$

$V_x = -0.6x + 14.4$

$M_x = -0.3x^2 + 7.2(x-4)$
$\qquad -7.2(x-20)$

3-21

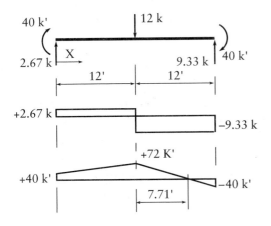

$0 \leq x \leq 12$

$V_x = +22.67$

$M_x = 40 + 2.67x$

$12 \leq x \leq 24$

$V_x = -9.33$

$M_x = 40 + 2.67x - 12(x-12)$

3-23

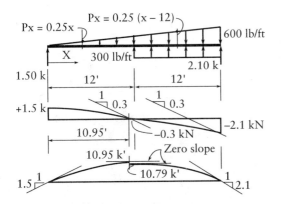

$0 \leq x \leq 12$

$V_x = 1.50 - 0.0125x^2$

$M_x = 1.50x - 0.00417x^3$

$12 \leq x \leq 24$

$V_x = -0.3 - 0.125(x-12)^2$

$M_x = 1.50x - 1.8(x-8)$
$\qquad -0.00417(x-12)^3$

3-25

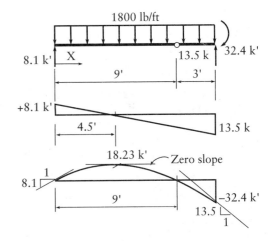

$0 \leq x \leq 12$

$V_x = 8.1 - 1.8x$

$M_x = 8.1x - 0.9x^2$

3-27

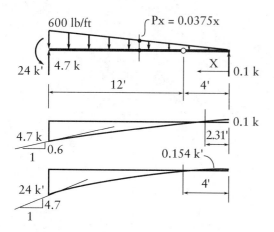

$0 \le x \le 16$

$$V_x = -0.1 + 0.01875x^2$$
$$M_x = +0.1x - 0.00625x^3$$

3-29

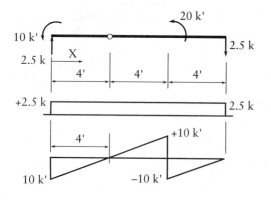

$0 \le x \le 8$

$$V_x = 2.5 \text{ k}$$
$$M_x = -10 + 2.5x$$

$8 \le x \le 12$

$$V_x = 2.5 \text{ k}$$
$$M_x = -30 + 2.5x$$

3-31

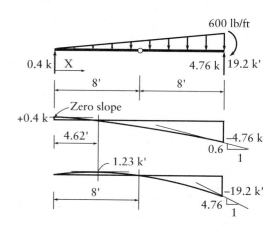

$0 \le x \le 16$

$$V_x = 0.4 - 0.01875x^2$$
$$M_x = 0.4x - 0.00625x^3$$

3-33

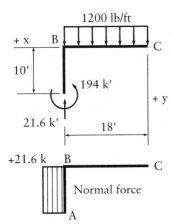

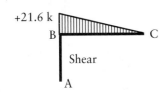

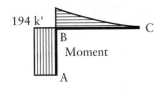

$0 \leq x \leq 18, \quad y = 0$

$\quad V_x = 1.2x$

$\quad M_x = +0.6x^2$

$\quad N_x = 0$

$x = 18, \quad 0 \leq y \leq 10$

$\quad V_y = 0$

$\quad M_y = +194 \text{ kip-ft}$

$\quad N_y = -21.6 \text{ kips (compr)}$

3-35

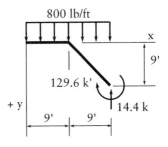

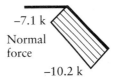

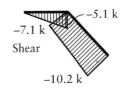

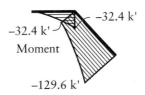

$0 \leq x \leq 18, \quad \text{all values of } y$

$\quad V_x = -0.8x$

$\quad M_x = -0.4x^2$

$\quad N_x = 0$

Resultants on sloping section:

$0 \leq x \leq 9, \quad y = 0$

$\quad V_s = V_x$

$\quad M_s = M_x$

$\quad N_x = 0$

$9 \leq x \leq 18, \quad y = x - 9$

$V_s = V_x \cos \alpha = -0.566x$

$M_s = M_x$

$N_s = -V_x \sin \alpha = -0.566x$

3-37

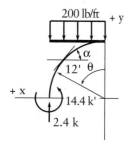

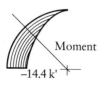

$x = 12 \sin \theta$

$y = 12 \cos \theta$

$\theta = \alpha$

$0 \leq \theta \leq \dfrac{\pi}{2}$

$V_x = -200x = -2.4 \sin \theta$

$M_x = -100x^2 = -14.4 \sin^2 \theta$

$N_x = 0$

Resultants on sloping section:

$0 \leq \theta \leq \dfrac{\pi}{2}$

$V_s = V_x \cos \alpha =$
$\qquad -2.4 \sin \theta \, (1 - \cos \theta) \, M_s$

$M_x = -14.4 \sin^2 \theta$

$N_s = V_x \sin \alpha = -2.4 \sin^2 \theta$

3-39

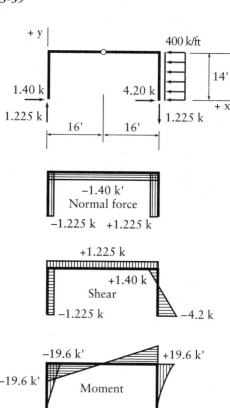

$x = 0, \quad 0 \leq y \leq 14$

$V_y = -1.40$

$M_y = -140y$

$N_y = -1.225$

$0 \leq x \leq 32, \quad y = 14$

$\quad V_x = +1.225$

$\quad M_x = -19.60 + 1.225x$

$\quad N_x = -1.40$

$x = 32, \quad 0 \leq y \leq 14$

$\quad V_y = -4.2 + 0.4y$

$\quad M_y = -4.2y + 0.2y^2$

$\quad N_y = +1.225$

3-41

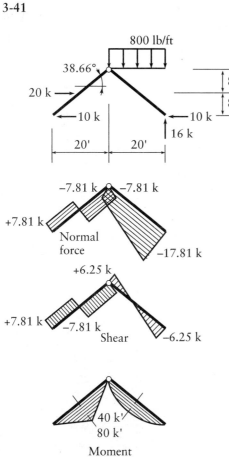

$0 \leq x \leq 5, \quad y = \dfrac{4}{5}x, \quad \theta = \alpha$

$20 \leq x \leq 40, \quad y = 16 - \dfrac{4}{5}x, \quad \theta = -\alpha$

$0 \leq x \leq 10, \quad y = \dfrac{4}{5}x$

$\quad V_x = 0$

$\quad M_x = +10y$

$\quad N_x = +10$

$0 \leq x \leq 20, \quad y = \dfrac{4}{5}x$

$\quad V_x = 0$

$\quad M_x = +10y - 20\,(y - 8)$

$\quad N_x = -10$

$20 \leq x \leq 40, \quad y = 16 - \dfrac{4}{5}x$

$\quad V_x = -0.8\,(20 - x)$

$\quad M_x = +10y - 20\,(y - 8) - 4\,(x - 20)^2$

$\quad N_x = -10$

Resultants along sloping sections:

$0 \leq x \leq 10, \quad y = +\dfrac{4}{5}x, \quad \alpha = -38.66°$

$\quad V_s = +7.81$

$\quad M_s = M_x$

$\quad N_s = +7.81$

$10 \leq x \leq 20, \quad y = +\dfrac{4}{5}x, \quad \alpha = -38.66°$

$\quad V_s = -7.81$

$\quad M_s = M_x$

$\quad N_s = -7.81$

$20 \leq x \leq 40$, $y = 16 - \dfrac{4}{5}x$, $\alpha = +38.66°$

$V_s = -0.625\,(20 - x) + 6.25$

$M_s = M_x$

$N_s = +0.5\,(20 - x) - 7.81$

Review Questions

1. $f = 22{,}900$ psi

3. $v = 15{,}280$ psi

5. Four commonly used cross-sectional resultants are moment, axial force, shear force, and torque.

7. The slope of the moment diagram is found simply by observing the magnitude of the shear V from the shear diagram:

$$\frac{dM}{dx} = +V$$

9. At a single concentrated load, the shear diagram jumps from one value just to the left of the load to another value just to the right of the load.

11. When the shear has only one value at a point and that value is zero, the moment diagram is continuous across the point and it reaches a maximum or minimum value at that point.

13. An inflection point occurs when the flexural curvature of a member changes from positive to negative; that is, flexural stress changes from tension on the bottom fibers to tension on the top fibers.

15. A point of contraflexure is another name for a point of inflection; the two terms are used interchangeably.

CHAPTER 4 EQUATIONS OF THE ELASTIC CURVE

Outside Problems

4-1 & 4-3 See the results in Table 4-1.

4-5 & 4-6

$0 \leq x \leq 5$:

$$\frac{dy}{dx} = +\frac{wL^3}{6EI}\left[1 - \frac{x^3}{L^3}\right] - \frac{wL^3}{192EI}$$

$$y = -\frac{wL^4}{24EI}\left[\frac{x^4}{L^4} - 4\frac{x}{L} + 3\right]$$

$$+ \frac{wL^4}{1920EI}\left[9 - 10\frac{x}{L}\right]$$

$5 \leq x \leq 10$:

$$\frac{dy}{dx} = +\frac{wL^3}{6EI}\left[1 - \frac{x^3}{L^3}\right]$$

$$- \frac{wL^3}{192EI}\left[1 - 16\left(\frac{x}{L} - \frac{1}{2}\right)^4\right]$$

$$y = -\frac{wL^4}{24EI}\left[\frac{x^4}{L^4} - 4\frac{x}{L} + 3\right]$$

$$+ \frac{wL^4}{1920EI}\left[32\left(\frac{x}{L} - \frac{1}{2}\right)^5 + 9 - 10\frac{x}{L}\right]$$

4-9 & 4-10

$0 \leq x \leq 4$:

$$\frac{dy}{dx} = +\frac{PL^2}{2EI}\left[1 - \frac{x^2}{L^2}\right] - \frac{PL^2}{8EI}$$

$$y = -\frac{PL^3}{6EI}\left[\frac{x^3}{L^3} - 3\frac{x}{L} + 2\right]$$

$$+ \frac{PL^3}{48EI}\left[6\left(1 - \frac{x}{L}\right) - 1\right]$$

$4 \leq x \leq 8$:

$$\frac{dy}{dx} = +\frac{PL^2}{2EI}\left[1 - \frac{x^2}{L^2}\right] - \frac{PL^2}{8EI}\left[1 - 4\left(\frac{x}{L} - \frac{1}{2}\right)^2\right]$$

$$y = -\frac{PL^3}{6EI}\left[\frac{x^3}{L^3} - 3\frac{x}{L} + 2\right]$$

$$+ \frac{PL^3}{48EI}\left[8\left(\frac{x}{L} - \frac{1}{2}\right)^3 + 6\left(1 - \frac{x}{L}\right) - 1\right]$$

4-13 Solution is given by the sum of:

Case 1, positive, $P = 2k$

Case 2, negative, with $n = \frac{1}{4}$, $P = 2k$

Case 3, positive, with $n = \frac{1}{2}$, $P = 2k$

Case 4, negative, with $n = \frac{3}{4}$, $P = 2k$

4-15 Solution is given by the sum of:

Case 3, positive, $w = 300$ lb/ft

Case 4, negative, $n = \frac{1}{2}$, $w = 600$ lb/ft

4-17 Solution is given by the sum of:

Case 5, positive, $p = 2400$ lb/ft

Case 6, negative, $n = \frac{1}{3}$, $p = 1600$ lb/ft

Case 4, negative, $n = \frac{1}{3}$, $w = 800$ lb/ft

Case 4, negative, $n = \frac{2}{3}$, $w = 800$ lb/ft

Case 6, positive, $n = \frac{2}{3}$, $p = 800$ lb/ft

4-19   Solution is given by the sum of:

Case 3, positive, $w = 800$ lb/ft

Case 5, negative, $p = 2400$ lb/ft

Case 6, positive, $n = \dfrac{1}{3}$, $p = 1600$ lb/ft

Case 6, positive, $n = \dfrac{2}{3}$, $p = 800$ lb/ft

4-21

$0 \leq x \leq 6$:

$$\frac{dy}{dx} = \frac{wL^3}{6EI_1}\left[1 - \frac{x^3}{L^3}\right] - \frac{wL^3}{48EI_1}\left[1 - \frac{I_1}{I_2}\right]$$

$$y = -\frac{wL^4}{24EI_1}\left[\frac{x^4}{L^4} - 4\frac{x}{L} + 3\right]$$

$$+ \frac{wL^4}{24EI_1}\left[\frac{1}{2}\left(1 - \frac{x}{L}\right) - \frac{1}{16}\right]\left[1 - \frac{I_1}{I_2}\right]$$

$6 \leq x \leq 12$:

$$\frac{dy}{dx} = \frac{wL^3}{6EI_1}\left[1 - \frac{x^3}{L^3}\right]$$

$$- \frac{wL^3}{48EI_1}\left[1 - 8\left(\frac{x}{L} - \frac{1}{2}\right)^3\right]\left[1 - \frac{I_1}{I_2}\right]$$

$$y = -\frac{wL^4}{24EI_1}\left[\frac{x^4}{L^4} - 4\frac{x}{L} + 3\right]$$

$$+ \frac{wL^4}{24EI_1}\left[\left(\frac{x}{L} - \frac{1}{2}\right)^4 + \frac{1}{2}\left(1 - \frac{x}{L}\right)\right.$$

$$\left. - \frac{1}{16}\right]\left[1 - \frac{I_1}{I_2}\right]$$

4-23

$0 \leq x \leq \dfrac{2}{3}L$:

$$\frac{dy}{dx} = -\frac{pL^3}{24EI_1}\left[1 - \frac{x^4}{L^4}\right] - \frac{pL^3}{8EI_1}\left[\frac{1}{81}\right]\left[1 - \frac{I_1}{I_2}\right]$$

$$y = -\frac{pL^4}{120EI_1}\left[\frac{x^5}{L^5} + 5\left(1 - \frac{x}{L}\right) - 1\right]$$

$$+ \frac{pL^4}{40EI_1}\left[\frac{5}{81}\left(1 - \frac{x}{L}\right) - \frac{1}{243}\right]\left[1 - \frac{I_1}{I_2}\right]$$

$\dfrac{2}{3}L \leq x \leq L$:

$$\frac{dy}{dx} = \frac{pL^3}{24EI_1}\left[1 - \frac{x^4}{L^4}\right]$$

$$- \frac{pL^3}{8EI_1}\left[\frac{1}{81} - \left(\frac{x}{L} - \frac{2}{3}\right)^4\right]\left[1 - \frac{I_1}{I_2}\right]$$

$$y = -\frac{pL^4}{120EI_1}\left[\frac{x^5}{L^5} + 5\left(1 - \frac{x}{L}\right) - 1\right]$$

$$+ \frac{pL^4}{40EI_1}\left[\left(\frac{x}{L} - \frac{2}{3}\right)^5\right.$$

$$\left. + \frac{5}{81}\left(1 - \frac{x}{L}\right) - \frac{1}{243}\right]\left[1 - \frac{I_1}{I_2}\right]$$

4-25 & 4-27   See the results in Table 4-2.

4-29 & 4-30

$0 \leq x \leq 19$:

$$\frac{dx}{dy} = -\frac{wL^3}{24EI}\left[1 - 6\frac{x^2}{L^2} + 4\frac{x^3}{L^3}\right]$$

$$+ \frac{wL^3}{180EI}\left[\frac{37}{32} - \left(\frac{15}{4}\right)\left(\frac{x^2}{L^2}\right)\right]$$

$$y = -\frac{wL^3}{24EI}\left[\frac{x}{L} - 2\frac{x^3}{L^3} + \frac{x^4}{L^4}\right]$$

$$+ \frac{wL^4}{180EI}\left[\left(\frac{37}{32}\right)\left(\frac{x}{L}\right) - \left(\frac{5}{4}\right)\left(\frac{x^3}{L^3}\right)\right]$$

$10 \le x \le 20$:

$$\frac{dx}{dy} = -\frac{wL^3}{24EI}\left[1 - 6\frac{x^2}{L^2} + 4\frac{x^3}{L^3}\right]$$
$$+\frac{wL^3}{180EI}\left[\frac{37}{32} + -\left(\frac{15}{4}\right)\left(\frac{x^2}{L^2}\right)\right]$$
$$+15\left(\frac{x}{L} - \frac{1}{2}\right)^4\right]$$

$$y = -\frac{wL^4}{24EI}\left[\frac{x}{L} - 2\frac{x^3}{L^3} + \frac{x^4}{L^4}\right]$$
$$+\frac{wL^4}{180EI}\left[\left(\frac{37}{32}\right)\left(\frac{x}{L}\right) - \left(\frac{5}{4}\right)\left(\frac{x^3}{L^3}\right)\right.$$
$$\left. + 3\left(\frac{x}{L} - \frac{1}{2}\right)^5\right]$$

4-33 & 4-34

$0 \le x \le 24$:

$$\frac{dx}{dy} = +\frac{wL^3}{24EI}\left[1 - 6\frac{x^2}{L^2} + 4\frac{x^3}{L^3}\right]$$
$$-\frac{wL^3}{180EI}\left[7 - 30\frac{x^2}{L^2} + 15\frac{x^4}{L^4}\right]$$

$$y = +\frac{wL^4}{24EI}\left[\frac{x}{L} - 2\frac{x^3}{L^3} + \frac{x^4}{L^4}\right]$$
$$-\frac{wL^4}{180EI}\left[7 - 10\frac{x^3}{L^3} + 3\frac{x^5}{L^5}\right]$$

4-37 Solution is given by the sum of:

Case 2, positive, $w = 1200$ lb/ft

Case 9, negative, $p = w = 1200$ lb/ft,

$$n = \frac{1}{3}$$

Case 10, negative, $p = w = 1200$ lb/ft,

$$n = \frac{1}{3}$$

4-39 Solution is given by the sum of:

Case 5, positive, $M = 40$ k', $\quad n = \frac{1}{3}$

Case 5, negative, $M = 40$ k', $\quad n = \frac{2}{3}$

4-41 Solution is given by the sum of:

Case 2, negative, $w = 1$ kip/ft

Case 9, positive, $p = 2$ kip/ft, $\quad n = \frac{1}{2}$

Case 10, positive, $p = 2$ kip/ft, $\quad n = \frac{1}{2}$

4-43 Solution is given by the sum of:

Case 2, negative, $w = 800$ lb/ft

Case 10, positive, $p = 1600$ lb/ft, $n = \frac{1}{2}$

Review Questions

1. The Bernoulli equation for beams is given by

$$\frac{1}{\rho_x} = \frac{M_x}{EI}$$

where ρ_x is the radius of curvature at point x
M_x is the moment at point x
I is the moment of inertia of the cross section
E is the modulus of elasticity of the material

3. Isotropic materials have the same mechanical properties in all directions, for both tensile and compressive loads.

5. The relationship between elastic modulus of elasticity E and shear modulus of elasticity G is given by

$$G = \frac{E}{2(1+\mu)}$$

where μ is Poisson's ratio.

7. The general differential equation for the elastic curve of a beam is given by

$$\frac{d^2y}{dx^2} = \frac{M_x}{EI_x}$$

where x and y are the coordinate axes
M_x is the moment at any point x
I_x is the moment of inertia at point x
E is the modulus of elasticity

CHAPTER 5 AREA MOMENT METHODS IN BEAMS

Outside Problems

5-1

$$\theta_A = \frac{A_m}{EI} = 0.00406 \text{ rad}$$

5-2

$$\Delta_A = t_{AB} = \frac{A_m \bar{x}_A}{EI} = -0.409 \text{ in.}$$

5-5

$$\theta_A = \frac{A_m}{EI} = 0.00618 \text{ rad}$$

5-6

$$\Delta_A = \frac{A_m \bar{x}_A}{EI} = 0.742 \text{ in.}$$

5-9

$$\theta_A = \frac{A_m}{EI} = 0.0104 \text{ rad}$$

5-10

$$\Delta_C = t_{AC} = +1.492 \text{ in.}$$

5-13

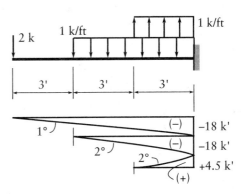

5-15

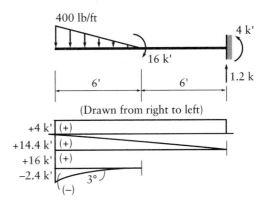

5-17

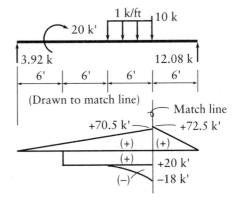

5-19

$$\theta_D = \frac{A_m}{EI} = -0.00295 \text{ rad}$$

5-20

$$\Delta_D = \frac{A_m \bar{x}_D}{EI} = -0.351 \text{ in.}$$

5-23

$$\theta_B = \frac{A_m}{EI} = 0.00245 \text{ rad}$$

5-24

$$\Delta_B = \frac{A_m \bar{x}_B}{EI} = 0.423 \text{ in.}$$

5-27

$$\theta_A = \frac{t_{BA}}{L} = 0.00883 \text{ rad}$$

5-28

$$\Delta_C = \frac{1}{2} t_{BA} - t_{CA} = 1.274 \text{ in.}$$

5-31

$$\theta_A = \frac{t_{CA} + \Delta_A}{L} = 0.00076 \text{ rad}$$

5-32

$$\Delta_A = \frac{32}{24} t_{BC} - t_{AC} = -0.175 \text{ in. (upward)}$$

5-35

$$\theta_E = \frac{t_{BC} - t_{DC}}{L} = +0.00083 \text{ rad}$$

5-36

$$\Delta_E = t_{EC} + t_{DC} - (t_{BC} - t_{DC}) \frac{20}{16}$$
$$= +0.107 \text{ in.}$$

5-39

$$\theta_A = \frac{A_m}{EI} = +0.0988 \text{ rad}$$

5-40

$$\Delta_C = t_{AC} = 1.19 \text{ in.}$$

5-43

$$\theta_A = \frac{A_M}{EI} = \frac{A_1}{EI_1} + \frac{A_2 + A_3 + A_4 + A_5 + A_6}{EI_2}$$
$$= 0.00808 \text{ rad}$$

5-44

$$\Delta_C = t_{BC} = \frac{A_M \bar{x}_B}{EI}$$

$$= \frac{A_2 \bar{x}_B + A_3 \bar{x}_B + A_4 \bar{x}_B + A_5 \bar{x}_B + A_6 \bar{x}_B}{EI_2}$$

$$= +34.12 \text{ mm}$$

Review Questions

1. Given two points A and B on the elastic curve of a beam, the angular change (in radians) from the tangent at A to the tangent at B can be computed as the area of the bending moment diagram between A and B, divided by EI; if the sign of the angular change is positive, the elastic curve cups upward (it smiles).

3. If the algebraic sign of the angle computed by the first area moment theorem is negative, the elastic curve cups downward (it frowns).

5. In the first area moment theorem, if the tangents cross above the elastic curve, the algebraic sign of the angle is negative.

CHAPTER 6   CLASSICAL ENERGY METHODS IN BEAMS AND FRAMES

Outside Problems

6-1

$$\theta_A = \int_0^L \frac{M_x \dfrac{\partial M_x}{\partial Q} ds}{EI_x} = -0.0090 \text{ rad} \atop \text{(opposite to } Q)$$

6-2

$$\Delta_A = \int_0^L \frac{M_x \dfrac{\partial M_x}{\partial Z} ds}{EI_x} \; -0.694 \text{ in.} \atop \text{(opposite to } Z)$$

6-5

$$\theta_A = \int_0^L \frac{M_x \dfrac{\partial M_x}{\partial Q} ds}{EI_x} = +0.00614 \text{ rad}$$

6-6

$$\Delta_A = \int_0^L \frac{M_x \dfrac{\partial M_x}{\partial Z} ds}{EI_x} = +0.385 \text{ in.}$$

6-9

$$2\theta_A = 2\int_0^{\frac{1}{2}L} \frac{M_x \dfrac{\partial M_x}{\partial Q} ds}{EI_x} = +0.00558 \text{ rad}$$

6-10

$$2\Delta_A = 2\int_0^{\frac{1}{2}L} \frac{M_x \dfrac{\partial M_x}{\partial Z} ds}{EI_x} = +0.402 \text{ in.}$$

6-13

$$\theta_A = \int_0^L \frac{M_x \dfrac{\partial M_x}{\partial Q} ds}{EI_x} = -0.01417 \text{ rad}$$

6-14

$$\Delta_A = \int_0^L \frac{M_x \dfrac{\partial M_x}{\partial Z} ds}{EI_x} = -1.121 \text{ in.}$$

6-17

$$\theta_C = \int_0^L \frac{M_x \dfrac{\partial M_x}{\partial Q} ds}{EI_x} = -0.0140 \text{ rad}$$

6-18

$$\Delta_C = \int_0^L \frac{M_x \dfrac{\partial M_x}{\partial Z} ds}{EI_x} = -16.80 \text{ mm}$$

6-21

$$\theta_C = \int_0^L \frac{M_x \dfrac{\partial M_x}{\partial Q} ds}{EI_x} = 0.00779 \text{ rad}$$

6-22

$$\Delta_{CY} = \int_0^L \frac{M_X \frac{\partial M_X}{\partial Z_Y} ds}{EI_X} = -1.121 \text{ in.}$$

$$\Delta_{CX} = 0$$

6-25

$$\theta_C = \int_0^L \frac{M_X \frac{\partial M_X}{\partial Q} ds}{EI_X} = 0.0244 \text{ rad}$$

6-26

$$\Delta_{CX} = \int_0^L \frac{M_X \frac{\partial M_X}{\partial Z_X} ds}{EI_X} = -1.548 \text{ in.}$$

$$\Delta_{CY} = \int_0^L \frac{M_X \frac{\partial M_X}{\partial Z_Y} dx}{EI_X} = -2.587 \text{ in.}$$

6-29

$$\theta_B = \int_0^L \frac{M_X \frac{\partial M_X}{\partial Q} ds}{EI_X} = +0.0124 \text{ rad}$$

6-30

$$\Delta_{BX} = \int_0^L \frac{M_X \frac{\partial M_X}{\partial Z_X} ds}{EI_X} = -4.204 \text{ in.}$$

$$\Delta_{BY} = \int_0^L \frac{M_X \frac{\partial M_X}{\partial Z_Y} dx}{EI_X} = +0.892 \text{ in.}$$

6-33

$$\theta_A = \int_0^L \frac{M_X \frac{\partial M_X}{\partial Q} ds}{EI_X} = 0.00525 \text{ rad}$$

6-34

$$\Delta_{AX} = \int_0^L \frac{M_X \frac{\partial M_X}{\partial Z_X} ds}{EI_X} = 1.792 \text{ in.}$$

$$\Delta_{AY} = 0$$

6-37

$$\theta_C = \int_0^L \frac{M_X \frac{\partial M_X}{\partial Q} ds}{EI_X} = 0.0106 \text{ rad}$$

6-38

$$\Delta_{CX} = \int_0^L \frac{M_X \frac{\partial M_X}{\partial Z_X} ds}{EI_X} = 2.082 \text{ in.}$$

$$\Delta_{CY} = 0$$

6-41

$$\theta_A = \int_0^L \frac{M_X \frac{\partial M_X}{\partial Q} ds}{EI_X} = -0.0154 \text{ rad}$$

6-42

$$\Delta_A = \int_0^L \frac{M_X \frac{\partial M_X}{\partial Z_Y} ds}{EI_X} = -2.324 \text{ in.}$$

Review Questions

1. In the energy methods, external work is generated when the applied loads move through the small structural deflections to their final positions; the work is then the average external force times the small distance moved.

3. In an elastic body under a general system of loads, the first partial derivative of the energy equation with respect to any one of the concentrated loads gives the displacement of that load along its line of action; the sign of the displacement is positive if the displacement is in the same direction as the load.

5. The only effect of a stepped cross section in a Castigliano solution is that the step produces another discontinuity in the integral.

7. Two types of structures that could require a numerical integration of the Castigliano solution are:

   1. Structures whose members have continuously varying cross sections and thus have continuously varying moments of inertia.
   2. Structures whose shape cannot be defined by a geometric equation, such as free-form sculptured shapes.

CHAPTER 7 UNIT LOAD METHOD IN BEAMS AND FRAMES

Outside Problems

7-1

$$\theta_A = \int_0^L \frac{M_X m_R ds}{EI_X} = -0.0090 \text{ rad}$$

7-2

$$\Delta_{AY} = \int_0^L \frac{M_X m_V ds}{EI_X} = -0.694 \text{ in.}$$

7-5

$$\theta_C = \int_0^L \frac{M_X m_R dx}{EI_X} = 0.00614 \text{ rad}$$

7-6

$$\Delta_C = \int_0^L \frac{M_X m_V dx}{EI_X} = 0.385 \text{ in.}$$

7-9

$$2\theta_A = 2\int_0^{\frac{1}{2}L} \frac{M_X m_R dx}{EI_X} = 0.00558 \text{ rad}$$

7-10

$$2\Delta_{AY} = 2\int_0^{\frac{1}{2}L} \frac{M_X m_V dx}{EI_X} = 0.402 \text{ in.}$$

7-13

$$\theta_A = 2\int_0^L \frac{M_X m_R dx}{EI_X} = -0.0142 \text{ rad}$$

7-14

$$\Delta_{AY} = 2\int_0^L \frac{M_X m_V dx}{EI_X} = -1.121 \text{ in.}$$

7-17

$$\theta_C = \int_0^L \frac{M_X m_R dx}{EI_X} = -0.0140 \text{ rad}$$

7-18

$$\Delta_{CY} = \int_0^L \frac{M_X m_V dx}{EI_X} = -16.80 \text{ mm}$$

7-21

$$\theta_C = 2\int_0^L \frac{M_X m_R ds}{EI_X} = -0.00779 \text{ rad}$$

7-22

$$\Delta_{CX} = 0$$

$$\Delta_{CY} = \int_0^L \frac{M_X m_V ds}{EI_X} = +1.121 \text{ in.}$$

7-25

$$\theta_C = \int_0^L \frac{M_X m_R ds}{EI_X} = 0.0244 \text{ rad}$$

7-26

$$\Delta_{CX} = \int_0^L \frac{M_X m_h ds}{EI_X} = -1.548 \text{ in.}$$

$$\Delta_{CY} = \int_0^L \frac{M_X m_V ds}{EI_X} = +2.587$$

7-29

$$\theta_B = \int_0^L \frac{M_X m_R ds}{EI_X} = +0.0124 \text{ rad}$$

7-30

$$\Delta_{BX} = \int_0^L \frac{M_X m_h ds}{EI_X} = -4.204 \text{ in.}$$

$$\Delta_{BY} = \int_0^L \frac{M_X m_V ds}{EI_X} = +0.892$$

7-33

$$2\theta_A = 2\int_0^{\frac{1}{2}L} \frac{M_X m_R ds}{EI_X} = -0.00525 \text{ rad}$$

7-34

$$\Delta_{AX} = 2\int_0^{\frac{1}{2}L} \frac{M_X m_h ds}{EI_X} = 1.792 \text{ in.}$$

$$\Delta_{AY} = 0$$

7-37

$$\theta_C = \int_0^L \frac{M_X m_R ds}{EI_X} = +0.0106 \text{ rad}$$

7-38

$$\Delta_{CX} = \int_0^L \frac{M_X m_h ds}{EI_X} = 2.083 \text{ in.}$$

$$\Delta_{CY} = 0$$

7-41

$$\theta_A = \int_0^L \frac{M_X m_R ds}{EI_X} = -0.0154 \text{ rad}$$

7-42

$$\Delta_{AY} = \int_0^L \frac{M_X m_V ds}{EI_X} = -2.324 \text{ in.}$$

Review Questions

1. In applications of the Castigliano solution, the unit load concept offers a convenient way to find the partial derivative of the moment equation.

3. The unit load method may be used when the cross section of a member is continuously variable.

5. In the unit load method, rotations are computed through the use of a unit moment rather than a unit force.

7. Unit moment and unit concentrated load may not be applied at the same time in the unit load method, since it would not be possible to distinguish between them in subsequent calculations.

CHAPTER 8 SIMPLE TRUSSES

Outside Problems

8-1

$R_{AY} = -14$ k   (in opposite direction)

$R_{CY} = 54$ k   (in direction shown)

$R_{CX} = 0$

8-3

$R_{JY} = 34$ k   (in direction shown)

$R_{AY} = -34$ k   (opposite to direction shown)

$R_{AX} = -26$ k   (opposite to direction shown)

8-5

$R_{IY} = 4$ k   (in direction shown)

$R_{MY} = 18$ k   (in direction shown)

$R_{BY} = -2$ k   (in opposite direction)

$R_{BX} = 0$

8-7

$R_G = 34.05$ k   (in direction shown)

$R_{AX} = 0.27$ k (in direction shown)

$R_{AY} = -6.58$ k (in opposite direction)

8-9

$R_{BY} = 6.07$ k (in direction shown)

$R_{AY} = 3.93$ k (in direction shown)

$R_{BX} = 10.45$ k (in direction shown)

$R_{AX} = 0.45$ k (in direction shown)

8-11

$R_{CY} = 10.5$ k (in direction shown)

$R_{CX} = 11.5$ k (in direction shown)

$R_{AY} = -0.5$ k (in opposite direction)

$R_{AX} = -0.5$ k (in opposite direction)

Review Questions

1. Three advantages that trusses have when compared to solid beams are:

   1. All material is stressed to optimum levels.
   2. Long spans may be bridged by using short members.
   3. Trusses are relatively lightweight.

3. The compression chord of trusses must be braced because of the lateral instability of the chord; it tends to roll sideways.

5. Since all truss members are specifically designed to carry only axial loads, any flexural loading could quickly overstress the member or (in the case of compression members) could contribute to premature buckling.

7. When long slender tension members are placed in compression, they will buckle at extremely low values of load; it is essential that any such load reversals be identified and provided for.

9. Secondary flexural stresses in truss members can become a problem in short heavy members; as a guide, the effects of secondary stresses are likely to become significant when the L/d (length-to-depth) ratio is less than about 10.

11. A Pratt truss has its diagonal members oriented to produce tension in them under full uniform loading of the truss; the diagonals in a Howe truss are oriented in the opposite direction, to produce compression in them under full uniform loading of the truss.

CHAPTER 9 FORCES IN TRUSS MEMBERS

Outside Problems

9-1 & 9-13

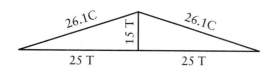

9-3 & 9-15

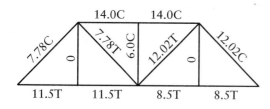

9-5 & 9-17

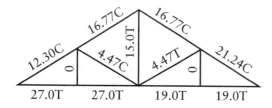

9-7 & 9-19

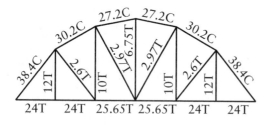

9-9 & 9-21

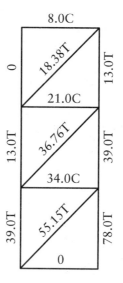

9-11 & 9-23

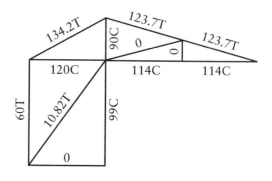

Findings for the Trusses of Problems 9-25 Through 9-31

PROBLEM NUMBER	STATICALLY DETERMINATE EXTERNALLY	j	m	h	$2(j - l) - h$	INTERNAL CHARACTERISTICS
9-25	indeterminate	12	21	1	21	determinate and stable
9-27	determinate	6	9	1	9	determinate and stable
9-29	determinate	5	7	1	7	determinate and stable
9-31	indeterminate	10	17	2	16	indeterminate and stable

9-33 The loaded counterdiagonals are those shown in the following sketch:

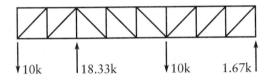

9-35 The loaded counterdiagonals are those shown in the following sketch:

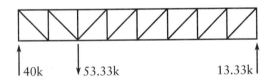

9-37 The loaded counterdiagonals are those shown in the following sketch:

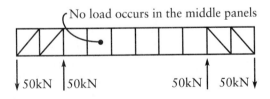

9-39 The loaded counterdiagonals are those shown in the following sketch:

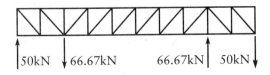

Review Questions

1. In the equilibrium equations of a particle, the equation of moment equilibrium ($\Sigma M_0 = 0$) is still valid, but it does not contribute anything to the solution.

3. In the method of joints, it is advisable to plan the sequence of joints in which the solution will be performed in order to prevent wasted effort when a joint has too many unknowns to be solvable.

5. A simple truss is formed by beginning with a base triangle, and then adding sets of two members and their included hinge until the final desired configuration is obtained.

7. The most reliable way to determine whether a truss is statically determinate internally is to check it to see whether it is properly formed; if it is properly formed, it is statically determinate internally.

9. A load reversal in a truss member may subject a long slender tension member (which can carry a large load in tension) to a compressive load that it cannot carry; the result could be collapse of the truss.

11. Counterdiagonals provide an effective way to relieve the problem of load reversals; the truss simply reconfigures itself such that the diagonals are always in tension.

CHAPTER 10 DEFORMATIONS IN SIMPLE TRUSSES

Outside Problems

10-1

$$\Delta = \sum_{0}^{m} \frac{T_i z_i L_i}{A_i E_i} = 0.658 \text{ in.}$$

10-3

$$\Delta_G = \sum \frac{T_i z_i L_i}{A_i E_i} = -0.06 \text{ in.} \quad \text{(up)}$$

10-5

$$\Delta_D = \sum \frac{T_i z_{Di} L_i}{A_i E_i} = 0.967 \text{ in. to the right}$$

10-6

$$\Delta_B = \sum \frac{T_i z_{Bi} L_i}{A_i E_i} = 0.330 \text{ in. to the right}$$

10-9

$$\Delta_{IV} = \sum \frac{T_i z_{IVi} L_i}{A_i E} = 0.840 \text{ in. downward}$$

10-10

$$\Delta_{GH} = \sum \frac{T_i z_{GHi} L_i}{A_i E} = 1.150 \text{ in. to the right}$$

10-13

With 30 kip load at A, $\Delta_F = 0$

With 30 kip load at I,
$\Delta_F = 0.07$ in. downward

With 30 kip load at H,
$\Delta_F = 0.29$ in. downward

With 30 kip load at G,
$\Delta_F = 0.69$ in. downward

With 30 kip load at F,
$\Delta_F = 1.88$ in. downward

10-15

With 40 kip load at A, $\Delta_J = 0$

With 40 kip load at L,
$\Delta_J = 0.18$ in. downward

With 40 kip load at K,
$\Delta_J = 0.28$ in. downward

With 40 kip load at J,
$\Delta_J = 0.36$ in. downward

With 40 kip load at I,
$\Delta_J = 0.28$ in. downward

With 40 kip load at H,
$\Delta_J = 0.18$ in. downward

With 40 kip load at G, $\Delta_J = 0$

10-17

$$\Delta_{AX} = \sum \frac{T_i z_i L_i}{A_i E} = 0.77 \text{ in. to the right}$$

10-19

$$\Delta_{GX} = \sum \frac{T_i z_i L_i}{A_i E} = 0.44 \text{ in. to the right}$$

Review Questions

1. The method of double integration yields the deformation curve for a smooth and continuous elastic curve; the method is not appropriate for trusses, with their segmented straight lines.

3. Using the unit load in truss analysis affords a means of finding the partial derivatives that is completely independent of the solution for the actual load conditions.

5. A counterdiagonal is one of the X-braces in a cross-braced truss panel; each such panel has two diagonal members rather than one.

7. The angle of rotation of a truss member is usually found by finding the deflections at each end of the member; the difference in deflection then indicates the angular rotation of the member.

CHAPTER 11 INFLUENCE LINES

Outside Problems

11-1 & 11-2

$M_{MAX} = -782 \text{ k} \cdot \text{ft}$

$V_{MAX} = +53 \text{ kips}$

11-5 & 11-6

$M_{MAX(+)} = +1218.5 \text{ k} \cdot \text{ft}$

$M_{MAX(-)} = -1312 \text{ k} \cdot \text{ft}$

11-9   The influence line is shown in the following sketch:

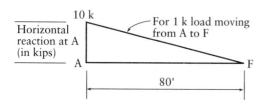

11-11   The influence line is shown in the following sketch:

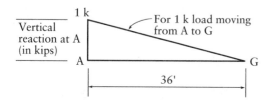

11-13   The influence line for member AC is shown in the following sketch:

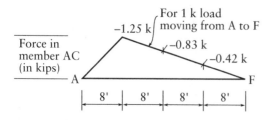

11-15   The influence line for member CJ is shown in the following sketch:

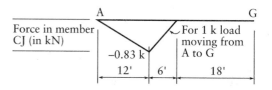

11-17 & 11-18

The influence line for deflection at F is shown in the following sketch:

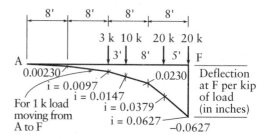

Deflection at F is given by:

$\Delta_F = -2.19 \text{ in.}$ (downward)

Review Questions

1.   An influence line, as it is used in structural analysis, is a graphic aid in computing the moments, shears, and forces that are produced by sets of moving loads.

3.   The use of influence lines has decreased in recent years, due to the increased use of digital computers in structural analysis; such graphic aids for a manual analysis no longer offer any particular advantages.

5.   The major objection to using influence lines relates to the large amount of labor that must be invested in producing the influence lines.

CHAPTER 12 EXTERNAL LOADS ON STRUCTURES

Review Questions

1. At about 70 feet in height, a structure's response to load begins to undergo significant change; tall buildings respond to lateral load much differently than low buildings do.

3. In structural analysis, dynamic loads are generally transformed into equivalent static loads; the structure is then designed to sustain these equivalent static loads.

5. The two types of gravity loads are dead loads and live loads.

7. Of the four major loads (dead, live, wind, and earthquake), only dead load can be determined accurately; the others are simply rough estimates that depend heavily on arbitrarily assumed conditions.

9. Usually, foundation settlement at any one foundation is limited to a nominal value, such as 1 inch or 25 mm. Any differential settlement between adjacent foundations will then be less than this amount, or roughly 3/4 inch or 20 mm. This amount of differential settlement is not seriously detrimental and its effects are usually relegated to the overall factor of safety.

11. Live loads are determined to suit the projected usage of the structure; minimum values are prescribed by the building code.

13. The overall wind load against the surface of a structure is generally constant, although it does increase somewhat with the height of the structure. At particular localized points of the surface, however, there can be concentrations of load due to particular features (such as notches, setbacks, and reveals). At such localized points, load concentration factors are applied to the overall wind pressure to be used only in that localized area.

15. Combinations of load that produce realistic "worst-case" conditions in a structure have evolved in engineering practice over many years of observations, to include many cases of failure analysis of actual structures. These combinations are generally prescribed by the building code.

17. The likelihood of maximum wind or earthquake load's occurring during the life of a structure is quite low. Consequently, an increase in allowable stress is permitted when such loads are being considered, even to the point of permitting some localized damage to occur as a result of this once-in-a-lifetime occurrence.

19. In addition to structural adequacy, the building code also governs requirements for electrical systems, plumbing, light and ventilation, and fire safety.

21. The building code has no authority over the builder's construction of falsework, formwork, or other ancillary construction.

23. To adopt a "model" building code, a municipality usually investigates the codes that are available, and then selects the one that best suits the local conditions and needs. The municipality then joins the organization that produces the model code; this includes paying both initial fees and continuing maintenance costs.

25. "Fireproof" buildings and "earthquake-resistant" buildings are designed not to collapse until the human occupants can be evacuated safely, even though the building may be so badly damaged that it must be torn down later and rebuilt.

CHAPTER 13 LOAD CALCULATIONS

Outside Problems

13-1 Dead load = 78 lb/ft^2

13-3 Dead load = 61 psf

13-5 Dead load = 48 psf

13-7 Dead load = 136 psf

Live Loads for Problems 13-9 through 13-15

PROBLEM NUMBER	STRUCTURE	LIVE LOAD
13-9	Private residential apartments	40 psf
13-11	Interior machinery and equipment rooms	150 psf±
13-13	School corridors	100 psf
13-15	Automobile parking garage ramps	150 psf

13-17 p = 16 psf

13-19

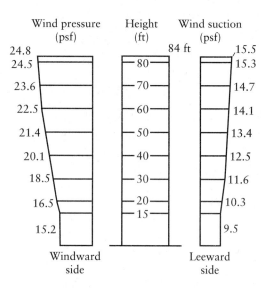

13-21 The design wind load for the overall triangular structure is 15% more than for a single vertical billboard; but the load on each of the two sloping billboards is much less than on a single billboard.

13-23

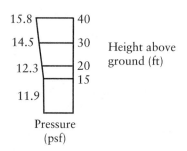

13-25 Base shear due to wind = 22,842 lb
Overturning moment due to wind = 1000.4 k · ft

13-27 The magnitude and locations of the base shears are shown in the following sketch:

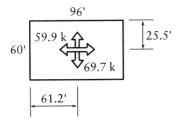

13-29 g-load = 10% of gravity loads

13-31 60% full

Review Questions

1. Building components that are accelerated at the same rate as the building frame are identified as dead loads. All other loads are live loads.

3. Shock-mounted equipment is not accelerated at the same rate as the building frame; it is classified as live load.

5. Under building load requirements for a randomly placed concentrated load, the members most likely to be affected are the floor joists, and the stress most likely to be affected is the shear stress.

7. Wind stagnation pressure is the pressure to be expected on a large vertical surface due to wind blowing directly against it.

9. Wind pressure increases slightly with height.

11. No suction is assumed to occur around a cylinder when it is subjected to wind load.

13. When a surface is inclined at about 40° from horizontal, the wind pressure is essentially zero, being neither pressure nor suction.

15. Localized increases in pressure can occur when a structure is subject to wind load; items located in such localities can be subjected to significantly higher pressures than the overall average pressure.

17. An "importance factor" is assigned to buildings that would house key functions following a disastrous wind or earthquake. Such buildings include hospitals, police stations, fire stations, and communications centers.

19. The resonant frequency of low, broad, rigid structures is so high that it is unlikely to be matched by any earthquake pulses.

CHAPTER 14 DISTRIBUTION OF LOADS WITHIN A STRUCTURE

14-1   Dead load delivered to the footing at A-1 = 81.7 kips

14-3   Dead load delivered to the footing at A-3 = 136.7 kips

14-5   Dead load delivered to the footing at B-1 = 123.1 kips

14-7   Dead load delivered to the footing at B-3 = 155.5 kips

14-9   Dead load delivered to the footing at A-1 = 27.8 kips

14-11   Dead load delivered to the footing at C-1 = 51.6 kips

14-13   Dead load delivered to the footing at A-4 = 50.2 kips

14-15   Dead load delivered to the footing at C-4 = 85.2 kips

14-17   Live load on the footing at A-1 = 21.60 kips

14-19   Live load on the footing at B-4 = 101.52 kips

14-21   Live load on the footing at B-2 = 86.40 kips

14-23   Live load on the footing at A-1 = 16.80 kips

14-25   Live load on the footing at B-3 = 100.8 kips

14-27   Live load on the footing at B-2 = 67.20 kips

14-29   Wind forces on the shear panels at each story are shown on the following sketches:

14-31   Wind forces on the shear panels at each story are shown on the following sketches:

14-33   For panels along lines *A* and *E*, with a panel width of 24 feet and with half the load going to each side, the shears are shown in the following sketches:

14-34 For panels along lines 1 and 5, with a
panel width of 18 feet and with half the
load going to each side, the shears are
shown in the following sketches:

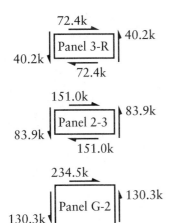

72.4k

Panel 3-R   40.2k

40.2k

72.4k

151.0k

Panel 2-3   83.9k

83.9k

151.0k

234.5k

Panel G-2   130.3k

130.3k

234.5k

CHAPTER 15   INDETERMINATE SINGLE-SPAN STRUCTURES

Outside Problems

15-1 & 15-3

See Table 15-1 for results.

15-5

$R_{AY} = 7.69$ kips $R_{BY} = 4.31$ kips

$M_{BA} = 31.44$ kip · ft

15-7

$R_{AY} = 29.70$ k $R_{BY} = 22.30$ k

$M_{BA} = 82.0$ k · ft

15-9

$R_{AY} = 46.49$ k $R_{BY} = 13.51$ k

$M_{BA} = 70.2$ k · ft

15-11

$R_{AY} = 42.38$ k $R_{BY} = 17.62$ k

$M_{BA} = 152.4$ k · ft

15-13

$R_{AY} = 8.72$ kN $R_{BY} = 14.08$ kN

$M_{BA} = 20.4$ kN · m

15-15 & 15-17

See Table 15-2 for results.

15-19

$R_{AY} = 9.75$ k $M_{AB} = 33.06$ k · ft

$R_{BY} = 2.25$ k $M_{BA} = 14.82$ k · ft

15-21

$R_{AY} = 22.84$ k $M_{AB} = 192.56$ k · ft

$R_{BY} = 37.16$ k $M_{BA} = 107.36$ k · ft

15-23

$M_{AB} = 114.2$ k · ft

$M_{BA} = 114.2$ k · ft

15-25

$R_{AX} = 4.76$ kips

15-27

$R_{AX} = 6.00$ kips $R_{DX} = 6.00$ kips

15-29

$R_{AX} = 385$ lb

15-31

$R_{AY} = 25.91$ kips $R_{DY} = 34.09$ kips

$R_{AX} = 12.27$ kips $R_{DX} = 12.27$ kips

15-33

$R_{AX} = 1.52$ kips

15-35

$R_{AX} = 2.40$ kips

15-37

$R_{AX} = 1.484$ kips

$R_{AY} = -0.071$ kips (up)

15-39

$R_{AX} = 16.29$ kips $\qquad R_{DX} = 14.91$ kips

15-41

$R_{AX} = 50$ kips $\qquad R_{BX} = 50$ kips

15-43

$R_{AX} = 82.355$ kips

CHAPTER 16 CONTINUOUS BEAMS AND FRAMES

Outside Problems

16-1

$R_{AY} = 9.92 \text{ k}$ $R_{BY} = 60.16 \text{ k}$

$R_{CY} = 19.92 \text{ k}$

16-3

$R_{AY} = 8.9 \text{ k}$ $R_{BY} = 54.1 \text{ k}$

$R_{CY} = 18.0 \text{ k}$

16-5

$R_{AY} = 0.5 \text{ k}$ (down)

$R_{BY} = 0.5 \text{ k}$ (down)

$R_{DY} = 54.5 \text{ k}$ (up)

$R_{CY} = 54.5 \text{ k}$ (up)

16-7

$R_{AX} = 4.8 \text{ k}$ (inward)

$R_{DX} = 4.8 \text{ k}$ (inward)

$R_{AY} = 18 \text{ k}$ (up)

$R_{DY} = 18 \text{ k}$ (up)

16-9   The horizontal forces are as follows:

$R_{AX} = 41.9 \text{ kN}$ (left)

$R_{DX} = 23.1 \text{ kN}$ (left)

The vertical forces R_{AY} and R_{DY} are statically determinate:

$R_{AY} = 10.83 \text{ kN}$ (down)

$R_{DY} = 10.83 \text{ kN}$ (up)

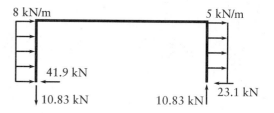

16-11

$R_{AX} = 13.54 \text{ kN}$ (right)

$R_{CX} = 11.46 \text{ kN}$ (right)

$R_{AY} = 5.20 \text{ kN}$ (down)

$R_{CY} = 5.20 \text{ kN}$ (up)

16-13

$R_{AX} = 9.07 \text{ k}$ (left)

$R_{DX} = 3.74 \text{ k}$ (left)

$R_{AY} = 2.73 \text{ k}$ (down)

$R_{DY} = 2.73 \text{ k}$ (up)

Final results are shown on the following sketch:

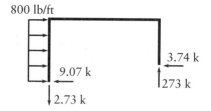

16-15

$R_{AX} = 7.58$ k (right)

$R_{FX} = 1.19$ k (left)

$R_{EX} = 6.39$ k (left)

The final reactions are shown in the following sketch (vertical reactions are found by summing the two cases):

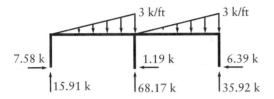

16-17

$R_{AX} = 0.10$ kN (left)

$R_{HX} = 0.57$ kN (right)

$R_{GX} = 0.02$ kN (right)

$R_{FX} = 0.68$ kN (left)

$R_{AY} = 0.40$ kN (down)

$R_{HY} = 2.95$ kN (up)

$R_{FY} = 7.18$ kN (up)

$R_{GY} = 15.62$ kN (up)

Final results are shown in the following sketch:

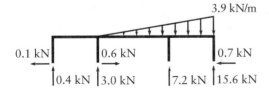

16-19

$R_{AX} = 5.16$ kips (right) $R_{FX} = 0$

$R_{EX} = 5.16$ kips (left)

$R_{AY} = 3.10$ kips

Final reactions are shown on the following sketch:

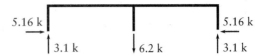

16-21

$R_{AX} = 9.03$ kips (right)

$R_{FX} = 9.03$ kips (left)

Final solution with moment diagram is given in the following sketch:

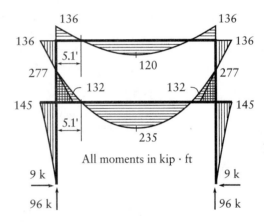

16-23

$R_{AY} = 6.39$ k (down)

$R_{GY} = 6.39$ k (down)

$R_{DY} = 12.78$ k (up)

Final results are shown on the following sketch:

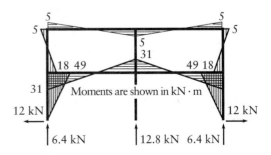

Index